ELECTRIC CIRCUITS

TENTH EDITION

James W. Nilsson • Susan A. Riedel

Electric Circuits

Custom Edition for Pennsylvania State University

Taken from:
Electric Circuits, Tenth Edition
by James W. Nilsson and Susan A. Riedel

Cover Art: Courtesy of Photodisc/Getty Images.

Taken from:

Electric Circuits, Tenth Edition
by James W. Nilsson and Susan A. Riedel
Copyright © 2015, 2008, 2005 by Pearson Education, Inc.
Published by Prentice Hall
Upper Saddle River, New Jersey 07458

This special edition published in cooperation with Pearson Learning Solutions.

Pearson Learning Solutions, 501 Boylston Street, Suite 900, Boston, MA 02116
A Pearson Education Company
www.pearsoned.com

Printed in the United States of America

 3 4 5 6 7 8 9 10 V092 18 17 16 15

000200010271922966

PJ

ISBN 10: 1-269-94932-2
ISBN 13: 978-1-269-94932-3

To Anna

Brief Contents

Contents

List of Examples

Chapter 8

Chapter 9

Chapter 10

Chapter 11

Chapter 14

Preface

The first edition of Electric Circuits, an introductory circuits text, was published in 1983. It included 100 worked examples and about 600 problems. It did not include a student workbook, supplements for PSpice or MultiSim, or any web support. Support for instructors was limited to a solution manual for the problems and enlarged copies of many text figures, suitable for making transparencies.

Much has changed in the 31 years since Electric Circuits first appeared, and during that time this text has evolved to better meet the needs of both students and their instructors. As an example, the text now includes about 150 worked examples, about 1850 problems, and extensive supplements and web content. The tenth edition is designed to revise and improve the material presented in the text, in its supplements, and on the web. Yet the fundamental goals of the text are unchanged. These goals are:

- To build an understanding of concepts and ideas explicitly in terms of previous learning. Students are constantly challenged by the need to layer new concepts on top of previous concepts they may still be struggling to master. This text provides an important focus on helping students understand how new concepts are related to and rely upon concepts previously presented.

- To emphasize the relationship between conceptual understanding and problem-solving approaches. Developing problem-solving skills continues to be the central challenge in a first-year circuits course. In this text we include numerous Examples that present problem-solving techniques followed by Assessment Problems that enable students to test their mastery of the material and techniques introduced. The problem-solving process we illustrate is based on concepts rather than the use of rote procedures. This encourages students to think about a problem before attempting to solve it.

- To provide students with a strong foundation of engineering practices. There are limited opportunities in a first-year circuit analysis course to introduce students to realistic engineering experiences. We continue to take advantage of the opportunities that do exist by including problems and examples that use realistic component values and represent realizable circuits. We include many problems related to the Practical Perspective problems that begin each chapter. We also include problems intended to stimulate the students' interest in engineering, where the problems require the type of insight typical of a practicing engineer.

WHY THIS EDITION?

The tenth edition revision of *Electric Circuits* began with a thorough review of the text. This review provided a clear picture of what matters most to instructors and their students and led to the following changes:

- Problem solving is fundamental to the study of circuit analysis. Having a wealth of new problems to assign and work is a key to success in any circuits course. Therefore, existing end-of-chapter problems were revised, and new end-of-chapter problems were added. As a result, more than 40% of the problems in the tenth edition have never appeared in any previous edition of the text.

- Both students and instructors want to know how the generalized techniques presented in a first-year circuit analysis course relate to problems faced by practicing engineers. The Practical Perspective problems provide this connection between circuit analysis and the real world. We have created new Practical Perspective problems for Chapters 2, 3, 6, 7, 8, and 10. Many of the new problems represent the world of the 21st century. Each Practical Perspective problem is solved, at least in part, at the end of the chapter, and additional end-of-chapter problems can be assigned to allow students to explore the Practical Perspective topic further.

- The PSpice and Multisim manuals have been revised to include screenshots from the most recent versions of these software simulation applications. Each manual presents the simulation material in the same order as the material is presented in the text. These manuals continue to include examples of circuits to be simulated that are drawn directly from the text. The text continues to indicate end-of-chapter problems that are good candidates for simulation using either PSpice or Multisim.

- Students who could benefit from additional examples and practice problems can use the Student Workbook, which has been revised to reflect changes to the tenth edition of the text. This workbook has examples and problems covering the following material: balancing power, simple resistive circuits, node voltage method, mesh current method, Thévenin and Norton equivalents, op amp circuits, first-order circuits, second-order circuits, AC steady-state analysis, and Laplace transform circuit analysis.

- The Student Workbook now includes access to Video Solutions, complete, step-by-step solution walkthroughs to representative homework problems.

- Learning Catalytics, a "bring your own device" student engagement, assessment, and classroom intelligence system is now available with the tenth edition. With Learning Catalytics you can:
  - Use open-ended questions to get into the minds of students to understand what they do or don't know and adjust lectures accordingly.
  - Use a wide variety of question types to sketch a graph, annotate a circuit diagram, compose numeric or algebraic answers, and more.
  - Access rich analytics to understand student performance.
  - Use pre-built questions or add your own to make Learning Catalytics fit your course exactly.

- MasteringEngineering is an online tutorial and assessment program that provides students with personalized feedback and hints and instructors with diagnostics to track students' progress. With the tenth edition, MasteringEngineering will offer new tutorial homework problems, Coaching Activities, and Adaptive Follow-Up assignments. Visit www.masteringengineering.com for more information.

HALLMARK FEATURES

Chapter Problems

Users of *Electric Circuits* have consistently rated the Chapter Problems as one of the book's most attractive features. In the tenth edition, there are over 1650 end-of-chapter problems with approximately 40% that have never appeared in a previous edition. Problems are organized at the end of each chapter by section.

Practical Perspectives

The tenth edition continues the use of Practical Perspectives introduced with the chapter openers. They offer examples of real-world circuits, taken from real-world devices. The Practical Perspectives for six of the chapters are brand new to this edition. Every chapter begins with a brief description of a practical application of the material that follows. Once the chapter material is presented, the chapter concludes with a quantitative analysis of the Practical Perspective application. A group of end-of-chapter problems directly relates to the Practical Perspective application. Solving some of these problems enables you to understand how to apply the chapter contents to the solution of a real-world problem.

Assessment Problems

Each chapter begins with a set of chapter objectives. At key points in the chapter, you are asked to stop and assess your mastery of a particular objective by solving one or more assessment problems. The answers to all of the assessment problems are given at the conclusion of each problem, so you can check your work. If you are able to solve the assessment problems for a given objective, you have mastered that objective. If you need more practice, several end-of-chapter problems that relate to the objective are suggested at the conclusion of the assessment problems.

Examples

Every chapter includes many examples that illustrate the concepts presented in the text in the form of a numeric example. There are nearly 150 examples in this text. The examples are intended to illustrate the application of a particular concept, and also to encourage good problem-solving skills.

Fundamental Equations and Concepts

Throughout the text, you will see fundamental equations and concepts set apart from the main text. This is done to help you focus on some of the key principles in electric circuits and to help you navigate through the important topics.

Integration of Computer Tools

Computer tools can assist students in the learning process by providing a visual representation of a circuit's behavior, validating a calculated solution, reducing the computational burden of more complex circuits, and iterating toward a desired solution using parameter variation. This computational support is often invaluable in the design process. The tenth edition includes the support of PSpice® and Multisim®, both popular computer tools for circuit simulation and analysis. Chapter problems suited for exploration with PSpice and Multisim are marked accordingly.

Design Emphasis

The tenth edition continues to support the emphasis on the design of circuits in many ways. First, many of the Practical Perspective discussions focus on the design aspects of the circuits. The accompanying Chapter Problems continue the discussion of the design issues in these practical examples. Second, design-oriented Chapter Problems have been labeled explicitly, enabling students and instructors to identify those problems with a design focus. Third, the identification of problems suited to exploration with PSpice or Multisim suggests design opportunities using these software tools. Fourth, some problems in nearly every chapter focus on the use of realistic component values in achieving a desired circuit design. Once such a problem has been analyzed, the student can proceed to a laboratory to build and test the circuit, comparing the analysis with the measured performance of the actual circuit.

Accuracy

All text and problems in the tenth edition have undergone our strict hallmark accuracy checking process, to ensure the most error-free book possible.

RESOURCES FOR STUDENTS

MasteringEngineering.   MasteringEngineering provides tutorial homework problems designed to emulate the instructor's office hour environment, guiding students through engineering concepts with self-paced individualized coaching. These in-depth tutorial homework problems provide students with feedback specific to their errors and optional hints that break problems down into simpler steps. Visit www.masteringengineering .com for more information.

Student Workbook.   This resource teaches students techniques for solving problems presented in the text. Organized by concepts, this is a valuable problem-solving resource for all levels of students.

   The Student Workbook now includes access to Video Solutions, complete, step-by-step solution walkthroughs to representative homework problems.

Introduction to Multisim and Introduction to PSpice Manuals—Updated for the tenth edition, these manuals are excellent resources for those wishing to integrate PSpice or Multisim into their classes.

RESOURCES FOR INSTRUCTORS

All instructor resources are available for download at www.pearson highered.com. If you are in need of a login and password for this site, please contact your local Pearson representative.

Instructor Solutions Manual—Fully worked-out solutions to Assessment Problems and end-of-chapter problems.

PowerPoint lecture images—All figures from the text are available in PowerPoint for your lecture needs. An additional set of full lecture slides with embedded assessment questions are available upon request.

MasteringEngineering.   This online tutorial and assessment program allows you to integrate dynamic homework with automated grading and personalized feedback. MasteringEngineering allows you to easily track the performance of your entire class on an assignment-by-assignment basis, or the detailed work of an individual student. For more information visit www.masteringengineeing.com.

Learning Catalytics—This "bring your own device" student engagement, assessment and classroom intelligence system enables you to measure student learning during class, and adjust your lectures accordingly. A wide variety of question and answer types allows you to author your own questions, or you can use questions already authored into the system. For more information visit www.learningcatalytics.com.

PREREQUISITES

In writing the first 12 chapters of the text, we have assumed that the reader has taken a course in elementary differential and integral calculus. We have also assumed that the reader has had an introductory physics course, at either the high school or university level, that introduces the concepts of energy, power, electric charge, electric current, electric potential, and electromagnetic fields. In writing the final six chapters, we have assumed the student has had, or is enrolled in, an introductory course in differential equations.

COURSE OPTIONS

The text has been designed for use in a one-semester, two-semester, or a three-quarter sequence.

- *Single-semester course:* After covering Chapters 1–4 and Chapters 6–10 (omitting Sections 7.7 and 8.5) the instructor can choose from Chapter 5 (operational amplifiers), Chapter 11 (three-phase circuits), Chapters 13 and 14 (Laplace methods), and Chapter 18 (Two-Port Circuits) to develop the desired emphasis.
- *Two-semester sequence:* Assuming three lectures per week, the first nine chapters can be covered during the first semester, leaving Chapters 10–18 for the second semester.
- *Academic quarter schedule:* The book can be subdivided into three parts: Chapters 1–6, Chapters 7–12, and Chapters 13–18.

The introduction to operational amplifier circuits in Chapter 5 can be omitted without interfering with the reading of subsequent chapters. For example, if Chapter 5 is omitted, the instructor can simply skip Section 7.7, Section 8.5, Chapter 15, and those assessment problems and end-of-chapter problems in the chapters following Chapter 5 that pertain to operational amplifiers.

There are several appendixes at the end of the book to help readers make effective use of their mathematical background. Appendix A reviews Cramer's method of solving simultaneous linear equations and simple matrix algebra; complex numbers are reviewed in Appendix B; Appendix C contains additional material on magnetically coupled coils and ideal transformers; Appendix D contains a brief discussion of the decibel; Appendix E is dedicated to Bode diagrams; Appendix F is devoted to an abbreviated table of trigonometric identities that are useful in circuit analysis; and an abbreviated table of useful integrals is given in Appendix G. Appendix H provides tables of common standard component values for resistors, inductors, and capacitors, to be used in solving many end-of-chapter problems. Selected Answers provides answers to selected end-of-chapter problems.

ACKNOWLEDGMENTS

There were many hard-working people behind the scenes at our publisher who deserve our thanks and gratitude for their efforts on behalf of the tenth edition. At Pearson, we would like to thank Andrew Gilfillan, Rose Kernan, Gregory Dulles, Tim Galligan, and Scott Disanno for their continued support and encouragement, their professional demeanor, their willingness to lend an ear, and their months of long hours and no weekends. The authors would also like to acknowledge the staff at Integra Software Solutions for their dedication and hard work in typesetting this text. The authors would also like to thank Kurt Norlin for his help in accuracy checking the text and problems.

We are very grateful for the many instructors and students who have done formal reviews of the text or offered positive feedback and suggestions for improvement more informally. We are pleased to receive email from instructors and students who use the book, even when they are pointing out an error we failed to catch in the review process. We have been contacted by people who use our text from all over the world, and we thank all of you for taking the time to do so. We use as many of your suggestions as possible to continue to improve the content, the pedagogy, and the presentation in this text. We are privileged to have the opportunity to impact the educational experience of the many thousands of future engineers who will use this text.

JAMES W. NILSSON
SUSAN A. RIEDEL

ELECTRIC CIRCUITS
TENTH EDITION

✓ CHAPTER OBJECTIVES

1 Understand and be able to use SI units and the standard prefixes for powers of 10.

2 Know and be able to use the definitions of *voltage* and *current*.

3 Know and be able to use the definitions of *power* and *energy*.

4 Be able to use the passive sign convention to calculate the power for an ideal basic circuit element given its voltage and current.

Circuit Variables

Electrical engineering is an exciting and challenging profession for anyone who has a genuine interest in, and aptitude for, applied science and mathematics. Over the past century and a half, electrical engineers have played a dominant role in the development of systems that have changed the way people live and work. Satellite communication links, telephones, digital computers, televisions, diagnostic and surgical medical equipment, assembly-line robots, and electrical power tools are representative components of systems that define a modern technological society. As an electrical engineer, you can participate in this ongoing technological revolution by improving and refining these existing systems and by discovering and developing new systems to meet the needs of our ever-changing society.

As you embark on the study of circuit analysis, you need to gain a feel for where this study fits into the hierarchy of topics that comprise an introduction to electrical engineering. Hence we begin by presenting an overview of electrical engineering, some ideas about an engineering point of view as it relates to circuit analysis, and a review of the international system of units.

We then describe generally what circuit analysis entails. Next, we introduce the concepts of voltage and current. We follow these concepts with discussion of an ideal basic element and the need for a polarity reference system. We conclude the chapter by describing how current and voltage relate to power and energy.

Practical Perspective

Balancing Power

One of the most important skills you will develop is the ability to check your answers for the circuits you design and analyze using the tools developed in this text. A common method used to check for valid answers is to balance the power in the circuit. The linear circuits we study have no net power, so the sum of the power associated with each circuit component must be zero. If the total power for the circuit is zero, we say that the power balances, but if the total power is not zero, we need to find the errors in our calculation.

As an example, we will consider a very simple model for the distribution of electricity to a typical home, as shown below. (Note that a more realistic model will be investigated in the Practical Perspective for Chapter 9.) The components labeled a and b represent the electrical source to the home. The components labeled c, d, and e represent the wires that carry the electrical current from the source to the devices in the home requiring electrical power. The components labeled f, g, and h represent lamps, televisions, hair dryers, refrigerators, and other devices that require power.

Once we have introduced the concepts of voltage, current, power, and energy, we will examine this circuit model in detail, and use a power balance to determine whether the results of analyzing this circuit are correct.

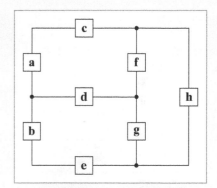

romakoma / Shutterstock

Elena Elisseeva / Alamy

3

1.1 Electrical Engineering: An Overview

Electrical engineering is the profession concerned with systems that produce, transmit, and measure electric signals. Electrical engineering combines the physicist's models of natural phenomena with the mathematician's tools for manipulating those models to produce systems that meet practical needs. Electrical systems pervade our lives; they are found in homes, schools, workplaces, and transportation vehicles everywhere. We begin by presenting a few examples from each of the five major classifications of electrical systems:

- communication systems
- computer systems
- control systems
- power systems
- signal-processing systems

Then we describe how electrical engineers analyze and design such systems.

Communication systems are electrical systems that generate, transmit, and distribute information. Well-known examples include television equipment, such as cameras, transmitters, receivers, and VCRs; radio telescopes, used to explore the universe; satellite systems, which return images of other planets and our own; radar systems, used to coordinate plane flights; and telephone systems.

Figure 1.1 depicts the major components of a modern telephone system. Starting at the left of the figure, inside a telephone, a microphone turns sound waves into electric signals. These signals are carried to a switching center where they are combined with the signals from tens, hundreds, or thousands of other telephones. The combined signals leave the switching center; their form depends on the distance they must travel. In our example, they are sent through wires in underground coaxial cables to a microwave transmission station. Here, the signals are transformed into microwave frequencies and broadcast from a transmission antenna through air and space, via a communications satellite, to a receiving antenna. The microwave receiving station translates the microwave signals into a form suitable for further transmission, perhaps as pulses of light to be sent through fiber-optic cable. On arrival at the second switching center, the combined signals are separated, and each is routed to the appropriate telephone, where an earphone acts as a speaker to convert the received electric signals back into sound waves. At each stage of the process, electric circuits operate on the signals. Imagine the challenge involved in designing, building, and operating each circuit in a way that guarantees that all of the hundreds of thousands of simultaneous calls have high-quality connections.

Computer systems use electric signals to process information ranging from word processing to mathematical computations. Systems range in size and power from pocket calculators to personal computers to supercomputers that perform such complex tasks as processing weather data and modeling chemical interactions of complex organic molecules. These systems include networks of microcircuits, or integrated circuits—postage-stampsized assemblies of hundreds, thousands, or millions of electrical components that often operate at speeds and power levels close to fundamental physical limits, including the speed of light and the thermodynamic laws.

Control systems use electric signals to regulate processes. Examples include the control of temperatures, pressures, and flow rates in an oil refinery; the fuel-air mixture in a fuel-injected automobile engine; mechanisms such as the motors, doors, and lights in elevators; and the locks in the

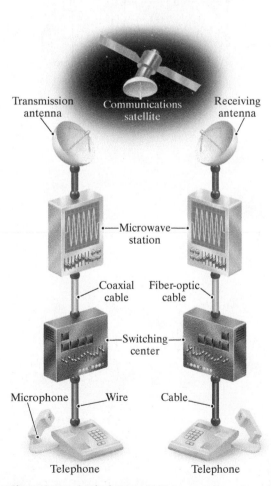

Figure 1.1 ▲ A telephone system.

Panama Canal. The autopilot and autolanding systems that help to fly and land airplanes are also familiar control systems.

Power systems generate and distribute electric power. Electric power, which is the foundation of our technology-based society, usually is generated in large quantities by nuclear, hydroelectric, and thermal (coal-, oil-, or gas-fired) generators. Power is distributed by a grid of conductors that crisscross the country. A major challenge in designing and operating such a system is to provide sufficient redundancy and control so that failure of any piece of equipment does not leave a city, state, or region completely without power.

Signal-processing systems act on electric signals that represent information. They transform the signals and the information contained in them into a more suitable form. There are many different ways to process the signals and their information. For example, image-processing systems gather massive quantities of data from orbiting weather satellites, reduce the amount of data to a manageable level, and transform the remaining data into a video image for the evening news broadcast. A computerized tomography (CT) scan is another example of an image-processing system. It takes signals generated by a special X-ray machine and transforms them into an image such as the one in Fig. 1.2. Although the original X-ray signals are of little use to a physician, once they are processed into a recognizable image the information they contain can be used in the diagnosis of disease and injury.

Considerable interaction takes place among the engineering disciplines involved in designing and operating these five classes of systems. Thus communications engineers use digital computers to control the flow of information. Computers contain control systems, and control systems contain computers. Power systems require extensive communications systems to coordinate safely and reliably the operation of components, which may be spread across a continent. A signal-processing system may involve a communications link, a computer, and a control system.

A good example of the interaction among systems is a commercial airplane, such as the one shown in Fig. 1.3. A sophisticated communications system enables the pilot and the air traffic controller to monitor the plane's location, permitting the air traffic controller to design a safe flight path for all of the nearby aircraft and enabling the pilot to keep the plane on its designated path. On the newest commercial airplanes, an onboard computer system is used for managing engine functions, implementing the navigation and flight control systems, and generating video information screens in the cockpit. A complex control system uses cockpit commands to adjust the position and speed of the airplane, producing the appropriate signals to the engines and the control surfaces (such as the wing flaps, ailerons, and rudder) to ensure the plane remains safely airborne and on the desired flight path. The plane must have its own power system to stay aloft and to provide and distribute the electric power needed to keep the cabin lights on, make the coffee, and show the movie. Signal-processing systems reduce the noise in air traffic communications and transform information about the plane's location into the more meaningful form of a video display in the cockpit. Engineering challenges abound in the design of each of these systems and their integration into a coherent whole. For example, these systems must operate in widely varying and unpredictable environmental conditions. Perhaps the most important engineering challenge is to guarantee that sufficient redundancy is incorporated in the designs to ensure that passengers arrive safely and on time at their desired destinations.

Although electrical engineers may be interested primarily in one area, they must also be knowledgeable in other areas that interact with this area of interest. This interaction is part of what makes electrical

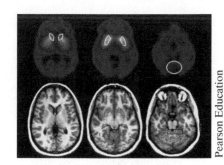

Pearson Education

Figure 1.2 ▲ A CT scan of an adult head.

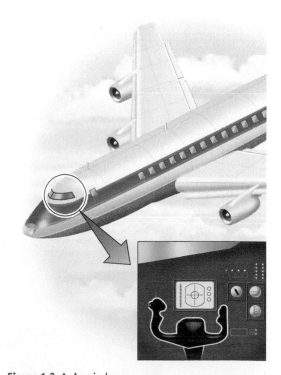

Figure 1.3 ▲ An airplane.

engineering a challenging and exciting profession. The emphasis in engineering is on making things work, so an engineer is free to acquire and use any technique, from any field, that helps to get the job done.

Circuit Theory

In a field as diverse as electrical engineering, you might well ask whether all of its branches have anything in common. The answer is yes—electric circuits. An **electric circuit** is a mathematical model that approximates the behavior of an actual electrical system. As such, it provides an important foundation for learning—in your later courses and as a practicing engineer—the details of how to design and operate systems such as those just described. The models, the mathematical techniques, and the language of circuit theory will form the intellectual framework for your future engineering endeavors.

Note that the term *electric circuit* is commonly used to refer to an actual electrical system as well as to the model that represents it. In this text, when we talk about an electric circuit, we always mean a model, unless otherwise stated. It is the modeling aspect of circuit theory that has broad applications across engineering disciplines.

Circuit theory is a special case of electromagnetic field theory: the study of static and moving electric charges. Although generalized field theory might seem to be an appropriate starting point for investigating electric signals, its application is not only cumbersome but also requires the use of advanced mathematics. Consequently, a course in electromagnetic field theory is not a prerequisite to understanding the material in this book. We do, however, assume that you have had an introductory physics course in which electrical and magnetic phenomena were discussed.

Three basic assumptions permit us to use circuit theory, rather than electromagnetic field theory, to study a physical system represented by an electric circuit. These assumptions are as follows:

1. *Electrical effects happen instantaneously throughout a system.* We can make this assumption because we know that electric signals travel at or near the speed of light. Thus, if the system is physically small, electric signals move through it so quickly that we can consider them to affect every point in the system simultaneously. A system that is small enough so that we can make this assumption is called a **lumped-parameter system**.

2. *The net charge on every component in the system is always zero.* Thus no component can collect a net excess of charge, although some components, as you will learn later, can hold equal but opposite separated charges.

3. *There is no magnetic coupling between the components in a system.* As we demonstrate later, magnetic coupling can occur *within* a component.

That's it; there are no other assumptions. Using circuit theory provides simple solutions (of sufficient accuracy) to problems that would become hopelessly complicated if we were to use electromagnetic field theory. These benefits are so great that engineers sometimes specifically design electrical systems to ensure that these assumptions are met. The importance of assumptions 2 and 3 becomes apparent after we introduce the basic circuit elements and the rules for analyzing interconnected elements.

However, we need to take a closer look at assumption 1. The question is, "How small does a physical system have to be to qualify as a lumped-parameter system?" We can get a quantitative handle on the question by noting that electric signals propagate by wave phenomena. If the wavelength of the signal is large compared to the physical dimensions of the system, we have a lumped-parameter system. The wavelength λ is the velocity divided by the repetition rate, or **frequency**, of the signal; that is, $\lambda = c/f$. The frequency f is measured in hertz (Hz). For example, power systems in the United States operate at 60 Hz. If we use the speed of light ($c = 3 \times 10^8$ m/s) as the velocity of propagation, the wavelength is 5×10^6 m. If the power system of interest is physically smaller than this wavelength, we can represent it as a lumped-parameter system and use circuit theory to analyze its behavior. How do we define *smaller*? A good rule is the *rule of 1/10th*: If the dimension of the system is 1/10th (or smaller) of the dimension of the wavelength, you have a lumped-parameter system. Thus, as long as the physical dimension of the power system is less than 5×10^5 m, we can treat it as a lumped-parameter system.

On the other hand, the propagation frequency of radio signals is on the order of 10^9 Hz. Thus the wavelength is 0.3 m. Using the rule of 1/10th, the relevant dimensions of a communication system that sends or receives radio signals must be less than 3 cm to qualify as a lumped-parameter system. Whenever any of the pertinent physical dimensions of a system under study approaches the wavelength of its signals, we must use electromagnetic field theory to analyze that system. Throughout this book we study circuits derived from lumped-parameter systems.

Problem Solving

As a practicing engineer, you will not be asked to solve problems that have already been solved. Whether you are trying to improve the performance of an existing system or creating a new system, you will be working on unsolved problems. As a student, however, you will devote much of your attention to the discussion of problems already solved. By reading about and discussing how these problems were solved in the past, and by solving related homework and exam problems on your own, you will begin to develop the skills to successfully attack the unsolved problems you'll face as a practicing engineer.

Some general problem-solving procedures are presented here. Many of them pertain to thinking about and organizing your solution strategy *before* proceeding with calculations.

1. *Identify what's given and what's to be found.* In problem solving, you need to know your destination before you can select a route for getting there. What is the problem asking you to solve or find? Sometimes the goal of the problem is obvious; other times you may need to paraphrase or make lists or tables of known and unknown information to see your objective.

   The problem statement may contain extraneous information that you need to weed out before proceeding. On the other hand, it may offer incomplete information or more complexities than can be handled given the solution methods at your disposal. In that case, you'll need to make assumptions to fill in the missing information or simplify the problem context. Be prepared to circle back and reconsider supposedly extraneous information and/or your assumptions if your calculations get bogged down or produce an answer that doesn't seem to make sense.

2. *Sketch a circuit diagram or other visual model.* Translating a verbal problem description into a visual model is often a useful step in the solution process. If a circuit diagram is already provided, you may need to add information to it, such as labels, values, or reference directions. You may also want to redraw the circuit in a simpler, but equivalent, form. Later in this text you will learn the methods for developing such simplified equivalent circuits.

3. *Think of several solution methods and decide on a way of choosing among them.* This course will help you build a collection of analytical tools, several of which may work on a given problem. But one method may produce fewer equations to be solved than another, or it may require only algebra instead of calculus to reach a solution. Such efficiencies, if you can anticipate them, can streamline your calculations considerably. Having an alternative method in mind also gives you a path to pursue if your first solution attempt bogs down.

4. *Calculate a solution.* Your planning up to this point should have helped you identify a good analytical method and the correct equations for the problem. Now comes the solution of those equations. Paper-and-pencil, calculator, and computer methods are all available for performing the actual calculations of circuit analysis. Efficiency and your instructor's preferences will dictate which tools you should use.

5. *Use your creativity.* If you suspect that your answer is off base or if the calculations seem to go on and on without moving you toward a solution, you should pause and consider alternatives. You may need to revisit your assumptions or select a different solution method. Or, you may need to take a less-conventional problem-solving approach, such as working backward from a solution. This text provides answers to all of the Assessment Problems and many of the Chapter Problems so that you may work backward when you get stuck. In the real world, you won't be given answers in advance, but you may have a desired problem outcome in mind from which you can work backward. Other creative approaches include allowing yourself to see parallels with other types of problems you've successfully solved, following your intuition or hunches about how to proceed, and simply setting the problem aside temporarily and coming back to it later.

6. *Test your solution.* Ask yourself whether the solution you've obtained makes sense. Does the magnitude of the answer seem reasonable? Is the solution physically realizable? You may want to go further and rework the problem via an alternative method. Doing so will not only test the validity of your original answer, but will also help you develop your intuition about the most efficient solution methods for various kinds of problems. In the real world, safety-critical designs are always checked by several independent means. Getting into the habit of checking your answers will benefit you as a student and as a practicing engineer.

These problem-solving steps cannot be used as a recipe to solve every problem in this or any other course. You may need to skip, change the order of, or elaborate on certain steps to solve a particular problem. Use these steps as a guideline to develop a problem-solving style that works for you.

1.2 The International System of Units

Engineers compare theoretical results to experimental results and compare competing engineering designs using quantitative measures. Modern engineering is a multidisciplinary profession in which teams of engineers work together on projects, and they can communicate their results in a meaningful way only if they all use the same units of measure. The International System of Units (abbreviated SI) is used by all the major engineering societies and most engineers throughout the world; hence we use it in this book.

TABLE 1.1   The International System of Units (SI)

Quantity	Basic Unit	Symbol
Length	meter	m
Mass	kilogram	kg
Time	second	s
Electric current	ampere	A
Thermodynamic temperature	degree kelvin	K
Amount of substance	mole	mol
Luminous intensity	candela	cd

National Institute of Standards and Technology Special Publication 330, 2008 Edition, Natl. Inst. Stand. Technol. Spec. Pub. 330, 2008 Ed., 96 pages (March 2008)

The SI units are based on seven *defined* quantities:

- length
- mass
- time
- electric current
- thermodynamic temperature
- amount of substance
- luminous intensity

These quantities, along with the basic unit and symbol for each, are listed in Table 1.1. Although not strictly SI units, the familiar time units of minute (60 s), hour (3600 s), and so on are often used in engineering calculations. In addition, defined quantities are combined to form **derived** units. Some, such as force, energy, power, and electric charge, you already know through previous physics courses. Table 1.2 lists the derived units used in this book.

In many cases, the SI unit is either too small or too large to use conveniently. Standard prefixes corresponding to powers of 10, as listed in Table 1.3, are then applied to the basic unit. All of these prefixes are correct, but engineers often use only the ones for powers divisible by 3; thus centi, deci, deka, and hecto are used rarely. Also, engineers often select the prefix that places the base number in the range between 1 and 1000. Suppose that a time calculation yields a result of 10^{-5} s, that is, 0.00001 s. Most engineers would describe this quantity as $10\,\mu$s, that is, $10^{-5} = 10 \times 10^{-6}$ s, rather than as 0.01 ms or 10,000,000 ps.

TABLE 1.2   Derived Units in SI

Quantity	Unit Name (Symbol)	Formula
Frequency	hertz (Hz)	s^{-1}
Force	newton (N)	$kg \cdot m/s^2$
Energy or work	joule (J)	$N \cdot m$
Power	watt (W)	J/s
Electric charge	coulomb (C)	$A \cdot s$
Electric potential	volt (V)	J/C
Electric resistance	ohm (Ω)	V/A
Electric conductance	siemens (S)	A/V
Electric capacitance	farad (F)	C/V
Magnetic flux	weber (Wb)	$V \cdot s$
Inductance	henry (H)	Wb/A

National Institute of Standards and Technology Special Publication 330, 2008 Edition, Natl. Inst. Stand. Technol. Spec. Pub. 330, 2008 Ed., 96 pages (March 2008)

TABLE 1.3   Standardized Prefixes to Signify Powers of 10

Prefix	Symbol	Power
atto	a	10^{-18}
femto	f	10^{-15}
pico	p	10^{-12}
nano	n	10^{-9}
micro	μ	10^{-6}
milli	m	10^{-3}
centi	c	10^{-2}
deci	d	10^{-1}
deka	da	10
hecto	h	10^{2}
kilo	k	10^{3}
mega	M	10^{6}
giga	G	10^{9}
tera	T	10^{12}

National Institute of Standards and Technology Special Publication 330, 2008 Edition, Natl. Inst. Stand. Technol. Spec. Pub. 330, 2008 Ed., 96 pages (March 2008)

Example 1.1 illustrates a method for converting from one set of units to another and also uses power-of-ten prefixes.

Example 1.1   Using SI Units and Prefixes for Powers of 10

If a signal can travel in a cable at 80% of the speed of light, what length of cable, in inches, represents 1 ns?

Solution

First, note that $1 \text{ ns} = 10^{-9}$ s. Also, recall that the speed of light $c = 3 \times 10^{8}$ m/s. Then, 80% of the speed of light is $0.8c = (0.8)(3 \times 10^{8}) = 2.4 \times 10^{8}$ m/s. Using a product of ratios, we can convert 80% of the speed of light from meters-per-second to inches-per-nanosecond. The result is the distance in inches traveled in 1 ns:

$$\frac{2.4 \times 10^{8} \text{ meters}}{1 \text{ second}} \cdot \frac{1 \text{ second}}{10^{9} \text{ nanoseconds}} \cdot \frac{100 \text{ centimeters}}{1 \text{ meter}} \cdot \frac{1 \text{ inch}}{2.54 \text{ centimeters}}$$

$$= \frac{(2.4 \times 10^{8})(100)}{(10^{9})(2.54)} = 9.45 \text{ inches/nanosecond}$$

Therefore, a signal traveling at 80% of the speed of light will cover 9.45 inches of cable in 1 nanosecond.

✓ ASSESSMENT PROBLEMS

Objective 1—Understand and be able to use SI units and the standard prefixes for powers of 10

1.1 Assume a telephone signal travels through a cable at two-thirds the speed of light. How long does it take the signal to get from New York City to Miami if the distance is approximately 1100 miles?

Answer: 8.85 ms.

1.2 How many dollars per millisecond would the federal government have to collect to retire a deficit of $100 billion in one year?

Answer: $3.17/ms.

NOTE: Also try Chapter Problems 1.1, 1.3, and 1.5.

1.3 Circuit Analysis: An Overview

Before becoming involved in the details of circuit analysis, we need to take a broad look at engineering design, specifically the design of electric circuits. The purpose of this overview is to provide you with a perspective on where circuit analysis fits within the whole of circuit design. Even though this book focuses on circuit analysis, we try to provide opportunities for circuit design where appropriate.

All engineering designs begin with a need, as shown in Fig. 1.4. This need may come from the desire to improve on an existing design, or it may be something brand-new. A careful assessment of the need results in design specifications, which are measurable characteristics of a proposed design. Once a design is proposed, the design specifications allow us to assess whether or not the design actually meets the need.

A concept for the design comes next. The concept derives from a complete understanding of the design specifications coupled with an insight into the need, which comes from education and experience. The concept may be realized as a sketch, as a written description, or in some other form. Often the next step is to translate the concept into a mathematical model. A commonly used mathematical model for electrical systems is a **circuit model**.

The elements that comprise the circuit model are called **ideal circuit components**. An ideal circuit component is a mathematical model of an actual electrical component, like a battery or a light bulb. It is important for the ideal circuit component used in a circuit model to represent the behavior of the actual electrical component to an acceptable degree of accuracy. The tools of **circuit analysis**, the focus of this book, are then applied to the circuit. Circuit analysis is based on mathematical techniques and is used to predict the behavior of the circuit model and its ideal circuit components. A comparison between the desired behavior, from the design specifications, and the predicted behavior, from circuit analysis, may lead to refinements in the circuit model and its ideal circuit elements. Once the desired and predicted behavior are in agreement, a physical prototype can be constructed.

The **physical prototype** is an actual electrical system, constructed from actual electrical components. Measurement techniques are used to determine the actual, quantitative behavior of the physical system. This actual behavior is compared with the desired behavior from the design specifications and the predicted behavior from circuit analysis. The comparisons may result in refinements to the physical prototype, the circuit model, or both. Eventually, this iterative process, in which models, components, and systems are continually refined, may produce a design that accurately matches the design specifications and thus meets the need.

From this description, it is clear that circuit analysis plays a very important role in the design process. Because circuit analysis is applied to circuit models, practicing engineers try to use mature circuit models so that the resulting designs will meet the design specifications in the first iteration. In this book, we use models that have been tested for between 20 and 100 years; you can assume that they are mature. The ability to model actual electrical systems with ideal circuit elements makes circuit theory extremely useful to engineers.

Saying that the interconnection of ideal circuit elements can be used to quantitatively predict the behavior of a system implies that we can describe the interconnection with mathematical equations. For the mathematical equations to be useful, we must write them in terms of measurable quantities. In the case of circuits, these quantities are voltage and current, which we discuss in Section 1.4. The study of circuit analysis involves understanding the behavior of each ideal circuit element in terms of its voltage and current and understanding the constraints imposed on the voltage and current as a result of interconnecting the ideal elements.

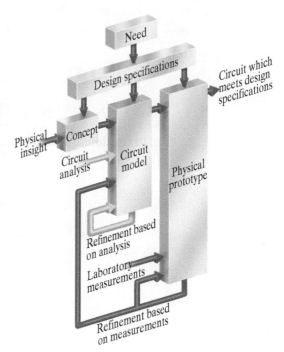

Figure 1.4 ▲ A conceptual model for electrical engineering design.

1.4   Voltage and Current

The concept of electric charge is the basis for describing all electrical phenomena. Let's review some important characteristics of electric charge.

- The charge is bipolar, meaning that electrical effects are described in terms of positive and negative charges.
- The electric charge exists in discrete quantities, which are integral multiples of the electronic charge, 1.6022×10^{-19} C.
- Electrical effects are attributed to both the separation of charge and charges in motion.

In circuit theory, the separation of charge creates an electric force (voltage), and the motion of charge creates an electric fluid (current).

The concepts of voltage and current are useful from an engineering point of view because they can be expressed quantitatively. Whenever positive and negative charges are separated, energy is expended. **Voltage** is the energy per unit charge created by the separation. We express this ratio in differential form as

Definition of voltage ▶

$$v = \frac{dw}{dq},$$ (1.1)

where

v = the voltage in volts,
w = the energy in joules,
q = the charge in coulombs.

The electrical effects caused by charges in motion depend on the rate of charge flow. The rate of charge flow is known as the **electric current**, which is expressed as

Definition of current ▶

$$i = \frac{dq}{dt},$$ (1.2)

where

i = the current in amperes,
q = the charge in coulombs,
t = the time in seconds.

Equations 1.1 and 1.2 are definitions for the magnitude of voltage and current, respectively. The bipolar nature of electric charge requires that we assign polarity references to these variables. We will do so in Section 1.5.

Although current is made up of discrete, moving electrons, we do not need to consider them individually because of the enormous number of them. Rather, we can think of electrons and their corresponding charge as one smoothly flowing entity. Thus, i is treated as a continuous variable.

One advantage of using circuit models is that we can model a component strictly in terms of the voltage and current at its terminals. Thus two physically different components could have the same relationship between the terminal voltage and terminal current. If they do, for purposes of circuit analysis, they are identical. Once we know how a component behaves at its terminals, we can analyze its behavior in a circuit. However, when developing circuit models, we are interested in a component's internal behavior. We might want to know, for example, whether charge conduction is taking place because of free electrons moving through the crystal lattice structure of a metal or whether it is because of electrons moving within the covalent bonds of a semiconductor material. However, these concerns are beyond the realm of circuit theory. In this book we use circuit models that have already been developed; we do not discuss how component models are developed.

1.5 The Ideal Basic Circuit Element

An **ideal basic circuit element** has three attributes: (1) it has only two terminals, which are points of connection to other circuit components; (2) it is described mathematically in terms of current and/or voltage; and (3) it cannot be subdivided into other elements. We use the word *ideal* to imply that a basic circuit element does not exist as a realizable physical component. However, as we discussed in Section 1.3, ideal elements can be connected in order to model actual devices and systems. We use the word *basic* to imply that the circuit element cannot be further reduced or subdivided into other elements. Thus the basic circuit elements form the building blocks for constructing circuit models, but they themselves cannot be modeled with any other type of element.

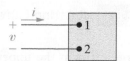

Figure 1.5 ▲ An ideal basic circuit element.

Figure 1.5 is a representation of an ideal basic circuit element. The box is blank because we are making no commitment at this time as to the type of circuit element it is. In Fig. 1.5, the voltage across the terminals of the box is denoted by v, and the current in the circuit element is denoted by i. The polarity reference for the voltage is indicated by the plus and minus signs, and the reference direction for the current is shown by the arrow placed alongside the current. The interpretation of these references given positive or negative numerical values of v and i is summarized in Table 1.4. Note that algebraically the notion of positive charge flowing in one direction is equivalent to the notion of negative charge flowing in the opposite direction.

The assignments of the reference polarity for voltage and the reference direction for current are entirely arbitrary. However, once you have assigned the references, you must write all subsequent equations to agree with the chosen references. The most widely used sign convention applied to these references is called the **passive sign convention**, which we use throughout this book. The passive sign convention can be stated as follows:

> Whenever the reference direction for the current in an element is in the direction of the reference voltage drop across the element (as in Fig. 1.5), use a positive sign in any expression that relates the voltage to the current. Otherwise, use a negative sign.

◀ **Passive sign convention**

We apply this sign convention in all the analyses that follow. Our purpose for introducing it even before we have introduced the different types of basic circuit elements is to impress on you the fact that the selection of polarity references along with the adoption of the passive sign convention is *not* a function of the basic elements nor the type of interconnections made with the basic elements. We present the application and interpretation of the passive sign convention in power calculations in Section 1.6.

Example 1.2 illustrates one use of the equation defining current.

TABLE 1.4   Interpretation of Reference Directions in Fig. 1.5

Positive Value	Negative Value
v voltage drop from terminal 1 to terminal 2	voltage rise from terminal 1 to terminal 2
or	*or*
voltage rise from terminal 2 to terminal 1	voltage drop from terminal 2 to terminal 1
i positive charge flowing from terminal 1 to terminal 2	positive charge flowing from terminal 2 to terminal 1
or	*or*
negative charge flowing from terminal 2 to terminal 1	negative charge flowing from terminal 1 to terminal 2

| Example 1.2 | **Relating Current and Charge** |

No charge exists at the upper terminal of the element in Fig. 1.5 for $t < 0$. At $t = 0$, a 5 A current begins to flow into the upper terminal.

a) Derive the expression for the charge accumulating at the upper terminal of the element for $t > 0$.

b) If the current is stopped after 10 seconds, how much charge has accumulated at the upper terminal?

Solution

a) From the definition of current given in Eq. 1.2, the expression for charge accumulation due to current flow is

$$q(t) = \int_0^t i(x)dx.$$

Therefore,

$$q(t) = \int_0^t 5dx = 5x \Big|_0^t = 5t - 5(0) = 5t \text{ C} \quad \text{for } t > 0.$$

b) The total charge that accumulates at the upper terminal in 10 seconds due to a 5 A current is $q(10) = 5(10) = 50$ C.

✓ ASSESSMENT PROBLEMS

Objective 2—Know and be able to use the definitions of *voltage* and *current*

1.3   The current at the terminals of the element in Fig. 1.5 is

$$i = 0, \qquad\qquad t < 0;$$

$$i = 20e^{-5000t} \text{ A}, \quad t \geq 0.$$

Calculate the total charge (in microcoulombs) entering the element at its upper terminal.

Answer: 4000 μC.

NOTE: Also try Chapter Problem 1.8.

1.4   The expression for the charge entering the upper terminal of Fig. 1.5 is

$$q = \frac{1}{\alpha^2} - \left(\frac{t}{\alpha} + \frac{1}{\alpha^2}\right)e^{-\alpha t} \text{ C}.$$

Find the maximum value of the current entering the terminal if $\alpha = 0.03679$ s^{-1}.

Answer: 10 A.

1.6 Power and Energy

Power and energy calculations also are important in circuit analysis. One reason is that although voltage and current are useful variables in the analysis and design of electrically based systems, the useful output of the system often is nonelectrical, and this output is conveniently expressed in terms of power or energy. Another reason is that all practical devices have limitations on the amount of power that they can handle. In the design process, therefore, voltage and current calculations by themselves are not sufficient.

We now relate power and energy to voltage and current and at the same time use the power calculation to illustrate the passive sign convention. Recall from basic physics that power is the time rate of expending or absorbing energy. (A water pump rated 75 kW can deliver more liters per second than one rated 7.5 kW.) Mathematically, energy per unit time is expressed in the form of a derivative, or

$$p = \frac{dw}{dt},$$ (1.3)   ◀ **Definition of power**

where

p = the power in watts,

w = the energy in joules,

i = the time in seconds.

Thus 1 W is equivalent to 1 J/s.

The power associated with the flow of charge follows directly from the definition of voltage and current in Eqs. 1.1 and 1.2, or

$$p = \frac{dw}{dt} = \left(\frac{dw}{dq}\right)\left(\frac{dq}{dt}\right),$$

so

$$p = vi$$ (1.4)   ◀ **Power equation**

where

p = the power in watts,

v = the voltage in volts,

i = the current in amperes.

Equation 1.4 shows that the **power** associated with a basic circuit element is simply the product of the current in the element and the voltage across the element. Therefore, power is a quantity associated with a pair of terminals, and we have to be able to tell from our calculation whether power is being delivered to the pair of terminals or extracted from it. This information comes from the correct application and interpretation of the passive sign convention.

If we use the passive sign convention, Eq. 1.4 is correct if the reference direction for the current is in the direction of the reference voltage drop across the terminals. Otherwise, Eq. 1.4 must be written with a minus sign. In other words, if the current reference is in the direction of a reference voltage rise across the terminals, the expression for the power is

$$p = -vi$$ (1.5)

The algebraic sign of power is based on charge movement through voltage drops and rises. As positive charges move through a drop in voltage, they lose energy, and as they move through a rise in voltage, they gain energy. Figure 1.6 summarizes the relationship between the polarity references for voltage and current and the expression for power.

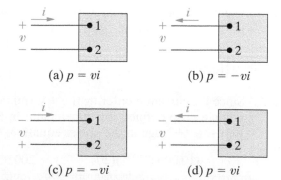

(a) $p = vi$ (b) $p = -vi$

(c) $p = -vi$ (d) $p = vi$

Figure 1.6 ▲ Polarity references and the expression for power.

We can now state the rule for interpreting the algebraic sign of power:

Interpreting algebraic sign of power ▶

> If the power is positive (that is, if $p > 0$), power is being delivered to the circuit inside the box. If the power is negative (that is, if $p < 0$), power is being extracted from the circuit inside the box.

For example, suppose that we have selected the polarity references shown in Fig. 1.6(b). Assume further that our calculations for the current and voltage yield the following numerical results:

$$i = 4 \text{ A} \quad \text{and} \quad v = -10 \text{ V}.$$

Then the power associated with the terminal pair 1,2 is

$$p = -(-10)(4) = 40 \text{ W}.$$

Thus the circuit inside the box is absorbing 40 W.

To take this analysis one step further, assume that a colleague is solving the same problem but has chosen the reference polarities shown in Fig. 1.6(c). The resulting numerical values are

$$i = -4 \text{ A}, \quad v = 10 \text{ V}, \quad \text{and} \quad p = 40 \text{ W}.$$

Note that interpreting these results in terms of this reference system gives the same conclusions that we previously obtained—namely, that the circuit inside the box is absorbing 40 W. In fact, any of the reference systems in Fig. 1.6 yields this same result.

Example 1.3 illustrates the relationship between voltage, current, power, and energy for an ideal basic circuit element and the use of the passive sign convention.

Example 1.3   Relating Voltage, Current, Power, and Energy

Assume that the voltage at the terminals of the element in Fig. 1.5, whose current was defined in Assessment Problem 1.3, is

$$v = 0 \qquad\qquad t < 0;$$
$$v = 10e^{-5000t} \text{ kV}, \qquad t \geq 0.$$

a) Calculate the power supplied to the element at 1 ms.

b) Calculate the total energy (in joules) delivered to the circuit element.

Solution

a) Since the current is entering the + terminal of the voltage drop defined for the element in Fig. 1.5, we use a "+" sign in the power equation.

$$p = vi = (10,000e^{-5000t})(20e^{-5000t}) = 200,000e^{-10,000t} \text{ W}.$$
$$p(0.001) = 200,000e^{-10,000t(0.001)} = 200,000e^{-10}$$
$$= 200,000(45.4 \times 10^{-6}) = 0.908 \text{ W}.$$

b) From the definition of power given in Eq. 1.3, the expression for energy is

$$w(t) = \int_0^t p(x)dx$$

To find the total energy delivered, integrate the expression for power from zero to infinity. Therefore,

$$w_{total} = \int_0^\infty 200,000e^{-10,000x} \, dx = \left. \frac{200,000e^{-10,000x}}{-10,000} \right|_0^\infty$$
$$= -20e^{-\infty} - (-20e^{-0}) = 0 + 20 = 20 \text{ J}.$$

Thus, the total energy supplied to the circuit element is 20 J.

✓ ASSESSMENT PROBLEMS

Objective 3—Know and use the definitions of *power* and *energy*; Objective 4—Be able to use the passive sign convention

1.5 Assume that a 20 V voltage drop occurs across an element from terminal 2 to terminal 1 and that a current of 4 A enters terminal 2.

a) Specify the values of v and i for the polarity references shown in Fig. 1.6(a)–(d).

b) State whether the circuit inside the box is absorbing or delivering power.

c) How much power is the circuit absorbing?

Answer: (a) Circuit 1.6(a): $v = -20$ V, $i = -4$ A;
circuit 1.6(b): $v = -20$ V, $i = 4$ A;
circuit 1.6(c): $v = 20$ V, $i = -4$ A;
circuit 1.6(d): $v = 20$ V, $i = 4$ A;

(b) absorbing;

(c) 80 W.

1.6 The voltage and current at the terminals of the circuit element in Fig 1.5 are zero for $t < 0$. For $t \geq 0$, they are

$$v = 80{,}000te^{-500t} \text{ V}, \qquad t \geq 0;$$

$$i = 15te^{-500t} \text{ A}, \qquad t \geq 0.$$

a) Find the time when the power delivered to the circuit element is maximum.

b) Find the maximum value of power.

c) Find the total energy delivered to the circuit element.

Answer: (a) 2 ms; (b) 649.6 mW; (c) 2.4 mJ.

1.7 A high-voltage direct-current (dc) transmission line between Celilo, Oregon and Sylmar, California is operating at 800 kV and carrying 1800 A, as shown. Calculate the power (in megawatts) at the Oregon end of the line and state the direction of power flow.

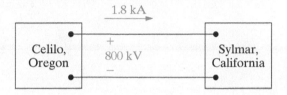

Answer: 1440 MW, Celilo to Sylmar

NOTE: Also try Chapter Problems 1.12, 1.19, and 1.24.

Practical Perspective

Balancing Power

A model of the circuitry that distributes power to a typical home is shown in Fig. 1.7 with voltage polarities and current directions defined for all of the circuit components. The results of circuit analysis give the values for all of these voltages and currents, which are summarized in Table 1.4. To determine whether or not the values given are correct, calculate the power associated with each component. Use the passive sign convention in the power calculations, as shown below.

$p_a = v_a i_a = (120)(-10) = -1200$ W $p_b = -v_b i_b = -(120)(9) = -1080$ W

$p_c = v_c i_c = (10)(10) = 100$ W $p_d = -v_d i_d = -(10)(1) = -10$ W

$p_e = v_e i_e = (-10)(-9) = 90$ W $p_f = -v_f i_f = -(-100)(5) = 500$ W

$p_g = v_g i_g = (120)(4) = 480$ W $p_h = v_h i_h = (-220)(-5) = 1100$ W

The power calculations show that components a, b, and d are supplying power, since the power values are negative, while components c, e, f, g, and h are absorbing power. Now check to see if the power balances by finding the total power supplied and the total power absorbed.

$$p_{\text{supplied}} = p_a + p_b + p_d = -1200 - 1080 - 10 = -2290 \text{ W}$$

$$p_{\text{absorbed}} = p_c + p_e + p_f + p_g + p_h$$

$$= 100 + 90 + 500 + 480 + 1100 = 2270 \text{ W}$$

$$p_{\text{supplied}} + p_{\text{absorbed}} = -2290 + 2270 = -20 \text{ W}$$

Something is wrong—if the values for voltage and current in this circuit are correct, the total power should be zero! There is an error in the data and we can find it from the calculated powers if the error exists in the sign of a single component. Note that if we divide the total power by 2, we get -10 W, which is the power calculated for component d. If the power for component d was $+10$ W, the total power would be 0. Circuit analysis techniques from upcoming chapters can be used to show that the current through component d should be -1 A, not $+1$ A given in Table 1.4.

TABLE 1.4 Volatage and current values for the circuit in Fig. 1.7.

Component	v(V)	i(A)
a	120	−10
b	120	9
c	10	10
d	10	1
e	−10	−9
f	−100	5
g	120	4
h	−220	−5

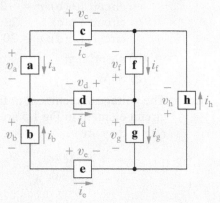

Figure 1.7 ▲ Circuit model for power distribution in a home, with voltages and currents defined.

Note: Assess your understanding of the Practical Perspective by trying Chapter Problems 1.34 and 1.35.

Summary

- The International System of Units (SI) enables engineers to communicate in a meaningful way about quantitative results. Table 1.1 summarizes the base SI units; Table 1.2 presents some useful derived SI units. (See pages 8 and 9.)

- Circuit analysis is based on the variables of voltage and current. (See page 11.)

- **Voltage** is the energy per unit charge created by charge separation and has the SI unit of volt ($v = dw/dq$). (See page 12.)

- **Current** is the rate of charge flow and has the SI unit of ampere ($i = dq/dt$). (See page 12.)

- The **ideal basic circuit element** is a two-terminal component that cannot be subdivided; it can be described mathematically in terms of its terminal voltage and current. (See page 12.)

- The **passive sign convention** uses a positive sign in the expression that relates the voltage and current at the terminals of an element when the reference direction for the current through the element is in the direction of the reference voltage drop across the element. (See page 13.)

- **Power** is energy per unit of time and is equal to the product of the terminal voltage and current; it has the SI unit of watt ($p = dw/dt = vi$). (See page 15.)

- The algebraic sign of power is interpreted as follows:

  - If $p > 0$, power is being delivered to the circuit or circuit component.

  - If $p < 0$, power is being extracted from the circuit or circuit component. (See page 16.)

Problems

Section 1.2

1.1 There are approximately 260 million passenger vehicles registered in the United States. Assume that the battery in the average vehicle stores 540 watt-hours (Wh) of energy. Estimate (in gigawatt-hours) the total energy stored in U.S. passenger vehicles.

1.2 A hand-held video player displays 480×320 picture elements (pixels) in each frame of the video. Each pixel requires 2 bytes of memory. Videos are displayed at a rate of 30 frames per second. How many hours of video will fit in a 32 gigabyte memory?

1.3 The 16 giga-byte (GB = 2^{30} bytes) flash memory chip for an MP3 player is 11 mm by 15 mm by 1 mm. This memory chip holds 20,000 photos.

    a) How many photos fit into a cube whose sides are 1 mm?

    b) How many bytes of memory are stored in a cube whose sides are 200 μm?

1.4 The line described in Assessment Problem 1.7 is 845 mi in length. The line contains four conductors, each weighing 2526 lb per 1000 ft. How many kilograms of conductor are in the line?

1.5 One liter (L) of paint covers approximately 10 m^2 of wall. How thick is the layer before it dries? (*Hint*: 1 L = 1 $\times$ 10^6 mm^3.)

1.6 Some species of bamboo can grow 250 mm/day. Assume individual cells in the plant are 10 μm long.

    a) How long, on average, does it take a bamboo stalk to grow 1 cell length?

    b) How many cell lengths are added in one week, on average?

Section 1.4

1.7 There is no charge at the upper terminal of the element in Fig. 1.5 for $t < 0$. At $t = 0$ a current of $125e^{-2500t}$ mA enters the upper terminal.

    a) Derive the expression for the charge that accumulates at the upper terminal for $t > 0$.

    b) Find the total charge that accumulates at the upper terminal.

    c) If the current is stopped at $t = 0.5$ ms, how much charge has accumulated at the upper terminal?

1.8 The current entering the upper terminal of Fig. 1.5 is

$$i = 20 \cos 5000t \text{ A.}$$

Assume the charge at the upper terminal is zero at the instant the current is passing through its maximum value. Find the expression for $q(t)$.

1.9 The current at the terminals of the element in Fig. 1.5 is

$$i = 0, \qquad\qquad t < 0;$$
$$i = 40te^{-500t} \text{ A,} \qquad t \geq 0.$$

    a) Find the expression for the charge accumulating at the upper terminal.

    b) Find the charge that has accumulated at $t = 1$ ms.

1.10 In electronic circuits it is not unusual to encounter currents in the microampere range. Assume a 35 μA current, due to the flow of electrons. What is the average number of electrons per second that flow past a fixed reference cross section that is perpendicular to the direction of flow?

1.11 How much energy is imparted to an electron as it flows through a 6 V battery from the positive to the negative terminal? Express your answer in attojoules.

Sections 1.5–1.6

1.12 The references for the voltage and current at the terminal of a circuit element are as shown in Fig. 1.6(d). The numerical values for v and i are 40 V and -10 A.

    a) Calculate the power at the terminals and state whether the power is being absorbed or delivered by the element in the box.

    b) Given that the current is due to electron flow, state whether the electrons are entering or leaving terminal 2.

    c) Do the electrons gain or lose energy as they pass through the element in the box?

1.13 Repeat Problem 1.12 with a voltage of -60 V.

1.14 Two electric circuits, represented by boxes A and B, are connected as shown in Fig. P1.14. The reference direction for the current i in the interconnection and the reference polarity for the voltage v across the interconnection are as shown in the figure. For each of the following sets of numerical values, calculate the power in the interconnection and state whether the power is flowing from A to B or vice versa.

a) $i = 6$ A, $\quad v = 30$ V

b) $i = -8$ A, $\quad v = -20$ V

c) $i = 4$ A, $\quad v = -60$ V

d) $i = -9$ A, $\quad v = 40$ V

Figure P1.14

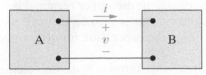

1.15 When a car has a dead battery, it can often be started by connecting the battery from another car across its terminals. The positive terminals are connected together as are the negative terminals. The connection is illustrated in Fig. P1.15. Assume the current i in Fig. P1.15 is measured and found to be 30 A.

a) Which car has the dead battery?

b) If this connection is maintained for 1 min, how much energy is transferred to the dead battery?

Figure P1.15

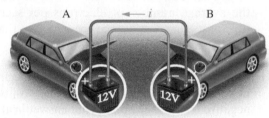

1.16 The manufacturer of a 1.5 V D flashlight battery says that the battery will deliver 9 mA for 40 continuous hours. During that time the voltage will drop from 1.5 V to 1.0 V. Assume the drop in voltage is linear with time. How much energy does the battery deliver in this 40 h interval?

1.17 One 12 V battery supplies 100 mA to a boom box. How much energy does the battery supply in 4 h?

1.18 The voltage and current at the terminals of the circuit element in Fig. 1.5 are zero for $t < 0$. For $t \geq 0$ they are

$$v = 15e^{-250t} \text{ V},$$
$$i = 40e^{-250t} \text{ mA}.$$

a) Calculate the power supplied to the element at 10 ms.

b) Calculate the total energy delivered to the circuit element.

1.19 The voltage and current at the terminals of the circuit element in Fig. 1.5 are zero for $t < 0$. For $t \geq 0$ they are

$$v = 75 - 75e^{-1000t} \text{ V},$$
$$i = 50e^{-1000t} \text{ mA}.$$

a) Find the maximum value of the power delivered to the circuit.

b) Find the total energy delivered to the element.

1.20 The voltage and current at the terminals of the circuit element in Fig. 1.5 are zero for $t < 0$. For $t \geq 0$ they are

$$v = 50e^{-1600t} - 50e^{-400t} \text{ V},$$
$$i = 5e^{-1600t} - 5e^{-400t} \text{ mA}.$$

a) Find the power at $t = 625 \ \mu$s.

b) How much energy is delivered to the circuit element between 0 and 625 μs?

c) Find the total energy delivered to the element.

1.21 The voltage and current at the terminals of the circuit element in Fig. 1.5 are zero for $t < 0$. For $t \geq 0$ they are

$$v = (1500t + 1)e^{-750t} \text{ V}, \quad t \geq 0;$$
$$i = 40e^{-750t} \text{ mA}, \quad\quad\quad t \geq 0.$$

a) Find the time when the power delivered to the circuit element is maximum.

b) Find the maximum value of p in milliwatts.

c) Find the total energy delivered to the circuit element in microjoules.

1.22 The voltage and current at the terminals of the circuit element in Fig. 1.5 are zero for $t < 0$. For $t \geq 0$ they are

$$v = (3200t + 4)e^{-1000t} \text{ V},$$
$$i = (128t + 0.16)e^{-1000t} \text{ A}.$$

a) At what instant of time is maximum power delivered to the element?

b) Find the maximum power in watts.

c) Find the total energy delivered to the element in microjoules.

1.23 The voltage and current at the terminals of the circuit element in Fig. 1.5 are zero for $t < 0$ and $t > 40$ s. In the interval between 0 and 40 s the expressions are

$$v = t(1 - 0.025t) \text{ V}, \quad 0 < t < 40 \text{ s};$$
$$i = 4 - 0.2t \text{ A}, \quad 0 < t < 40 \text{ s}.$$

a) At what instant of time is the power being delivered to the circuit element maximum?

b) What is the power at the time found in part (a)?

c) At what instant of time is the power being extracted from the circuit element maximum?

d) What is the power at the time found in part (c)?

e) Calculate the net energy delivered to the circuit at 0, 10, 20, 30 and 40 s.

1.24 The voltage and current at the terminals of the circuit element in Fig. 1.5 are zero for $t < 0$. For $t \geq 0$ they are

$$v = 400e^{-100t} \sin 200t \text{ V},$$
$$i = 5e^{-100t} \sin 200t \text{ A}.$$

a) Find the power absorbed by the element at $t = 10$ ms.

b) Find the total energy absorbed by the element.

1.25 The voltage and current at the terminals of the element in Fig. 1.5 are

$$v = 250 \cos 800\pi t \text{ V}, \quad i = 8 \sin 800\pi t \text{ A}.$$

a) Find the maximum value of the power being delivered to the element.

b) Find the maximum value of the power being extracted from the element.

c) Find the average value of p in the interval $0 \leq t \leq 2.5$ ms.

d) Find the average value of p in the interval $0 \leq t \leq 15.625$ ms.

1.26 The voltage and current at the terminals of an automobile battery during a charge cycle are shown in Fig. P1.26.

a) Calculate the total charge transferred to the battery.

b) Calculate the total energy transferred to the battery.

c) Find the total energy delivered to the element.

Figure P1.26

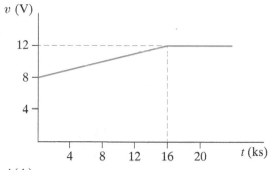

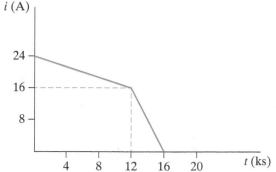

1.27 The voltage and current at the terminals of the circuit element in Fig. 1.5 are shown in Fig. P1.27.

a) Sketch the power versus t plot for $0 \leq t \leq 80$ ms.

b) Calculate the energy delivered to the circuit element at $t = 10, 30,$ and 80 ms.

Figure P1.27

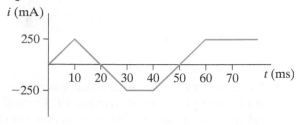

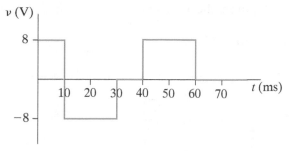

1.28 An industrial battery is charged over a period of several hours at a constant voltage of 120 V. Initially, the current is 10 mA and increases linearly to 15 mA in 10 ks. From 10 ks to 20 ks, the current is constant at 15 mA. From 20 ks to 30 ks the current decreases linearly to 10 mA. At 30 ks the power is disconnected from the battery.

a) Sketch the current from $t = 0$ to $t = 30$ ks.

b) Sketch the power delivered to the battery from $t = 0$ to $t = 30$ ks.

c) Using the sketch of the power, find the total energy delivered to the battery.

1.29 The numerical values for the currents and voltages in the circuit in Fig. P1.29 are given in Table P1.29. Find the total power developed in the circuit.

Figure P1.29

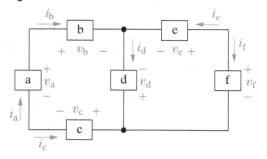

TABLE P1.29

Element	Voltage (V)	Current (mA)
a	40	−4
b	−24	−4
c	−16	4
d	−80	−1.5
e	40	2.5
f	120	−2.5

1.30 The numerical values of the voltages and currents in the interconnection seen in Fig. P1.30 are given in Table P1.30. Does the interconnection satisfy the power check?

Figure P1.30

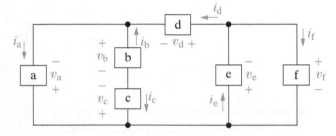

TABLE P1.30

Element	Voltage (kV)	Current (μA)
a	−3	−250
b	4	−400
c	1	400
d	1	150
e	−4	200
f	4	50

1.31 Assume you are an engineer in charge of a project and one of your subordinate engineers reports that the interconnection in Fig. P1.31 does not pass the power check. The data for the interconnection are given in Table P1.31.

a) Is the subordinate correct? Explain your answer.

b) If the subordinate is correct, can you find the error in the data?

Figure P1.31

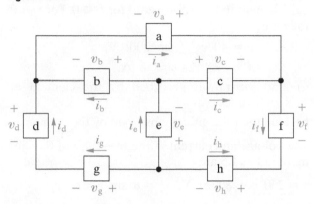

TABLE P1.31

Element	Voltage (V)	Current (A)
a	46.16	6.0
b	14.16	4.72
c	−32.0	−6.4
d	22.0	1.28
e	−33.6	−1.68
f	66.0	0.4
g	2.56	1.28
h	−0.4	0.4

1.32 The voltage and power values for each of the elements shown in Fig. P1.32 are given in Table P1.32.

a) Show that the interconnection of the elements satisfies the power check.

b) Find the value of the current through each of the elements using the values of power and voltage and the current directions shown in the figure.

Figure P1.32

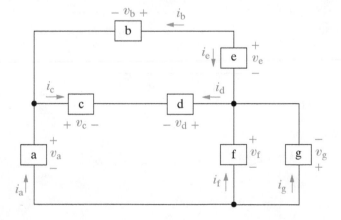

TABLE P1.32

Element	Power (kW)	Voltage (V)
a	0.6 supplied	400
b	0.05 supplied	−100
c	0.4 absorbed	200
d	0.6 supplied	300
e	0.1 absorbed	−200
f	2.0 absorbed	500
g	1.25 supplied	−500

TABLE P1.33

Element	Power (mW)	Current (mA)
a	175	25
b	375	75
c	150	−50
d	−320	40
e	160	20
f	120	−30
g	−660	55

1.33 The current and power for each of the interconnected elements in Fig. P1.33 is measured. The values are listed in Table P1.33.

a) Show that the interconnection satisfies the power check.

b) Identify the elements that absorb power.

c) Find the voltage for each of the elements in the interconnection, using the values of power and current and the voltage polarities shown in the figure.

Figure P1.33

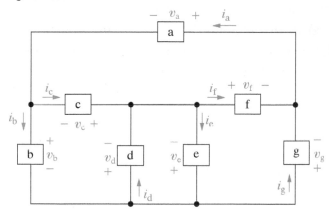

1.34 Show that the power balances for the circuit shown in Fig. 1.7, using the voltage and current values given in Table 1.4, with the value of the current for component d changed to −1 A.

1.35 Suppose there is no power lost in the wires used to distribute power in a typical home.

a) Create a new model for the power distribution circuit by modifying the circuit shown in Fig 1.7. Use the same names, voltage polarities, and current directions for the components that remain in this modified model.

b) The following voltages and currents are calculated for the components:

$$v_a = 120 \text{ V} \qquad i_a = -10 \text{ A}$$
$$v_b = 120 \text{ V} \qquad i_b = 10 \text{ A}$$
$$v_f = -120 \text{ V} \qquad i_f = 3 \text{ A}$$
$$v_g = 120 \text{ V}$$
$$v_h = -240 \text{ V} \qquad i_h = -7 \text{ A}$$

If the power in this modified model balances, what is the value of the current in component g?

Circuit Elements

✓ CHAPTER OBJECTIVES

1 Understand the symbols for and the behavior of the following ideal basic circuit elements: independent voltage and current sources, dependent voltage and current sources, and resistors.

2 Be able to state Ohm's law, Kirchhoff's current law, and Kirchhoff's voltage law, and be able to use these laws to analyze simple circuits.

3 Know how to calculate the power for each element in a simple circuit and be able to determine whether or not the power balances for the whole circuit.

There are five ideal basic circuit elements: voltage sources, current sources, resistors, inductors, and capacitors. In this chapter we discuss the characteristics of voltage sources, current sources, and resistors. Although this may seem like a small number of elements with which to begin analyzing circuits, many practical systems can be modeled with just sources and resistors. They are also a useful starting point because of their relative simplicity; the mathematical relationships between voltage and current in sources and resistors are algebraic. Thus you will be able to begin learning the basic techniques of circuit analysis with only algebraic manipulations.

We will postpone introducing inductors and capacitors until Chapter 6, because their use requires that you solve integral and differential equations. However, the basic analytical techniques for solving circuits with inductors and capacitors are the same as those introduced in this chapter. So, by the time you need to begin manipulating more difficult equations, you should be very familiar with the methods of writing them.

Practical Perspective

Heating with Electric Radiators

You want to heat your small garage using a couple of electric radiators. The power and voltage requirements for each radiator are 1200 W, 240 V. But you are not sure how to wire the radiators to the power supplied to the garage. Should you use the wiring diagram on the left, or the one on the right? Does it make any difference?

Once you have studied the material in this chapter, you will be able to answer these questions and determine how to heat the garage. The Practical Perspective at the end of this chapter guides you through the analysis of two circuits based on the two wiring diagrams shown below.

style-photography.de/fotolia

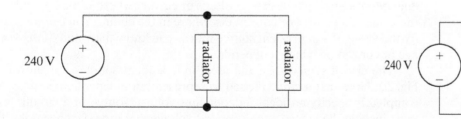

2.1 Voltage and Current Sources

Before discussing ideal voltage and current sources, we need to consider the general nature of electrical sources. An **electrical source** is a device that is capable of converting nonelectric energy to electric energy and vice versa. A discharging battery converts chemical energy to electric energy, whereas a battery being charged converts electric energy to chemical energy. A dynamo is a machine that converts mechanical energy to electric energy and vice versa. If operating in the mechanical-to-electric mode, it is called a generator. If transforming from electric to mechanical energy, it is referred to as a motor. The important thing to remember about these sources is that they can either deliver or absorb electric power, generally maintaining either voltage or current. This behavior is of particular interest for circuit analysis and led to the creation of the ideal voltage source and the ideal current source as basic circuit elements. The challenge is to model practical sources in terms of the ideal basic circuit elements.

An **ideal voltage source** is a circuit element that maintains a prescribed voltage across its terminals regardless of the current flowing in those terminals. Similarly, an **ideal current source** is a circuit element that maintains a prescribed current through its terminals regardless of the voltage across those terminals. These circuit elements do not exist as practical devices—they are idealized models of actual voltage and current sources.

Using an ideal model for current and voltage sources places an important restriction on how we may describe them mathematically. Because an ideal voltage source provides a steady voltage, even if the current in the element changes, it is impossible to specify the current in an ideal voltage source as a function of its voltage. Likewise, if the only information you have about an ideal current source is the value of current supplied, it is impossible to determine the voltage across that current source. We have sacrificed our ability to relate voltage and current in a practical source for the simplicity of using ideal sources in circuit analysis.

Ideal voltage and current sources can be further described as either independent sources or dependent sources. An **independent source** establishes a voltage or current in a circuit without relying on voltages or currents elsewhere in the circuit. The value of the voltage or current supplied is specified by the value of the independent source alone. In contrast, a **dependent source** establishes a voltage or current whose value depends on the value of a voltage or current elsewhere in the circuit. You cannot specify the value of a dependent source unless you know the value of the voltage or current on which it depends.

The circuit symbols for the ideal independent sources are shown in Fig. 2.1. Note that a circle is used to represent an independent source. To completely specify an ideal independent voltage source in a circuit, you must include the value of the supplied voltage and the reference polarity, as shown in Fig. 2.1(a). Similarly, to completely specify an ideal independent current source, you must include the value of the supplied current and its reference direction, as shown in Fig. 2.1(b).

The circuit symbols for the ideal dependent sources are shown in Fig. 2.2. A diamond is used to represent a dependent source. Both the

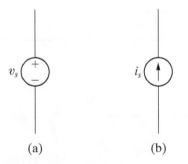

(a)   (b)

Figure 2.1 ▲ The circuit symbols for (a) an ideal independent voltage source and (b) an ideal independent current source.

dependent current source and the dependent voltage source may be controlled by either a voltage or a current elsewhere in the circuit, so there are a total of four variations, as indicated by the symbols in Fig. 2.2. Dependent sources are sometimes called **controlled sources**.

To completely specify an ideal dependent voltage-controlled voltage source, you must identify the controlling voltage, the equation that permits you to compute the supplied voltage from the controlling voltage, and the reference polarity for the supplied voltage. In Fig. 2.2(a), the controlling voltage is named v_x, the equation that determines the supplied voltage v_s is

$$v_s = \mu v_x,$$

and the reference polarity for v_s is as indicated. Note that μ is a multiplying constant that is dimensionless.

Similar requirements exist for completely specifying the other ideal dependent sources. In Fig. 2.2(b), the controlling current is i_x, the equation for the supplied voltage v_s is

$$v_s = \rho i_x,$$

the reference polarity is as shown, and the multiplying constant ρ has the dimension volts per ampere. In Fig. 2.2(c), the controlling voltage is v_x, the equation for the supplied current i_s is

$$i_s = \alpha v_x,$$

the reference direction is as shown, and the multiplying constant α has the dimension amperes per volt. In Fig. 2.2(d), the controlling current is i_x, the equation for the supplied current i_s is

$$i_s = \beta i_x,$$

the reference direction is as shown, and the multiplying constant β is dimensionless.

Finally, in our discussion of ideal sources, we note that they are examples of active circuit elements. An **active element** is one that models a device capable of generating electric energy. **Passive elements** model physical devices that cannot generate electric energy. Resistors, inductors, and capacitors are examples of passive circuit elements. Examples 2.1 and 2.2 illustrate how the characteristics of ideal independent and dependent sources limit the types of permissible interconnections of the sources.

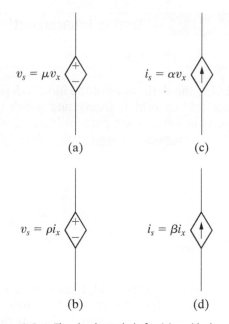

Figure 2.2 ▲ The circuit symbols for (a) an ideal dependent voltage-controlled voltage source, (b) an ideal dependent current-controlled voltage source, (c) an ideal dependent voltage-controlled current source, and (d) an ideal dependent current-controlled current source.

Example 2.1   Testing Interconnections of Ideal Sources

Using the definitions of the ideal independent voltage and current sources, state which interconnections in Fig. 2.3 are permissible and which violate the constraints imposed by the ideal sources.

Solution

Connection (a) is valid. Each source supplies voltage across the same pair of terminals, marked a,b. This requires that each source supply the same voltage with the same polarity, which they do.

Connection (b) is valid. Each source supplies current through the same pair of terminals, marked a,b. This requires that each source supply the same current in the same direction, which they do.

Connection (c) is not permissible. Each source supplies voltage across the same pair of terminals, marked a,b. This requires that each source supply the same voltage with the same polarity, which they do not.

Connection (d) is not permissible. Each source supplies current through the same pair of terminals, marked a,b. This requires that each source supply the same current in the same direction, which they do not.

Connection (e) is valid. The voltage source supplies voltage across the pair of terminals marked a,b. The current source supplies current through the same pair of terminals. Because an ideal voltage source supplies the same voltage regardless of the current, and an ideal current source supplies the same current regardless of the voltage, this is a permissible connection.

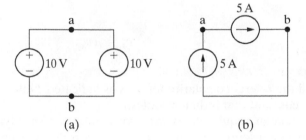

(a)   (b)

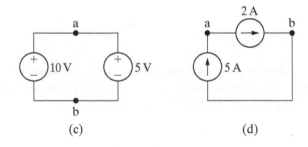

(c)   (d)

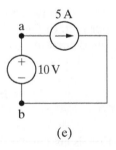

(e)

Figure 2.3 ▲ The circuits for Example 2.1.

| Example 2.2 | **Testing Interconnections of Ideal Independent and Dependent Sources** |

Using the definitions of the ideal independent and dependent sources, state which interconnections in Fig. 2.4 are valid and which violate the constraints imposed by the ideal sources.

Solution

Connection (a) is invalid. Both the independent source and the dependent source supply voltage across the same pair of terminals, labeled a,b. This requires that each source supply the same voltage with the same polarity. The independent source supplies 5 V, but the dependent source supplies 15 V.

Connection (b) is valid. The independent voltage source supplies voltage across the pair of terminals marked a,b. The dependent current source supplies current through the same pair of terminals. Because an ideal voltage source supplies the same voltage regardless of current, and an ideal current source supplies the same current regardless of voltage, this is an allowable connection.

Connection (c) is valid. The independent current source supplies current through the pair of terminals marked a,b. The dependent voltage source supplies voltage across the same pair of terminals. Because an ideal current source supplies the same current regardless of voltage, and an ideal voltage source supplies the same voltage regardless of current, this is an allowable connection.

Connection (d) is invalid. Both the independent source and the dependent source supply current through the same pair of terminals, labeled a,b. This requires that each source supply the same current in the same reference direction. The independent source supplies 2 A, but the dependent source supplies 6 A in the opposite direction.

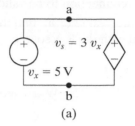

(a)

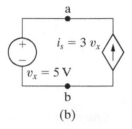

(b)

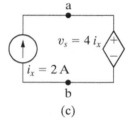

(c)

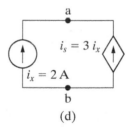

(d)

Figure 2.4 ▲ The circuits for Example 2.2.

✓ASSESSMENT PROBLEMS

Objective 1—Understand ideal basic circuit elements

2.1 For the circuit shown,

   a) What value of v_g is required in order for the interconnection to be valid?

   b) For this value of v_g, find the power associated with the 8 A source.

Answer: (a) −2 V;

   (b) −16 W (16 W delivered).

2.2 For the circuit shown,

   a) What value of α is required in order for the interconnection to be valid?

   b) For the value of α calculated in part (a), find the power associated with the 25 V source.

Answer: (a) 0.6 A/V;

   (b) 375 W (375 W absorbed).

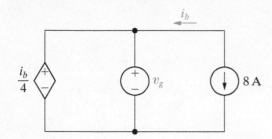

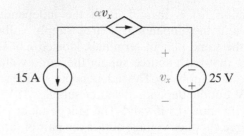

NOTE: Also try Chapter Problems 2.6 and 2.7.

2.2 Electrical Resistance (Ohm's Law)

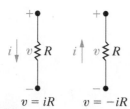

Figure 2.5 ▲ The circuit symbol for a resistor having a resistance R.

Resistance is the capacity of materials to impede the flow of current or, more specifically, the flow of electric charge. The circuit element used to model this behavior is the **resistor**. Figure 2.5 shows the circuit symbol for the resistor, with R denoting the resistance value of the resistor.

Conceptually, we can understand resistance if we think about the moving electrons that make up electric current interacting with and being resisted by the atomic structure of the material through which they are moving. In the course of these interactions, some amount of electric energy is converted to thermal energy and dissipated in the form of heat. This effect may be undesirable. However, many useful electrical devices take advantage of resistance heating, including stoves, toasters, irons, and space heaters.

Most materials exhibit measurable resistance to current. The amount of resistance depends on the material. Metals such as copper and aluminum have small values of resistance, making them good choices for wiring used to conduct electric current. In fact, when represented in a circuit diagram, copper or aluminum wiring isn't usually modeled as a resistor; the resistance of the wire is so small compared to the resistance of other elements in the circuit that we can neglect the wiring resistance to simplify the diagram.

For purposes of circuit analysis, we must reference the current in the resistor to the terminal voltage. We can do so in two ways: either in the direction of the voltage drop across the resistor or in the direction of the voltage rise across the resistor, as shown in Fig. 2.6. If we choose the former, the relationship between the voltage and current is

$$v = iR,$$
$$v = -iR$$

Figure 2.6 ▲ Two possible reference choices for the current and voltage at the terminals of a resistor, and the resulting equations.

Ohm's law ▶

$$v = iR, \tag{2.1}$$

where

$$v = \text{the voltage in volts,}$$

$$i = \text{the current in amperes,}$$

$$R = \text{the resistance in ohms.}$$

If we choose the second method, we must write

$$v = -iR, \tag{2.2}$$

where v, i, and R are, as before, measured in volts, amperes, and ohms, respectively. The algebraic signs used in Eqs. 2.1 and 2.2 are a direct consequence of the passive sign convention, which we introduced in Chapter 1.

Equations 2.1 and 2.2 are known as **Ohm's law** after Georg Simon Ohm, a German physicist who established its validity early in the nineteenth century. Ohm's law is the algebraic relationship between voltage and current for a resistor. In SI units, resistance is measured in ohms. The Greek letter omega (Ω) is the standard symbol for an ohm. The circuit diagram symbol for an 8 Ω resistor is shown in Fig. 2.7.

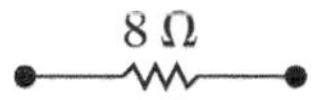

Ohm's law expresses the voltage as a function of the current. However, expressing the current as a function of the voltage also is convenient. Thus, from Eq. 2.1,

$$i = \frac{v}{R}, \tag{2.3}$$

or, from Eq. 2.2,

$$i = -\frac{v}{R}. \tag{2.4}$$

The reciprocal of the resistance is referred to as **conductance**, is symbolized by the letter G, and is measured in siemens (S). Thus,

$$G = \frac{1}{R} \text{ S.} \tag{2.5}$$

An 8 Ω resistor has a conductance value of 0.125 S. In much of the professional literature, the unit used for conductance is the mho (ohm spelled backward), which is symbolized by an inverted omega (℧). Therefore we may also describe an 8 Ω resistor as having a conductance of 0.125 mho, (℧).

We use ideal resistors in circuit analysis to model the behavior of physical devices. Using the qualifier *ideal* reminds us that the resistor model makes several simplifying assumptions about the behavior of actual resistive devices. The most important of these simplifying assumptions is that the resistance of the ideal resistor is constant and its value does not vary over time. Most actual resistive devices do not have constant resistance, and their resistance does vary over time. The ideal resistor model can be used to represent a physical device whose resistance doesn't vary much from some constant value over the time period of interest in the circuit analysis. In this book we assume that the simplifying assumptions about resistance devices are valid, and we thus use ideal resistors in circuit analysis.

We may calculate the power at the terminals of a resistor in several ways. The first approach is to use the defining equation and simply calculate

Figure 2.7 ▲ The circuit symbol for an 8 Ω resistor.

the product of the terminal voltage and current. For the reference systems shown in Fig. 2.6, we write

$$p = vi \qquad (2.6)$$

when $v = iR$ and

$$p = -vi \qquad (2.7)$$

when $v = -iR$.

A second method of expressing the power at the terminals of a resistor expresses power in terms of the current and the resistance. Substituting Eq. 2.1 into Eq. 2.6, we obtain

$$p = vi = (iR)i$$

so

Power in a resistor in terms of current ▶

$$p = i^2 R. \qquad (2.8)$$

Likewise, substituting Eq. 2.2 into Eq. 2.7, we have

$$p = -vi = -(-iR)i = i^2 R. \qquad (2.9)$$

Equations 2.8 and 2.9 are identical and demonstrate clearly that, regardless of voltage polarity and current direction, the power at the terminals of a resistor is positive. Therefore, a resistor absorbs power from the circuit.

A third method of expressing the power at the terminals of a resistor is in terms of the voltage and resistance. The expression is independent of the polarity references, so

Power in a resistor in terms of voltage ▶

$$p = \frac{v^2}{R}. \qquad (2.10)$$

Sometimes a resistor's value will be expressed as a conductance rather than as a resistance. Using the relationship between resistance and conductance given in Eq. 2.5, we may also write Eqs. 2.9 and 2.10 in terms of the conductance, or

$$p = \frac{i^2}{G}, \qquad (2.11)$$

$$p = v^2 G. \qquad (2.12)$$

Equations 2.6–2.12 provide a variety of methods for calculating the power absorbed by a resistor. Each yields the same answer. In analyzing a circuit, look at the information provided and choose the power equation that uses that information directly.

Example 2.3 illustrates the application of Ohm's law in conjunction with an ideal source and a resistor. Power calculations at the terminals of a resistor also are illustrated.

| Example 2.3 | **Calculating Voltage, Current, and Power for a Simple Resistive Circuit** |

In each circuit in Fig. 2.8, either the value of v or i is not known.

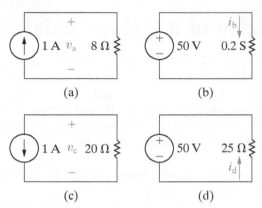

Figure 2.8 ▲ The circuits for Example 2.3.

a) Calculate the values of v and i.

b) Determine the power dissipated in each resistor.

Solution

a) The voltage v_a in Fig. 2.8(a) is a drop in the direction of the current in the resistor. Therefore,

$$v_a = (1)(8) = 8 \text{ V}.$$

The current i_b in the resistor with a conductance of 0.2 S in Fig. 2.8(b) is in the direction of the voltage drop across the resistor. Thus

$$i_b = (50)(0.2) = 10 \text{ A}.$$

The voltage v_c in Fig. 2.8(c) is a rise in the direction of the current in the resistor. Hence

$$v_c = -(1)(20) = -20 \text{ V}.$$

The current i_d in the 25 Ω resistor in Fig. 2.8(d) is in the direction of the voltage rise across the resistor. Therefore

$$i_d = \frac{-50}{25} = -2 \text{ A}.$$

b) The power dissipated in each of the four resistors is

$$P_{8\Omega} = \frac{(8)^2}{8} = (1)^2(8) = 8 \text{ W},$$

$$P_{0.2S} = (50)^2(0.2) = 500 \text{ W},$$

$$P_{20\Omega} = \frac{(-20)^2}{20} = (1)^2(20) = 20 \text{ W},$$

$$P_{25\Omega} = \frac{(50)^2}{25} = (-2)^2(25) = 100 \text{ W}.$$

✓ ASSESSMENT PROBLEMS

Objective 2—Be able to state and use Ohm's Law . . .

2.3   For the circuit shown,

a) If $v_g = 1$ kV and $i_g = 5$ mA, find the value of R and the power absorbed by the resistor.

b) If $i_g = 75$ mA and the power delivered by the voltage source is 3 W, find v_g, R, and the power absorbed by the resistor.

c) If $R = 300$ Ω and the power absorbed by R is 480 mW, find i_g and v_g.

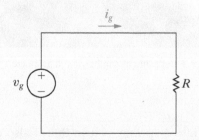

Answer: (a) 200 kΩ, 5 W;

(b) 40 V, 533.33 Ω, 3 W;

(c) 40 mA, 12 V.

2.4   For the circuit shown,

a) If $i_g = 0.5$ A and $G = 50$ mS, find v_g and the power delivered by the current source.

b) If $v_g = 15$ V and the power delivered to the conductor is 9 W, find the conductance G and the source current i_g.

c) If $G = 200$ μS and the power delivered to the conductance is 8 W, find i_g and v_g.

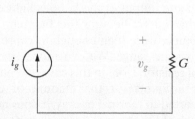

Answer: (a) 10 V, 5 W;

(b) 40 mS, 0.6 A;

(c) 40 mA, 200 V.

NOTE: *Also try Chapter Problems 2.11 and 2.12.*

Having introduced the general characteristics of ideal sources and resistors, we next show how to use these elements to build the circuit model of a practical system.

2.3 Construction of a Circuit Model

We have already stated that one reason for an interest in the basic circuit elements is that they can be used to construct circuit models of practical systems. The skill required to develop a circuit model of a device or system is as complex as the skill required to solve the derived circuit. Although this text emphasizes the skills required to solve circuits, you also will need other skills in the practice of electrical engineering, and one of the most important is modeling.

We develop circuit models in the next two examples. In Example 2.4 we construct a circuit model based on a knowledge of the behavior of the system's components and how the components are interconnected. In Example 2.5 we create a circuit model by measuring the terminal behavior of a device.

Example 2.4   **Constructing a Circuit Model of a Flashlight**

Construct a circuit model of a flashlight.

Solution

We chose the flashlight to illustrate a practical system because its components are so familiar. Figure 2.9 shows a photograph of a widely available flashlight.

When a flashlight is regarded as an electrical system, the components of primary interest are the batteries, the lamp, the connector, the case, and the switch. We now consider the circuit model for each component.

A dry-cell battery maintains a reasonably constant terminal voltage if the current demand is not excessive. Thus if the dry-cell battery is operating within its intended limits, we can model it with an ideal voltage source. The prescribed voltage then is constant and equal to the sum of two dry-cell values.

The ultimate output of the lamp is light energy, which is achieved by heating the filament in the lamp to a temperature high enough to cause radiation in the visible range. We can model the lamp with an ideal resistor. Note in this case that although the resistor accounts for the amount of electric energy converted to thermal energy, it does not predict how much of the thermal energy is converted to light energy. The resistor used to represent the lamp does predict the steady current drain on the batteries, a characteristic of the system that also is of interest. In this model, R_l symbolizes the lamp resistance.

The connector used in the flashlight serves a dual role. First, it provides an electrical conductive path between the dry cells and the case. Second, it is

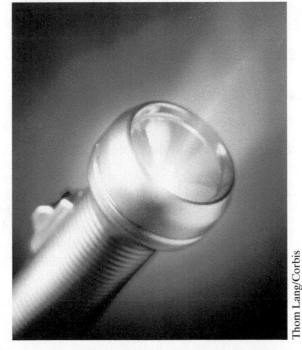

Figure 2.9 ▲ A flashlight can be viewed as an electrical system.

Thom Lang/Corbis

formed into a springy coil so that it also can apply mechanical pressure to the contact between the batteries and the lamp. The purpose of this mechanical pressure is to maintain contact between the two dry cells and between the dry cells and the lamp. Hence, in choosing the wire for the connector, we may find that its mechanical properties are more important than its electrical properties for the flashlight design. Electrically, we can model the connector with an ideal resistor, labeled R_1.

The case also serves both a mechanical and an electrical purpose. Mechanically, it contains all the other components and provides a grip for the person using it. Electrically, it provides a connection between other elements in the flashlight. If the case is metal, it conducts current between the batteries and the lamp. If it is plastic, a metal strip inside the case connects the coiled connector to the switch. Either way, an ideal resistor, which we denote R_c, models the electrical connection provided by the case.

The final component is the switch. Electrically, the switch is a two-state device. It is either ON or OFF. An ideal switch offers no resistance to the current when it is in the ON state, but it offers infinite resistance to current when it is in the OFF state. These two states represent the limiting values of a resistor; that is, the ON state corresponds to a resistor with a numerical value of zero, and the OFF state corresponds to a resistor with a numerical value of infinity. The two extreme values have the descriptive names **short circuit** ($R = 0$) and **open circuit** ($R = \infty$). Figure 2.10(a) and (b) show the graphical representation of a short circuit and an open circuit, respectively. The symbol shown in Fig. 2.10(c) represents the fact that a switch can be either a short circuit or an open circuit, depending on the position of its contacts.

We now construct the circuit model of the flashlight. Starting with the dry-cell batteries, the positive terminal of the first cell is connected to the negative terminal of the second cell, as shown in Fig. 2.11. The positive terminal of the second cell is connected to one terminal of the lamp. The other terminal of the lamp makes contact with one side of the switch, and the other side of the switch is connected to the metal case. The metal case is then connected to the negative terminal of the first dry cell by means of the metal spring. Note that the elements form a closed path or circuit. You can see the closed path formed by the connected elements in Fig. 2.11. Figure 2.12 shows a circuit model for the flashlight.

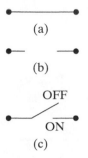

(a)

(b)

OFF

ON

(c)

Figure 2.10 ▲ Circuit symbols. (a) Short circuit. (b) Open circuit. (c) Switch.

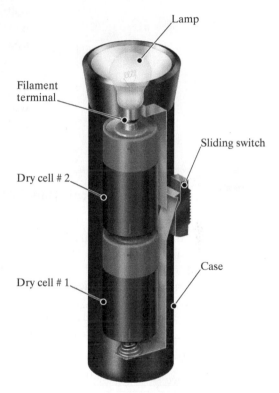

Figure 2.11 ▲ The arrangement of flashlight components.

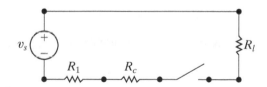

Figure 2.12 ▲ A circuit model for a flashlight.

We can make some general observations about modeling from our flashlight example: First, in developing a circuit model, the *electrical* behavior of each physical component is of primary interest. In the flashlight model, three very different physical components—a lamp, a coiled wire, and a metal case—are all represented by the same circuit element (a resistor), because the electrical phenomenon taking place in each is the same. Each is presenting resistance to the current flowing through the circuit.

Second, circuit models may need to account for undesired as well as desired electrical effects. For example, the heat resulting from the resistance in the lamp produces the light, a desired effect. However, the heat resulting from the resistance in the case and coil represents an unwanted or parasitic effect. It drains the dry cells and produces no useful output. Such parasitic effects must be considered or the resulting model may not adequately represent the system.

And finally, modeling requires approximation. Even for the basic system represented by the flashlight, we made simplifying assumptions in developing the circuit model. For example, we assumed an ideal switch, but in practical switches, contact resistance may be high enough to interfere with proper operation of the system. Our model does not predict this behavior. We also assumed that the coiled connector exerts enough pressure to eliminate any contact resistance between the dry cells. Our model does not predict the effect of inadequate pressure. Our use of an ideal voltage source ignores any internal dissipation of energy in the dry cells, which might be due to the parasitic heating just mentioned. We could account for this by adding an ideal resistor between the source and the lamp resistor. Our model assumes the internal loss to be negligible.

In modeling the flashlight as a circuit, we had a basic understanding of and access to the internal components of the system. However, sometimes we know only the terminal behavior of a device and must use this information in constructing the model. Example 2.5 explores such a modeling problem.

Example 2.5   Constructing a Circuit Model Based on Terminal Measurements

The voltage and current are measured at the terminals of the device illustrated in Fig. 2.13(a), and the values of v_t and i_t are tabulated in Fig. 2.13(b). Construct a circuit model of the device inside the box.

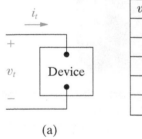

v_t (V)	i_t (A)
−40	−10
−20	−5
0	0
20	5
40	10

(a)   (b)

Figure 2.13 ▲ The (a) device and (b) data for Example 2.5.

Solution

Plotting the voltage as a function of the current yields the graph shown in Fig. 2.14(a). The equation of the line in this figure illustrates that the terminal voltage is directly proportional to the terminal current, $v_t = 4i_t$. In terms of Ohm's law, the device inside the box behaves like a 4 Ω resistor. Therefore, the circuit model for the device inside the box is a 4 Ω resistor, as seen in Fig. 2.14(b).

We come back to this technique of using terminal characteristics to construct a circuit model after introducing Kirchhoff's laws and circuit analysis.

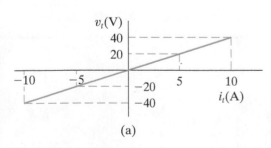

(a)

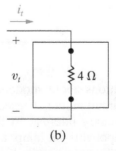

(b)

Figure 2.14 ▲ (a) The values of v_t versus i_t for the device in Fig. 2.13. (b) The circuit model for the device in Fig. 2.13.

NOTE: Assess your understanding of this example by trying Chapter Problems 2.14 and 2.15.

2.4 Kirchhoff's Laws

A circuit is said to be solved when the voltage across and the current in every element have been determined. Ohm's law is an important equation for deriving such solutions. However, Ohm's law may not be enough to provide a complete solution. As we shall see in trying to solve the flashlight circuit from Example 2.4, we need to use two more important algebraic relationships, known as Kirchhoff's laws, to solve most circuits.

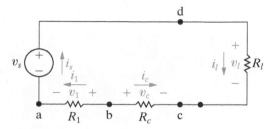

Figure 2.15 ▲ Circuit model of the flashlight with assigned voltage and current variables.

We begin by redrawing the circuit as shown in Fig. 2.15, with the switch in the ON state. Note that we have also labeled the current and voltage variables associated with each resistor and the current associated with the voltage source. Labeling includes reference polarities, as always. For convenience, we attach the same subscript to the voltage and current labels as we do to the resistor labels. In Fig. 2.15, we also removed some of the terminal dots of Fig. 2.12 and have inserted nodes. Terminal dots are the start and end points of an individual circuit element. A **node** is a point where two or more circuit elements meet. It is necessary to identify nodes in order to use Kirchhoff's current law, as we will see in a moment. In Fig. 2.15, the nodes are labeled a, b, c, and d. Node d connects the battery and the lamp and in essence stretches all the way across the top of the diagram, though we label a single point for convenience. The dots on either side of the switch indicate its terminals, but only one is needed to represent a node, so only one is labeled node c.

For the circuit shown in Fig. 2.15, we can identify seven unknowns: $i_s, i_1, i_c, i_l, v_1, v_c,$ and v_l. Recall that v_s is a known voltage, as it represents the sum of the terminal voltages of the two dry cells, a constant voltage of 3 V. The problem is to find the seven unknown variables. From algebra, you know that to find n unknown quantities you must solve n simultaneous independent equations. From our discussion of Ohm's law in Section 2.2, you know that three of the necessary equations are

$$v_1 = i_1 R_1, \tag{2.13}$$

$$v_c = i_c R_c, \tag{2.14}$$

$$v_l = i_l R_l. \tag{2.15}$$

What about the other four equations?

The interconnection of circuit elements imposes constraints on the relationship between the terminal voltages and currents. These constraints are referred to as Kirchhoff's laws, after Gustav Kirchhoff, who first stated them in a paper published in 1848. The two laws that state the constraints in mathematical form are known as Kirchhoff's current law and Kirchhoff's voltage law.

We can now state **Kirchhoff's current law**:

> The algebraic sum of all the currents at any node in a circuit equals zero.

◀ **Kirchhoff's current law (KCL)**

To use Kirchhoff's current law, an algebraic sign corresponding to a reference direction must be assigned to every current at the node. Assigning a positive sign to a current leaving a node requires assigning a negative sign to a current entering a node. Conversely, giving a negative sign to a current leaving a node requires giving a positive sign to a current entering a node.

Applying Kirchhoff's current law to the four nodes in the circuit shown in Fig. 2.15, using the convention that currents leaving a node are considered positive, yields four equations:

$$\text{node a} \qquad i_s - i_1 = 0, \tag{2.16}$$

$$\text{node b} \qquad i_1 + i_c = 0, \tag{2.17}$$

$$\text{node c} \qquad -i_c - i_l = 0, \tag{2.18}$$

$$\text{node d} \qquad i_l - i_s = 0. \tag{2.19}$$

Note that Eqs. 2.16–2.19 are not an independent set, because any one of the four can be derived from the other three. In any circuit with n nodes, $n - 1$ independent current equations can be derived from Kirchhoff's current law.[1] Let's disregard Eq. 2.19 so that we have six independent equations, namely, Eqs. 2.13–2.18. We need one more, which we can derive from Kirchhoff's voltage law.

Before we can state Kirchhoff's voltage law, we must define a **closed path** or **loop**. Starting at an arbitrarily selected node, we trace a closed path in a circuit through selected basic circuit elements and return to the original node without passing through any intermediate node more than once. The circuit shown in Fig. 2.15 has only one closed path or loop. For example, choosing node a as the starting point and tracing the circuit clockwise, we form the closed path by moving through nodes d, c, b, and back to node a. We can now state **Kirchhoff's voltage law**:

Kirchhoff's voltage law (KVL) ▶ | The algebraic sum of all the voltages around any closed path in a circuit equals zero.

To use Kirchhoff's voltage law, we must assign an algebraic sign (reference direction) to each voltage in the loop. As we trace a closed path, a voltage will appear either as a rise or a drop in the tracing direction. Assigning a positive sign to a voltage rise requires assigning a negative sign to a voltage drop. Conversely, giving a negative sign to a voltage rise requires giving a positive sign to a voltage drop.

We now apply Kirchhoff's voltage law to the circuit shown in Fig. 2.15. We elect to trace the closed path clockwise, assigning a positive algebraic sign to voltage drops. Starting at node d leads to the expression

$$v_l - v_c + v_1 - v_s = 0, \tag{2.20}$$

which represents the seventh independent equation needed to find the seven unknown circuit variables mentioned earlier.

The thought of having to solve seven simultaneous equations to find the current delivered by a pair of dry cells to a flashlight lamp is not very appealing. Thus in the coming chapters we introduce you to analytical techniques that will enable you to solve a simple one-loop circuit by writing a single equation. However, before moving on to a discussion of these circuit techniques, we need to make several observations about the detailed analysis of the flashlight circuit. In general, these observations are true and therefore are important to the discussions in subsequent chapters. They also support the contention that the flashlight circuit can be solved by defining a single unknown.

---

[1] We say more about this observation in Chapter 4.

First, note that if you know the current in a resistor, you also know the voltage across the resistor, because current and voltage are directly related through Ohm's law. Thus you can associate one unknown variable with each resistor, either the current or the voltage. Choose, say, the current as the unknown variable. Then, once you solve for the unknown current in the resistor, you can find the voltage across the resistor. In general, if you know the current in a passive element, you can find the voltage across it, greatly reducing the number of simultaneous equations to be solved. For example, in the flashlight circuit, we eliminate the voltages v_c, v_l, and v_1 as unknowns. Thus at the outset we reduce the analytical task to solving four simultaneous equations rather than seven.

The second general observation relates to the consequences of connecting only two elements to form a node. According to Kirchhoff's current law, when only two elements connect to a node, if you know the current in one of the elements, you also know it in the second element. In other words, you need define only one unknown current for the two elements. When just two elements connect at a single node, the elements are said to be **in series**. The importance of this second observation is obvious when you note that each node in the circuit shown in Fig. 2.15 involves only two elements. Thus you need to define only one unknown current. The reason is that Eqs. 2.16–2.18 lead directly to

$$i_s = i_1 = -i_c = i_l, \qquad (2.21)$$

which states that if you know any one of the element currents, you know them all. For example, choosing to use i_s as the unknown eliminates i_1, i_c, and i_l. The problem is reduced to determining one unknown, namely, i_s.

Examples 2.6 and 2.7 illustrate how to write circuit equations based on Kirchhoff's laws. Example 2.8 illustrates how to use Kirchhoff's laws and Ohm's law to find an unknown current. Example 2.9 expands on the technique presented in Example 2.5 for constructing a circuit model for a device whose terminal characteristics are known.

Example 2.6	**Using Kirchhoff's Current Law**

Sum the currents at each node in the circuit shown in Fig. 2.16. Note that there is no connection dot (•) in the center of the diagram, where the 4 Ω branch crosses the branch containing the ideal current source i_a.

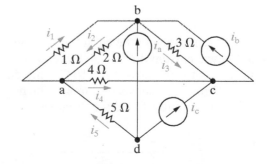

Figure 2.16 ▲ The circuit for Example 2.6.

Solution

In writing the equations, we use a positive sign for a current leaving a node. The four equations are

node a $i_1 + i_4 - i_2 - i_5 = 0,$

node b $i_2 + i_3 - i_1 - i_b - i_a = 0,$

node c $i_b - i_3 - i_4 - i_c = 0,$

node d $i_5 + i_a + i_c = 0.$

Example 2.7 | Using Kirchhoff's Voltage Law

Sum the voltages around each designated path in the circuit shown in Fig. 2.17.

Solution

In writing the equations, we use a positive sign for a voltage drop. The four equations are

path a $-v_1 + v_2 + v_4 - v_b - v_3 = 0,$

path b $-v_a + v_3 + v_5 = 0,$

path c $v_b - v_4 - v_c - v_6 - v_5 = 0,$

path d $-v_a - v_1 + v_2 - v_c + v_7 - v_d = 0.$

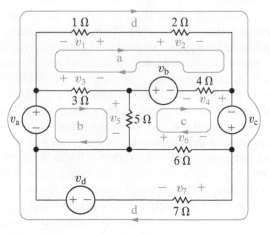

Figure 2.17 ▲ The circuit for Example 2.7.

Example 2.8 | Applying Ohm's Law and Kirchhoff's Laws to Find an Unknown Current

a) Use Kirchhoff's laws and Ohm's law to find i_o in the circuit shown in Fig. 2.18.

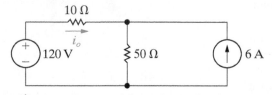

Figure 2.18 ▲ The circuit for Example 2.8.

b) Test the solution for i_o by verifying that the total power generated equals the total power dissipated.

Solution

a) We begin by redrawing the circuit and assigning an unknown current to the 50 Ω resistor and unknown voltages across the 10 Ω and 50 Ω resistors. Figure 2.19 shows the circuit. The nodes are labeled a, b, and c to aid the discussion.

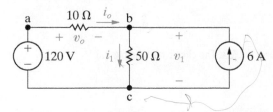

Figure 2.19 ▲ The circuit shown in Fig. 2.18, with the unknowns i_1, v_o, and v_1 defined.

Because i_o also is the current in the 120 V source, we have two unknown currents and

therefore must derive two simultaneous equations involving i_o and i_1. We obtain one of the equations by applying Kirchhoff's current law to either node b or c. Summing the currents at node b and assigning a positive sign to the currents leaving the node gives

$$i_1 - i_o - 6 = 0.$$

We obtain the second equation from Kirchhoff's voltage law in combination with Ohm's law. Noting from Ohm's law that v_o is $10i_o$ and v_1 is $50i_1$, we sum the voltages around the closed path cabc to obtain

$$-120 + 10i_o + 50i_1 = 0.$$

In writing this equation, we assigned a positive sign to voltage drops in the clockwise direction. Solving these two equations for i_o and i_1 yields

$$i_o = -3 \text{ A} \qquad \text{and} \qquad i_1 = 3 \text{ A}.$$

b) The power dissipated in the 50 Ω resistor is

$$p_{50\Omega} = (3)^2(50) = 450 \text{ W}.$$

The power dissipated in the 10 Ω resistor is

$$p_{10\Omega} = (-3)^2(10) = 90 \text{ W}.$$

The power delivered to the 120 V source is

$$p_{120V} = -120i_o = -120(-3) = 360 \text{ W}.$$

The power delivered to the 6 A source is

$$p_{6A} = -v_1(6), \quad \text{but} \quad v_1 = 50i_1 = 150 \text{ V}.$$

Therefore

$$p_{6A} = -150(6) = -900 \text{ W}.$$

The 6 A source is delivering 900 W, and the 120 V source is absorbing 360 W. The total power absorbed is $360 + 450 + 90 = 900$ W. Therefore, the solution verifies that the power delivered equals the power absorbed.

Example 2.9   Constructing a Circuit Model Based on Terminal Measurements

The terminal voltage and terminal current were measured on the device shown in Fig. 2.20(a), and the values of v_t and i_t are tabulated in Fig. 2.20(b).

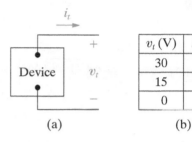

v_t (V)	i_t (A)
30	0
15	3
0	6

(a)   (b)

Figure 2.20 ▲ (a) Device and (b) data for Example 2.9.

a) Construct a circuit model of the device inside the box.

b) Using this circuit model, predict the power this device will deliver to a 10 Ω resistor.

Solution

a) Plotting the voltage as a function of the current yields the graph shown in Fig. 2.21(a). The equation of the line plotted is

$$v_t = 30 - 5i_t.$$

Now we need to identify the components of a circuit model that will produce the same relationship between voltage and current. Kirchhoff's voltage law tells us that the voltage drops across two components in series. From the equation, one of those components produces a 30 V drop regardless of the current. This component can be modeled as an ideal independent voltage source. The other component produces a positive voltage drop in the direction of the current i_t. Because the voltage drop is proportional to the current, Ohm's law tells us that this component can be modeled as an ideal resistor with a value of 5 Ω. The resulting circuit model is depicted in the dashed box in Fig. 2.21(b).

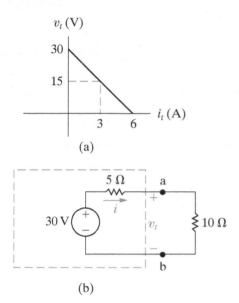

(a)

(b)

Figure 2.21 ▲ (a) The graph of v_t versus i_t for the device in Fig. 2.20(a). (b) The resulting circuit model for the device in Fig. 2.20(a), connected to a 10 Ω resistor.

b) Now we attach a 10 Ω resistor to the device in Fig. 2.21(b) to complete the circuit. Kirchhoff's current law tells us that the current in the 10 Ω resistor is the same as the current in the 5 Ω resistor. Using Kirchhoff's voltage law and Ohm's law, we can write the equation for the voltage drops around the circuit, starting at the voltage source and proceeding clockwise:

$$-30 + 5i + 10i = 0.$$

Solving for i, we get

$$i = 2 \text{ A}.$$

Because this is the value of current flowing in the 10 Ω resistor, we can use the power equation $p = i^2R$ to compute the power delivered to this resistor:

$$p_{10\Omega} = (2)^2(10) = 40 \text{ W}.$$

✓ ASSESSMENT PROBLEMS

Objective 2—Be able to state and use Ohm's law and Kirchhoff's current and voltage laws

2.5 For the circuit shown, calculate (a) i_5; (b) v_1; (c) v_2; (d) v_5; and (e) the power delivered by the 24 V source.

Answer: (a) 2 A;

(b) −4 V;

(c) 6 V;

(d) 14 V;

(e) 48 W.

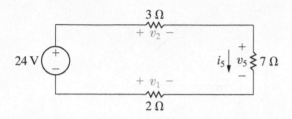

2.6 Use Ohm's law and Kirchhoff's laws to find the value of R in the circuit shown.

Answer: $R = 4\ \Omega$.

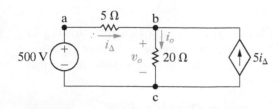

2.7 a) The terminal voltage and terminal current were measured on the device shown. The values of v_t and i_t are provided in the table. Using these values, create the straight line plot of v_t versus i_t. Compute the equation of the line and use the equation to construct a circuit model for the device using an ideal voltage source and a resistor.

b) Use the model constructed in (a) to predict the power that the device will deliver to a 25 Ω resistor.

Answer: (a) A 25 V source in series with a 100 Ω resistor;

(b) 1 W.

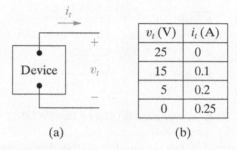

v_t (V)	i_t (A)
25	0
15	0.1
5	0.2
0	0.25

(a)   (b)

2.8 Repeat Assessment Problem 2.7 but use the equation of the graphed line to construct a circuit model containing an ideal current source and a resistor.

Answer: (a) A 0.25 A current source connected between the terminals of a 100 Ω resistor;

(b) 1 W.

NOTE: Also try Chapter Problems 2.18, 2.19, 2.29, and 2.31.

2.5 Analysis of a Circuit Containing Dependent Sources

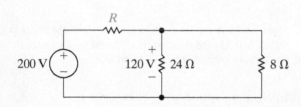

Figure 2.22 ▲ A circuit with a dependent source.

We conclude this introduction to elementary circuit analysis with a discussion of a circuit that contains a dependent source, as depicted in Fig. 2.22.

We want to use Kirchhoff's laws and Ohm's law to find v_o in this circuit. Before writing equations, it is good practice to examine the circuit diagram closely. This will help us identify the information that is known and the information we must calculate. It may also help us devise a strategy for solving the circuit using only a few calculations.

A look at the circuit in Fig. 2.22 reveals that

- Once we know i_o, we can calculate v_o using Ohm's law.
- Once we know i_Δ, we also know the current supplied by the dependent source $5i_\Delta$.
- The current in the 500 V source is i_Δ.

There are thus two unknown currents, i_Δ and i_o. We need to construct and solve two independent equations involving these two currents to produce a value for v_o.

From the circuit, notice the closed path containing the voltage source, the 5 Ω resistor, and the 20 Ω resistor. We can apply Kirchhoff's voltage law around this closed path. The resulting equation contains the two unknown currents:

$$500 = 5i_\Delta + 20i_o. \tag{2.22}$$

Now we need to generate a second equation containing these two currents. Consider the closed path formed by the 20 Ω resistor and the dependent current source. If we attempt to apply Kirchhoff's voltage law to this loop, we fail to develop a useful equation, because we don't know the value of the voltage across the dependent current source. In fact, the voltage across the dependent source is v_o, which is the voltage we are trying to compute. Writing an equation for this loop does not advance us toward a solution. For this same reason, we do not use the closed path containing the voltage source, the 5 Ω resistor, and the dependent source.

There are three nodes in the circuit, so we turn to Kirchhoff's current law to generate the second equation. Node a connects the voltage source and the 5 Ω resistor; as we have already observed, the current in these two elements is the same. Either node b or node c can be used to construct the second equation from Kirchhoff's current law. We select node b and produce the following equation:

$$i_o = i_\Delta + 5i_\Delta = 6i_\Delta. \tag{2.23}$$

Solving Eqs. 2.22 and 2.23 for the currents, we get

$$i_\Delta = 4 \text{ A,}$$

$$i_o = 24 \text{ A.} \tag{2.24}$$

Using Eq. 2.24 and Ohm's law for the 20 Ω resistor, we can solve for the voltage v_o:

$$v_o = 20i_o = 480 \text{ V.}$$

Think about a circuit analysis strategy before beginning to write equations. As we have demonstrated, not every closed path provides an opportunity to write a useful equation based on Kirchhoff's voltage law. Not every node provides for a useful application of Kirchhoff's current law. Some preliminary thinking about the problem can help in selecting the most fruitful approach and the most useful analysis tools for a particular problem. Choosing a good approach and the appropriate tools will usually reduce the number and complexity of equations to be solved. Example 2.10 illustrates another application of Ohm's law and Kirchhoff's laws to a circuit with a dependent source. Example 2.11 involves a much more complicated circuit, but with a careful choice of analysis tools, the analysis is relatively uncomplicated.

Example 2.10   Applying Ohm's Law and Kirchhoff's Laws to Find an Unknown Voltage

a) Use Kirchhoff's laws and Ohm's law to find the voltage v_o as shown in Fig. 2.23.

b) Show that your solution is consistent with the constraint that the total power developed in the circuit equals the total power dissipated.

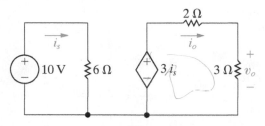

Figure 2.23 ▲ The circuit for Example 2.10.

Solution

a) A close look at the circuit in Fig. 2.23 reveals that:
- There are two closed paths, the one on the left with the current i_s and the one on the right with the current i_o.
- Once i_o is known, we can compute v_o.

We need two equations for the two currents. Because there are two closed paths and both have voltage sources, we can apply Kirchhoff's voltage law to each to give the following equations:

$$10 = 6i_s,$$

$$3i_s = 2i_o + 3i_o.$$

Solving for the currents yields

$$i_s = 1.67 \text{ A},$$

$$i_o = 1 \text{ A}.$$

Applying Ohm's law to the 3 Ω resistor gives the desired voltage:

$$v_o = 3i_o = 3 \text{ V}.$$

b) To compute the power delivered to the voltage sources, we use the power equation in the form $p = vi$. The power delivered to the independent voltage source is

$$p = (10)(-1.67) = -16.7 \text{ W}.$$

The power delivered to the dependent voltage source is

$$p = (3i_s)(-i_o) = (5)(-1) = -5 \text{ W}.$$

Both sources are developing power, and the total developed power is 21.7 W.

To compute the power delivered to the resistors, we use the power equation in the form $p = i^2 R$. The power delivered to the 6 Ω resistor is

$$p = (1.67)^2(6) = 16.7 \text{ W}.$$

The power delivered to the 2 Ω resistor is

$$p = (1)^2(2) = 2 \text{ W}.$$

The power delivered to the 3 Ω resistor is

$$p = (1)^2(3) = 3 \text{ W}.$$

The resistors all dissipate power, and the total power dissipated is 21.7 W, equal to the total power developed in the sources.

The circuit in Fig. 2.24 represents a common configuration encountered in the analysis and design of transistor amplifiers. Assume that the values of all the circuit elements—R_1, R_2, R_C, R_E, V_{CC}, and V_0—are known.

a) Develop the equations needed to determine the current in each element of this circuit.

b) From these equations, devise a formula for computing i_B in terms of the circuit element values.

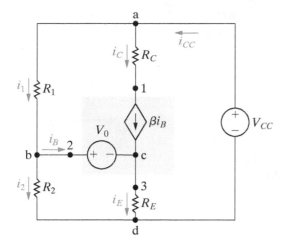

Figure 2.24 ▲ The circuit for Example 2.11.

Solution

A careful examination of the circuit reveals a total of six unknown currents, designated i_1, i_2, i_B, i_C, i_E, and i_{CC}. In defining these six unknown currents, we used the observation that the resistor R_C is in series with the dependent current source βi_B. We now must derive six independent equations involving these six unknowns.

a) We can derive three equations by applying Kirchhoff's current law to any three of the nodes a, b, c, and d. Let's use nodes a, b, and c and label the currents away from the nodes as positive:

$$(1)\quad i_1 + i_C - i_{CC} = 0,$$

$$(2)\quad i_B + i_2 - i_1 = 0,$$

$$(3)\quad i_E - i_B - i_C = 0.$$

A fourth equation results from imposing the constraint presented by the series connection of R_C and the dependent source:

$$(4)\quad i_C = \beta i_B.$$

We turn to Kirchhoff's voltage law in deriving the remaining two equations. We need to select two closed paths in order to use Kirchhoff's voltage law. Note that the voltage across the dependent current source is unknown, and that it cannot be determined from the source current βi_B. Therefore, we must select two closed paths that do not contain this dependent current source.

We choose the paths bcdb and badb and specify voltage drops as positive to yield

$$(5)\quad V_0 + i_E R_E - i_2 R_2 = 0,$$

$$(6)\quad -i_1 R_1 + V_{CC} - i_2 R_2 = 0.$$

b) To get a single equation for i_B in terms of the known circuit variables, you can follow these steps:

- Solve Eq. (6) for i_1, and substitute this solution for i_1 into Eq. (2).
- Solve the transformed Eq. (2) for i_2, and substitute this solution for i_2 into Eq. (5).
- Solve the transformed Eq. (5) for i_E, and substitute this solution for i_E into Eq. (3). Use Eq. (4) to eliminate i_C in Eq. (3).
- Solve the transformed Eq. (3) for i_B, and rearrange the terms to yield

$$i_B = \frac{(V_{CC}R_2)/(R_1 + R_2) - V_0}{(R_1 R_2)/(R_1 + R_2) + (1 + \beta)R_E}. \quad (2.25)$$

Problem 2.31 asks you to verify these steps. Note that once we know i_B, we can easily obtain the remaining currents.

✓ ASSESSMENT PROBLEMS

Objective 3—Know how to calculate power for each element in a simple circuit

2.9 For the circuit shown find (a) the current i_1 in microamperes, (b) the voltage v in volts, (c) the total power generated, and (d) the total power absorbed.

Answer: (a) 25 μA;

(b) –2 V;

(c) 6150 μW;

(d) 6150 μW.

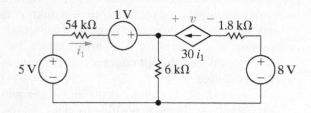

c) the power delivered by the independent current source,

d) the power delivered by the controlled current source,

e) the total power dissipated in the two resistors.

Answer: (a) 70 V;

(b) 210 W;

(c) 300 W;

(d) 40 W;

(e) 130 W.

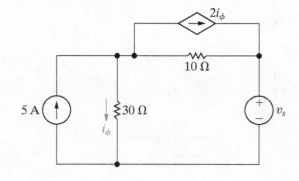

2.10 The current i_ϕ in the circuit shown is 2 A. Calculate

a) v_s,

b) the power absorbed by the independent voltage source,

NOTE: Also try Chapter Problems 2.32 and 2.33.

Practical Perspective

Heating with Electric Radiators

Let's determine which of the two wiring diagrams introduced at the beginning of this chapter should be used to wire the electric radiators to the power supplied to the garage. We begin with the diagram shown in Fig. 2.25. We can turn this into a circuit by modeling the radiators as resistors. The resulting circuit is shown in Fig. 2.26. Note that each radiator has the same resistance, R, and is labeled with a voltage and current value.

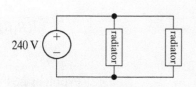

Figure 2.25 A wiring diagram for two radiators.

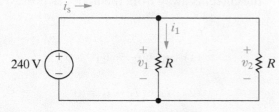

Figure 2.26 A circuit based on Fig. 2.25.

To find the unknown voltages and currents for the circuit in Fig. 2.26, begin by writing a KVL equation for the left side of the circuit:

$$-240 + v_1 = 0 \quad \Rightarrow \quad v_1 = 240\ V.$$

Now write a KVL equation for the right side of this circuit:

$$-v_1 + v_2 = 0 \quad \Rightarrow \quad v_2 = v_1 = 240 \, V.$$

Remember that the power and voltage specifications for each radiator are 1200 W, 240 V. Therefore the configuration shown in Fig. 2.25 satisfies the voltage specification, since each radiator would have a supplied voltage of 240 V.

Next, calculate the value of resistance R that will correctly model each radiator. We want the power associated with each radiator to be 1200 W. Use the equation for resistor power that involves the resistance and the voltage:

$$P_1 = \frac{v_1^2}{R} = \frac{v_2^2}{R} = P_2 \quad \Rightarrow \quad R = \frac{v_1^2}{P_1} = \frac{240^2}{1200} = 48 \, \Omega.$$

Each radiator can be modeled as a 48 Ω resistor with a voltage drop of 240 V and power of 1200 W. The total power for two radiators is thus 2400 W.

Finally, calculate the power supplied by the 240 V source. To do this, calculate the current in the voltage source, i_s, by writing a KCL equation at the top node in Fig. 2.26, and use that current to calculate the power for the voltage source.

$$-i_s + i_1 + i_2 = 0 \quad \Rightarrow \quad i_s = i_1 + i_2 = \frac{v_1}{R} + \frac{v_2}{R} = \frac{240}{48} + \frac{240}{48} = 10 \, A.$$

$$P_s = -(240)(i_s) = -(240)(10) = -2400 \, W.$$

Thus, the total power in the circuit is $-2400 + 2400 = 0$, so the power balances.

Now look at the other wiring diagram for the radiators, shown in Fig. 2.27. We know that the radiators can be modeled using 48 Ω resistors, which are used to turn the wiring diagram into the circuit in Fig. 2.28.

Start analyzing the circuit in Fig. 2.28 by writing a KVL equation:

$$-240 + v_x + v_y = 0 \quad \Rightarrow \quad v_x + v_y = 240.$$

Next, write a KCL equation at the node labeled a:

$$-i_x + i_y = 0 \quad \Rightarrow \quad i_x = i_y = i.$$

The current in the two resistors is the same, and we can use that current in Ohm's Law equations to replace the two unknown voltages in the KVL equation:

$$48i = 48i = 240 = 96i \quad \Rightarrow \quad i = \frac{240}{96} = 2.5 \, A.$$

Use the current in the two resistors to calculate the power for the two radiators.

$$P_x = P_y = Ri^2 = (48)(2.5)^2 = 300 \, W.$$

Thus, if the radiators are wired as shown in Fig. 2.27, their total power will be only 600 W. This is insufficient to heat the garage.

Therefore, the way the radiators are wired has a big impact on the amount of heat that will be supplied. When they are wired using the diagram in Fig. 2.25, 2400 W of power will be available, but when they are wired using the diagram in Fig. 2.27, only 600 W of power will be available.

NOTE: Assess your understanding of the Practical Perspective by solving Chapter Problems 2.41–2.43.

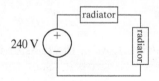

Figure 2.27 Another way to wire two radiators.

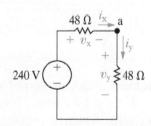

Figure 2.28 A circuit based on Fig. 2.27.

Summary

- The circuit elements introduced in this chapter are voltage sources, current sources, and resistors:
  - An **ideal voltage source** maintains a prescribed voltage regardless of the current in the device. An **ideal current source** maintains a prescribed current regardless of the voltage across the device. Voltage and current sources are either **independent**, that is, not influenced by any other current or voltage in the circuit; or **dependent**, that is, determined by some other current or voltage in the circuit. (See pages 26 and 27.)
  - A **resistor** constrains its voltage and current to be proportional to each other. The value of the proportional constant relating voltage and current in a resistor is called its **resistance** and is measured in ohms. (See page 30.)

- **Ohm's law** establishes the proportionality of voltage and current in a resistor. Specifically,

$$v = iR$$

if the current flow in the resistor is in the direction of the voltage drop across it, or

$$v = -iR$$

if the current flow in the resistor is in the direction of the voltage rise across it. (See page 31.)

- By combining the equation for power, $p = vi$, with Ohm's law, we can determine the power absorbed by a resistor:

$$p = i^2R = v^2/R.$$

(See page 32.)

- Circuits are described by nodes and closed paths. A **node** is a point where two or more circuit elements join. When just two elements connect to form a node, they are said to be **in series**. A **closed path** is a loop traced through connecting elements, starting and ending at the same node and encountering intermediate nodes only once each. (See pages 37–39.)

- The voltages and currents of interconnected circuit elements obey Kirchhoff's laws:
  - **Kirchhoff's current law** states that the algebraic sum of all the currents at any node in a circuit equals zero. (See page 37.)
  - **Kirchhoff's voltage law** states that the algebraic sum of all the voltages around any closed path in a circuit equals zero. (See page 38.)

- A circuit is solved when the voltage across and the current in every element have been determined. By combining an understanding of independent and dependent sources, Ohm's law, and Kirchhoff's laws, we can solve many simple circuits.

Problems

Section 2.1

2.1 a) Is the interconnection of ideal sources in the circuit in Fig. P2.1 valid? Explain.

   b) Identify which sources are developing power and which sources are absorbing power.

   c) Verify that the total power developed in the circuit equals the total power absorbed.

   d) Repeat (a)–(c), reversing the polarity of the 20 V source.

Figure P2.1

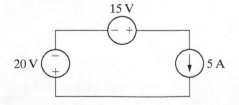

2.2 If the interconnection in Fig. P2.2 is valid, find the total power developed in the circuit. If the interconnection is not valid, explain why.

Figure P2.2

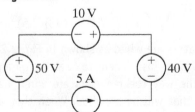

2.3 If the interconnection in Fig. P2.3 is valid, find the power developed by the current sources. If the interconnection is not valid, explain why.

Figure P2.3

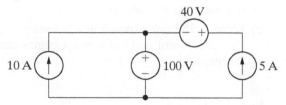

2.4 If the interconnection in Fig. P2.4 is valid, find the total power developed by the voltage sources. If the interconnection is not valid, explain why.

Figure P2.4

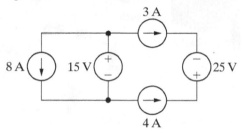

2.5 The interconnection of ideal sources can lead to an indeterminate solution. With this thought in mind, explain why the solutions for v_1 and v_2 in the circuit in Fig. P2.5 are not unique.

Figure P2.5

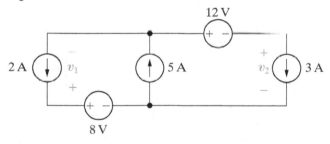

2.6 Consider the interconnection shown in Fig. P2.6.

 a) What value of v_1 is required to make this a valid interconnection?

 b) For this value of v_1, find the power associated with the voltage source.

Figure P2.6

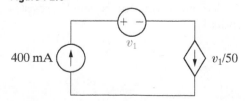

2.7 Consider the interconnection shown in Fig. P2.7.

 a) What value of α is required to make this a valid interconnection?

 b) For this value of α, find the power associated with the current source.

 c) Is the current source supplying or absorbing power?

Figure P2.7

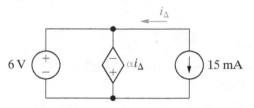

2.8 a) Is the interconnection in Fig. P2.8 valid? Explain.

 b) Can you find the total energy developed in the circuit? Explain.

Figure P2.8

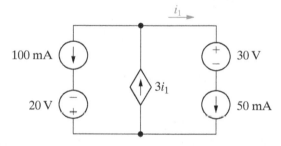

2.9 If the interconnection in Fig. P2.9 is valid, find the total power developed in the circuit. If the interconnection is not valid, explain why.

Figure P2.9

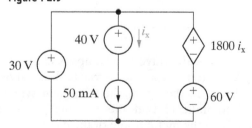

2.10 Find the total power developed in the circuit in Fig. P2.10 if $v_o = 5$ V.

Figure P2.10

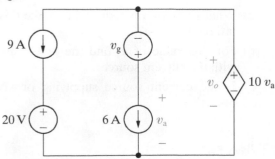

Sections 2.2–2.3

2.11 For the circuit shown in Fig. P2.11
   a) Find v.
   b) Find the power absorbed by the resistor.
   c) Reverse the direction of the current source and repeat parts (a) and (b).

Figure P2.11

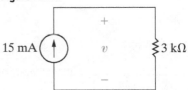

2.12 For the circuit shown in Fig. P2.12
   a) Find i.
   b) Find the power supplied by the voltage source.
   c) Reverse the polarity of the voltage source and repeat parts (a) and (b).

Figure P2.12

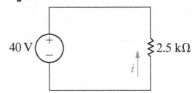

2.13 A pair of automotive headlamps is connected to a 12 V battery via the arrangement shown in Fig. P2.13. In the figure, the triangular symbol ▼ is used to indicate that the terminal is connected directly to the metal frame of the car.

   a) Construct a circuit model using resistors and an independent voltage source.
   b) Identify the correspondence between the ideal circuit element and the symbol component that it represents.

Figure P2.13

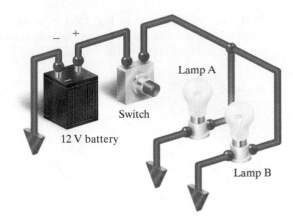

2.14 The terminal voltage and terminal current were measured on the device shown in Fig. P2.14(a). The values of v and i are given in the table of Fig. P2.14(b). Use the values in the table to construct a circuit model for the device consisting of a single resistor from Appendix H.

Figure P2.14

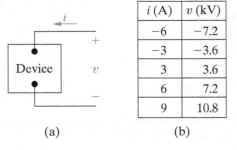

i (A)	v (kV)
−6	−7.2
−3	−3.6
3	3.6
6	7.2
9	10.8

(a)   (b)

2.15 A variety of voltage source values were applied to the device shown in Fig. P2.15(a). The power absorbed by the device for each value of voltage is recorded in the table given in Fig. P2.15(b). Use the values in the table to construct a circuit model for the device consisting of a single resistor from Appendix H.

Figure P2.15

(a)

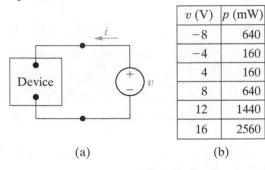

v (V)	p (mW)
−8	640
−4	160
4	160
8	640
12	1440
16	2560

(b)

2.16 A variety of current source values were applied to the device shown in Fig. P2.16(a). The power absorbed by the device for each value of current is recorded in the table given in Fig. P2.16(b). Use the values in the table to construct a circuit model for the device consisting of a single resistor from Appendix H.

Figure P2.16

(a)

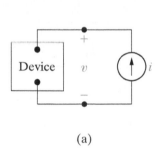

i (mA)	p (mW)
0.5	8.25
1.0	33.00
1.5	74.25
2.0	132.00
2.5	206.25
3.0	297.00

(b)

Section 2.4

2.17 Consider the circuit shown in Fig. P2.17.

a) Find v_o using Kirchoff's laws and Ohm's law.

b) Test the solution for v_o by verifying that the total power supplied equals the total power absorbed.

Figure P2.17

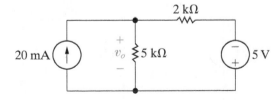

2.18 Given the circuit shown in Fig. P2.18, find

PSPICE MULTISIM

a) the value of i_a,

b) the value of i_b,

c) the value of v_o,

d) the power dissipated in each resistor,

c) the power delivered by the 50 V source.

Figure P2.18

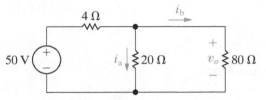

2.19 a) Find the currents i_1 and i_2 in the circuit in Fig. P2.19.

PSPICE MULTISIM

b) Find the voltage v_o.

c) Verify that the total power developed equals the total power dissipated.

Figure P2.19

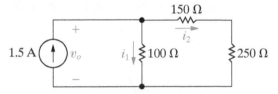

2.20 The current i_x in the circuit shown in Fig. P2.20 is 50 mA and the voltage v_x is 3.5 V. Find (a) i_1; (b) v_1; (c) v_g; and (d) the power supplied by the voltage source.

Figure P2.20

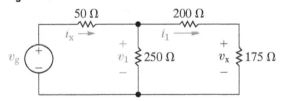

2.21 The current i_a in the circuit shown in Fig. P2.21 is 2 mA. Find (a) i_o; (b) i_g; and (c) the power delivered by the independent current source.

PSPICE MULTISIM

Figure P2.21

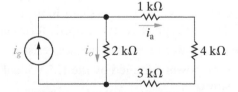

2.22 The current i_o in the circuit in Fig. P2.22 is 1 A.

PSPICE MULTISIM

a) Find i_1.

b) Find the power dissipated in each resistor.

c) Verify that the total power dissipated in the circuit equals the power developed by the 150 V source.

Figure P2.22

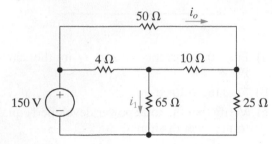

2.23 The variable resistor R in the circuit in Fig. P2.23 is
PSPICE   adjusted until i_0 equals 10 mA. Find the value of R.
MULTISIM

Figure P2.23

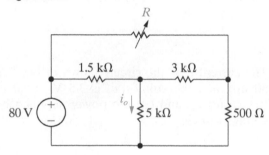

2.24 For the circuit shown in Fig. P2.24, find (a) R and
PSPICE   (b) the power supplied by the 240 V source.
MULTISIM

Figure P2.24

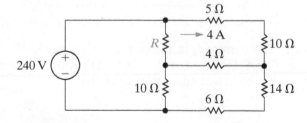

2.25 The voltage across the 16 Ω resistor in the circuit in
PSPICE   Fig. P2.25 is 80 V, positive at the upper terminal.
MULTISIM
  a) Find the power dissipated in each resistor.
  b) Find the power supplied by the 125 V ideal voltage source.
  c) Verify that the power supplied equals the total power dissipated.

Figure P2.25

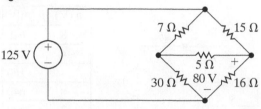

2.26 The currents i_a and i_b in the circuit in Fig. P2.26 are
PSPICE   4 A and −2 A, respectively.
MULTISIM
  a) Find i_g.
  b) Find the power dissipated in each resistor.
  c) Find v_g.
  d) Show that the power delivered by the current source is equal to the power absorbed by all the other elements.

Figure P2.26

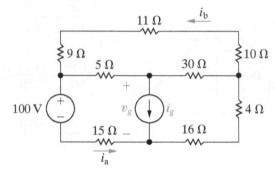

2.27 The currents i_1 and i_2 in the circuit in Fig. P2.27 are 21 A and 14 A, respectively.
  a) Find the power supplied by each voltage source.
  b) Show that the total power supplied equals the total power dissipated in the resistors.

Figure P2.27

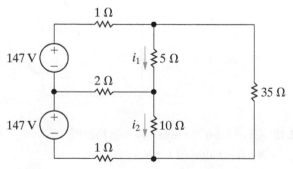

2.28 The voltage and current were measured at the terminals of the device shown in Fig. P2.28(a). The results are tabulated in Fig. P2.28(b).

a) Construct a circuit model for this device using an ideal voltage source in series with a resistor.

b) Use the model to predict the value of i_t when v_t is zero.

Figure P2.28

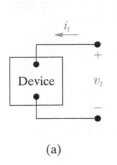

v_t (V)	i_t (A)
50	0
66	2
82	4
98	6
114	8
130	10

(a)   (b)

2.29 The voltage and current were measured at the terminals of the device shown in Fig. P2.29(a). The results are tabulated in Fig. P2.29(b).

a) Construct a circuit model for this device using an ideal current source in parallel with a resistor.

b) Use the model to predict the amount of power the device will deliver to a 20 Ω resistor.

Figure P2.29

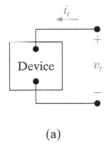

v_t (V)	i_t (A)
100	0
120	4
140	8
160	12
180	16

(a)   (b)

2.30 The table in Fig. P2.30(a) gives the relationship between the terminal current and voltage of the practical constant current source shown in Fig. P2.30(b).

a) Plot i_s versus v_s.

b) Construct a circuit model of this current source that is valid for $0 \le v_s \le 75$ V, based on the equation of the line plotted in (a).

c) Use your circuit model to predict the current delivered to a 2.5 kΩ resistor.

d) Use your circuit model to predict the open-circuit voltage of the current source.

e) What is the actual open-circuit voltage?

f) Explain why the answers to (d) and (e) are not the same.

Figure P2.30

i_s (mA)	v_s (V)
20.0	0
17.5	25
15.0	50
12.5	75
9.0	100
4.0	125
0.0	140

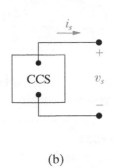

(a)   (b)

2.31 The table in Fig. P2.31(a) gives the relationship between the terminal voltage and current of the practical constant voltage source shown in Fig. P2.31(b).

a) Plot v_s versus i_s.

b) Construct a circuit model of the practical source that is valid for $0 \le i_s \le 24$ mA, based on the equation of the line plotted in (a). (Use an ideal voltage source in series with an ideal resistor.)

c) Use your circuit model to predict the current delivered to a 1 kΩ resistor connected to the terminals of the practical source.

d) Use your circuit model to predict the current delivered to a short circuit connected to the terminals of the practical source.

e) What is the actual short-circuit current?

f) Explain why the answers to (d) and (e) are not the same.

Figure P2.31

v_s (V)	i_s (mA)
24	0
22	8
20	16
18	24
15	32
10	40
0	48

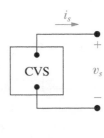

(a)   (b)

2.32 For the circuit shown in Fig. P2.32, find v_o and the total power supplied in the circuit.

Figure P2.32

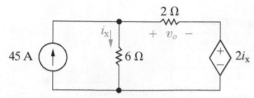

2.33 For the circuit shown in Fig. P2.33, find v_o and the total power absorbed in the circuit.

Figure P2.33

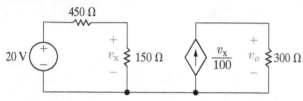

2.34 Consider the circuit shown in Fig. P2.34.

a) Find i_o.

b) Verify the value of i_o by showing that the power generated in the circuit equals the power absorbed in the circuit.

Figure P2.34

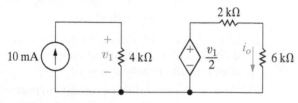

2.35 Find (a) i_o, (b) i_1, and (c) i_2 in the circuit in Fig. P2.35.

PSPICE

MULTISIM

Figure P2.35

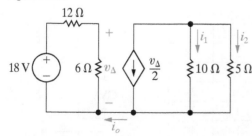

2.36 For the circuit shown in Fig. P2.36, calculate (a) i_Δ and v_o and (b) show that the power developed equals the power absorbed.

Figure P2.36

PSPICE

MULTISIM

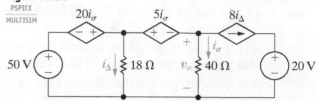

2.37 Find v_1 and v_g in the circuit shown in Fig. P2.37 when v_o equals 5 V. (*Hint:* Start at the right end of the circuit and work back toward v_g.)

Figure P2.37

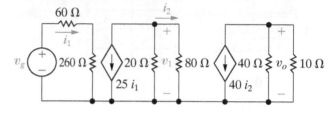

2.38 Derive Eq. 2.25. *Hint:* Use Eqs. (3) and (4) from Example 2.11 to express i_E as a function of i_B. Solve Eq. (2) for i_2 and substitute the result into both Eqs. (5) and (6). Solve the "new" Eq. (6) for i_1 and substitute this result into the "new" Eq. (5). Replace i_E in the "new" Eq. (5) and solve for i_B. Note that because i_{CC} appears only in Eq. (1), the solution for i_B involves the manipulation of only five equations.

2.39 For the circuit shown in Fig. 2.24, $R_1 = 40\,\text{k}\Omega$, $R_2 = 60\,\text{k}\Omega$, $R_C = 750\,\Omega$, $R_E = 120\,\Omega$, $V_{CC} = 10\,\text{V}$, $V_0 = 600\,\text{mV}$, and $\beta = 49$. Calculate i_B, i_C, i_E, v_{3d}, $v_{bd}, i_2, i_1, v_{ab}, i_{CC}$, and v_{13}. (*Note:* In the double subscript notation on voltage variables, the first subscript is positive with respect to the second subscript. See Fig. P2.39.)

PSPICE

MULTISIM

Figure P2.39

Sections 2.1–2.5

2.40 It is often desirable in designing an electric wiring system to be able to control a single appliance from two or more locations, for example, to control a lighting fixture from both the top and bottom of a

DESIGN
PROBLEM

stairwell. In home wiring systems, this type of control is implemented with three-way and four-way switches. A three-way switch is a three-terminal, two-position switch, and a four-way switch is a four-terminal, two-position switch. The switches are shown schematically in Fig. P2.40(a), which illustrates a three-way switch, and P2.40(b), which illustrates a four-way switch.

a) Show how two three-way switches can be connected between a and b in the circuit in Fig. P2.40(c) so that the lamp *l* can be turned ON or OFF from two locations.

b) If the lamp (appliance) is to be controlled from more than two locations, four-way switches are used in conjunction with two three-way switches. One four-way switch is required for each location in excess of two. Show how one four-way switch plus two three-way switches can be connected between a and b in Fig. P2.40(c) to control the lamp from three locations. (*Hint:* The four-way switch is placed between the three-way switches.)

Figure P2.40

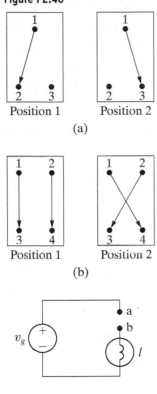

(a)

(b)

(c)

2.41 Suppose you want to add a third radiator to your garage that is identical to the two radiators you have already installed. All three radiators can be modeled by 48 Ω resistors. Using the wiring diagram shown in Fig. P2.41, calculate the total power for the three radiators.

Figure P2.41

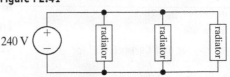

2.42 Repeat Problem 2.41 using the wiring diagram shown in Fig. P2.42. Compare the total radiator power in this configuration with the total radiator power in the configuration shown in Fig. P2.41.

Figure P2.42

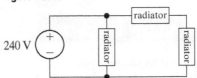

2.43 Repeat Problem 2.41 using the wiring diagram shown in Fig. P2.43. Compare the total radiator power in this configuration with the total radiator power in the configuration shown in Fig. P2.41.

Figure P2.43

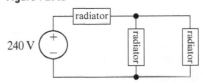

2.44 Repeat Problem 2.41 using the wiring diagram shown in Fig. P2.44. Compare the total radiator power in this configuration with the total radiator power in the configuration shown in Fig. P2.41.

Figure P2.44

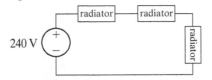

Simple Resistive Circuits

✓ CHAPTER OBJECTIVES

1 Be able to recognize resistors connected in series and in parallel and use the rules for combining series-connected resistors and parallel-connected resistors to yield equivalent resistance.

2 Know how to design simple voltage-divider and current-divider circuits.

3 Be able to use voltage division and current division appropriately to solve simple circuits.

4 Be able to determine the reading of an ammeter when added to a circuit to measure current; be able to determine the reading of a voltmeter when added to a circuit to measure voltage.

5 Understand how a Wheatstone bridge is used to measure resistance.

6 Know when and how to use delta-to-wye equivalent circuits to solve simple circuits.

Our analytical toolbox now contains Ohm's law and Kirchhoff's laws. In Chapter 2 we used these tools in solving simple circuits. In this chapter we continue applying these tools, but on more-complex circuits. The greater complexity lies in a greater number of elements with more complicated interconnections. This chapter focuses on reducing such circuits into simpler, equivalent circuits. We continue to focus on relatively simple circuits for two reasons: (1) It gives us a chance to acquaint ourselves thoroughly with the laws underlying more sophisticated methods, and (2) it allows us to be introduced to some circuits that have important engineering applications.

The sources in the circuits discussed in this chapter are limited to voltage and current sources that generate either constant voltages or currents; that is, voltages and currents that are invariant with time. Constant sources are often called **dc sources**. The *dc* stands for *direct current*, a description that has a historical basis but can seem misleading now. Historically, a direct current was defined as a current produced by a constant voltage. Therefore, a constant voltage became known as a direct current, or dc, voltage. The use of *dc* for *constant* stuck, and the terms *dc current* and *dc voltage* are now universally accepted in science and engineering to mean constant current and constant voltage.

Practical Perspective

Resistive Touch Screens

Some mobile phones and tablet computers use resistive touch screens, created by applying a transparent resistive material to the glass or acrylic screens. Two screens are typically used, separated by a transparent insulating layer. The resulting touch screen can be modeled by a grid of resistors in the x-direction and a grid of resistors in the y-direction, as shown in the figure on the right.

A separate electronic circuit applies a voltage drop across the grid in the x-direction, between the points a and b in the circuit, then removes that voltage and applies a voltage drop across the grid in the y-direction (between points c and d),

and continues to repeat this process. When the screen is touched, the two resistive layers are pressed together, creating a voltage that is sensed in the x-grid and another voltage that is sensed in the y-grid. These two voltages precisely locate the point where the screen was touched.

How is the voltage created by touching the screen related to the position where the screen was touched? How are the properties of the grids used to calculate the touch position? We will answer these questions in the Practical Perspective at the end of this chapter. The circuit analysis required to answer these questions uses some circuit analysis tools developed next.

Denis Semenchenko / Shutterstock

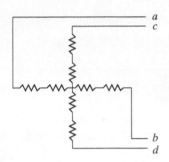

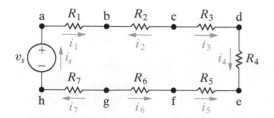

Figure 3.1 ▲ Resistors connected in series.

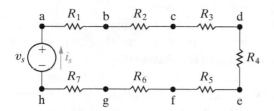

Figure 3.2 ▲ Series resistors with a single unknown current i_s.

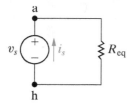

Figure 3.3 ▲ A simplified version of the circuit shown in Fig. 3.2.

Combining resistors in series ▶

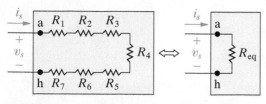

Figure 3.4 ▲ The black box equivalent of the circuit shown in Fig. 3.2.

3.1 Resistors in Series

In Chapter 2, we said that when just two elements connect at a single node, they are said to be in series. **Series-connected circuit elements** carry the same current. The resistors in the circuit shown in Fig. 3.1 are connected in series. We can show that these resistors carry the same current by applying Kirchhoff's current law to each node in the circuit. The series interconnection in Fig. 3.1 requires that

$$i_s = i_1 = -i_2 = i_3 = i_4 = -i_5 = -i_6 = i_7, \tag{3.1}$$

which states that if we know any one of the seven currents, we know them all. Thus we can redraw Fig. 3.1 as shown in Fig. 3.2, retaining the identity of the single current i_s.

To find i_s, we apply Kirchhoff's voltage law around the single closed loop. Defining the voltage across each resistor as a drop in the direction of i_s gives

$$-v_s + i_sR_1 + i_sR_2 + i_sR_3 + i_sR_4 + i_sR_5 + i_sR_6 + i_sR_7 = 0, \tag{3.2}$$

or

$$v_s = i_s(R_1 + R_2 + R_3 + R_4 + R_5 + R_6 + R_7). \tag{3.3}$$

The significance of Eq. 3.3 for calculating i_s is that the seven resistors can be replaced by a single resistor whose numerical value is the sum of the individual resistors, that is,

$$R_{eq} = R_1 + R_2 + R_3 + R_4 + R_5 + R_6 + R_7 \tag{3.4}$$

and

$$v_s = i_sR_{eq}. \tag{3.5}$$

Thus we can redraw Fig. 3.2 as shown in Fig. 3.3.

In general, if k resistors are connected in series, the equivalent single resistor has a resistance equal to the sum of the k resistances, or

$$R_{eq} = \sum_{i=1}^{k} R_i = R_1 + R_2 + \cdots + R_k. \tag{3.6}$$

Note that the resistance of the equivalent resistor is always larger than that of the largest resistor in the series connection.

Another way to think about this concept of an equivalent resistance is to visualize the string of resistors as being inside a black box. (An electrical engineer uses the term **black box** to imply an opaque container; that is, the contents are hidden from view. The engineer is then challenged to model the contents of the box by studying the relationship between the voltage and current at its terminals.) Determining whether the box contains k resistors or a single equivalent resistor is impossible. Figure 3.4 illustrates this method of studying the circuit shown in Fig. 3.2.

3.2 Resistors in Parallel

When two elements connect at a single node pair, they are said to be in parallel. **Parallel-connected circuit elements** have the same voltage across their terminals. The circuit shown in Fig. 3.5 illustrates resistors connected in parallel. Don't make the mistake of assuming that two elements are parallel connected merely because they are lined up in parallel in a circuit diagram. The defining characteristic of parallel-connected elements is that they have the same voltage across their terminals. In Fig. 3.6, you can see that R_1 and R_3 are not parallel connected because, between their respective terminals, another resistor dissipates some of the voltage.

Resistors in parallel can be reduced to a single equivalent resistor using Kirchhoff's current law and Ohm's law, as we now demonstrate. In the circuit shown in Fig. 3.5, we let the currents i_1, i_2, i_3, and i_4 be the currents in the resistors R_1 through R_4, respectively. We also let the positive reference direction for each resistor current be down through the resistor, that is, from node a to node b. From Kirchhoff's current law,

$$i_s = i_1 + i_2 + i_3 + i_4. \tag{3.7}$$

The parallel connection of the resistors means that the voltage across each resistor must be the same. Hence, from Ohm's law,

$$i_1 R_1 = i_2 R_2 = i_3 R_3 = i_4 R_4 = v_s. \tag{3.8}$$

Therefore,

$$i_1 = \frac{v_s}{R_1},$$

$$i_2 = \frac{v_s}{R_2},$$

$$i_3 = \frac{v_s}{R_3}, \quad \text{and}$$

$$i_4 = \frac{v_s}{R_4}. \tag{3.9}$$

Substituting Eq. 3.9 into Eq. 3.7 yields

$$i_s = v_s \left(\frac{1}{R_1} + \frac{1}{R_2} + \frac{1}{R_3} + \frac{1}{R_4} \right), \tag{3.10}$$

from which

$$\frac{i_s}{v_s} = \frac{1}{R_{eq}} = \frac{1}{R_1} + \frac{1}{R_2} + \frac{1}{R_3} + \frac{1}{R_4}. \tag{3.11}$$

Equation 3.11 is what we set out to show: that the four resistors in the circuit shown in Fig. 3.5 can be replaced by a single equivalent resistor. The circuit shown in Fig. 3.7 illustrates the substitution. For k resistors connected in parallel, Eq. 3.11 becomes

$$\frac{1}{R_{eq}} = \sum_{i=1}^{k} \frac{1}{R_i} = \frac{1}{R_1} + \frac{1}{R_2} + \cdots + \frac{1}{R_k}. \tag{3.12}$$

◀ **Combining resistors in parallel**

Note that the resistance of the equivalent resistor is always smaller than the resistance of the smallest resistor in the parallel connection. Sometimes,

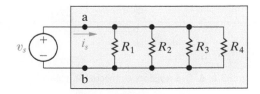

Figure 3.5 ▲ Resistors in parallel.

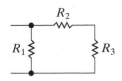

Figure 3.6 ▲ Nonparallel resistors.

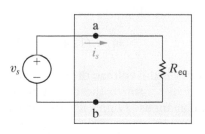

Figure 3.7 ▲ Replacing the four parallel resistors shown in Fig. 3.5 with a single equivalent resistor.

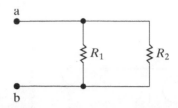

Figure 3.8 ▲ Two resistors connected in parallel.

using conductance when dealing with resistors connected in parallel is more convenient. In that case, Eq. 3.12 becomes

$$G_{eq} = \sum_{i=1}^{k} G_i = G_1 + G_2 + \cdots + G_k. \qquad (3.13)$$

Many times only two resistors are connected in parallel. Figure 3.8 illustrates this special case. We calculate the equivalent resistance from Eq. 3.12:

$$\frac{1}{R_{eq}} = \frac{1}{R_1} + \frac{1}{R_2} = \frac{R_2 + R_1}{R_1 R_2}, \qquad (3.14)$$

or

$$R_{eq} = \frac{R_1 R_2}{R_1 + R_2}. \qquad (3.15)$$

Thus for just two resistors in parallel the equivalent resistance equals the product of the resistances divided by the sum of the resistances. Remember that you can only use this result in the special case of just two resistors in parallel. Example 3.1 illustrates the usefulness of these results.

Example 3.1   Applying Series-Parallel Simplification

Find i_s, i_1, and i_2 in the circuit shown in Fig. 3.9.

Solution

We begin by noting that the 3 Ω resistor is in series with the 6 Ω resistor. We therefore replace this series combination with a 9 Ω resistor, reducing the circuit to the one shown in Fig. 3.10(a). We now can replace the parallel combination of the 9 Ω and 18 Ω resistors with a single resistance of $(18 \times 9)/(18 + 9)$, or 6 Ω. Figure 3.10(b) shows this further reduction of the circuit. The nodes x and y marked on all diagrams facilitate tracing through the reduction of the circuit.

From Fig. 3.10(b) you can verify that i_s equals 120/10, or 12 A. Figure 3.11 shows the result at this point in the analysis. We added the voltage v_1 to help clarify the subsequent discussion. Using Ohm's law we compute the value of v_1:

$$v_1 = (12)(6) = 72 \text{ V}. \qquad (3.16)$$

But v_1 is the voltage drop from node x to node y, so we can return to the circuit shown in Fig. 3.10(a) and again use Ohm's law to calculate i_1 and i_2. Thus,

$$i_1 = \frac{v_1}{18} = \frac{72}{18} = 4 \text{ A}, \qquad (3.17)$$

$$i_2 = \frac{v_1}{9} = \frac{72}{9} = 8 \text{ A}. \qquad (3.18)$$

We have found the three specified currents by using series-parallel reductions in combination with Ohm's law.

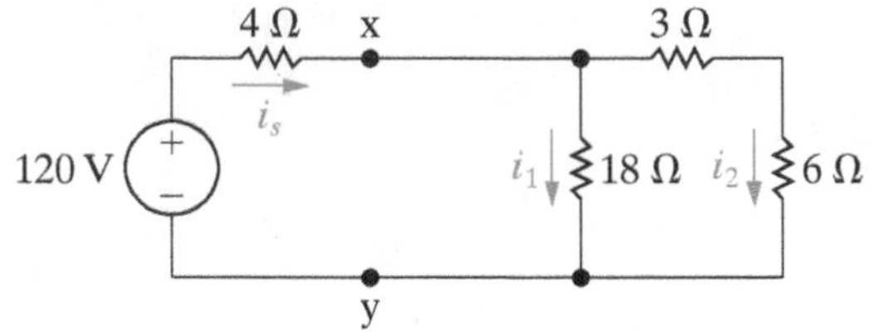

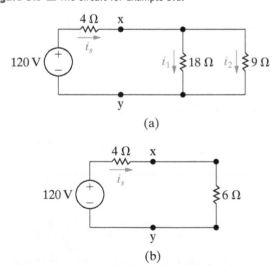

Figure 3.9 ▲ The circuit for Example 3.1.

Figure 3.10 ▲ A simplification of the circuit shown in Fig. 3.9.

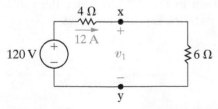

Figure 3.11 ▲ The circuit of Fig. 3.10(b) showing the numerical value of i_s.

Before leaving Example 3.1, we suggest that you take the time to show that the solution satisfies Kirchhoff's current law at every node and Kirchhoff's voltage law around every closed path. (Note that there are three closed paths that can be tested.) Showing that the power delivered by the voltage source equals the total power dissipated in the resistors also is informative. (See Problems 3.1 and 3.2.)

✓**ASSESSMENT PROBLEM**

Objective 1—Be able to recognize resistors connected in series and in parallel

3.1   For the circuit shown, find (a) the voltage v, (b) the power delivered to the circuit by the current source, and (c) the power dissipated in the 10 Ω resistor.

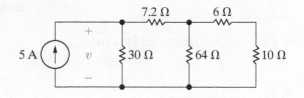

Answer: (a) 60 V;

(b) 300 W;

(c) 57.6 W.

NOTE: Also try Chapter Problems 3.3–3.6.

3.3 The Voltage-Divider and Current-Divider Circuits

At times—especially in electronic circuits—developing more than one voltage level from a single voltage supply is necessary. One way of doing this is by using a **voltage-divider circuit**, such as the one in Fig. 3.12.

We analyze this circuit by directly applying Ohm's law and Kirchhoff's laws. To aid the analysis, we introduce the current i as shown in Fig. 3.12(b). From Kirchhoff's current law, R_1 and R_2 carry the same current. Applying Kirchhoff's voltage law around the closed loop yields

$$v_s = iR_1 + iR_2, \tag{3.19}$$

or

$$i = \frac{v_s}{R_1 + R_2}. \tag{3.20}$$

Now we can use Ohm's law to calculate v_1 and v_2:

$$v_1 = iR_1 = v_s\frac{R_1}{R_1 + R_2}, \tag{3.21}$$

$$v_2 = iR_2 = v_s\frac{R_2}{R_1 + R_2}. \tag{3.22}$$

Equations 3.21 and 3.22 show that v_1 and v_2 are fractions of v_s. Each fraction is the ratio of the resistance across which the divided voltage is defined to the sum of the two resistances. Because this ratio is always less than 1.0, the divided voltages v_1 and v_2 are always less than the source voltage v_s.

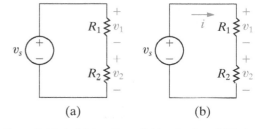

Figure 3.12 ▲ (a) A voltage-divider circuit and (b) the voltage-divider circuit with current i indicated.

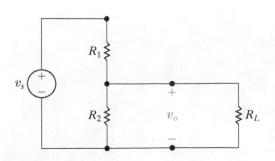

Figure 3.13 ▲ A voltage divider connected to a load R_L.

If you desire a particular value of v_2, and v_s is specified, an infinite number of combinations of R_1 and R_2 yield the proper ratio. For example, suppose that v_s equals 15 V and v_2 is to be 5 V. Then $v_2/v_s = \frac{1}{3}$ and, from Eq. 3.22, we find that this ratio is satisfied whenever $R_2 = \frac{1}{2}R_1$. Other factors that may enter into the selection of R_1, and hence R_2, include the power losses that occur in dividing the source voltage and the effects of connecting the voltage-divider circuit to other circuit components.

Consider connecting a resistor R_L in parallel with R_2, as shown in Fig. 3.13. The resistor R_L acts as a load on the voltage-divider circuit. A **load** on any circuit consists of one or more circuit elements that draw power from the circuit. With the load R_L connected, the expression for the output voltage becomes

$$v_o = \frac{R_{\text{eq}}}{R_1 + R_{\text{eq}}} v_s, \tag{3.23}$$

where

$$R_{\text{eq}} = \frac{R_2 R_L}{R_2 + R_L}. \tag{3.24}$$

Substituting Eq. 3.24 into Eq. 3.23 yields

$$v_o = \frac{R_2}{R_1[1 + (R_2/R_L)] + R_2} v_s. \tag{3.25}$$

Note that Eq. 3.25 reduces to Eq. 3.22 as $R_L \to \infty$, as it should. Equation 3.25 shows that, as long as $R_L \gg R_2$, the voltage ratio v_o/v_s is essentially undisturbed by the addition of the load on the divider.

Another characteristic of the voltage-divider circuit of interest is the sensitivity of the divider to the tolerances of the resistors. By *tolerance* we mean a range of possible values. The resistances of commercially available resistors always vary within some percentage of their stated value. Example 3.2 illustrates the effect of resistor tolerances in a voltage-divider circuit.

Example 3.2 **Analyzing the Voltage-Divider Circuit**

The resistors used in the voltage-divider circuit shown in Fig. 3.14 have a tolerance of $\pm10\%$. Find the maximum and minimum value of v_o.

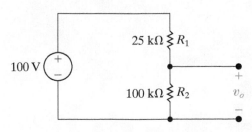

Figure 3.14 ▲ The circuit for Example 3.2.

Solution

From Eq. 3.22, the maximum value of v_o occurs when R_2 is 10% high and R_1 is 10% low, and the minimum value of v_o occurs when R_2 is 10% low and R_1 is 10% high. Therefore

$$v_o(\text{max}) = \frac{(100)(110)}{110 + 22.5} = 83.02 \text{ V},$$

$$v_o(\text{min}) = \frac{(100)(90)}{90 + 27.5} = 76.60 \text{ V}.$$

Thus, in making the decision to use 10% resistors in this voltage divider, we recognize that the no-load output voltage will lie between 76.60 and 83.02 V.

The Current-Divider Circuit

The **current-divider circuit** shown in Fig. 3.15 consists of two resistors connected in parallel across a current source. The current divider is designed to divide the current i_s between R_1 and R_2. We find the relationship between the current i_s and the current in each resistor (that is, i_1 and i_2) by directly applying Ohm's law and Kirchhoff's current law. The voltage across the parallel resistors is

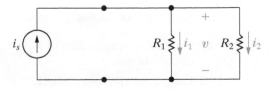

Figure 3.15 ▲ The current-divider circuit.

$$v = i_1 R_1 = i_2 R_2 = \frac{R_1 R_2}{R_1 + R_2} i_s. \tag{3.26}$$

From Eq. 3.26,

$$i_1 = \frac{R_2}{R_1 + R_2} i_s, \tag{3.27}$$

$$i_2 = \frac{R_1}{R_1 + R_2} i_s. \tag{3.28}$$

Equations 3.27 and 3.28 show that the current divides between two resistors in parallel such that the current in one resistor equals the current entering the parallel pair multiplied by the other resistance and divided by the sum of the resistors. Example 3.3 illustrates the use of the current-divider equation.

Example 3.3   **Analyzing a Current-Divider Circuit**

Find the power dissipated in the 6 Ω resistor shown in Fig. 3.16.

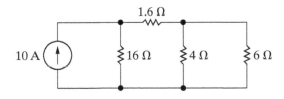

Figure 3.16 ▲ The circuit for Example 3.3.

Solution

First, we must find the current in the resistor by simplifying the circuit with series-parallel reductions. Thus, the circuit shown in Fig. 3.16 reduces to the one shown in Fig. 3.17. We find the current i_o by using the formula for current division:

$$i_o = \frac{16}{16 + 4}(10) = 8 \text{ A}.$$

Note that i_o is the current in the 1.6 Ω resistor in Fig. 3.16. We now can further divide i_o between the 6 Ω and 4 Ω resistors. The current in the 6 Ω resistor is

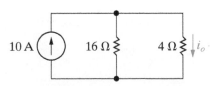

Figure 3.17 ▲ A simplification of the circuit shown in Fig. 3.16.

$$i_6 = \frac{4}{6 + 4}(8) = 3.2 \text{ A},$$

and the power dissipated in the 6 Ω resistor is
$p = (3.2)^2(6) = 61.44 \text{ W}.$

✓ASSESSMENT PROBLEMS

Objective 2—Know how to design simple voltage-divider and current-divider circuits

3.2 a) Find the no-load value of v_o in the circuit shown.

b) Find v_o when R_L is 150 kΩ.

c) How much power is dissipated in the 25 kΩ resistor if the load terminals are accidentally short-circuited?

d) What is the maximum power dissipated in the 75 kΩ resistor?

3.3 a) Find the value of R that will cause 4 A of current to flow through the 80 Ω resistor in the circuit shown.

b) How much power will the resistor R from part (a) need to dissipate?

c) How much power will the current source generate for the value of R from part (a)?

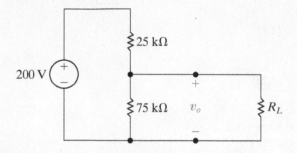

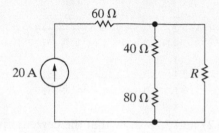

Answer: (a) 150 V;

(b) 133.33 V;

(c) 1.6 W;

(d) 0.3 W.

Answer: (a) 30 Ω;

(b) 7680 W;

(c) 33,600 W.

NOTE: Also try Chapter Problems 3.12, 3.14, and 3.16.

3.4 Voltage Division and Current Division

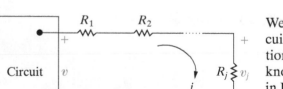

Figure 3.18 ▲ Circuit used to illustrate voltage division.

We can now generalize the results from analyzing the voltage divider circuit in Fig. 3.12 and the current-divider circuit in Fig. 3.15. The generalizations will yield two additional and very useful circuit analysis techniques known as **voltage division** and **current division**. Consider the circuit shown in Fig. 3.18.

The box on the left can contain a single voltage source or any other combination of basic circuit elements that results in the voltage v shown in the figure. To the right of the box are n resistors connected in series. We are interested in finding the voltage drop v_j across an arbitrary resistor R_j in terms of the voltage v. We start by using Ohm's law to calculate i, the current through all of the resistors in series, in terms of the current v and the n resistors:

$$i = \frac{v}{R_1 + R_2 + \cdots + R_n} = \frac{v}{R_{eq}}. \tag{3.29}$$

The equivalent resistance, R_{eq}, is the sum of the n resistor values because the resistors are in series, as shown in Eq. 3.6. We apply Ohm's law a second time to calculate the voltage drop v_j across the resistor R_j, using the current i calculated in Eq. 3.29:

$$v_j = iR_j = \frac{R_j}{R_{eq}} v.$$

(3.30)   ◀ **Voltage-division equation**

Note that we used Eq. 3.29 to obtain the right-hand side of Eq. 3.30. Equation 3.30 is the voltage division equation. It says that the voltage drop v_j across a single resistor R_j from a collection of series-connected resistors is proportional to the total voltage drop v across the set of series-connected resistors. The constant of proportionality is the ratio of the single resistance to the equivalent resistance of the series connected set of resistors, or R_j/R_{eq}.

Now consider the circuit shown in Fig. 3.19. The box on the left can contain a single current source or any other combination of basic circuit elements that results in the current i shown in the figure. To the right of the box are n resistors connected in parallel. We are interested in finding the current i_j through an arbitrary resistor R_j in terms of the current i. We start by using Ohm's law to calculate v, the voltage drop across each of the resistors in parallel, in terms of the current i and the n resistors:

$$v = i(R_1 \| R_2 \| \dots \| R_n) = iR_{eq}.$$

(3.31)

The equivalent resistance of n resistors in parallel, R_{eq}, can be calculated using Eq. 3.12. We apply Ohm's law a second time to calculate the current i_j through the resistor R_j, using the voltage v calculated in Eq. 3.31:

$$i_j = \frac{v}{R_j} = \frac{R_{eq}}{R_j} i.$$

(3.32)   ◀ **Current-division equation**

Note that we used Eq. 3.31 to obtain the right-hand side of Eq. 3.32. Equation 3.32 is the current division equation. It says that the current i through a single resistor R_j from a collection of parallel-connected resistors is proportional to the total current i supplied to the set of parallel-connected resistors. The constant of proportionality is the ratio of the equivalent resistance of the parallel-connected set of resistors to the single resistance, or R_{eq}/R_j. Note that the constant of proportionality in the current division equation is the inverse of the constant of proportionality in the voltage division equation!

Example 3.4 uses voltage division and current division to solve for voltages and currents in a circuit.

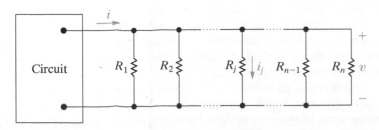

Figure 3.19 ▲ Circuit used to illustrate current division.

Example 3.4   Using Voltage Division and Current Division to Solve a Circuit

Use current division to find the current i_o and use voltage division to find the voltage v_o for the circuit in Fig. 3.20.

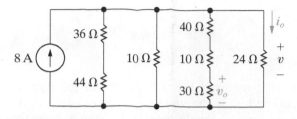

Figure 3.20 ▲ The circuit for Example 3.4.

Solution

We can use Eq. 3.32 if we can find the equivalent resistance of the four parallel branches containing resistors. Symbolically,

$$R_{eq} = (36 + 44)\|10\|(40 + 10 + 30)\|24$$

$$= 80\|10\|80\|24 = \cfrac{1}{\cfrac{1}{80} + \cfrac{1}{10} + \cfrac{1}{80} + \cfrac{1}{24}} = 6\ \Omega.$$

Applying Eq. 3.32,

$$i_o = \frac{6}{24}(8\ \text{A}) = 2\ \text{A}.$$

We can use Ohm's law to find the voltage drop across the 24 Ω resistor:

$$v = (24)(2) = 48\ \text{V}.$$

This is also the voltage drop across the branch containing the 40 Ω, the 10 Ω, and the 30 Ω resistors in series. We can then use voltage division to determine the voltage drop v_o across the 30 Ω resistor given that we know the voltage drop across the series-connected resistors, using Eq. 3.30. To do this, we recognize that the equivalent resistance of the series-connected resistors is 40 + 10 + 30 = 80 Ω:

$$v_o = \frac{30}{80}(48\ \text{V}) = 18\ \text{V}.$$

✓ ASSESSMENT PROBLEM

Objective 3—Be able to use voltage and current division to solve simple circuits

3.4 a) Use voltage division to determine the voltage v_o across the 40 Ω resistor in the circuit shown.

b) Use v_o from part (a) to determine the current through the 40 Ω resistor, and use this current and current division to calculate the current in the 30 Ω resistor.

c) How much power is absorbed by the 50 Ω resistor?

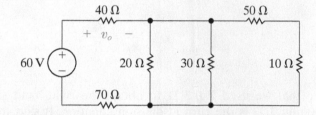

Answer: (a) 20 V;

(b) 166.67 mA;

(c) 347.22 mW.

NOTE: Also try Chapter Problems 3.25 and 3.26.

3.5 Measuring Voltage and Current

When working with actual circuits, you will often need to measure voltages and currents. We will spend some time discussing several measuring devices here and in the next section, because they are relatively simple to analyze and offer practical examples of the current- and voltage-divider configurations we have just studied.

An **ammeter** is an instrument designed to measure current; it is placed in series with the circuit element whose current is being measured. A **voltmeter** is an instrument designed to measure voltage; it is placed in parallel with the element whose voltage is being measured. An ideal ammeter or voltmeter has no effect on the circuit variable it is designed to measure.

That is, an ideal ammeter has an equivalent resistance of 0 Ω and functions as a short circuit in series with the element whose current is being measured. An ideal voltmeter has an infinite equivalent resistance and thus functions as an open circuit in parallel with the element whose voltage is being measured. The configurations for an ammeter used to measure the current in R_1 and for a voltmeter used to measure the voltage in R_2 are depicted in Fig. 3.21. The ideal models for these meters in the same circuit are shown in Fig. 3.22.

There are two broad categories of meters used to measure continuous voltages and currents: digital meters and analog meters. **Digital meters** measure the continuous voltage or current signal at discrete points in time, called the sampling times. The signal is thus converted from an analog signal, which is continuous in time, to a digital signal, which exists only at discrete instants in time. A more detailed explanation of the workings of digital meters is beyond the scope of this text and course. However, you are likely to see and use digital meters in lab settings because they offer several advantages over analog meters. They introduce less resistance into the circuit to which they are connected, they are easier to connect, and the precision of the measurement is greater due to the nature of the readout mechanism.

Analog meters are based on the d'Arsonval meter movement which implements the readout mechanism. A d'Arsonval meter movement consists of a movable coil placed in the field of a permanent magnet. When current flows in the coil, it creates a torque on the coil, causing it to rotate and move a pointer across a calibrated scale. By design, the deflection of the pointer is directly proportional to the current in the movable coil. The coil is characterized by both a voltage rating and a current rating. For example, one commercially available meter movement is rated at 50 mV and 1 mA. This means that when the coil is carrying 1 mA, the voltage drop across the coil is 50 mV and the pointer is deflected to its full-scale position. A schematic illustration of a d'Arsonval meter movement is shown in Fig. 3.23.

An analog ammeter consists of a d'Arsonval movement in parallel with a resistor, as shown in Fig. 3.24. The purpose of the parallel resistor is to limit the amount of current in the movement's coil by shunting some of it through R_A. An analog voltmeter consists of a d'Arsonval movement in series with a resistor, as shown in Fig. 3.25. Here, the resistor is used to limit the voltage drop across the meter's coil. In both meters, the added resistor determines the full-scale reading of the meter movement.

From these descriptions we see that an actual meter is nonideal; both the added resistor and the meter movement introduce resistance in the circuit to which the meter is attached. In fact, any instrument used to make physical measurements extracts energy from the system while making measurements. The more energy extracted by the instruments, the more severely the measurement is disturbed. A real ammeter has an equivalent resistance that is not zero, and it thus effectively adds resistance to the circuit in series with the element whose current the ammeter is reading. A real voltmeter has an equivalent resistance that is not infinite, so it effectively adds resistance to the circuit in parallel with the element whose voltage is being read.

How much these meters disturb the circuit being measured depends on the effective resistance of the meters compared with the resistance in the circuit. For example, using the rule of 1/10th, the effective resistance of an ammeter should be no more than 1/10th of the value of the smallest resistance in the circuit to be sure that the current being measured is nearly the same with or without the ammeter. But in an analog meter, the value of resistance is determined by the desired full-scale reading we wish to make, and it cannot be arbitrarily selected. The following examples illustrate the calculations involved in determining the resistance needed in an analog ammeter or voltmeter. The examples also consider the resulting effective resistance of the meter when it is inserted in a circuit.

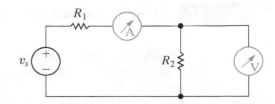

Figure 3.21 ▲ An ammeter connected to measure the current in R_1, and a voltmeter connected to measure the voltage across R_2.

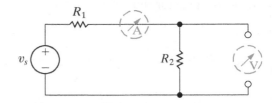

Figure 3.22 ▲ A short-circuit model for the ideal ammeter, and an open-circuit model for the ideal voltmeter.

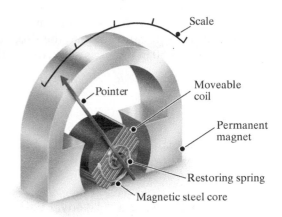

Figure 3.23 ▲ A schematic diagram of a d'Arsonval meter movement.

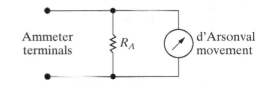

Figure 3.24 ▲ A dc ammeter circuit.

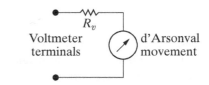

Figure 3.25 ▲ A dc voltmeter circuit.

Example 3.5 Using a d'Arsonval Ammeter

a) A 50 mV, 1 mA d'Arsonval movement is to be used in an ammeter with a full-scale reading of 10 mA. Determine R_A.

b) Repeat (a) for a full-scale reading of 1 A.

c) How much resistance is added to the circuit when the 10 mA ammeter is inserted to measure current?

d) Repeat (c) for the 1 A ammeter.

Solution

a) From the statement of the problem, we know that when the current at the terminals of the ammeter is 10 mA, 1 mA is flowing through the meter coil, which means that 9 mA must be diverted through R_A. We also know that when the movement carries 1 mA, the drop across its terminals is 50 mV. Ohm's law requires that

$$9 \times 10^{-3} R_A = 50 \times 10^{-3},$$

or

$$R_A = 50/9 = 5.555 \ \Omega.$$

b) When the full-scale deflection of the ammeter is 1 A, R_A must carry 999 mA when the movement carries 1 mA. In this case, then,

$$999 \times 10^{-3} R_A = 50 \times 10^{-3},$$

or

$$R_A = 50/999 \approx 50.05 \ \text{m}\Omega.$$

c) Let R_m represent the equivalent resistance of the ammeter. For the 10 mA ammeter,

$$R_m = \frac{50 \ \text{mV}}{10 \ \text{mA}} = 5 \ \Omega,$$

or, alternatively,

$$R_m = \frac{(50)(50/9)}{50 + (50/9)} = 5 \ \Omega.$$

d) For the 1 A ammeter

$$R_m = \frac{50 \ \text{mV}}{1 \ \text{A}} = 0.050 \ \Omega,$$

or, alternatively,

$$R_m = \frac{(50)(50/999)}{50 + (50/999)} = 0.050 \ \Omega.$$

Example 3.6 Using a d'Arsonval Voltmeter

a) A 50 mV, 1 mA d'Arsonval movement is to be used in a voltmeter in which the full-scale reading is 150 V. Determine R_v.

b) Repeat (a) for a full-scale reading of 5 V.

c) How much resistance does the 150 V meter insert into the circuit?

d) Repeat (c) for the 5 V meter.

Solution

a) Full-scale deflection requires 50 mV across the meter movement, and the movement has a resistance of 50 Ω. Therefore we apply Eq. 3.22 with $R_1 = R_v, R_2 = 50, v_s = 150,$ and $v_2 = 50$ mV:

$$50 \times 10^{-3} = \frac{50}{R_v + 50}(150).$$

Solving for R_v gives

$$R_v = 149{,}950 \ \Omega.$$

b) For a full-scale reading of 5 V,

$$50 \times 10^{-3} = \frac{50}{R_v + 50}(5),$$

or

$$R_v = 4950 \ \Omega.$$

c) If we let R_m represent the equivalent resistance of the meter,

$$R_m = \frac{150 \ \text{V}}{10^{-3} \ \text{A}} = 150{,}000 \ \Omega,$$

or, alternatively,

$$R_m = 149{,}950 + 50 = 150{,}000 \ \Omega.$$

d) Then,

$$R_m = \frac{5 \ \text{V}}{10^{-3} \ \text{A}} = 5000 \ \Omega,$$

or, alternatively,

$$R_m = 4950 + 50 = 5000 \ \Omega.$$

Objective 4—Be able to determine the reading of ammeters and voltmeters

3.5 a) Find the current in the circuit shown.

   b) If the ammeter in Example 3.5(a) is used to measure the current, what will it read?

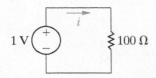

3.6 a) Find the voltage v across the 75 kΩ resistor in the circuit shown.

   b) If the 150 V voltmeter of Example 3.6(a) is used to measure the voltage, what will be the reading?

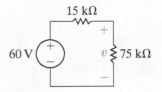

Answer: (a) 10 mA;

   (b) 9.524 mA.

Answer: (a) 50 V;

   (b) 46.15 V.

NOTE: Also try Chapter Problems 3.34 and 3.37.

3.6 Measuring Resistance— The Wheatstone Bridge

Many different circuit configurations are used to measure resistance. Here we will focus on just one, the Wheatstone bridge. The Wheatstone bridge circuit is used to precisely measure resistances of medium values, that is, in the range of 1 Ω to 1 MΩ. In commercial models of the Wheatstone bridge, accuracies on the order of ±0.1% are possible. The bridge circuit consists of four resistors, a dc voltage source, and a detector. The resistance of one of the four resistors can be varied, which is indicated in Fig. 3.26 by the arrow through R_3. The dc voltage source is usually a battery, which is indicated by the battery symbol for the voltage source v in Fig. 3.26. The detector is generally a d'Arsonval movement in the microamp range and is called a galvanometer. Figure 3.26 shows the circuit arrangement of the resistances, battery, and detector where R_1, R_2, and R_3 are known resistors and R_x is the unknown resistor.

To find the value of R_x, we adjust the variable resistor R_3 until there is no current in the galvanometer. We then calculate the unknown resistor from the simple expression

$$R_x = \frac{R_2}{R_1}R_3.$$ (3.33)

The derivation of Eq. 3.33 follows directly from the application of Kirchhoff's laws to the bridge circuit. We redraw the bridge circuit as Fig. 3.27 to show the currents appropriate to the derivation of Eq. 3.33. When i_g is zero, that is, when the bridge is balanced, Kirchhoff's current law requires that

$$i_1 = i_3,$$ (3.34)

$$i_2 = i_x.$$ (3.35)

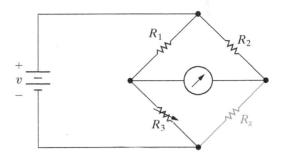

Figure 3.26 ▲ The Wheatstone bridge circuit.

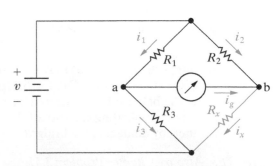

Figure 3.27 ▲ A balanced Wheatstone bridge ($i_g = 0$).

Now, because i_g is zero, there is no voltage drop across the detector, and therefore points a and b are at the same potential. Thus when the bridge is balanced, Kirchhoff's voltage law requires that

$$i_3 R_3 = i_x R_x, \tag{3.36}$$
$$i_1 R_1 = i_2 R_2. \tag{3.37}$$

Combining Eqs. 3.34 and 3.35 with Eq. 3.36 gives

$$i_1 R_3 = i_2 R_x. \tag{3.38}$$

We obtain Eq. 3.33 by first dividing Eq. 3.38 by Eq. 3.37 and then solving the resulting expression for R_x:

$$\frac{R_3}{R_1} = \frac{R_x}{R_2}, \tag{3.39}$$

from which

$$R_x = \frac{R_2}{R_1} R_3. \tag{3.40}$$

Now that we have verified the validity of Eq. 3.33, several comments about the result are in order. First, note that if the ratio R_2/R_1 is unity, the unknown resistor R_x equals R_3. In this case, the bridge resistor R_3 must vary over a range that includes the value R_x. For example, if the unknown resistance were 1000 Ω and R_3 could be varied from 0 to 100 Ω, the bridge could never be balanced. Thus to cover a wide range of unknown resistors, we must be able to vary the ratio R_2/R_1. In a commercial Wheatstone bridge, R_1 and R_2 consist of decimal values of resistances that can be switched into the bridge circuit. Normally, the decimal values are 1, 10, 100, and 1000 Ω so that the ratio R_2/R_1 can be varied from 0.001 to 1000 in decimal steps. The variable resistor R_3 is usually adjustable in integral values of resistance from 1 to 11,000 Ω.

Although Eq. 3.33 implies that R_x can vary from zero to infinity, the practical range of R_x is approximately 1 Ω to 1 MΩ. Lower resistances are difficult to measure on a standard Wheatstone bridge because of thermoelectric voltages generated at the junctions of dissimilar metals and because of thermal heating effects—that is, $i^2 R$ effects. Higher resistances are difficult to measure accurately because of leakage currents. In other words, if R_x is large, the current leakage in the electrical insulation may be comparable to the current in the branches of the bridge circuit.

✓ ASSESSMENT PROBLEM

Objective 5—Understand how a Wheatstone bridge is used to measure resistance

3.7 The bridge circuit shown is balanced when $R_1 = 100\ \Omega$, $R_2 = 1000\ \Omega$, and $R_3 = 150\ \Omega$. The bridge is energized from a 5 V dc source.

a) What is the value of R_x?

b) Suppose each bridge resistor is capable of dissipating 250 mW. Can the bridge be left in the balanced state without exceeding the power-dissipating capacity of the resistors, thereby damaging the bridge?

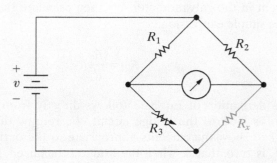

Answer: (a) 1500 Ω;

(b) yes.

NOTE: Also try Chapter Problem 3.51.

3.7 Delta-to-Wye (Pi-to-Tee) Equivalent Circuits

The bridge configuration in Fig. 3.26 introduces an interconnection of resistances that warrants further discussion. If we replace the galvanometer with its equivalent resistance R_m, we can draw the circuit shown in Fig. 3.28. We cannot reduce the interconnected resistors of this circuit to a single equivalent resistance across the terminals of the battery if restricted to the simple series or parallel equivalent circuits introduced earlier in this chapter. The interconnected resistors can be reduced to a single equivalent resistor by means of a delta-to-wye (Δ-to-Y) or pi-to-tee (π-to-T) equivalent circuit.[1]

The resistors R_1, R_2, and R_m (or R_3, R_m and R_x) in the circuit shown in Fig. 3.28 are referred to as a **delta (Δ) interconnection** because the interconnection looks like the Greek letter Δ. It also is referred to as a **pi interconnection** because the Δ can be shaped into a π without disturbing the electrical equivalence of the two configurations. The electrical equivalence between the Δ and π interconnections is apparent in Fig. 3.29.

The resistors R_1, R_m, and R_3 (or R_2, R_m and R_x) in the circuit shown in Fig. 3.28 are referred to as a **wye (Y) interconnection** because the interconnection can be shaped to look like the letter Y. It is easier to see the Y shape when the interconnection is drawn as in Fig. 3.30. The Y configuration also is referred to as a **tee (T) interconnection** because the Y structure can be shaped into a T structure without disturbing the electrical equivalence of the two structures. The electrical equivalence of the Y and the T configurations is apparent from Fig. 3.30.

Figure 3.31 illustrates the Δ-to-Y (or π-to-T) equivalent circuit transformation. Note that we cannot transform the Δ interconnection into the Y interconnection simply by changing the shape of the interconnections. Saying the Δ-connected circuit is equivalent to the Y-connected circuit means that the Δ configuration can be replaced with a Y configuration to make the terminal behavior of the two configurations identical. Thus if each circuit is placed in a black box, we can't tell by external measurements whether the box contains a set of Δ-connected resistors or a set of Y-connected resistors. This condition is true only if the resistance between corresponding terminal pairs is the same for each box. For example, the resistance between terminals a and b must be the same whether we use the Δ-connected set or the Y-connected set. For each pair of terminals in the Δ-connected circuit, the equivalent resistance can be computed using series and parallel simplifications to yield

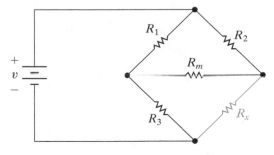

Figure 3.28 ▲ A resistive network generated by a Wheatstone bridge circuit.

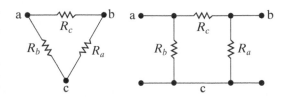

Figure 3.29 ▲ A Δ configuration viewed as a π configuration.

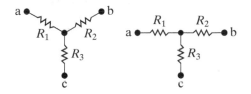

Figure 3.30 ▲ A Y structure viewed as a T structure.

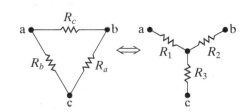

Figure 3.31 ▲ The Δ-to-Y transformation.

$$R_{\mathrm{ab}} = \frac{R_c(R_a + R_b)}{R_a + R_b + R_c} = R_1 + R_2, \qquad (3.41)$$

$$R_{\mathrm{bc}} = \frac{R_a(R_b + R_c)}{R_a + R_b + R_c} = R_2 + R_3, \qquad (3.42)$$

$$R_{\mathrm{ca}} = \frac{R_b(R_c + R_a)}{R_a + R_b + R_c} = R_1 + R_3. \qquad (3.43)$$

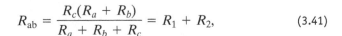

---

[1] Δ and Y structures are present in a variety of useful circuits, not just resistive networks. Hence the Δ-to-Y transformation is a helpful tool in circuit analysis.

Straightforward algebraic manipulation of Eqs. 3.41–3.43 gives values for the Y-connected resistors in terms of the Δ-connected resistors required for the Δ-to-Y equivalent circuit:

$$R_1 = \frac{R_b R_c}{R_a + R_b + R_c}, \tag{3.44}$$

$$R_2 = \frac{R_c R_a}{R_a + R_b + R_c}, \tag{3.45}$$

$$R_3 = \frac{R_a R_b}{R_a + R_b + R_c}. \tag{3.46}$$

Reversing the Δ-to-Y transformation also is possible. That is, we can start with the Y structure and replace it with an equivalent Δ structure. The expressions for the three Δ-connected resistors as functions of the three Y-connected resistors are

$$R_a = \frac{R_1 R_2 + R_2 R_3 + R_3 R_1}{R_1}, \tag{3.47}$$

$$R_b = \frac{R_1 R_2 + R_2 R_3 + R_3 R_1}{R_2}, \tag{3.48}$$

$$R_c = \frac{R_1 R_2 + R_2 R_3 + R_3 R_1}{R_3}. \tag{3.49}$$

Example 3.7 illustrates the use of a Δ-to-Y transformation to simplify the analysis of a circuit.

Example 3.7 Applying a Delta-to-Wye Transform

Find the current and power supplied by the 40 V source in the circuit shown in Fig. 3.32.

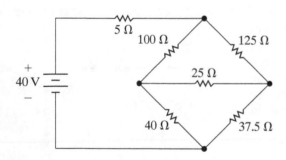

Figure 3.32 ▲ The circuit for Example 3.7.

Solution

We are interested only in the current and power drain on the 40 V source, so the problem has been solved once we obtain the equivalent resistance across the terminals of the source. We can find this equivalent resistance easily after replacing either the upper Δ (100, 125, 25 Ω) or the lower Δ (40, 25, 37.5 Ω) with its equivalent Y. We choose to replace the upper Δ. We then compute the three

Y resistances, defined in Fig. 3.33, from Eqs. 3.44 to 3.46. Thus,

$$R_1 = \frac{100 \times 125}{250} = 50\ \Omega,$$

$$R_2 = \frac{125 \times 25}{250} = 12.5\ \Omega,$$

$$R_3 = \frac{100 \times 25}{250} = 10\ \Omega.$$

Substituting the Y-resistors into the circuit shown in Fig. 3.32 produces the circuit shown in Fig. 3.34. From Fig. 3.34, we can easily calculate the resistance across the terminals of the 40 V source by series-parallel simplifications:

$$R_{eq} = 55 + \frac{(50)(50)}{100} = 80\ \Omega.$$

The final step is to note that the circuit reduces to an 80 Ω resistor across a 40 V source, as shown in Fig. 3.35, from which it is apparent that the 40 V source delivers 0.5 A and 20 W to the circuit.

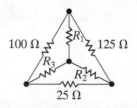

Figure 3.33 ▲ The equivalent Y resistors.

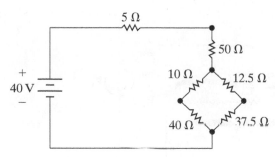

Figure 3.34 ▲ A transformed version of the circuit shown in Fig. 3.32.

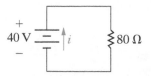

Figure 3.35 ▲ The final step in the simplification of the circuit shown in Fig. 3.32.

✓**ASSESSMENT PROBLEM**

Objective 6—Know when and how to use delta-to-wye equivalent circuits

3.8   Use a Y-to-Δ transformation to find the voltage v in the circuit shown.

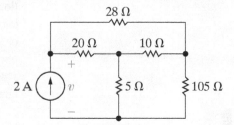

Answer: 35 V.

NOTE: Also try Chapter Problems 3.60, 3.62, and 3.63.

Practical Perspective

Resistive Touch Screens

Begin by analyzing the resistive grid in the x-direction. We model the resistance of the grid in the x-direction with the resistance R_x, as shown in Fig. 3.34. The x-location where the screen is touched is indicated by the arrow. The resulting voltage drop across the resistance αR_x is V_x. Touching the screen effectively divides the total resistance, R_x, into two separate resistances αR_x and $(1 - \alpha)R_x$.

From the figure you can see that when the touch is on the far right side of the screen, $\alpha = 0$, and $V_x = 0$. Similarly, when the touch is on the far left side of the screen, $\alpha = 1$, and $V_x = V_s$. If the touch is in between the two edges of the screen, the value of α is between 0 and 1 and the two parts of the resistance R_x form a voltage divider. We can calculate the voltage V_x using the equation for voltage division:

$$V_x = \frac{\alpha R_x}{\alpha R_x + (1 - \alpha)R_x}V_s = \frac{\alpha R_x}{R_x}V_s = \alpha V_s.$$

We can find the value of α, which represents the location of the touch point with respect the far right side of the screen, by dividing the voltage

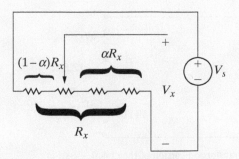

Figure 3.36 ▲ The resistive touch screen grid in the *x*-direction.

across the grid resistance starting at the touch point, V_x, by the voltage applied across the entire resistive grid in the *x*-direction, V_s :

$$\alpha = \frac{V_x}{V_s}.$$

Now we want to use the value of α to determine the *x*-coordinate of the touch location on the screen. Typically the screen coordinates are specified in terms of pixels (short for "picture elements"). For example, the screen of a mobile phone would be divided into a grid of pixels with p_x pixels in the *x*-direction, and p_y pixels in the *y*-direction. Each pixel is identified by its *x*-location (a number between 0 and $p_x - 1$) and its *y*-location (a number between 0 and $p_y - 1$). The pixel with the location (0, 0) is in the upper left hand corner of the screen, as shown in Fig. 3.37.

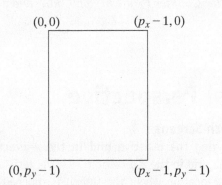

Figure 3.37 ▲ The pixel coordinates of a screen with p_x pixels in the *x*-direction and p_y pixels in the *y*-direction.

Since α represents the location of the touch point with respect to the right side of the screen, $(1 - \alpha)$ represents the location of the touch point with respect to the left side of the screen. Therefore, the *x*-coordinate of the pixel corresponding to the touch point is

$$x = (1 - \alpha)p_x.$$

Note that the value of *x* is capped at $(p_x - 1)$.

Using the model of the resistive screen grid in the *y*-direction shown in Fig. 3.38, it is easy to show that the voltage created by a touch at the arrow is given by

$$V_y = \beta V_s.$$

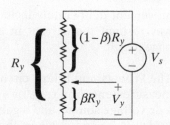

Figure 3.38 ▲ The resistive touch screen grid in the y-direction.

Therefore, the y-coordinate of the pixel corresponding to the touch point is

$$y = (1 - \beta)p_y,$$

where the value of y is capped at $(p_y - 1)$. (See Problem 3.72.)

NOTE: Assess your understanding of the Practical Perspective by solving Chapter Problems 3.72–3.75.

Summary

- **Series resistors** can be combined to obtain a single equivalent resistance according to the equation

$$R_{eq} = \sum_{i=1}^{k} R_i = R_1 + R_2 + \cdots + R_k.$$

(See page 58.)

- **Parallel resistors** can be combined to obtain a single equivalent resistance according to the equation

$$\frac{1}{R_{eq}} = \sum_{i=1}^{k} \frac{1}{R_i} = \frac{1}{R_1} + \frac{1}{R_2} + \cdots + \frac{1}{R_k}.$$

When just two resistors are in parallel, the equation for equivalent resistance can be simplified to give

$$R_{eq} = \frac{R_1 R_2}{R_1 + R_2}.$$

(See pages 59–60.)

- When voltage is divided between series resistors, as shown in the figure, the voltage across each resistor can be found according to the equations

$$v_1 = \frac{R_1}{R_1 + R_2} v_s,$$

$$v_2 = \frac{R_2}{R_1 + R_2} v_s.$$

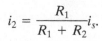

(See page 61.)

- When current is divided between parallel resistors, as shown in the figure, the current through each resistor can be found according to the equations

$$i_1 = \frac{R_2}{R_1 + R_2} i_s.$$

$$i_2 = \frac{R_1}{R_1 + R_2} i_s.$$

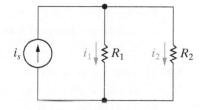

(See page 63.)

- **Voltage division** is a circuit analysis tool that is used to find the voltage drop across a single resistance from a collection of series-connected resistances when the voltage drop across the collection is known:

$$v_j = \frac{R_j}{R_{eq}} v,$$

where v_j is the voltage drop across the resistance R_j and v is the voltage drop across the series-connected resistances whose equivalent resistance is R_{eq}. (See page 65.)

- **Current division** is a circuit analysis tool that is used to find the current through a single resistance from a collection of parallel-connected resistances when the current into the collection is known:

$$I_j = \frac{R_{eq}}{R_j} i,$$

where i_j is the current through the resistance R_j and i is the current into the parallel-connected resistances whose equivalent resistance is R_{eq}. (See page 65.)

- A **voltmeter** measures voltage and must be placed in parallel with the voltage being measured. An ideal voltmeter has infinite internal resistance and thus does not alter the voltage being measured. (See page 66.)

- An **ammeter** measures current and must be placed in series with the current being measured. An ideal ammeter has zero internal resistance and thus does not alter the current being measured. (See page 66.)

- **Digital meters** and **analog meters** have internal resistance, which influences the value of the circuit variable being measured. Meters based on the d'Arsonval meter

movement deliberately include internal resistance as a way to limit the current in the movement's coil. (See page 67.)

- The **Wheatstone bridge** circuit is used to make precise measurements of a resistor's value using four resistors, a dc voltage source, and a galvanometer. A Wheatstone bridge is balanced when the resistors obey Eq. 3.33, resulting in a galvanometer reading of 0 A. (See page 69.)

- A circuit with three resistors connected in a Δ configuration (or a π configuration) can be transformed into an equivalent circuit in which the three resistors are Y connected (or T connected). The Δ-to-Y transformation is given by Eqs. 3.44–3.46; the Y-to-Δ transformation is given by Eqs. 3.47–3.49. (See page 72.)

Problems

Sections 3.1–3.2

3.1 a) Show that the solution of the circuit in Fig. 3.9 (see Example 3.1) satisfies Kirchhoff's current law at junctions x and y.

     PSPICE
     MULTISIM

     b) Show that the solution of the circuit in Fig. 3.9 satisfies Kirchhoff's voltage law around every closed loop.

3.2 a) Find the power dissipated in each resistor in the circuit shown in Fig. 3.9.

     PSPICE
     MULTISIM

     b) Find the power delivered by the 120 V source.

     c) Show that the power delivered equals the power dissipated.

3.3 For each of the circuits shown in Fig. P3.3,

     a) identify the resistors connected in series,

     b) simplify the circuit by replacing the series-connected resistors with equivalent resistors.

3.4 For each of the circuits shown in Fig. P3.4,

     a) identify the resistors connected in parallel,

     b) simplify the circuit by replacing the parallel-connected resistors with equivalent resistors.

3.5 For each of the circuits shown in Fig. P3.3,

     a) find the equivalent resistance seen by the source,

     b) find the power developed by the source.

Figure P3.3

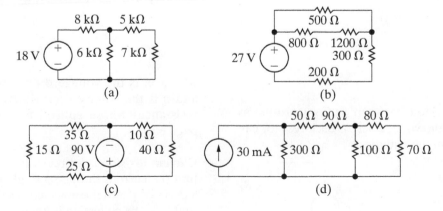

Figure P3.4

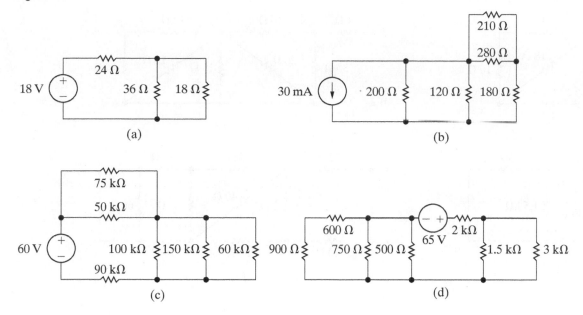

(a)

(b)

(c)

(d)

3.6 For each of the circuits shown in Fig. P3.4,
    a) find the equivalent resistance seen by the source,
    b) find the power developed by the source.

3.7 a) In the circuits in Fig. P3.7(a)–(d), find the equivalent resistance seen by the source.
    b) For each circuit find the power delivered by the source.

PSPICE
MULTISIM

Figure P3.7

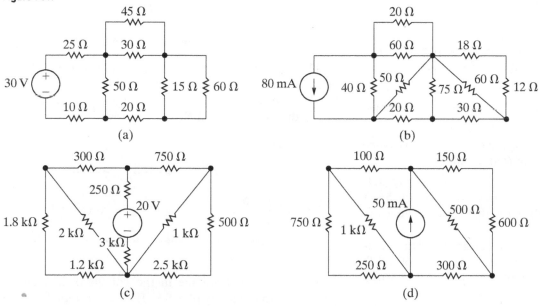

(a)

(b)

(c)

(d)

3.8 Find the equivalent resistance R_{ab} for each of the circuits in Fig. P3.8.

PSPICE
MULTISIM

3.9 Find the equivalent resistance R_{ab} for each of the circuits in Fig. P3.9.

PSPICE
MULTISIM

Figure P3.8

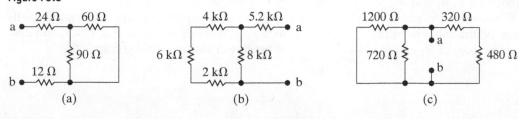

(a)

(b)

(c)

Figure P3.9

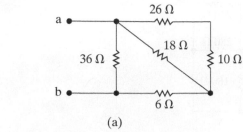

(a)

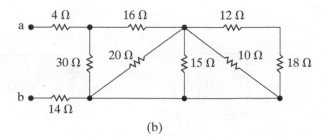

(b)

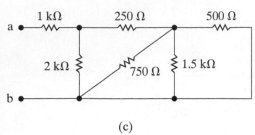

(c)

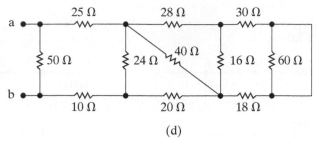

(d)

3.10 a) Find an expression for the equivalent resistance of two resistors of value R in series.

b) Find an expression for the equivalent resistance of n resistors of value R in series.

c) Using the results of (a), design a resistive network with an equivalent resistance of $3\text{ k}\Omega$ using two resistors with the same value from Appendix H.

d) Using the results of (b), design a resistive network with an equivalent resistance of $4\text{ k}\Omega$ using a minimum number of identical resistors from Appendix H.

3.11 a) Find an expression for the equivalent resistance of two resistors of value R in parallel.

b) Find an expression for the equivalent resistance of n resistors of value R in parallel.

c) Using the results of (a), design a resistive network with an equivalent resistance of $5\text{ k}\Omega$ using two resistors with the same value from Appendix H.

d) Using the results of (b), design a resistive network with an equivalent resistance of $4\text{ k}\Omega$ using a minimum number of identical resistors from Appendix H.

Section 3.3

3.12 a) Calculate the no-load voltage v_o for the voltage-divider circuit shown in Fig. P3.12.

DESIGN
PROBLEM

PSPICE

MULTISIM

b) Calculate the power dissipated in R_1 and R_2.

c) Assume that only 0.5 W resistors are available. The no-load voltage is to be the same as in (a). Specify the smallest ohmic values of R_1 and R_2.

Figure P3.12

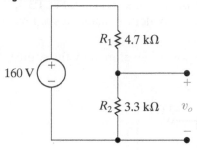

3.13 In the voltage-divider circuit shown in Fig. P3.13, the no-load value of v_o is 4 V. When the load resistance R_L is attached across the terminals a and b, v_o drops to 3 V. Find R_L.

PSPICE

MULTISIM

Figure P3.13

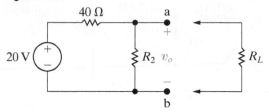

3.14 The no-load voltage in the voltage-divider circuit shown in Fig. P3.14 is 8 V. The smallest load resistor that is ever connected to the divider is $3.6\text{ k}\Omega$. When the divider is loaded, v_o is not to drop below 7.5 V.

DESIGN
PROBLEM

PSPICE

MULTISIM

a) Design the divider circuit to meet the specifications just mentioned. Specify the numerical values of R_1 and R_2.

b) Assume the power ratings of commercially available resistors are 1/16, 1/8, 1/4, 1, and 2 W. What power rating would you specify?

Figure P3.14

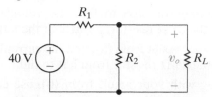

3.15 Assume the voltage divider in Fig. P3.14 has been constructed from 1 W resistors. What is the smallest resistor from Appendix H that can be used as R_L before one of the resistors in the divider is operating at its dissipation limit?

3.16 Find the power dissipated in the 5 Ω resistor in the

PSPICE   current divider circuit in Fig. P3.16.

MULTISIM

Figure P3.16

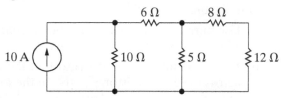

3.17 For the current divider circuit in Fig. P3.17 calculate

PSPICE   a) i_o and v_o.

MULTISIM

b) the power dissipated in the 6 Ω resistor.

c) the power developed by the current source.

Figure P3.17

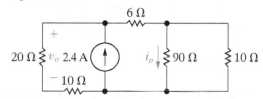

3.18 Specify the resistors in the current divider circuit in

DESIGN   Fig. P3.18 to meet the following design criteria:

PROBLEM

$$i_g = 50 \text{ mA}; v_g = 25 \text{ V}; i_1 = 0.6i_2;$$
$$i_3 = 2i_2; \text{ and } i_4 = 4i_1.$$

Figure P3.18

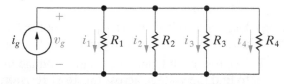

3.19 There is often a need to produce more than one

DESIGN   voltage using a voltage divider. For example, the

PROBLEM   memory components of many personal computers require voltages of -12 V, 5 V, and $+12$ V, all with respect to a common reference terminal. Select the values of R_1, R_2, and R_3 in the circuit in Fig. P3.19 to meet the following design requirements:

a) The total power supplied to the divider circuit by the 24 V source is 80 W when the divider is unloaded.

b) The three voltages, all measured with respect to the common reference terminal, are $v_1 = 12$ V, $v_2 = 5$ V, and $v_3 = -12$ V.

Figure P3.19

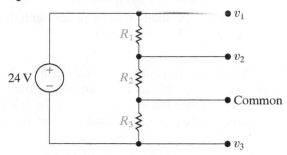

3.20 a) The voltage divider in Fig. P3.20(a) is loaded

PSPICE   with the voltage divider shown in Fig. P3.20(b);

MULTISIM   that is, a is connected to a', and b is connected to b'. Find v_o.

b) Now assume the voltage divider in Fig. P3.20(b) is connected to the voltage divider in Fig. P3.20(a) by means of a current-controlled voltage source as shown in Fig. P3.20(c). Find v_o.

c) What effect does adding the dependent-voltage source have on the operation of the voltage divider that is connected to the 380 V source?

Figure P3.20

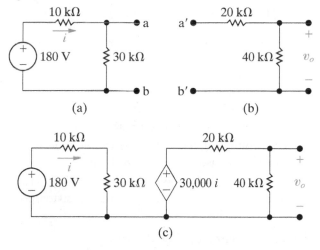

3.21 A voltage divider like that in Fig. 3.13 is to be

DESIGN   designed so that $v_o = kv_s$ at no load ($R_L = \infty$) and

PROBLEM $v_o = \alpha v_s$ at full load ($R_L = R_o$). Note that by definition $\alpha < k < 1$.

a) Show that

$$R_1 = \frac{k - \alpha}{\alpha k} R_o$$

and

$$R_2 = \frac{k - \alpha}{\alpha(1 - k)} R_o.$$

b) Specify the numerical values of R_1 and R_2 if $k = 0.85, \alpha = 0.80$, and $R_o = 34\ k\Omega$.

c) If $v_s = 60$ V, specify the maximum power that will be dissipated in R_1 and R_2.

d) Assume the load resistor is accidentally short circuited. How much power is dissipated in R_1 and R_2?

3.22 a) Show that the current in the kth branch of the circuit in Fig. P3.22(a) is equal to the source current i_g times the conductance of the kth branch divided by the sum of the conductances, that is,

PSPICE
MULTISIM

$$i_k = \frac{i_g G_k}{G_1 + G_2 + G_3 + \cdots + G_k + \cdots + G_N}.$$

b) Use the result derived in (a) to calculate the current in the $5\ \Omega$ resistor in the circuit in Fig. P3.22(b).

Figure P3.22

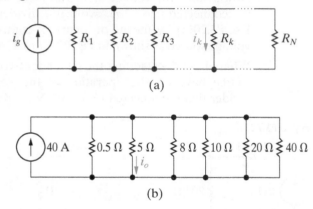

(a)

(b)

Section 3.4

3.23 Look at the circuit in Fig. P3.3(a).

a) Use voltage division to find the voltage across the 6 kΩ resistor, positive at the top.

b) Use the result from part (a) and voltage division to find the voltage across the 5 kΩ resistor, positive on the left.

3.24 Look at the circuit in Fig. P3.3(d).

a) Use current division to find the current in the 50 Ω resistor from left to right.

b) Use the result from part (a) and current division to find the current in the 70 Ω resistor from top to bottom.

3.25 Look at the circuit in Fig. P3.7(a).

a) Use voltage division to find the voltage drop across the 25 Ω resistor, positive at the left.

b) Using your result from (a), find the current flowing in the 25 Ω resistor from left to right.

c) Starting with your result from (b), use current division to find the current in the 50 Ω resistor from top to bottom.

d) Using your result from part (c), find the voltage drop across the 50 Ω resistor, positive at the top.

e) Starting with your result from (d), use voltage division to find the voltage drop across the 60 Ω resistor, positive at the top.

3.26 Attach a 450 mA current source between the terminals a–b in Fig. P3.9(a), with the current arrow pointing up.

a) Use current division to find the current in the 36 Ω resistor from top to bottom.

b) Use the result from part (a) to find the voltage across the 36 Ω resistor, positive at the top.

c) Use the result from part (b) and voltage division to find the voltage across the 18 Ω resistor, positive at the top.

d) Use the result from part (c) and voltage division to find the voltage across the 10 Ω resistor, positive at the top.

3.27 Attach a 6 V voltage source between the terminals a–b in Fig. P3.9(b), with the positive terminal at the top.

a) Use voltage division to find the voltage across the 4 Ω resistor, positive at the top.

b) Use the result from part (a) to find the current in the 4 Ω resistor from left to right.

c) Use the result from part (b) and current division to find the current in the 16 Ω resistor from left to right.

d) Use the result from part (c) and current division to find the current in the 10 Ω resistor from top to bottom.

e) Use the result from part (d) to find the voltage across the 10 Ω resistor, positive at the top.

f) Use the result from part (e) and voltage division to find the voltage across the 18 Ω resistor, positive at the top.

3.28 a) Find the voltage v_x in the circuit in Fig. P3.28 using voltage and/or current division.

PSPICE
MULTISIM

b) Replace the 18 V source with a general voltage source equal to V_s. Assume V_s is positive at the upper terminal. Find v_x as a function of V_s.

Figure P3.28

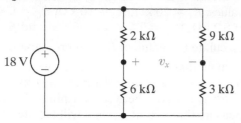

3.29 Find v_o in the circuit in Fig. P3.29 using voltage and/or current division.

PSPICE
MULTISIM

Figure P3.29

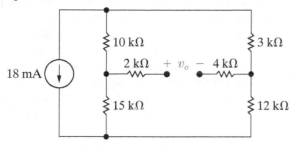

3.30 Find v_1 and v_2 in the circuit in Fig. P3.30 using voltage and/or current division.

PSPICE
MULTISIM

Figure P3.30

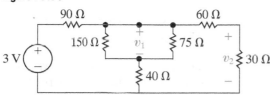

3.31 For the circuit in Fig. P3.31, find i_g and then use current division to find i_o.

Figure P3.31

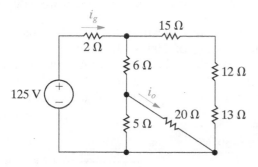

3.32 For the circuit in Fig. P3.32, calculate i_1 and i_2 using current division.

PSPICE
MULTISIM

Figure P3.32

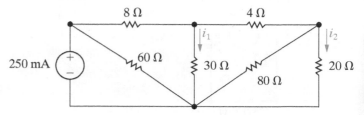

3.33 A d'Arsonval ammeter is shown in Fig. P3.33.

a) Calculate the value of the shunt resistor, R_A, to give a full-scale current reading of 5 A.

b) How much resistance is added to a circuit when the 5 A ammeter in part (a) is inserted to measure current?

c) Calculate the value of the shunt resistor, R_A, to give a full-scale current reading of 100 mA.

d) How much resistance is added to a circuit when the 100 mA ammeter in part (c) is inserted to measure current?

Figure P3.33

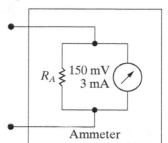

3.34 A shunt resistor and a 50 mV, 1 mA d'Arsonval movement are used to build a 5 A ammeter. A resistance of 20 mΩ is placed across the terminals of the ammeter. What is the new full-scale range of the ammeter?

3.35 A d'Arsonval movement is rated at 2 mA and
DESIGN 200 mV. Assume 1 W precision resistors are avail-
PROBLEM able to use as shunts. What is the largest full-scale-reading ammeter that can be designed using a single resistor? Explain.

3.36 a) Show for the ammeter circuit in Fig. P3.36 that the current in the d'Arsonval movement is always 1/25th of the current being measured.

b) What would the fraction be if the 100 mV, 2 mA movement were used in a 5 A ammeter?

c) Would you expect a uniform scale on a dc d'Arsonval ammeter?

Figure P3.36

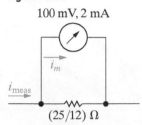

100 mV, 2 mA

i_m

i_{meas}

$(25/12)$ Ω

3.37 A d'Arsonval voltmeter is shown in Fig. P3.37. Find the value of R_v for each of the following full-scale readings: (a) 50 V, (b) 5 V, (c) 250 mV, and (d) 25 mV.

Figure P3.37

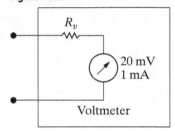

R_v

20 mV
1 mA

Voltmeter

3.38 Suppose the d'Arsonval voltmeter described in Problem 3.37 is used to measure the voltage across the 45 Ω resistor in Fig. P3.38.

a) What will the voltmeter read?

b) Find the percentage of error in the voltmeter reading if

$$\% \text{ error} = \left(\frac{\text{measured value}}{\text{true value}} - 1 \right) \times 100.$$

Figure P3.38

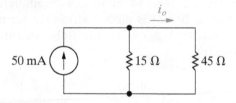

i_o

50 mA   15 Ω 45 Ω

3.39 The ammeter in the circuit in Fig. P3.39 has a resistance of 0.1 Ω. Using the definition of the percentage error in a meter reading found in Problem 3.38, what is the percentage of error in the reading of this ammeter?

Figure P3.39

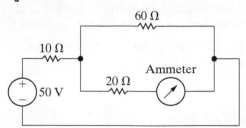

60 Ω

10 Ω

Ammeter

20 Ω

50 V

3.40 The ammeter described in Problem 3.39 is used to measure the current i_o in the circuit in Fig. P3.38. What is the percentage of error in the measured value?

3.41 The elements in the circuit in Fig. 2.24 have the following values: $R_1 = 20$ kΩ, $R_2 = 80$ kΩ, $R_C = 0.82$ kΩ, $R_E = 0.2$ kΩ, $V_{CC} = 7.5$ V, $V_0 = 0.6$ V, and $\beta = 39$.

PSPICE
MULTISIM

a) Calculate the value of i_B in microamperes.

b) Assume that a digital multimeter, when used as a dc ammeter, has a resistance of 1 kΩ. If the meter is inserted between terminals b and 2 to measure the current i_B, what will the meter read?

c) Using the calculated value of i_B in (a) as the correct value, what is the percentage of error in the measurement?

3.42 You have been told that the dc voltage of a power supply is about 350 V. When you go to the instrument room to get a dc voltmeter to measure the power supply voltage, you find that there are only two dc voltmeters available. One voltmeter is rated 300 V full scale and has a sensitivity of 900 Ω/V. The other voltmeter is rated 150 V full scale and has a sensitivity of 1200 Ω/V. (*Hint:* you can find the effective resistance of a voltmeter by multiplying its rated full-scale voltage and its sensitivity.)

a) How can you use the two voltmeters to check the power supply voltage?

b) What is the maximum voltage that can be measured?

c) If the power supply voltage is 320 V, what will each voltmeter read?

3.43 Assume that in addition to the two voltmeters described in Problem 3.42, a 50 kΩ precision resistor is also available. The 50 kΩ resistor is connected in series with the series-connected voltmeters. This circuit is then connected across the terminals of the power supply. The reading on the 300 V meter is 205.2 V and the reading on the 150 V meter is 136.8 V. What is the voltage of the power supply?

3.44 The voltmeter shown in Fig. P3.44(a) has a full-scale reading of 500 V. The meter movement is rated 100 mV and 0.5 mA. What is the percentage of error in the meter reading if it is used to measure the voltage v in the circuit of Fig. P3.44(b)?

Figure P3.44

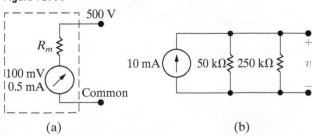

500 V

R_m

100 mV
0.5 mA

Common

10 mA   50 kΩ 250 kΩ v

(a)   (b)

3.45 The voltage-divider circuit shown in Fig. P3.45 is designed so that the no-load output voltage is 7/9ths of the input voltage. A d'Arsonval voltmeter having a sensitivity of 100 Ω/V and a full-scale rating of 200 V is used to check the operation of the circuit.

a) What will the voltmeter read if it is placed across the 180 V source?

b) What will the voltmeter read if it is placed across the 70 kΩ resistor?

c) What will the voltmeter read if it is placed across the 20 kΩ resistor?

d) Will the voltmeter readings obtained in parts (b) and (c) add to the reading recorded in part (a)? Explain why or why not.

Figure P3.45

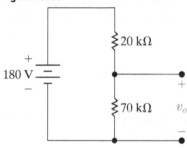

3.46 Assume in designing the multirange voltmeter shown in Fig. P3.46 that you ignore the resistance of the meter movement.

DESIGN PROBLEM

a) Specify the values of R_1, R_2, and R_3.

b) For each of the three ranges, calculate the percentage of error that this design strategy produces.

Figure P3.46

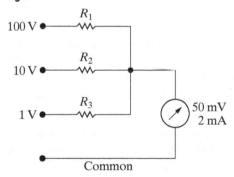

3.47 The circuit model of a dc voltage source is shown in Fig. P3.47. The following voltage measurements are made at the terminals of the source: (1) With the terminals of the source open, the voltage is measured at 50 mV, and (2) with a 15 MΩ resistor connected to the terminals, the voltage is measured at 48.75 mV. All measurements are made with a digital voltmeter that has a meter resistance of 10 MΩ.

a) What is the internal voltage of the source (v_s) in millivolts?

b) What is the internal resistance of the source (R_s) in kilo-ohms?

Figure P3.47

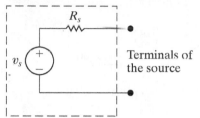

3.48 Design a d'Arsonval voltmeter that will have the three voltage ranges shown in Fig. P3.48.

DESIGN PROBLEM

a) Specify the values of R_1, R_2, and R_3.

b) Assume that a 750 kΩ resistor is connected between the 150 V terminal and the common terminal. The voltmeter is then connected to an unknown voltage using the common terminal and the 300 V terminal. The voltmeter reads 288 V. What is the unknown voltage?

c) What is the maximum voltage the voltmeter in (b) can measure?

Figure P3.48

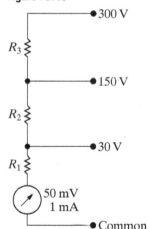

3.49 A 600 kΩ resistor is connected from the 200 V terminal to the common terminal of a dual-scale voltmeter, as shown in Fig. P3.49(a). This modified voltmeter is then used to measure the voltage across the 360 kΩ resistor in the circuit in Fig. P3.49(b).

a) What is the reading on the 500 V scale of the meter?

b) What is the percentage of error in the measured voltage?

Figure P3.49

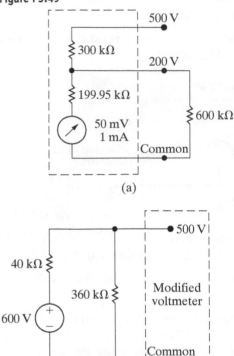

(a)

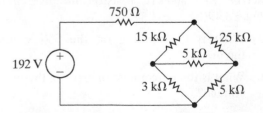

(b)

Section 3.6

3.50 Assume the ideal voltage source in Fig. 3.26 is
PSPICE replaced by an ideal current source. Show that
MULTISIM Eq. 3.33 is still valid.

3.51 The bridge circuit shown in Fig. 3.26 is energized
PSPICE from a 24 V dc source. The bridge is balanced when
MULTISIM $R_1 = 500 \ \Omega$, $R_2 = 1000 \ \Omega$, and $R_3 = 750 \ \Omega$.

a) What is the value of R_x?

b) How much current (in milliamperes) does the dc
source supply?

c) Which resistor in the circuit absorbs the most
power? How much power does it absorb?

d) Which resistor absorbs the least power? How
much power does it absorb?

3.52 Find the power dissipated in the 3 kΩ resistor in the
PSPICE circuit in Fig. P3.52.
MULTISIM

Figure P3.52

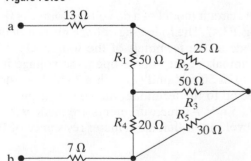

3.53 Find the detector current i_d in the unbalanced
bridge in Fig. P3.53 if the voltage drop across the
detector is negligible.

Figure P3.53

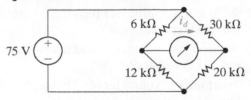

3.54 In the Wheatstone bridge circuit shown in Fig. 3.26,
PSPICE the ratio R_2/R_1 can be set to the following values:
MULTISIM 0.001, 0.01, 0.1, 1, 10, 100, and 1000. The resistor R_3
can be varied from 1 to 11,110 Ω, in increments of
1 Ω. An unknown resistor is known to lie between
4 and 5 Ω. What should be the setting of the R_2/R_1
ratio so that the unknown resistor can be measured
to four significant figures?

Section 3.7

3.55 Find the current and power supplied by the 40 V
source in the circuit for Example 3.7 (Fig. 3.32) by
replacing the lower Δ (25, 37.5, and 40 Ω) with its
equivalent Y.

3.56 Find the current and power supplied by the 40 V
source in the circuit for Example 3.7 (Fig. 3.32) by
replacing the Y on the left (25, 40, and 100 Ω) with
its equivalent Δ.

3.57 Find the current and power supplied by the 40 V
source in the circuit for Example 3.7 (Fig. 3.32) by
replacing the Y on the right (25, 37.5, and 125 Ω)
with its equivalent Δ.

3.58 a) Find the equivalent resistance R_{ab} in the circuit
PSPICE   in Fig. P3.58 by using a Y-to-Δ transformation
MULTISIM   involving resistors R_2, R_3, and R_5.

b) Repeat (a) using a Δ-to-Y transformation involving resistors R_3, R_4, and R_5.

c) Give two additional Δ-to-Y or Y-to-Δ transformations that could be used to find R_{ab}.

Figure P3.58

3.59 Use a Δ-to-Y transformation to find the voltages v_1 and v_2 in the circuit in Fig. P3.59.

Figure P3.59

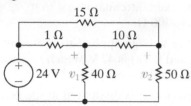

3.60
a) Find the resistance seen by the ideal voltage source in the circuit in Fig. P3.60.

b) If v_{ab} equals 400 V, how much power is dissipated in the 31 Ω resistor?

Figure P3.60

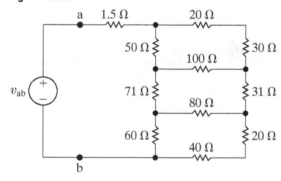

3.61 Use a Y-to-Δ transformation to find (a) i_o; (b) i_1; (c) i_2; and (d) the power delivered by the ideal current source in the circuit in Fig. P3.61.

Figure P3.61

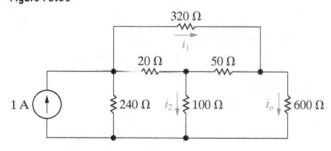

3.62 Find i_o and the power dissipated in the 140 Ω resistor in the circuit in Fig. P3.62.

Figure P3.62

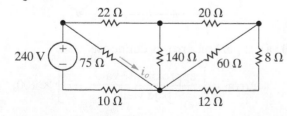

3.63 For the circuit shown in Fig. P3.63, find (a) i_1, (b) v, (c) i_2, and (d) the power supplied by the voltage source.

Figure P3.63

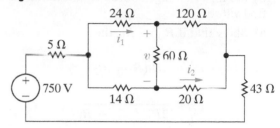

3.64 Show that the expressions for Δ conductances as functions of the three Y conductances are

$$G_a = \frac{G_2 G_3}{G_1 + G_2 + G_3},$$

$$G_b = \frac{G_1 G_3}{G_1 + G_2 + G_3},$$

$$G_c = \frac{G_1 G_2}{G_1 + G_2 + G_3},$$

where

$$G_a = \frac{1}{R_a}, \quad G_1 = \frac{1}{R_1}, \quad \text{etc.}$$

3.65 Derive Eqs. 3.44–3.49 from Eqs. 3.41–3.43. The following two hints should help you get started in the right direction:

1) To find R_1 as a function of R_a, R_b, and R_c, first subtract Eq. 3.42 from Eq. 3.43 and then add this result to Eq. 3.41. Use similar manipulations to find R_2 and R_3 as functions of R_a, R_b, and R_c.

2) To find R_b as a function of R_1, R_2, and R_3, take advantage of the derivations obtained by hint (1), namely, Eqs. 3.44–3.46. Note that these equations can be divided to obtain

$$\frac{R_2}{R_3} = \frac{R_c}{R_b}, \quad \text{or} \quad R_c = \frac{R_2}{R_3} R_b,$$

and

$$\frac{R_1}{R_2} = \frac{R_b}{R_a}, \quad \text{or} \quad R_a = \frac{R_2}{R_1} R_b.$$

Now use these ratios in Eq. 3.43 to eliminate R_a and R_c. Use similar manipulations to find R_a and R_c as functions of R_1, R_2, and R_3.

Sections 3.1–3.7

3.66 Resistor networks are sometimes used as volume-control circuits. In this application, they are referred to as *resistance attenuators* or *pads*.

A typical fixed-attenuator pad is shown in Fig. P3.66. In designing an attenuation pad, the circuit designer will select the values of R_1 and R_2 so that the ratio of v_o/v_i and the resistance seen by the input voltage source R_{ab} both have a specified value.

a) Show that if $R_{ab} = R_L$, then

$$R_L^2 = 4R_1(R_1 + R_2),$$

$$\frac{v_o}{v_i} = \frac{R_2}{2R_1 + R_2 + R_L}.$$

b) Select the values of R_1 and R_2 so that $R_{ab} = R_L = 300 \ \Omega$ and $v_o/v_i = 0.5$.

c) Choose values from Appendix H that are closest to R_1 and R_2 from part (b). Calculate the percent error in the resulting values for R_{ab} and v_0/v_1 if these new resistor values are used.

Figure P3.66

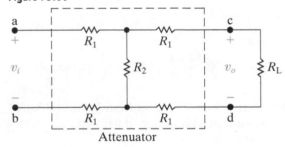

Attenuator

3.67 a) The fixed-attenuator pad shown in Fig. P3.67 is called a *bridged tee*. Use a Y-to-Δ transformation to show that $R_{ab} = R_L$ if $R = R_L$.

DESIGN
PROBLEM

b) Show that when $R = R_L$, the voltage ratio v_o/v_i equals 0.50.

Figure P3.67

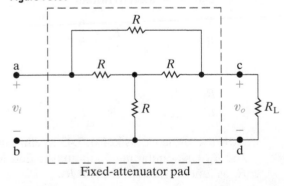

Fixed-attenuator pad

3.68 The design equations for the bridged-tee attenuator circuit in Fig. P3.68 are

PSPICE
MULTISIM

$$R_2 = \frac{2RR_L^2}{3R^2 - R_L^2},$$

$$\frac{v_o}{v_i} = \frac{3R - R_L}{3R + R_L},$$

when R_2 has the value just given.

a) Design a fixed attenuator so that $v_i = 3.5v_o$ when $R_L = 300 \ \Omega$.

b) Assume the voltage applied to the input of the pad designed in (a) is 42 V. Which resistor in the pad dissipates the most power?

c) How much power is dissipated in the resistor in part (b)?

d) Which resistor in the pad dissipates the least power?

e) How much power is dissipated in the resistor in part (d)?

Figure P3.68

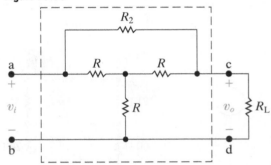

3.69 a) For the circuit shown in Fig. P3.69 the bridge is balanced when $\Delta R = 0$. Show that if $\Delta R \ll R_o$ the bridge output voltage is approximately

PSPICE
MULTISIM

$$v_o \approx \frac{-\Delta R R_4}{(R_o + R_4)^2} v_{in}$$

b) Given $R_2 = 1 \ k\Omega$, $R_3 = 500 \ \Omega$, $R_4 = 5 \ k\Omega$, and $v_{in} = 6 \ V$, what is the approximate bridge output voltage if ΔR is 3% of R_o?

c) Find the actual value of v_o in part (b).

Figure P3.69

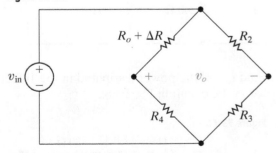

3.70 a) If percent error is defined as

$$\% \text{ error} = \left[\frac{\text{approximate value}}{\text{true value}} - 1 \right] \times 100,$$

show that the percent error in the approximation of v_o in Problem 3.69 is

$$\% \text{ error} = \frac{-(\Delta R)R_3}{(R_2 + R_3)R_4} \times 100.$$

b) Calculate the percent error in v_o, using the values in Problem 3.69(b).

3.71 Assume the error in v_o in the bridge circuit in Fig. P3.69 is not to exceed 0.5%. What is the largest percent change in R_o that can be tolerated?

DESIGN PROBLEM

3.72 a) Using Fig. 3.38 derive the expression for the voltage V_y.

b) Assuming that there are p_y pixels in the y-direction, derive the expression for the y-coordinate of the touch point, using the result from part (a).

3.73 A resistive touch screen has 5 V applied to the grid in the x-direction and in the y-direction. The screen has 480 pixels in the x-direction and 800 pixels in

PRACTICAL PERSPECTIVE
PSPICE
MULTISIM

the y-direction. When the screen is touched, the voltage in the x-grid is 1 V and the voltage in the y-grid is 3.75 V.)

a) Calculate the values of α and β.

a) Calculate the x- and y-coordinates of the pixel at the point where the screen was touched.

3.74 A resistive touch screen has 640 pixels in the x-direction and 1024 pixels in the y-direction. The resistive grid has 8 V applied in both the x- and y-directions. The pixel coordinates at the touch point are (480, 192). Calculate the voltages V_x and V_y.

PRACTICAL PERSPECTIVE
DESIGN PROBLEM
PSPICE
MULTISIM

3.75 Suppose the resistive touch screen described in Problem 3.74 is simultaneously touched at two points, one with coordinates (480, 192) and the other with coordinates (240, 384).

a) Calculate the voltage measured in the x- and y-grids.

b) Which touch point has your calculation in (a) identified?

Techniques of Circuit Analysis

✓ CHAPTER OBJECTIVES

1 Understand and be able to use the node-voltage method to solve a circuit.

2 Understand and be able to use the mesh-current method to solve a circuit.

3 Be able to decide whether the node-voltage method or the mesh-current method is the preferred approach to solving a particular circuit.

4 Understand source transformation and be able to use it to solve a circuit.

5 Understand the concept of the Thévenin and Norton equivalent circuits and be able to construct a Thévenin or Norton equivalent for a circuit.

6 Know the condition for maximum power transfer to a resistive load and be able to calculate the value of the load resistor that satisfies this condition.

So far, we have analyzed relatively simple resistive circuits by applying Kirchhoff's laws in combination with Ohm's law. We can use this approach for all circuits, but as they become structurally more complicated and involve more and more elements, this direct method soon becomes cumbersome. In this chapter we introduce two powerful techniques of circuit analysis that aid in the analysis of complex circuit structures: the node-voltage method and the mesh-current method. These techniques give us two systematic methods of describing circuits with the minimum number of simultaneous equations.

In addition to these two general analytical methods, in this chapter we also discuss other techniques for simplifying circuits. We have already demonstrated how to use series-parallel reductions and Δ-to-Y transformations to simplify a circuit's structure. We now add source transformations and Thévenin and Norton equivalent circuits to those techniques.

We also consider two other topics that play a role in circuit analysis. One, maximum power transfer, considers the conditions necessary to ensure that the power delivered to a resistive load by a source is maximized. Thévenin equivalent circuits are used in establishing the maximum power transfer conditions. The final topic in this chapter, superposition, looks at the analysis of circuits with more than one independent source.

Practical Perspective

Circuits with Realistic Resistors

In the last chapter we began to explore the effect of imprecise resistor values on the performance of a circuit; specifically, on the performance of a voltage divider. Resistors are manufactured for only a small number of discrete values, and any given resistor from a batch of resistors will vary from its stated value within some tolerance. Resistors with tighter tolerance, say 1%, are more expensive than resistors with greater tolerance, say 10%. Therefore, in a circuit that uses many resistors, it would be important to understand which resistor's value has the greatest impact on the expected performance of the circuit.

In other words, we would like to predict the effect of varying each resistor's value on the output of the circuit. If we know that a particular resistor must be very close to its stated value for the circuit to function correctly, we can then decide to spend the extra money necessary to achieve a tighter tolerance on that resistor's value.

Exploring the effect of a circuit component's value on the circuit's output is known as **sensitivity analysis**. Once we have presented additional circuit analysis techniques, the topic of sensitivity analysis will be examined.

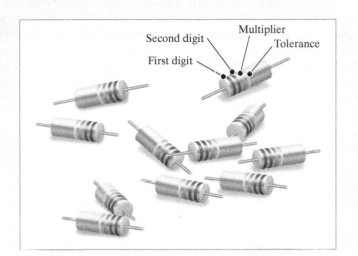

Ocean/Corbis

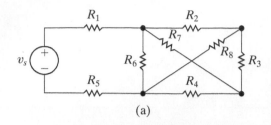

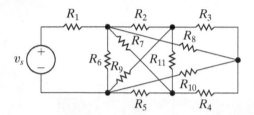

Figure 4.1 ▲ (a) A planar circuit. (b) The same circuit redrawn to verify that it is planar.

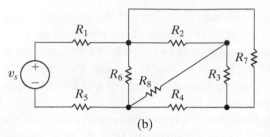

Figure 4.2 ▲ A nonplanar circuit.

4.1 Terminology

To discuss the more involved methods of circuit analysis, we must define a few basic terms. So far, all the circuits presented have been **planar circuits**—that is, those circuits that can be drawn on a plane with no crossing branches. A circuit that is drawn with crossing branches still is considered planar if it can be redrawn with no crossover branches. For example, the circuit shown in Fig. 4.1(a) can be redrawn as Fig. 4.1(b); the circuits are equivalent because all the node connections have been maintained. Therefore, Fig. 4.1(a) is a planar circuit because it can be redrawn as one. Figure 4.2 shows a nonplanar circuit—it cannot be redrawn in such a way that all the node connections are maintained and no branches overlap. The node-voltage method is applicable to both planar and nonplanar circuits, whereas the mesh-current method is limited to planar circuits.

Describing a Circuit—The Vocabulary

In Section 1.5 we defined an ideal basic circuit element. When basic circuit elements are interconnected to form a circuit, the resulting interconnection is described in terms of nodes, paths, branches, loops, and meshes. We defined both a node and a closed path, or loop, in Section 2.4. Here we restate those definitions and then define the terms *path, branch,* and *mesh.* For your convenience, all of these definitions are presented in Table 4.1. Table 4.1 also includes examples of each definition taken from the circuit in Fig. 4.3, which are developed in Example 4.1.

Example 4.1 **Identifying Node, Branch, Mesh and Loop in a Circuit**

For the circuit in Fig. 4.3, identify

a) all nodes.

b) all essential nodes.

c) all branches.

d) all essential branches.

e) all meshes.

f) two paths that are not loops or essential branches.

g) two loops that are not meshes.

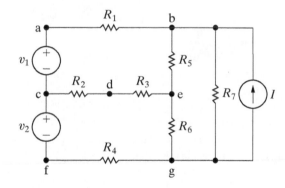

Figure 4.3 ▲ A circuit illustrating nodes, branches, meshes, paths, and loops.

Solution

a) The nodes are a, b, c, d, e, f, and g.

b) The essential nodes are b, c, e, and g.

c) The branches are v_1, v_2, R_1, R_2, R_3, R_4, R_5, R_6, R_7, and I.

d) The essential branches are $v_1 - R_1$, $R_2 - R_3$, $v_2 - R_4$, R_5, R_6, R_7, and I.

e) The meshes are $v_1 - R_1 - R_5 - R_3 - R_2$, $v_2 - R_2 - R_3 - R_6 - R_4$, $R_5 - R_7 - R_6$, and $R_7 - I$.

f) $R_1 - R_5 - R_6$ is a path, but it is not a loop (because it does not have the same starting and ending nodes), nor is it an essential branch (because it does not connect two essential nodes). $v_2 - R_2$ is also a path but is neither a loop nor an essential branch, for the same reasons.

g) $v_1 - R_1 - R_5 - R_6 - R_4 - v_2$ is a loop but is not a mesh, because there are two loops within it. $I - R_5 - R_6$ is also a loop but not a mesh.

NOTE: Assess your understanding of this material by trying Chapter Problems 4.1 and 4.5.

TABLE 4.1 Terms for Describing Circuits

Name	Definition	Example From Fig. 4.3
node	A point where two or more circuit elements join	a
essential node	A node where three or more circuit elements join	b
path	A trace of adjoining basic elements with no elements included more than once	$v_1 - R_1 - R_5 - R_6$
branch	A path that connects two nodes	R_1
essential branch	A path which connects two essential nodes without passing through an essential node	$v_1 - R_1$
loop	A path whose last node is the same as the starting node	$v_1 - R_1 - R_5 - R_6 - R_4 - v_2$
mesh	A loop that does not enclose any other loops	$v_1 - R_1 - R_5 - R_3 - R_2$
planar circuit	A circuit that can be drawn on a plane with no crossing branches	Fig. 4.3 is a planar circuit Fig. 4.2 is a nonplanar circuit

Simultaneous Equations—How Many?

The number of unknown currents in a circuit equals the number of branches, b, where the current is not known. For example, the circuit shown in Fig. 4.3 has nine branches in which the current is unknown. Recall that we must have b independent equations to solve a circuit with b unknown currents. If we let n represent the number of nodes in the circuit, we can derive $n - 1$ independent equations by applying Kirchhoff's current law to any set of $n - 1$ nodes. (Application of the current law to the nth node does not generate an independent equation, because this equation can be derived from the previous $n - 1$ equations. See Problem 4.5.) Because we need b equations to describe a given circuit and because we can obtain $n - 1$ of these equations from Kirchhoff's current law, we must apply Kirchhoff's voltage law to loops or meshes to obtain the remaining $b - (n - 1)$ equations.

Thus by counting nodes, meshes, and branches where the current is unknown, we have established a systematic method for writing the necessary number of equations to solve a circuit. Specifically, we apply Kirchhoff's current law to $n - 1$ nodes and Kirchhoff's voltage law to $b - (n - 1)$ loops (or meshes). These observations also are valid in terms of essential nodes and essential branches. Thus if we let n_e represent the number of essential nodes and b_e the number of essential branches where the current is unknown, we can apply Kirchhoff's current law at $n_e - 1$ nodes and Kirchhoff's voltage law around $b_e - (n_e - 1)$ loops or meshes. In circuits, the number of essential nodes is less than or equal to the number of nodes, and the number of essential branches is less than or equal to the number of branches. Thus it is often convenient to use essential nodes and essential branches when analyzing a circuit, because they produce fewer independent equations to solve.

A circuit may consist of disconnected parts. An example of such a circuit is examined in Problem 4.3. The statements pertaining to the number of equations that can be derived from Kirchhoff's current law, $n - 1$, and voltage law, $b - (n - 1)$, apply to connected circuits. If a circuit has n nodes and b branches and is made up of s parts, the current law can be

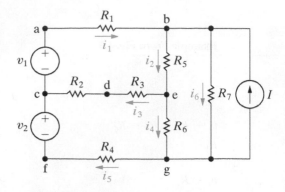

Figure 4.4 ▲ The circuit shown in Fig. 4.3 with six unknown branch currents defined.

applied $n - s$ times, and the voltage law $b - n + s$ times. Any two separate parts can be connected by a single conductor. This connection always causes two nodes to form one node. Moreover, no current exists in the single conductor, so any circuit made up of s disconnected parts can always be reduced to a connected circuit.

The Systematic Approach—An Illustration

We now illustrate this systematic approach by using the circuit shown in Fig. 4.4. We write the equations on the basis of essential nodes and branches. The circuit has four essential nodes and six essential branches, denoted $i_1 - i_6$, for which the current is unknown.

We derive three of the six simultaneous equations needed by applying Kirchhoff's current law to any three of the four essential nodes. We use the nodes b, c, and e to get

$$-i_1 + i_2 + i_6 - I = 0,$$

$$i_1 - i_3 - i_5 = 0,$$

$$i_3 + i_4 - i_2 = 0. \tag{4.1}$$

We derive the remaining three equations by applying Kirchhoff's voltage law around three meshes. Because the circuit has four meshes, we need to dismiss one mesh. We choose $R_7 - I$, because we don't know the voltage across I.[1]

Using the other three meshes gives

$$R_1 i_1 + R_5 i_2 + i_3(R_2 + R_3) - v_1 = 0,$$

$$-i_3(R_2 + R_3) + i_4 R_6 + i_5 R_4 - v_2 = 0,$$

$$-i_2 R_5 + i_6 R_7 - i_4 R_6 = 0. \tag{4.2}$$

Rearranging Eqs. 4.1 and 4.2 to facilitate their solution yields the set

$$-i_1 + i_2 + 0i_3 + 0i_4 + 0i_5 + i_6 = I,$$

$$i_1 + 0i_2 - i_3 + 0i_4 - i_5 + 0i_6 = 0,$$

$$0i_1 - i_2 + i_3 + i_4 + 0i_5 + 0i_6 = 0,$$

$$R_1 i_1 + R_5 i_2 + (R_2 + R_3)i_3 + 0i_4 + 0i_5 + 0i_6 = v_1,$$

$$0i_1 + 0i_2 - (R_2 + R_3)i_3 + R_6 i_4 + R_4 i_5 + 0i_6 = v_2,$$

$$0i_1 - R_5 i_2 + 0i_3 - R_6 i_4 + 0i_5 + R_7 i_6 = 0. \tag{4.3}$$

Note that summing the current at the nth node (g in this example) gives

$$i_5 - i_4 - i_6 + I = 0. \tag{4.4}$$

---

[1] We say more about this decision in Section 4.7.

Equation 4.4 is not independent, because we can derive it by summing Eqs. 4.1 and then multiplying the sum by −1. Thus Eq. 4.4 is a linear combination of Eqs. 4.1 and therefore is not independent of them. We now carry the procedure one step further. By introducing new variables, we can describe a circuit with just $n - 1$ equations or just $b - (n - 1)$ equations. Therefore these new variables allow us to obtain a solution by manipulating fewer equations, a desirable goal even if a computer is to be used to obtain a numerical solution.

The new variables are known as node voltages and mesh currents. The node-voltage method enables us to describe a circuit in terms of $n_e - 1$ equations; the mesh-current method enables us to describe a circuit in terms of $b_e - (n_e - 1)$ equations. We begin in Section 4.2 with the node-voltage method.

NOTE: Assess your understanding of this material by trying Chapter Problems 4.2 and 4.3.

4.2 Introduction to the Node-Voltage Method

We introduce the node-voltage method by using the essential nodes of the circuit. The first step is to make a neat layout of the circuit so that no branches cross over and to mark clearly the essential nodes on the circuit diagram, as in Fig. 4.5. This circuit has three essential nodes ($n_e = 3$); therefore, we need two ($n_e - 1$) node-voltage equations to describe the circuit. The next step is to select one of the three essential nodes as a reference node. Although theoretically the choice is arbitrary, practically the choice for the reference node often is obvious. For example, the node with the most branches is usually a good choice. The optimum choice of the reference node (if one exists) will become apparent after you have gained some experience using this method. In the circuit shown in Fig. 4.5, the lower node connects the most branches, so we use it as the reference node. We flag the chosen reference node with the symbol ▼, as in Fig. 4.6.

After selecting the reference node, we define the node voltages on the circuit diagram. A **node voltage** is defined as the voltage rise from the reference node to a nonreference node. For this circuit, we must define two node voltages, which are denoted v_1 and v_2 in Fig. 4.6.

We are now ready to generate the node-voltage equations. We do so by first writing the current leaving each branch connected to a nonreference node as a function of the node voltages and then summing these currents to zero in accordance with Kirchhoff's current law. For the circuit in Fig. 4.6, the current away from node 1 through the 1 Ω resistor is the voltage drop across the resistor divided by the resistance (Ohm's law). The voltage drop across the resistor, in the direction of the current away from the node, is $v_1 - 10$. Therefore the current in the 1 Ω resistor is $(v_1 - 10)/1$. Figure 4.7 depicts these observations. It shows the 10 V–1 Ω branch, with the appropriate voltages and current.

This same reasoning yields the current in every branch where the current is unknown. Thus the current away from node 1 through the 5 Ω resistor is $v_1/5$, and the current away from node 1 through the 2 Ω resistor is $(v_1 - v_2)/2$. The sum of the three currents leaving node 1 must equal zero; therefore the node-voltage equation derived at node 1 is

$$\frac{v_1 - 10}{1} + \frac{v_1}{5} + \frac{v_1 - v_2}{2} = 0. \tag{4.5}$$

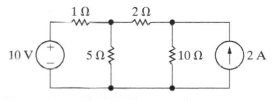

Figure 4.5 ▲ A circuit used to illustrate the node-voltage method of circuit analysis.

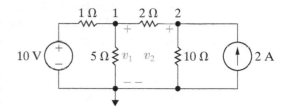

Figure 4.6 ▲ The circuit shown in Fig. 4.5 with a reference node and the node voltages.

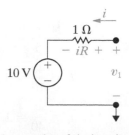

Figure 4.7 ▲ Computation of the branch current i.

The node-voltage equation derived at node 2 is

$$\frac{v_2 - v_1}{2} + \frac{v_2}{10} - 2 = 0. \qquad (4.6)$$

Note that the first term in Eq. 4.6 is the current away from node 2 through the $2\ \Omega$ resistor, the second term is the current away from node 2 through the $10\ \Omega$ resistor, and the third term is the current away from node 2 through the current source.

Equations 4.5 and 4.6 are the two simultaneous equations that describe the circuit shown in Fig. 4.6 in terms of the node voltages v_1 and v_2. Solving for v_1 and v_2 yields

$$v_1 = \frac{100}{11} = 9.09\ \text{V}$$

$$v_2 = \frac{120}{11} = 10.91\ \text{V}.$$

Once the node voltages are known, all the branch currents can be calculated. Once these are known, the branch voltages and powers can be calculated. Example 4.2 illustrates the use of the node-voltage method.

Example 4.2   Using the Node-Voltage Method

a) Use the node-voltage method of circuit analysis to find the branch currents i_a, i_b, and i_c in the circuit shown in Fig. 4.8.

b) Find the power associated with each source, and state whether the source is delivering or absorbing power.

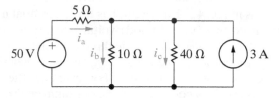

Figure 4.8 ▲ The circuit for Example 4.2.

Solution

a) We begin by noting that the circuit has two essential nodes; thus we need to write a single node-voltage expression. We select the lower node as the reference node and define the unknown node voltage as v_1. Figure 4.9 illustrates these decisions. Summing the currents away from node 1 generates the node-voltage equation

$$\frac{v_1 - 50}{5} + \frac{v_1}{10} + \frac{v_1}{40} - 3 = 0.$$

Solving for v_1 gives

$$v_1 = 40\ \text{V}.$$

Hence

$$i_a = \frac{50 - 40}{5} = 2\ \text{A},$$

$$i_b = \frac{40}{10} = 4\ \text{A},$$

$$i_c = \frac{40}{40} = 1\ \text{A}.$$

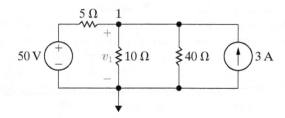

Figure 4.9 ▲ The circuit shown in Fig. 4.8 with a reference node and the unknown node voltage v_1.

b) The power associated with the 50 V source is

$$p_{50V} = -50i_a = -100\ \text{W (delivering)}.$$

The power associated with the 3 A source is

$$p_{3A} = -3v_1 = -3(40) = -120\ \text{W (delivering)}.$$

We check these calculations by noting that the total delivered power is 220 W. The total power absorbed by the three resistors is $4(5) + 16(10) + 1(40)$, or 220 W, as we calculated and as it must be.

✓ASSESSMENT PROBLEMS

Objective 1—Understand and be able to use the node-voltage method

4.1 a) For the circuit shown, use the node-voltage method to find v_1, v_2, and i_1.

b) How much power is delivered to the circuit by the 15 A source?

c) Repeat (b) for the 5 A source

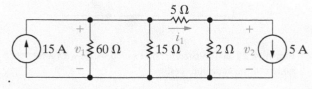

Answer: (a) 60 V, 10 V, 10 A;

(b) 900 W;

(c) −50 W.

NOTE: *Also try Chapter Problems 4.6, 4.11, and 4.13.*

4.2 Use the node-voltage method to find v in the circuit shown.

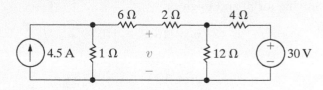

Answer: 15 V.

4.3 The Node-Voltage Method and Dependent Sources

If the circuit contains dependent sources, the node-voltage equations must be supplemented with the constraint equations imposed by the presence of the dependent sources. Example 4.3 illustrates the application of the node-voltage method to a circuit containing a dependent source.

Example 4.3 **Using the Node-Voltage Method with Dependent Sources**

Use the node-voltage method to find the power dissipated in the 5 Ω resistor in the circuit shown in Fig. 4.10.

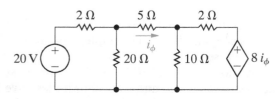

Figure 4.10 ▲ The circuit for Example 4.3.

Solution

We begin by noting that the circuit has three essential nodes. Hence we need two node-voltage equations to describe the circuit. Four branches terminate

on the lower node, so we select it as the reference node. The two unknown node voltages are defined on the circuit shown in Fig. 4.11. Summing the currents away from node 1 generates the equation

$$\frac{v_1 - 20}{2} + \frac{v_1}{20} + \frac{v_1 - v_2}{5} = 0.$$

Summing the currents away from node 2 yields

$$\frac{v_2 - v_1}{5} + \frac{v_2}{10} + \frac{v_2 - 8i_\phi}{2} = 0.$$

As written, these two node-voltage equations contain three unknowns, namely, v_1, v_2, and i_ϕ. To eliminate i_ϕ we must express this controlling current in terms of the node voltages, or

$$i_\phi = \frac{v_1 - v_2}{5}.$$

Substituting this relationship into the node 2 equation simplifies the two node-voltage equations to

$$0.75v_1 - 0.2v_2 = 10,$$

$$-v_1 + 1.6v_2 = 0.$$

Solving for v_1 and v_2 gives

$$v_1 = 16 \text{ V}$$

and

$$v_2 = 10 \text{ V}.$$

Then,

$$i_\phi = \frac{16 - 10}{5} = 1.2 \text{ A},$$

$$p_{5\Omega} = (1.44)(5) = 7.2 \text{ W}.$$

A good exercise to build your problem-solving intuition is to reconsider this example, using node 2 as the reference node. Does it make the analysis easier or harder?

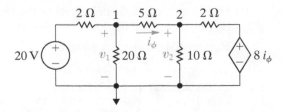

Figure 4.11 ▲ The circuit shown in Fig. 4.10, with a reference node and the node voltages.

ASSESSMENT PROBLEM

Objective 1—Understand and be able to use the node-voltage method

4.3   a) Use the node-voltage method to find the power associated with each source in the circuit shown.
   b) State whether the source is delivering power to the circuit or extracting power from the circuit.

Answer: (a) $p_{50V} = -150 \text{ W}$, $p_{3i_1} = -144 \text{ W}$,
   $p_{5A} = -80 \text{ W}$;
   (b) all sources are delivering power to the circuit.

NOTE: Also try Chapter Problems 4.18 and 4.19.

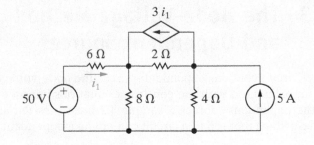

4.4 The Node-Voltage Method: Some Special Cases

When a voltage source is the only element between two essential nodes, the node-voltage method is simplified. As an example, look at the circuit in Fig. 4.12. There are three essential nodes in this circuit, which means that two simultaneous equations are needed. From these three essential nodes, a reference node has been chosen and two other nodes have been labeled. But the 100 V source constrains the voltage between node 1 and the reference node to 100 V. This means that there is only one unknown node voltage (v_2). Solution of this circuit thus involves only a single node-voltage equation at node 2:

$$\frac{v_2 - v_1}{10} + \frac{v_2}{50} - 5 = 0. \tag{4.7}$$

But $v_1 = 100 \text{ V}$, so Eq. 4.7 can be solved for v_2:

$$v_2 = 125 \text{ V}. \tag{4.8}$$

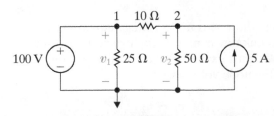

Figure 4.12 ▲ A circuit with a known node voltage.

Knowing v_2, we can calculate the current in every branch. You should verify that the current into node 1 in the branch containing the independent voltage source is 1.5 A.

In general, when you use the node-voltage method to solve circuits that have voltage sources connected directly between essential nodes, the number of unknown node voltages is reduced. The reason is that, whenever a voltage source connects two essential nodes, it constrains the difference between the node voltages at these nodes to equal the voltage of the source. Taking the time to see if you can reduce the number of unknowns in this way will simplify circuit analysis.

Suppose that the circuit shown in Fig. 4.13 is to be analyzed using the node-voltage method. The circuit contains four essential nodes, so we anticipate writing three node-voltage equations. However, two essential nodes are connected by an independent voltage source, and two other essential nodes are connected by a current-controlled dependent voltage source. Hence, there actually is only one unknown node voltage.

Choosing which node to use as the reference node involves several possibilities. Either node on each side of the dependent voltage source looks attractive because, if chosen, one of the node voltages would be known to be either $+10i_\phi$ (left node is the reference) or $-10i_\phi$ (right node is the reference). The lower node looks even better because one node voltage is immediately known (50 V) and five branches terminate there. We therefore opt for the lower node as the reference.

Figure 4.14 shows the redrawn circuit, with the reference node flagged and the node voltages defined. Also, we introduce the current i because we cannot express the current in the dependent voltage source branch as a function of the node voltages v_2 and v_3. Thus, at node 2

$$\frac{v_2 - v_1}{5} + \frac{v_2}{50} + i = 0, \tag{4.9}$$

and at node 3

$$\frac{v_3}{100} - i - 4 = 0. \tag{4.10}$$

We eliminate i simply by adding Eqs. 4.9 and 4.10 to get

$$\frac{v_2 - v_1}{5} + \frac{v_2}{50} + \frac{v_3}{100} - 4 = 0. \tag{4.11}$$

The Concept of a Supernode

Equation 4.11 may be written directly, without resorting to the intermediate step represented by Eqs. 4.9 and 4.10. To do so, we consider nodes 2 and 3 to be a single node and simply sum the currents away from the node in terms of the node voltages v_2 and v_3. Figure 4.15 illustrates this approach.

When a voltage source is between two essential nodes, we can combine those nodes to form a **supernode**. Obviously, Kirchhoff's current law must hold for the supernode. In Fig. 4.15, starting with the 5 Ω branch and moving counterclockwise around the supernode, we generate the equation

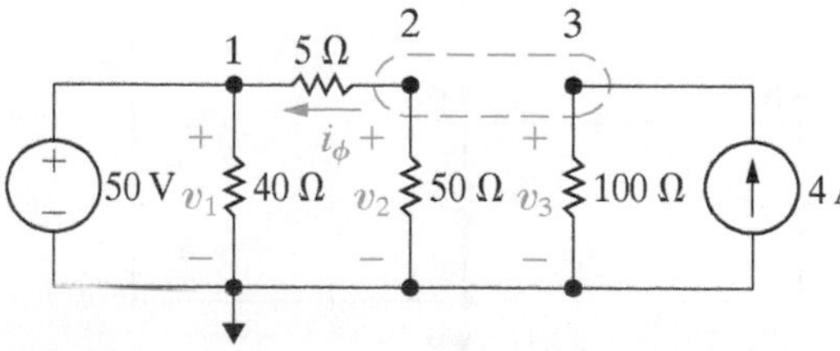

$$\frac{v_2 - v_1}{5} + \frac{v_2}{50} + \frac{v_3}{100} - 4 = 0, \tag{4.12}$$

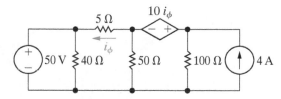

Figure 4.13 ▲ A circuit with a dependent voltage source connected between nodes.

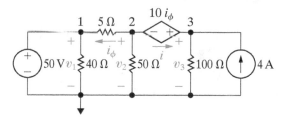

Figure 4.14 ▲ The circuit shown in Fig. 4.13. with the selected node voltages defined.

Figure 4.15 ▲ Considering nodes 2 and 3 to be a supernode.

which is identical to Eq. 4.11. Creating a supernode at nodes 2 and 3 has made the task of analyzing this circuit easier. It is therefore always worth taking the time to look for this type of shortcut before writing any equations.

After Eq. 4.12 has been derived, the next step is to reduce the expression to a single unknown node voltage. First we eliminate v_1 from the equation because we know that $v_1 = 50$ V. Next we express v_3 as a function of v_2:

$$v_3 = v_2 + 10i_\phi. \tag{4.13}$$

We now express the current controlling the dependent voltage source as a function of the node voltages:

$$i_\phi = \frac{v_2 - 50}{5}. \tag{4.14}$$

Using Eqs. 4.13 and 4.14 and $v_1 = 50$ V reduces Eq. 4.12 to

$$v_2\left(\frac{1}{50} + \frac{1}{5} + \frac{1}{100} + \frac{10}{500}\right) = 10 + 4 + 1,$$

$$v_2(0.25) = 15,$$

$$v_2 = 60 \text{ V}.$$

From Eqs. 4.13 and 4.14:

$$i_\phi = \frac{60 - 50}{5} = 2 \text{ A},$$

$$v_3 = 60 + 20 = 80 \text{ V}.$$

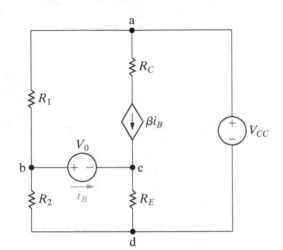

Figure 4.16 ▲ The transistor amplifier circuit shown in Fig. 2.24.

Node-Voltage Analysis of the Amplifier Circuit

Let's use the node-voltage method to analyze the circuit first introduced in Section 2.5 and shown again in Fig. 4.16.

When we used the branch-current method of analysis in Section 2.5, we faced the task of writing and solving six simultaneous equations. Here we will show how nodal analysis can simplify our task.

The circuit has four essential nodes: Nodes a and d are connected by an independent voltage source as are nodes b and c. Therefore the problem reduces to finding a single unknown node voltage, because $(n_e - 1) - 2 = 1$. Using d as the reference node, combine nodes b and c into a supernode, label the voltage drop across R_2 as v_b, and label the voltage drop across R_E as v_c, as shown in Fig. 4.17. Then,

$$\frac{v_b}{R_2} + \frac{v_b - V_{CC}}{R_1} + \frac{v_c}{R_E} - \beta i_B = 0. \tag{4.15}$$

We now eliminate both v_c and i_B from Eq. 4.15 by noting that

$$v_c = (i_B + \beta i_B)R_E, \tag{4.16}$$

$$v_c = v_b - V_0. \tag{4.17}$$

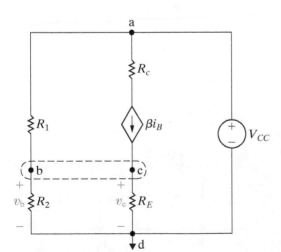

Figure 4.17 ▲ The circuit shown in Fig. 4.16, with voltages and the supernode identified.

Substituting Eqs. 4.16 and 4.17 into Eq. 4.15 yields

$$v_b \left[\frac{1}{R_1} + \frac{1}{R_2} + \frac{1}{(1 + \beta)R_E} \right] = \frac{V_{CC}}{R_1} + \frac{V_0}{(1 + \beta)R_E}. \qquad (4.18)$$

Solving Eq. 4.18 for v_b yields

$$v_b = \frac{V_{CC}R_2(1 + \beta)R_E + V_0R_1R_2}{R_1R_2 + (1 + \beta)R_E(R_1 + R_2)}. \qquad (4.19)$$

Using the node-voltage method to analyze this circuit reduces the problem from manipulating six simultaneous equations (see Problem 2.27) to manipulating three simultaneous equations. You should verify that, when Eq. 4.19 is combined with Eqs. 4.16 and 4.17, the solution for i_B is identical to Eq. 2.25. (See Problem 4.30.)

✓ ASSESSMENT PROBLEMS

Objective 1—Understand and be able to use the node-voltage method

4.4 Use the node-voltage method to find v_o in the circuit shown.

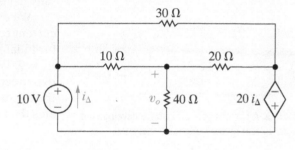

Answer: 24 V.

4.5 Use the node-voltage method to find v in the circuit shown.

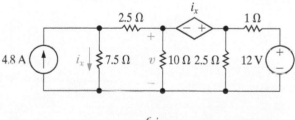

Answer: 8 V.

4.6 Use the node-voltage method to find v_1 in the circuit shown.

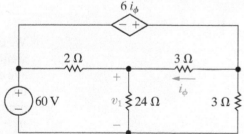

Answer: 48 V.

NOTE: Also try Chapter Problems 4.22, 4.23, and 4.26.

4.5 Introduction to the Mesh-Current Method

As stated in Section 4.1, the mesh-current method of circuit analysis enables us to describe a circuit in terms of $b_e - (n_e - 1)$ equations. Recall that a mesh is a loop with no other loops inside it. The circuit in Fig. 4.1(b) is shown again in Fig. 4.18, with current arrows inside each loop to distinguish it. Recall also that the mesh-current method is applicable only to planar circuits. The

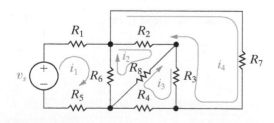

Figure 4.18 ▲ The circuit shown in Fig. 4.1(b), with the mesh currents defined.

circuit in Fig. 4.18 contains seven essential branches where the current is unknown and four essential nodes. Therefore, to solve it via the mesh-current method, we must write four $[7 - (4 - 1)]$ mesh-current equations.

A **mesh current** is the current that exists only in the perimeter of a mesh. On a circuit diagram it appears as either a closed solid line or an almost-closed solid line that follows the perimeter of the appropriate mesh. An arrowhead on the solid line indicates the reference direction for the mesh current. Figure 4.18 shows the four mesh currents that describe the circuit in Fig. 4.1(b). Note that by definition, mesh currents automatically satisfy Kirchhoff's current law. That is, at any node in the circuit, a given mesh current both enters and leaves the node.

Figure 4.18 also shows that identifying a mesh current in terms of a branch current is not always possible. For example, the mesh current i_2 is not equal to any branch current, whereas mesh currents i_1, i_3, and i_4 can be identified with branch currents. Thus measuring a mesh current is not always possible; note that there is no place where an ammeter can be inserted to measure the mesh current i_2. The fact that a mesh current can be a fictitious quantity doesn't mean that it is a useless concept. On the contrary, the mesh-current method of circuit analysis evolves quite naturally from the branch-current equations.

We can use the circuit in Fig. 4.19 to show the evolution of the mesh-current technique. We begin by using the branch currents (i_1, i_2, and i_3) to formulate the set of independent equations. For this circuit, $b_e = 3$ and $n_e = 2$. We can write only one independent current equation, so we need two independent voltage equations. Applying Kirchhoff's current law to the upper node and Kirchhoff's voltage law around the two meshes generates the following set of equations:

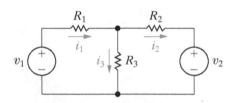

Figure 4.19 ▲ A circuit used to illustrate development of the mesh-current method of circuit analysis.

$$i_1 = i_2 + i_3, \tag{4.20}$$

$$v_1 = i_1 R_1 + i_3 R_3, \tag{4.21}$$

$$-v_2 = i_2 R_2 - i_3 R_3. \tag{4.22}$$

We reduce this set of three equations to a set of two equations by solving Eq. 4.20 for i_3 and then substituting this expression into Eqs. 4.21 and 4.22:

$$v_1 = i_1(R_1 + R_3) - i_2 R_3, \tag{4.23}$$

$$-v_2 = -i_1 R_3 + i_2(R_2 + R_3). \tag{4.24}$$

We can solve Eqs. 4.23 and 4.24 for i_1 and i_2 to replace the solution of three simultaneous equations with the solution of two simultaneous equations. We derived Eqs. 4.23 and 4.24 by substituting the $n_e - 1$ current equations into the $b_e - (n_e - 1)$ voltage equations. The value of the mesh-current method is that, by defining mesh currents, we automatically eliminate the $n_e - 1$ current equations. Thus the mesh-current method is equivalent to a systematic substitution of the $n_e - 1$ current equations into the $b_e - (n_e - 1)$ voltage equations. The mesh currents in Fig. 4.19 that are equivalent to eliminating the branch current i_3 from Eqs. 4.21 and 4.22 are shown in Fig. 4.20. We now apply Kirchhoff's voltage law around the two meshes, expressing all voltages across resistors in terms of the mesh currents, to get the equations

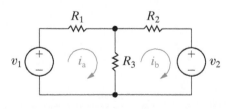

Figure 4.20 ▲ Mesh currents i_a and i_b.

$$v_1 = i_a R_1 + (i_a - i_b)R_3, \tag{4.25}$$

$$-v_2 = (i_b - i_a)R_3 + i_b R_2. \tag{4.26}$$

Collecting the coefficients of i_a and i_b in Eqs. 4.25 and 4.26 gives

$$v_1 = i_a(R_1 + R_3) - i_b R_3, \tag{4.27}$$

$$-v_2 = -i_a R_3 + i_b(R_2 + R_3). \tag{4.28}$$

Note that Eqs. 4.27 and 4.28 and Eqs. 4.23 and 4.24 are identical in form, with the mesh currents i_a and i_b replacing the branch currents i_1 and i_2. Note also that the branch currents shown in Fig. 4.19 can be expressed in terms of the mesh currents shown in Fig. 4.20, or

$$i_1 = i_a, \tag{4.29}$$

$$i_2 = i_b, \tag{4.30}$$

$$i_3 = i_a - i_b. \tag{4.31}$$

The ability to write Eqs. 4.29–4.31 by inspection is crucial to the mesh-current method of circuit analysis. Once you know the mesh currents, you also know the branch currents. And once you know the branch currents, you can compute any voltages or powers of interest.

Example 4.4 illustrates how the mesh-current method is used to find source powers and a branch voltage.

Example 4.4   Using the Mesh-Current Method

a) Use the mesh-current method to determine the power associated with each voltage source in the circuit shown in Fig. 4.21.

b) Calculate the voltage v_o across the 8 Ω resistor.

Solution

a) To calculate the power associated with each source, we need to know the current in each source. The circuit indicates that these source currents will be identical to mesh currents. Also, note that the circuit has seven branches where

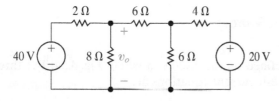

Figure 4.21 ▲ The circuit for Example 4.4.

the current is unknown and five nodes. Therefore we need three $[b - (n - 1) = 7 - (5 - 1)]$ mesh-current equations to describe the circuit. Figure 4.22 shows the three mesh currents used to describe the circuit in Fig. 4.21. If we assume that the voltage drops are positive, the three mesh equations are

$$-40 + 2i_a + 8(i_a - i_b) = 0,$$

$$8(i_b - i_a) + 6i_b + 6(i_b - i_c) = 0,$$

$$6(i_c - i_b) + 4i_c + 20 = 0. \tag{4.32}$$

Your calculator can probably solve these equations, or you can use a computer tool. Cramer's method is a useful tool when solving three or more simultaneous equations by hand. You can review this important tool in Appendix A. Reorganizing Eqs. 4.32 in anticipation of using your calculator, a computer program, or Cramer's method gives

$$10i_a - 8i_b + 0i_c = 40;$$

$$-8i_a + 20i_b - 6i_c = 0;$$

$$0i_a - 6i_b + 10i_c = -20. \tag{4.33}$$

The three mesh currents are

$$i_a = 5.6 \text{ A},$$

$$i_b = 2.0 \text{ A},$$

$$i_c = -0.80 \text{ A}.$$

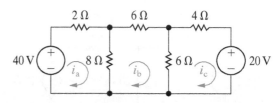

Figure 4.22 ▲ The three mesh currents used to analyze the circuit shown in Fig. 4.21.

The mesh current i_a is identical with the branch current in the 40 V source, so the power associated with this source is

$$p_{40V} = -40i_a = -224 \text{ W}.$$

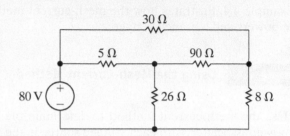

The minus sign means that this source is delivering power to the network. The current in the 20 V source is identical to the mesh current i_c; therefore

$$p_{20V} = 20i_c = -16 \text{ W}.$$

The 20 V source also is delivering power to the network.

b) The branch current in the 8 Ω resistor in the direction of the voltage drop v_o is $i_a - i_b$. Therefore

$$v_o = 8(i_a - i_b) = 8(3.6) = 28.8 \text{ V}.$$

✓ **ASSESSMENT PROBLEM**

Objective 2—Understand and be able to use the mesh-current method

4.7   Use the mesh-current method to find (a) the power delivered by the 80 V source to the circuit shown and (b) the power dissipated in the 8 Ω resistor.

Answer: (a) 400 W;
(b) 50 W.

NOTE: Also try Chapter Problems 4.32 and 4.36.

4.6 The Mesh-Current Method and Dependent Sources

If the circuit contains dependent sources, the mesh-current equations must be supplemented by the appropriate constraint equations. Example 4.5 illustrates the application of the mesh-current method when the circuit includes a dependent source.

Example 4.5   Using the Mesh-Current Method with Dependent Sources

Use the mesh-current method of circuit analysis to determine the power dissipated in the 4 Ω resistor in the circuit shown in Fig. 4.23.

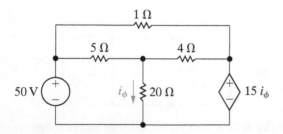

Figure 4.23 ▲ The circuit for Example 4.5.

Solution

This circuit has six branches where the current is unknown and four nodes. Therefore we need three mesh currents to describe the circuit. They are

defined on the circuit shown in Fig. 4.24. The three mesh-current equations are

$$50 = 5(i_1 - i_2) + 20(i_1 - i_3),$$

$$0 = 5(i_2 - i_1) + 1i_2 + 4(i_2 - i_3),$$

$$0 = 20(i_3 - i_1) + 4(i_3 - i_2) + 15i_\phi. \quad (4.34)$$

We now express the branch current controlling the dependent voltage source in terms of the mesh currents as

$$i_\phi = i_1 - i_3, \quad (4.35)$$

which is the supplemental equation imposed by the presence of the dependent source. Substituting Eq. 4.35 into Eqs. 4.34 and collecting the coefficients of i_1, i_2, and i_3 in each equation generates

$$50 = 25i_1 - 5i_2 - 20i_3,$$

$$0 = -5i_1 + 10i_2 - 4i_3,$$

$$0 = -5i_1 - 4i_2 + 9i_3.$$

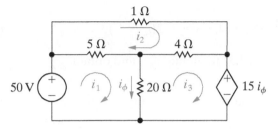

Figure 4.24 ▲ The circuit shown in Fig. 4.23 with the three mesh currents.

Because we are calculating the power dissipated in the 4 Ω resistor, we compute the mesh currents i_2 and i_3:

$$i_2 = 26 \text{ A},$$

$$i_3 = 28 \text{ A}.$$

The current in the 4 Ω resistor oriented from left to right is $i_3 - i_2$, or 2 A. Therefore the power dissipated is

$$p_{4\Omega} = (i_3 - i_2)^2(4) = (2)^2(4) = 16 \text{ W}.$$

What if you had not been told to use the mesh-current method? Would you have chosen the node-voltage method? It reduces the problem to finding one unknown node voltage because of the presence of two voltage sources between essential nodes. We present more about making such choices later.

✓ASSESSMENT PROBLEMS

Objective 2—Understand and be able to use the mesh-current method

4.8 a) Determine the number of mesh-current equations needed to solve the circuit shown.

   b) Use the mesh-current method to find how much power is being delivered to the dependent voltage source.

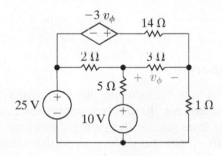

NOTE: *Also try Chapter Problems 4.39 and 4.40.*

Answer: (a) 3;
       (b) −36 W.

4.9 Use the mesh-current method to find v_o in the circuit shown.

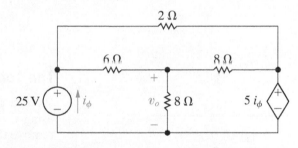

Answer: 16 V.

4.7 The Mesh-Current Method: Some Special Cases

When a branch includes a current source, the mesh-current method requires some additional manipulations. The circuit shown in Fig. 4.25 depicts the nature of the problem.

We have defined the mesh currents i_a, i_b, and i_c, as well as the voltage across the 5 A current source, to aid the discussion. Note that the circuit contains five essential branches where the current is unknown and four essential nodes. Hence we need to write two $[5 - (4 - 1)]$ mesh-current

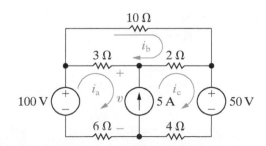

Figure 4.25 ▲ A circuit illustrating mesh analysis when a branch contains an independent current source.

equations to solve the circuit. The presence of the current source reduces the three unknown mesh currents to two such currents, because it constrains the difference between i_a and i_c to equal 5 A. Hence, if we know i_a, we know i_c, and vice versa.

However, when we attempt to sum the voltages around either mesh a or mesh c, we must introduce into the equations the unknown voltage across the 5 A current source. Thus, for mesh a:

$$100 = 3(i_a - i_b) + v + 6i_a, \tag{4.36}$$

and for mesh c:

$$-50 = 4i_c - v + 2(i_c - i_b). \tag{4.37}$$

We now add Eqs. 4.36 and 4.37 to eliminate v and obtain

$$50 = 9i_a - 5i_b + 6i_c. \tag{4.38}$$

Summing voltages around mesh b gives

$$0 = 3(i_b - i_a) + 10i_b + 2(i_b - i_c). \tag{4.39}$$

We reduce Eqs. 4.38 and 4.39 to two equations and two unknowns by using the constraint that

$$i_c - i_a = 5. \tag{4.40}$$

We leave to you the verification that, when Eq. 4.40 is combined with Eqs. 4.38 and 4.39, the solutions for the three mesh currents are

$$i_a = 1.75 \text{ A}, \quad i_b = 1.25 \text{ A}, \quad \text{and} \quad i_c = 6.75 \text{ A}.$$

The Concept of a Supermesh

We can derive Eq. 4.38 without introducing the unknown voltage v by using the concept of a supermesh. To create a supermesh, we mentally remove the current source from the circuit by simply avoiding this branch when writing the mesh-current equations. We express the voltages around the supermesh in terms of the original mesh currents. Figure 4.26 illustrates the supermesh concept. When we sum the voltages around the supermesh (denoted by the dashed line), we obtain the equation

$$-100 + 3(i_a - i_b) + 2(i_c - i_b) + 50 + 4i_c + 6i_a = 0, \tag{4.41}$$

which reduces to

$$50 = 9i_a - 5i_b + 6i_c. \tag{4.42}$$

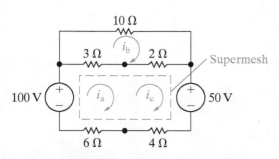

Figure 4.26 ▲ The circuit shown in Fig. 4.25, illustrating the concept of a supermesh.

Note that Eqs. 4.42 and 4.38 are identical. Thus the supermesh has eliminated the need for introducing the unknown voltage across the current source. Once again, taking time to look carefully at a circuit to identify a shortcut such as this provides a big payoff in simplifying the analysis.

Mesh-Current Analysis of the Amplifier Circuit

We can use the circuit first introduced in Section 2.5 (Fig. 2.24) to illustrate how the mesh-current method works when a branch contains a dependent current source. Figure 4.27 shows that circuit, with the three mesh currents denoted i_a, i_b, and i_c. This circuit has four essential nodes and five essential branches where the current is unknown. Therefore we know that the circuit can be analyzed in terms of two $[5 - (4 - 1)]$ mesh-current equations. Although we defined three mesh currents in Fig. 4.27, the dependent current source forces a constraint between mesh currents i_a and i_c, so we have only two unknown mesh currents. Using the concept of the supermesh, we redraw the circuit as shown in Fig. 4.28.

We now sum the voltages around the supermesh in terms of the mesh currents i_a, i_b, and i_c to obtain

$$R_1 i_a + v_{CC} + R_E(i_c - i_b) - V_0 = 0. \tag{4.43}$$

The mesh b equation is

$$R_2 i_b + V_0 + R_E(i_b - i_c) = 0. \tag{4.44}$$

The constraint imposed by the dependent current source is

$$\beta i_B = i_a - i_c. \tag{4.45}$$

The branch current controlling the dependent current source, expressed as a function of the mesh currents, is

$$i_B = i_b - i_a. \tag{4.46}$$

From Eqs. 4.45 and 4.46,

$$i_c = (1 + \beta)i_a - \beta i_b. \tag{4.47}$$

We now use Eq. 4.47 to eliminate i_c from Eqs. 4.43 and 4.44:

$$[R_1 + (1 + \beta)R_E]i_a - (1 + \beta)R_E i_b = V_0 - V_{CC}, \tag{4.48}$$

$$-(1 + \beta)R_E i_a + [R_2 + (1 + \beta)R_E]i_b = -V_0. \tag{4.49}$$

You should verify that the solution of Eqs. 4.48 and 4.49 for i_a and i_b gives

$$i_a = \frac{V_0 R_2 - V_{CC} R_2 - V_{CC}(1 + \beta)R_E}{R_1 R_2 + (1 + \beta)R_E(R_1 + R_2)}, \tag{4.50}$$

$$i_b = \frac{-V_0 R_1 - (1 + \beta)R_E V_{CC}}{R_1 R_2 + (1 + \beta)R_E(R_1 + R_2)}. \tag{4.51}$$

We also leave you to verify that, when Eqs. 4.50 and 4.51 are used to find i_B, the result is the same as that given by Eq. 2.25.

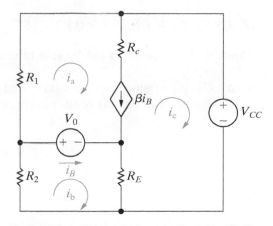

Figure 4.27 ▲ The circuit shown in Fig. 2.24 with the mesh currents i_a, i_b, and i_c.

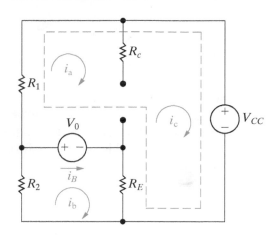

Figure 4.28 ▲ The circuit shown in Fig. 4.27, depicting the supermesh created by the presence of the dependent current source.

✓**ASSESSMENT PROBLEMS**

Objective 2—Understand and be able to use the mesh-current method

4.10 Use the mesh-current method to find the power dissipated in the 2 Ω resistor in the circuit shown.

Answer: 72 W.

4.11 Use the mesh-current method to find the mesh current i_a in the circuit shown.

Answer: 15 A.

4.12 Use the mesh-current method to find the power dissipated in the 1 Ω resistor in the circuit shown.

Answer: 36 W.

NOTE: Also try Chapter Problems 4.43, 4.47, 4.49, and 4.52.

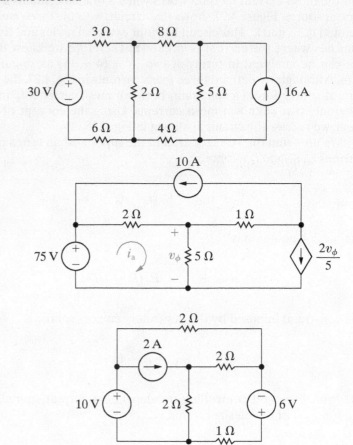

4.8 The Node-Voltage Method Versus the Mesh-Current Method

The greatest advantage of both the node-voltage and mesh-current methods is that they reduce the number of simultaneous equations that must be manipulated. They also require the analyst to be quite systematic in terms of organizing and writing these equations. It is natural to ask, then, "When is the node-voltage method preferred to the mesh-current method and vice versa?" As you might suspect, there is no clear-cut answer. Asking a number of questions, however, may help you identify the more efficient method before plunging into the solution process:

• Does one of the methods result in fewer simultaneous equations to solve?

• Does the circuit contain supernodes? If so, using the node-voltage method will permit you to reduce the number of equations to be solved.

- Does the circuit contain supermeshes? If so, using the mesh-current method will permit you to reduce the number of equations to be solved.

- Will solving some portion of the circuit give the requested solution? If so, which method is most efficient for solving just the pertinent portion of the circuit?

Perhaps the most important observation is that, for any situation, some time spent thinking about the problem in relation to the various analytical approaches available is time well spent. Examples 4.6 and 4.7 illustrate the process of deciding between the node-voltage and mesh-current methods.

Example 4.6   Understanding the Node-Voltage Method Versus Mesh-Current Method

Find the power dissipated in the 300 Ω resistor in the circuit shown in Fig. 4.29.

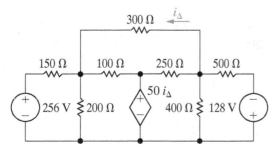

Figure 4.29 ▲ The circuit for Example 4.6.

Solution

To find the power dissipated in the 300 Ω resistor, we need to find either the current in the resistor or the voltage across it. The mesh-current method yields the current in the resistor; this approach requires solving five simultaneous mesh equations, as depicted in Fig. 4.30. In writing the five equations, we must include the constraint $i_\Delta = -i_b$.

Before going further, let's also look at the circuit in terms of the node-voltage method. Note that, once we know the node voltages, we can calculate either the current in the 300 Ω resistor or the voltage across it. The circuit has four essential nodes, and therefore only three node-voltage equations are required to describe the circuit. Because of the dependent voltage source between two essential nodes, we have to sum the currents at only two nodes. Hence the problem is reduced to writing two node-voltage equations and a constraint equation. Because the node-voltage method requires only three simultaneous equations, it is the more attractive approach.

Once the decision to use the node-voltage method has been made, the next step is to select a reference node. Two essential nodes in the circuit in Fig. 4.29 merit consideration. The first is the reference node in Fig. 4.31. If this node is selected, one of the unknown node voltages is the voltage across the

300 Ω resistor, namely, v_2 in Fig. 4.31. Once we know this voltage, we calculate the power in the 300 Ω resistor by using the expression

$$p_{300\Omega} = v_2^2/300.$$

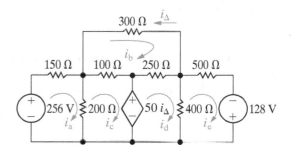

Figure 4.30 ▲ The circuit shown in Fig. 4.29, with the five mesh currents.

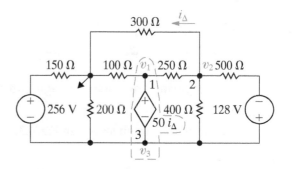

Figure 4.31 ▲ The circuit shown in Fig. 4.29, with a reference node.

Note that, in addition to selecting the reference node, we defined the three node voltages v_1, v_2, and v_3 and indicated that nodes 1 and 3 form a super-node, because they are connected by a dependent voltage source. It is understood that a node voltage is a rise from the reference node; therefore, in Fig. 4.31, we have not placed the node voltage polarity references on the circuit diagram.

The second node that merits consideration as the reference node is the lower node in the circuit, as shown in Fig. 4.32. It is attractive because it has the most branches connected to it, and the node-voltage equations are thus easier to write. However, to find either the current in the 300 Ω resistor or the voltage across it requires an additional calculation once we know the node voltages v_a and v_c. For example, the current in the 300 Ω resistor is $(v_c - v_a)/300$, whereas the voltage across the resistor is $v_c - v_a$.

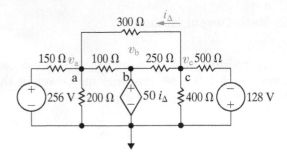

Figure 4.32 ▲ The circuit shown in Fig. 4.29 with an alternative reference node.

We compare these two possible reference nodes by means of the following sets of equations. The first set pertains to the circuit shown in Fig. 4.31, and the second set is based on the circuit shown in Fig. 4.32.

- Set 1 (Fig 4.31)
  At the supernode,

$$\frac{v_1}{100} + \frac{v_1 - v_2}{250} + \frac{v_3}{200} + \frac{v_3 - v_2}{400} + \frac{v_3 - (v_2 + 128)}{500}$$

$$+ \frac{v_3 + 256}{150} = 0.$$

At v_2,

$$\frac{v_2}{300} + \frac{v_2 - v_1}{250} + \frac{v_2 - v_3}{400} + \frac{v_2 + 128 - v_3}{500} = 0.$$

From the supernode, the constraint equation is

$$v_3 = v_1 - 50i_\Delta = v_1 - \frac{v_2}{6}.$$

- Set 2 (Fig 4.32)
  At v_a,

$$\frac{v_a}{200} + \frac{v_a - 256}{150} + \frac{v_a - v_b}{100} + \frac{v_a - v_c}{300} = 0.$$

At v_c,

$$\frac{v_c}{400} + \frac{v_c + 128}{500} + \frac{v_c - v_b}{250} + \frac{v_c - v_a}{300} = 0.$$

From the supernode, the constraint equation is

$$v_b = 50i_\Delta = \frac{50(v_c - v_a)}{300} = \frac{v_c - v_a}{6}.$$

You should verify that the solution of either set leads to a power calculation of 16.57 W dissipated in the 300 Ω resistor.

Example 4.7   Comparing the Node-Voltage and Mesh-Current Methods

Find the voltage v_o in the circuit shown in Fig. 4.33.

Solution

At first glance, the node-voltage method looks appealing, because we may define the unknown voltage as a node voltage by choosing the lower terminal of the dependent current source as the reference node. The circuit has four essential nodes and two voltage-controlled dependent sources, so the node-voltage method requires manipulation of three node-voltage equations and two constraint equations.

Let's now turn to the mesh-current method for finding v_o. The circuit contains three meshes, and we can use the leftmost one to calculate v_o. If we

let i_a denote the leftmost mesh current, then $v_o = 193 - 10i_a$. The presence of the two current sources reduces the problem to manipulating a single supermesh equation and two constraint equations. Hence the mesh-current method is the more attractive technique here.

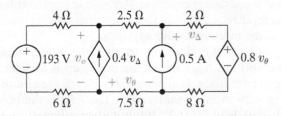

Figure 4.33 ▲ The circuit for Example 4.7.

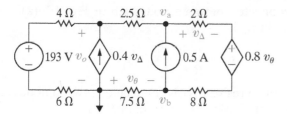

Figure 4.34 ▲ The circuit shown in Fig. 4.33 with the three mesh currents.

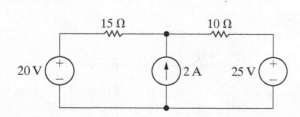

Figure 4.35 ▲ The circuit shown in Fig. 4.33 with node voltages.

To help you compare the two approaches, we summarize both methods. The mesh-current equations are based on the circuit shown in Fig. 4.34, and the node-voltage equations are based on the circuit shown in Fig. 4.35. The supermesh equation is

$$193 = 10i_a + 10i_b + 10i_c + 0.8v_\theta,$$

and the constraint equations are

$$i_b - i_a = 0.4v_\Delta = 0.8i_c;$$

$$v_\theta = -7.5i_b; \text{ and}$$

$$i_c - i_b = 0.5.$$

We use the constraint equations to write the super-mesh equation in terms of i_a:

$$160 = 80i_a, \quad \text{or} \quad i_a = 2 \text{ A},$$

$$v_o = 193 - 20 = 173 \text{ V}.$$

The node-voltage equations are

$$\frac{v_o - 193}{10} - 0.4v_\Delta + \frac{v_o - v_a}{2.5} = 0,$$

$$\frac{v_a - v_o}{2.5} - 0.5 + \frac{v_a - (v_b + 0.8v_\theta)}{10} = 0,$$

$$\frac{v_b}{7.5} + 0.5 + \frac{v_b + 0.8v_\theta - v_a}{10} = 0.$$

The constraint equations are

$$v_\theta = -v_b, \quad v_\Delta = \left[\frac{v_a - (v_b + 0.8v_\theta)}{10} \right] 2.$$

We use the constraint equations to reduce the node-voltage equations to three simultaneous equations involving v_o, v_a, and v_b. You should verify that the node-voltage approach also gives $v_o = 173$ V.

✓ ASSESSMENT PROBLEMS

Objective 3—Deciding between the node-voltage and mesh-current methods

4.13 Find the power delivered by the 2 A current source in the circuit shown.

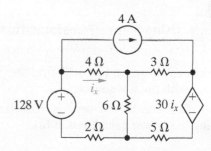

Answer: 70 W.

4.14 Find the power delivered by the 4 A current source in the circuit shown.

Answer: 40 W.

NOTE: *Also try Chapter Problems 4.54 and 4.56.*

4.9 Source Transformations

Even though the node-voltage and mesh-current methods are powerful techniques for solving circuits, we are still interested in methods that can be used to simplify circuits. Series-parallel reductions and Δ-to-Y transformations are

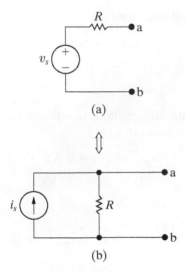

Figure 4.36 ▲ Source transformations.

already on our list of simplifying techniques. We begin expanding this list with source transformations. A **source transformation**, shown in Fig. 4.36, allows a voltage source in series with a resistor to be replaced by a current source in parallel with the same resistor or vice versa. The double-headed arrow emphasizes that a source transformation is bilateral; that is, we can start with either configuration and derive the other.

We need to find the relationship between v_s and i_s that guarantees the two configurations in Fig. 4.36 are equivalent with respect to nodes a,b. Equivalence is achieved if any resistor R_L experiences the same current flow, and thus the same voltage drop, whether connected between nodes a,b in Fig. 4.36(a) or Fig. 4.36(b).

Suppose R_L is connected between nodes a,b in Fig. 4.36(a). Using Ohm's law, the current in R_L is

$$i_L = \frac{v_s}{R + R_L}. \tag{4.52}$$

Now suppose the same resistor R_L is connected between nodes a,b in Fig. 4.36(b). Using current division, the current in R_L is

$$i_L = \frac{R}{R + R_L} i_s. \tag{4.53}$$

If the two circuits in Fig. 4.36 are equivalent, these resistor currents must be the same. Equating the right-hand sides of Eqs. 4.52 and 4.53 and simplifying,

$$i_s = \frac{v_s}{R}. \tag{4.54}$$

When Eq. 4.54 is satisfied for the circuits in Fig. 4.36, the current in R_L is the same for both circuits in the figure for all values of R_L. If the current through R_L is the same in both circuits, then the voltage drop across R_L is the same in both circuits, and the circuits are equivalent at nodes a,b.

If the polarity of v_s is reversed, the orientation of i_s must be reversed to maintain equivalence.

Example 4.8 illustrates the usefulness of making source transformations to simplify a circuit-analysis problem.

Example 4.8   Using Source Transformations to Solve a Circuit

a) For the circuit shown in Fig. 4.37, find the power associated with the 6 V source.

b) State whether the 6 V source is absorbing or delivering the power calculated in (a).

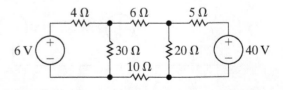

Figure 4.37 ▲ The circuit for Example 4.8.

Solution

a) If we study the circuit shown in Fig. 4.37, knowing that the power associated with the 6 V source is of interest, several approaches come to mind. The circuit has four essential nodes and six essential branches where the current is unknown. Thus we can find the current in the branch containing the 6 V source by solving either three $[6 - (4 - 1)]$ mesh-current equations or three $[4 - 1]$ node-voltage equations. Choosing the mesh-current approach involves solving for the mesh current that corresponds to the branch current in the 6 V source. Choosing the node-voltage approach involves solving for the voltage across the 30 Ω resistor, from which the branch current in the 6 V source can be calculated. But by focusing on just one branch current, we can first simplify the circuit by using source transformations.

We must reduce the circuit in a way that pre-serves the identity of the branch containing the 6 V source. We have no reason to preserve the identity of the branch containing the 40 V source. Beginning with

this branch, we can transform the 40 V source in series with the 5 Ω resistor into an 8 A current source in parallel with a 5 Ω resistor, as shown in Fig. 4.38(a).

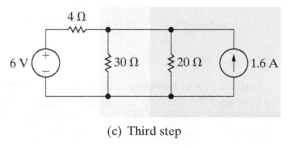

(a) First step

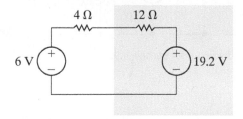

(b) Second step

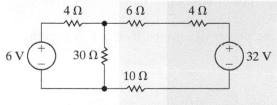

(c) Third step

(d) Fourth step

Figure 4.38 ▲ Step-by-step simplification of the circuit shown in Fig. 4.37.

Next, we can replace the parallel combination of the 20 Ω and 5 Ω resistors with a 4 Ω resistor. This 4 Ω resistor is in parallel with the 8 A source and therefore can be replaced with a 32 V source in series with a 4 Ω resistor, as shown in Fig. 4.38(b). The 32 V source is in series with 20 Ω of resistance and, hence, can be replaced by a current source of 1.6 A in parallel with 20 Ω, as shown in Fig. 4.38(c). The 20 Ω and 30 Ω parallel resistors can be reduced to a single 12 Ω resistor. The parallel combination of the 1.6 A current source

and the 12 Ω resistor transforms into a voltage source of 19.2 V in series with 12 Ω. Figure 4.38(d) shows the result of this last transformation. The current in the direction of the voltage drop across the 6 V source is $(19.2 - 6)/16$, or 0.825 A. Therefore the power associated with the 6 V source is

$$p_{6V} = (0.825)(6) = 4.95 \text{ W}.$$

b) The voltage source is absorbing power.

A question that arises from use of the source transformation depicted in Fig. 4.38 is, "What happens if there is a resistance R_p in parallel with the voltage source or a resistance R_s in series with the current source?" In both cases, the resistance has no effect on the equivalent circuit that pre-dicts behavior with respect to terminals a,b. Figure 4.39 summarizes this observation.

The two circuits depicted in Fig. 4.39(a) are equivalent with respect to terminals a,b because they produce the same voltage and current in any resistor R_L inserted between nodes a,b. The same can be said for the cir-cuits in Fig. 4.39(b). Example 4.9 illustrates an application of the equiva-lent circuits depicted in Fig. 4.39.

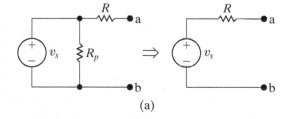

(a)

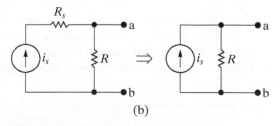

(b)

Figure 4.39 ▲ Equivalent circuits containing a resistance in parallel with a voltage source or in series with a current source.

Example 4.9   Using Special Source Transformation Techniques

a) Use source transformations to find the voltage v_o in the circuit shown in Fig. 4.40.

b) Find the power developed by the 250 V voltage source.

c) Find the power developed by the 8 A current source.

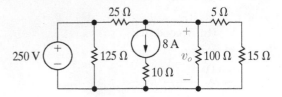

Figure 4.40 ▲ The circuit for Example 4.9.

Solution

a) We begin by removing the 125 Ω and 10 Ω resistors, because the 125 Ω resistor is connected across the 250 V voltage source and the 10 Ω resistor is connected in series with the 8 A current source. We also combine the series-connected resistors into a single resistance of 20 Ω. Figure 4.41 shows the simplified circuit.

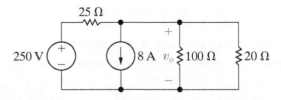

Figure 4.41 ▲ A simplified version of the circuit shown in Fig. 4.40.

We now use a source transformation to replace the 250 V source and 25 Ω resistor with a 10 A source in parallel with the 25 Ω resistor, as shown in Fig. 4.42. We can now simplify the circuit shown in Fig. 4.42 by using Kirchhoff's current law to combine the parallel current sources into a single source. The parallel resistors combine into a single resistor. Figure 4.43 shows the result. Hence $v_o = 20$ V.

b) The current supplied by the 250 V source equals the current in the 125 Ω resistor plus the current in the 25 Ω resistor. Thus

$$i_s = \frac{250}{125} + \frac{250 - 20}{25} = 11.2 \text{ A}.$$

Therefore the power developed by the voltage source is

$$p_{250\text{V}}(\text{developed}) = (250)(11.2) = 2800 \text{ W}.$$

c) To find the power developed by the 8 A current source, we first find the voltage across the source. If we let v_s represent the voltage across the source, positive at the upper terminal of the source, we obtain

$$v_s + 8(10) = v_o = 20, \quad \text{or} \quad v_s = -60 \text{ V},$$

and the power developed by the 8 A source is 480 W. Note that the 125 Ω and 10 Ω resistors do not affect the value of v_o but do affect the power calculations.

Figure 4.42 ▲ The circuit shown in Fig. 4.41 after a source transformation.

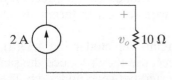

Figure 4.43 ▲ The circuit shown in Fig. 4.42 after combining sources and resistors.

✓**ASSESSMENT PROBLEM**

Objective 4—Understand source transformation

4.15   a) Use a series of source transformations to
find the voltage v in the circuit shown.

b) How much power does the 120 V source
deliver to the circuit?

Answer: (a) 48 V;

(b) 374.4 W.

NOTE: Also try Chapter Problems 4.61 and 4.62.

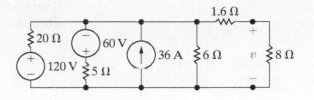

4.10 Thévenin and Norton Equivalents

At times in circuit analysis, we want to concentrate on what happens at
a specific pair of terminals. For example, when we plug a toaster into an
outlet, we are interested primarily in the voltage and current at the terminals of the toaster. We have little or no interest in the effect that connecting the toaster has on voltages or currents elsewhere in the circuit
supplying the outlet. We can expand this interest in terminal behavior
to a set of appliances, each requiring a different amount of power.
We then are interested in how the voltage and current delivered at the
outlet change as we change appliances. In other words, we want to focus
on the behavior of the circuit supplying the outlet, but only at the outlet terminals.

Thévenin and Norton equivalents are circuit simplification techniques
that focus on terminal behavior and thus are extremely valuable aids in
analysis. Although here we discuss them as they pertain to resistive circuits, Thévenin and Norton equivalent circuits may be used to represent
any circuit made up of linear elements.

We can best describe a Thévenin equivalent circuit by reference to
Fig. 4.44, which represents any circuit made up of sources (both independent and dependent) and resistors. The letters a and b denote the
pair of terminals of interest. Figure 4.44(b) shows the Thévenin equivalent. Thus, a **Thévenin equivalent circuit** is an independent voltage
source V_{Th} in series with a resistor R_{Th}, which replaces an interconnection of sources and resistors. This series combination of V_{Th} and R_{Th} is
equivalent to the original circuit in the sense that, if we connect the
same load across the terminals a,b of each circuit, we get the same voltage and current at the terminals of the load. This equivalence holds for
all possible values of load resistance.

To represent the original circuit by its Thévenin equivalent, we must
be able to determine the Thévenin voltage V_{Th} and the Thévenin resistance R_{Th}. First, we note that if the load resistance is infinitely large, we
have an open-circuit condition. The open-circuit voltage at the terminals
a,b in the circuit shown in Fig. 4.44(b) is V_{Th}. By hypothesis, this must be

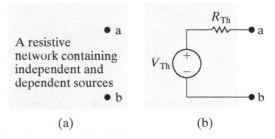

Figure 4.44 ▲ (a) A general circuit. (b) The Thévenin
equivalent circuit.

the same as the open-circuit voltage at the terminals a,b in the original circuit. Therefore, to calculate the Thévenin voltage V_{Th}, we simply calculate the open-circuit voltage in the original circuit.

Reducing the load resistance to zero gives us a short-circuit condition. If we place a short circuit across the terminals a,b of the Thévenin equivalent circuit, the short-circuit current directed from a to b is

$$i_{sc} = \frac{V_{Th}}{R_{Th}}. \qquad (4.55)$$

By hypothesis, this short-circuit current must be identical to the short-circuit current that exists in a short circuit placed across the terminals a,b of the original network. From Eq. 4.55,

$$R_{Th} = \frac{V_{Th}}{i_{sc}}. \qquad (4.56)$$

Thus the Thévenin resistance is the ratio of the open-circuit voltage to the short-circuit current.

Finding a Thévenin Equivalent

To find the Thévenin equivalent of the circuit shown in Fig. 4.45, we first calculate the open-circuit voltage of v_{ab}. Note that when the terminals a,b are open, there is no current in the 4 Ω resistor. Therefore the open-circuit voltage v_{ab} is identical to the voltage across the 3 A current source, labeled v_1. We find the voltage by solving a single node-voltage equation. Choosing the lower node as the reference node, we get

$$\frac{v_1 - 25}{5} + \frac{v_1}{20} - 3 = 0. \qquad (4.57)$$

Solving for v_1 yields

$$v_1 = 32 \text{ V}. \qquad (4.58)$$

Hence the Thévenin voltage for the circuit is 32 V.

The next step is to place a short circuit across the terminals and calculate the resulting short-circuit current. Figure 4.46 shows the circuit with the short in place. Note that the short-circuit current is in the direction of the open-circuit voltage drop across the terminals a,b. If the short-circuit current is in the direction of the open-circuit voltage rise across the terminals, a minus sign must be inserted in Eq. 4.56.

The short-circuit current (i_{sc}) is found easily once v_2 is known. Therefore the problem reduces to finding v_2 with the short in place. Again, if we use the lower node as the reference node, the equation for v_2 becomes

$$\frac{v_2 - 25}{5} + \frac{v_2}{20} - 3 + \frac{v_2}{4} = 0. \qquad (4.59)$$

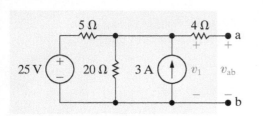

Figure 4.45 ▲ A circuit used to illustrate a Thévenin equivalent.

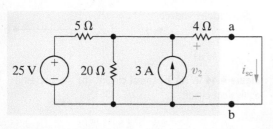

Figure 4.46 ▲ The circuit shown in Fig. 4.45 with terminals a and b short-circuited.

Solving Eq. 4.59 for v_2 gives

$$v_2 = 16 \text{ V}. \qquad (4.60)$$

Hence, the short-circuit current is

$$i_{sc} = \frac{16}{4} = 4 \text{ A}. \qquad (4.61)$$

We now find the Thévenin resistance by substituting the numerical results from Eqs. 4.58 and 4.61 into Eq. 4.56:

$$R_{Th} = \frac{V_{Th}}{i_{sc}} = \frac{32}{4} = 8 \text{ }\Omega. \qquad (4.62)$$

Figure 4.47 shows the Thévenin equivalent for the circuit shown in Fig. 4.45. You should verify that, if a 24 Ω resistor is connected across the terminals a,b in Fig. 4.45, the voltage across the resistor will be 24 V and the current in the resistor will be 1 A, as would be the case with the Thévenin circuit in Fig. 4.47. This same equivalence between the circuit in Figs. 4.45 and 4.47 holds for any resistor value connected between nodes a,b.

The Norton Equivalent

A **Norton equivalent circuit** consists of an independent current source in parallel with the Norton equivalent resistance. We can derive it from a Thévenin equivalent circuit simply by making a source transformation. Thus the Norton current equals the short-circuit current at the terminals of interest, and the Norton resistance is identical to the Thévenin resistance.

Using Source Transformations

Sometimes we can make effective use of source transformations to derive a Thévenin or Norton equivalent circuit. For example, we can derive the Thévenin and Norton equivalents of the circuit shown in Fig. 4.45 by making the series of source transformations shown in Fig. 4.48. This technique is most useful when the network contains only independent sources. The presence of dependent sources requires retaining the identity of the controlling voltages and/or currents, and this constraint usually prohibits continued reduction of the circuit by source transformations. We discuss the problem of finding the Thévenin equivalent when a circuit contains dependent sources in Example 4.10.

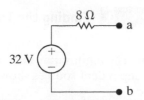

Figure 4.47 ▲ The Thévenin equivalent of the circuit shown in Fig. 4.45.

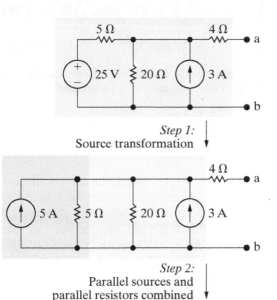

Step 1:
Source transformation

Step 2:
Parallel sources and
parallel resistors combined

Step 3:
Source transformation; series
resistors combined, producing
the Thévenin equivalent circuit

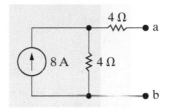

Step 4:
Source transformation, producing
the Norton equivalent circuit

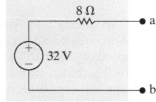

Figure 4.48 ▲ Step-by-step derivation of the Thévenin and Norton equivalents of the circuit shown in Fig. 4.45.

Example 4.10   Finding the Thévenin Equivalent of a Circuit with a Dependent Source

Find the Thévenin equivalent for the circuit containing dependent sources shown in Fig. 4.49.

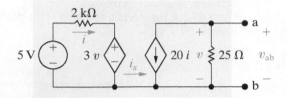

Figure 4.49 ▲ A circuit used to illustrate a Thévenin equivalent when the circuit contains dependent sources.

Solution

The first step in analyzing the circuit in Fig. 4.49 is to recognize that the current labeled i_x must be zero. (Note the absence of a return path for i_x to enter the left-hand portion of the circuit.) The open-circuit, or Thévenin, voltage will be the voltage across the 25 Ω resistor. With $i_x = 0$,

$$V_{Th} = v_{ab} = (-20i)(25) = -500i.$$

The current i is

$$i = \frac{5 - 3v}{2000} = \frac{5 - 3V_{Th}}{2000}.$$

In writing the equation for i, we recognize that the Thévenin voltage is identical to the control voltage. When we combine these two equations, we obtain

$$V_{Th} = -5 \text{ V}.$$

To calculate the short-circuit current, we place a short circuit across a,b. When the terminals a,b are shorted together, the control voltage v is reduced to zero. Therefore, with the short in place, the circuit shown in Fig. 4.49 becomes the one shown in Fig. 4.50. With the short circuit shunting the 25 Ω resistor, all the current from the dependent current source appears in the short, so

$$i_{sc} = -20i.$$

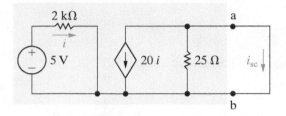

Figure 4.50 ▲ The circuit shown in Fig. 4.49 with terminals a and b short-circuited.

As the voltage controlling the dependent voltage source has been reduced to zero, the current controlling the dependent current source is

$$i = \frac{5}{2000} = 2.5 \text{ mA}.$$

Combining these two equations yields a short-circuit current of

$$i_{sc} = -20(2.5) = -50 \text{ mA}.$$

From i_{sc} and V_{Th} we get

$$R_{Th} = \frac{V_{Th}}{i_{sc}} = \frac{-5}{-50} \times 10^3 = 100 \ \Omega.$$

Figure 4.51 illustrates the Thévenin equivalent for the circuit shown in Fig. 4.49. Note that the reference polarity marks on the Thévenin voltage source in Fig. 4.51 agree with the preceding equation for V_{Th}.

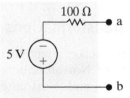

Figure 4.51 ▲ The Thévenin equivalent for the circuit shown in Fig. 4.49.

✓ ASSESSMENT PROBLEMS

Objective 5—Understand Thévenin and Norton equivalents

4.16 Find the Thévenin equivalent circuit with respect to the terminals a,b for the circuit shown.

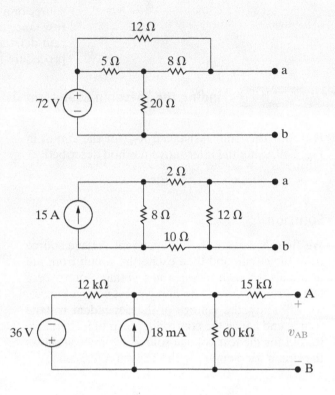

Answer: $V_{ab} = V_{Th} = 64.8\ \text{V}$, $R_{Th} = 6\ \Omega$.

4.17 Find the Norton equivalent circuit with respect to the terminals a,b for the circuit shown.

Answer: $I_N = 6\ \text{A}$ (directed toward a), $R_N = 7.5\ \Omega$.

4.18 A voltmeter with an internal resistance of $100\ \text{k}\Omega$ is used to measure the voltage v_{AB} in the circuit shown. What is the voltmeter reading?

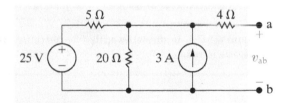

Answer: 120 V.

NOTE: Also try Chapter Problems 4.64, 4.68, and 4.72.

4.11 More on Deriving a Thévenin Equivalent

The technique for determining R_{Th} that we discussed and illustrated in Section 4.10 is not always the easiest method available. Two other methods generally are simpler to use. The first is useful if the network contains only independent sources. To calculate R_{Th} for such a network, we first deactivate all independent sources and then calculate the resistance seen looking into the network at the designated terminal pair. A voltage source is deactivated by replacing it with a short circuit. A current source is deactivated by replacing it with an open circuit. For example, consider the circuit shown in Fig. 4.52. Deactivating the independent sources simplifies the circuit to the one shown in Fig. 4.53. The resistance seen looking into the terminals a,b is denoted R_{ab}, which consists of the 4 Ω resistor in series with the parallel combinations of the 5 and 20 Ω resistors. Thus,

$$R_{ab} = R_{Th} = 4 + \frac{5 \times 20}{25} = 8\ \Omega. \tag{4.63}$$

Note that the derivation of R_{Th} with Eq. 4.63 is much simpler than the same derivation with Eqs. 4.57–4.62.

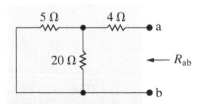

Figure 4.52 ▲ A circuit used to illustrate a Thévenin equivalent.

Figure 4.53 ▲ The circuit shown in Fig. 4.52 after deactivation of the independent sources.

If the circuit or network contains dependent sources, an alternative procedure for finding the Thévenin resistance R_{Th} is as follows. We first deactivate all independent sources, and we then apply either a test voltage source or a test current source to the Thévenin terminals a,b. The Thévenin resistance equals the ratio of the voltage across the test source to the current delivered by the test source. Example 4.11 illustrates this alternative procedure for finding R_{Th}, using the same circuit as Example 4.10.

| Example 4.11 | Finding the Thévenin Equivalent Using a Test Source |

Find the Thévenin resistance R_{Th} for the circuit in Fig. 4.49, using the alternative method described.

Solution

We first deactivate the independent voltage source from the circuit and then excite the circuit from the terminals a,b with either a test voltage source or a test current source. If we apply a test voltage source, we will know the voltage of the dependent voltage source and hence the controlling current i. Therefore we opt for the test voltage source. Figure 4.54 shows the circuit for computing the Thévenin resistance.

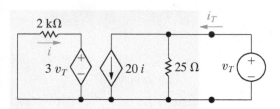

Figure 4.54 ▲ An alternative method for computing the Thévenin resistance.

The externally applied test voltage source is denoted v_T, and the current that it delivers to the circuit is labeled i_T. To find the Thévenin resistance, we simply solve the circuit shown in Fig. 4.54 for the ratio of the voltage to the current at the test source; that is, $R_{\mathrm{Th}} = v_T/i_T$. From Fig. 4.54,

$$i_T = \frac{v_T}{25} + 20i, \qquad (4.64)$$

$$i = \frac{-3v_T}{2} \text{ mA}. \qquad (4.65)$$

We then substitute Eq. 4.65 into Eq. 4.64 and solve the resulting equation for the ratio v_T/i_T:

$$i_T = \frac{v_T}{25} - \frac{60v_T}{2000}, \qquad (4.66)$$

$$\frac{i_T}{v_T} = \frac{1}{25} - \frac{6}{200} = \frac{50}{5000} = \frac{1}{100}. \qquad (4.67)$$

From Eqs. 4.66 and 4.67,

$$R_{\mathrm{Th}} = \frac{v_T}{i_T} = 100 \ \Omega. \qquad (4.68)$$

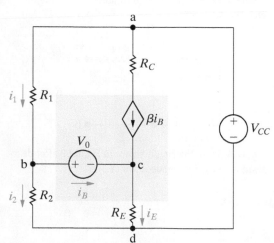

Figure 4.55 ▲ The application of a Thévenin equivalent in circuit analysis.

In general, these computations are easier than those involved in computing the short-circuit current. Moreover, in a network containing only resistors and dependent sources, you must use the alternative method, because the ratio of the Thévenin voltage to the short-circuit current is indeterminate. That is, it is the ratio 0/0.

Using the Thévenin Equivalent in the Amplifier Circuit

At times we can use a Thévenin equivalent to reduce one portion of a circuit to greatly simplify analysis of the larger network. Let's return to the circuit first introduced in Section 2.5 and subsequently analyzed in Sections 4.4 and 4.7. To aid our discussion, we redrew the circuit and identified the branch currents of interest, as shown in Fig. 4.55.

As our previous analysis has shown, i_B is the key to finding the other branch currents. We redraw the circuit as shown in Fig. 4.56 to prepare to replace the subcircuit to the left of V_0 with its Thévenin equivalent. You

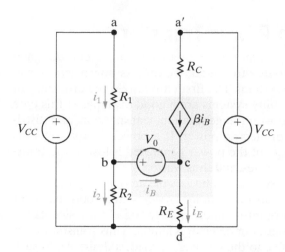

Figure 4.56 ▲ A modified version of the circuit shown in Fig. 4.55.

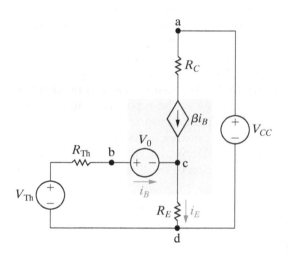

Figure 4.57 ▲ The circuit shown in Fig. 4.56 modified by a Thévenin equivalent.

should be able to determine that this modification has no effect on the branch currents i_1, i_2, i_B, and i_E.

Now we replace the circuit made up of V_{CC}, R_1, and R_2 with a Thévenin equivalent, with respect to the terminals b,d. The Thévenin voltage and resistance are

$$V_{Th} = \frac{V_{CC}R_2}{R_1 + R_2},$$ (4.69)

$$R_{Th} = \frac{R_1R_2}{R_1 + R_2}.$$ (4.70)

With the Thévenin equivalent, the circuit in Fig. 4.56 becomes the one shown in Fig. 4.57.

We now derive an equation for i_B simply by summing the voltages around the left mesh. In writing this mesh equation, we recognize that $i_E = (1 + \beta)i_B$. Thus,

$$V_{Th} = R_{Th}i_B + V_0 + R_E(1 + \beta)i_B,$$ (4.71)

from which

$$i_B = \frac{V_{Th} - V_0}{R_{Th} + (1 + \beta)R_E}.$$ (4.72)

When we substitute Eqs. 4.69 and 4.70 into Eq. 4.72, we get the same expression obtained in Eq. 2.25. Note that when we have incorporated the Thévenin equivalent into the original circuit, we can obtain the solution for i_B by writing a single equation.

✓ ASSESSMENT PROBLEMS

Objective 5—Understand Thévenin and Norton equivalents

4.19 Find the Thévenin equivalent circuit with respect to the terminals a,b for the circuit shown.

Answer: $V_{Th} = v_{ab} = 8\text{ V}$, $R_{Th} = 1\ \Omega$.

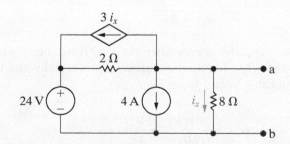

4.20 Find the Thévenin equivalent circuit with respect to the terminals a,b for the circuit shown. (*Hint:* Define the voltage at the leftmost node as v, and write two nodal equations with V_{Th} as the right node voltage.)

Answer: $V_{Th} = v_{ab} = 30\text{ V}$, $R_{Th} = 10\ \Omega$.

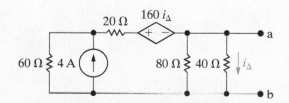

NOTE: Also try Chapter Problems 4.74 and 4.79.

4.12 Maximum Power Transfer

Circuit analysis plays an important role in the analysis of systems designed to transfer power from a source to a load. We discuss power transfer in terms of two basic types of systems. The first emphasizes the efficiency of the power transfer. Power utility systems are a good example of this type because they are concerned with the generation, transmission, and distribution of large quantities of electric power. If a power utility system is inefficient, a large percentage of the power generated is lost in the transmission and distribution processes, and thus wasted.

The second basic type of system emphasizes the amount of power transferred. Communication and instrumentation systems are good examples because in the transmission of information, or data, via electric signals, the power available at the transmitter or detector is limited. Thus, transmitting as much of this power as possible to the receiver, or load, is desirable. In such applications the amount of power being transferred is small, so the efficiency of transfer is not a primary concern. We now consider maximum power transfer in systems that can be modeled by a purely resistive circuit.

Maximum power transfer can best be described with the aid of the circuit shown in Fig. 4.58. We assume a resistive network containing independent and dependent sources and a designated pair of terminals, a,b, to which a load, R_L, is to be connected. The problem is to determine the value of R_L that permits maximum power delivery to R_L. The first step in this process is to recognize that a resistive network can always be replaced by its Thévenin equivalent. Therefore, we redraw the circuit shown in Fig. 4.58 as the one shown in Fig. 4.59. Replacing the original network by its Thévenin equivalent greatly simplifies the task of finding R_L. Derivation of R_L requires expressing the power dissipated in R_L as a function of the three circuit parameters V_{Th}, R_{Th}, and R_L. Thus

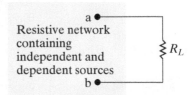

Figure 4.58 ▲ A circuit describing maximum power transfer.

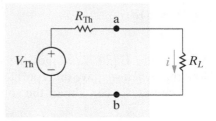

Figure 4.59 ▲ A circuit used to determine the value of R_L for maximum power transfer.

$$p = i^2 R_L = \left(\frac{V_{Th}}{R_{Th} + R_L} \right)^2 R_L. \tag{4.73}$$

Next, we recognize that for a given circuit, V_{Th} and R_{Th} will be fixed. Therefore the power dissipated is a function of the single variable R_L. To find the value of R_L that maximizes the power, we use elementary calculus. We begin by writing an equation for the derivative of p with respect to R_L:

$$\frac{dp}{dR_L} = V_{Th}^2 \left[\frac{(R_{Th} + R_L)^2 - R_L \cdot 2(R_{Th} + R_L)}{(R_{Th} + R_L)^4} \right]. \tag{4.74}$$

The derivative is zero and p is maximized when

$$(R_{Th} + R_L)^2 = 2R_L(R_{Th} + R_L). \tag{4.75}$$

Solving Eq. 4.75 yields

Condition for maximum power transfer ▶

$$R_L = R_{Th}. \tag{4.76}$$

Thus maximum power transfer occurs when the load resistance R_L equals the Thévenin resistance R_{Th}. To find the maximum power delivered to R_L, we simply substitute Eq. 4.76 into Eq. 4.73:

$$p_{max} = \frac{V_{Th}^2 R_L}{(2R_L)^2} = \frac{V_{Th}^2}{4R_L}. \tag{4.77}$$

The analysis of a circuit when the load resistor is adjusted for maximum power transfer is illustrated in Example 4.12.

Example 4.12   Calculating the Condition for Maximum Power Transfer

a) For the circuit shown in Fig. 4.60, find the value of R_L that results in maximum power being transferred to R_L.

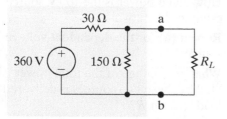

Figure 4.60 ▲ The circuit for Example 4.12.

b) Calculate the maximum power that can be delivered to R_L.

c) When R_L is adjusted for maximum power transfer, what percentage of the power delivered by the 360 V source reaches R_L?

Solution

a) The Thévenin voltage for the circuit to the left of the terminals a,b is

$$V_{Th} = \frac{150}{180}(360) = 300 \text{ V}.$$

The Thévenin resistance is

$$R_{Th} = \frac{(150)(30)}{180} = 25 \ \Omega.$$

Replacing the circuit to the left of the terminals a,b with its Thévenin equivalent gives us the circuit shown in Fig. 4.61, which indicates that R_L must equal 25 Ω for maximum power transfer.

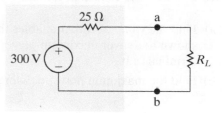

Figure 4.61 ▲ Reduction of the circuit shown in Fig. 4.60 by means of a Thévenin equivalent.

b) The maximum power that can be delivered to R_L is

$$p_{max} = \left(\frac{300}{50}\right)^2 (25) = 900 \text{ W}.$$

c) When R_L equals 25 Ω, the voltage v_{ab} is

$$v_{ab} = \left(\frac{300}{50}\right)(25) = 150 \text{ V}.$$

From Fig. 4.60, when v_{ab} equals 150 V, the current in the voltage source in the direction of the voltage rise across the source is

$$i_s = \frac{360 - 150}{30} = \frac{210}{30} = 7 \text{ A}.$$

Therefore, the source is delivering 2520 W to the circuit, or

$$p_s = -i_s(360) = -2520 \text{ W}.$$

The percentage of the source power delivered to the load is

$$\frac{900}{2520} \times 100 = 35.71\%.$$

✓ ASSESSMENT PROBLEMS

Objective 6—Know the condition for and calculate maximum power transfer to resistive load

4.21 a) Find the value of R that enables the circuit shown to deliver maximum power to the terminals a,b.

b) Find the maximum power delivered to R.

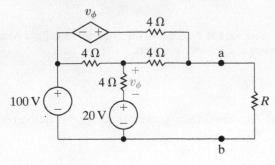

Answer: (a) 3 Ω;

(b) 1.2 kW.

NOTE: Also try Chapter Problems 4.88 and 4.90.

4.22 Assume that the circuit in Assessment Problem 4.21 is delivering maximum power to the load resistor R.

a) How much power is the 100 V source delivering to the network?

b) Repeat (a) for the dependent voltage source.

c) What percentage of the total power generated by these two sources is delivered to the load resistor R?

Answer: (a) 3000 W;

(b) 800 W;

(c) 31.58%.

4.13 Superposition

A linear system obeys the principle of **superposition**, which states that whenever a linear system is excited, or driven, by more than one independent source of energy, the total response is the sum of the individual responses. An individual response is the result of an independent source acting alone. Because we are dealing with circuits made up of interconnected linear-circuit elements, we can apply the principle of superposition directly to the analysis of such circuits when they are driven by more than one independent energy source. At present, we restrict the discussion to simple resistive networks; however, the principle is applicable to any linear system.

Superposition is applied in both the analysis and the design of circuits. In analyzing a complex circuit with multiple independent voltage and current sources, there are often fewer, simpler equations to solve when the effects of the independent sources are considered one at a time. Applying superposition can thus simplify circuit analysis. Be aware, though, that sometimes applying superposition actually complicates the analysis, producing more equations to solve than with an alternative method. Superposition is required only if the independent sources in a circuit are fundamentally different. In these early chapters, all independent sources are dc sources, so superposition is not required. We introduce superposition here in anticipation of later chapters in which circuits will require it.

Superposition is applied in design to synthesize a desired circuit response that could not be achieved in a circuit with a single source. If the desired circuit response can be written as a sum of two or more terms, the response can be realized by including one independent source for each term of the response. This approach to the design of circuits with complex responses allows a designer to consider several simple designs instead of one complex design.

We demonstrate the superposition principle by using it to find the branch currents in the circuit shown in Fig. 4.62. We begin by finding the branch currents resulting from the 120 V voltage source. We denote those currents with a prime. Replacing the ideal current source with an open circuit deactivates it; Fig. 4.63 shows this. The branch currents in this circuit are the result of only the voltage source.

We can easily find the branch currents in the circuit in Fig. 4.63 once we know the node voltage across the 3 Ω resistor. Denoting this voltage v_1, we write

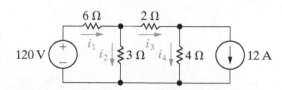

Figure 4.62 ▲ A circuit used to illustrate superposition.

$$\frac{v_1 - 120}{6} + \frac{v_1}{3} + \frac{v_1}{2 + 4} = 0, \qquad (4.78)$$

from which

$$v_1 = 30 \text{ V}. \qquad (4.79)$$

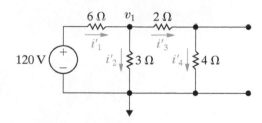

Figure 4.63 ▲ The circuit shown in Fig. 4.62 with the current source deactivated.

Now we can write the expressions for the branch currents $i_1' - i_4'$ directly:

$$i_1' = \frac{120 - 30}{6} = 15 \text{ A}, \qquad (4.80)$$

$$i_2' = \frac{30}{3} = 10 \text{ A}, \qquad (4.81)$$

$$i_3' = i_4' = \frac{30}{6} = 5 \text{ A}. \qquad (4.82)$$

To find the component of the branch currents resulting from the current source, we deactivate the ideal voltage source and solve the circuit shown in Fig. 4.64. The double-prime notation for the currents indicates they are the components of the total current resulting from the ideal current source.

We determine the branch currents in the circuit shown in Fig. 4.64 by first solving for the node voltages across the 3 and 4 Ω resistors, respectively. Figure 4.65 shows the two node voltages. The two node-voltage equations that describe the circuit are

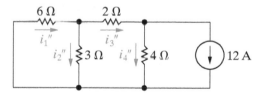

Figure 4.64 ▲ The circuit shown in Fig. 4.62 with the voltage source deactivated.

$$\frac{v_3}{3} + \frac{v_3}{6} + \frac{v_3 - v_4}{2} = 0, \qquad (4.83)$$

$$\frac{v_4 - v_3}{2} + \frac{v_4}{4} + 12 = 0. \qquad (4.84)$$

Solving Eqs. 4.83 and 4.84 for v_3 and v_4, we get

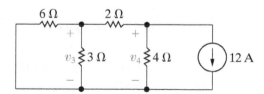

Figure 4.65 ▲ The circuit shown in Fig. 4.64 showing the node voltages v_3 and v_4.

$$v_3 = -12 \text{ V}, \qquad (4.85)$$

$$v_4 = -24 \text{ V}. \qquad (4.86)$$

Now we can write the branch currents i_1'' through i_4'' directly in terms of the node voltages v_3 and v_4:

$$i_1'' = \frac{-v_3}{6} = \frac{12}{6} = 2 \text{ A}, \qquad (4.87)$$

$$i_2'' = \frac{v_3}{3} = \frac{-12}{3} = -4 \text{ A}, \tag{4.88}$$

$$i_3'' = \frac{v_3 - v_4}{2} = \frac{-12 + 24}{2} = 6 \text{ A}, \tag{4.89}$$

$$i_4'' = \frac{v_4}{4} = \frac{-24}{4} = -6 \text{ A}. \tag{4.90}$$

To find the branch currents in the original circuit, that is, the currents i_1, i_2, i_3, and i_4 in Fig. 4.62, we simply add the currents given by Eqs. 4.87–4.90 to the currents given by Eqs. 4.80–4.82:

$$i_1 = i_1' + i_1'' = 15 + 2 = 17 \text{ A}, \tag{4.91}$$

$$i_2 = i_2' + i_2'' = 10 - 4 = 6 \text{ A}, \tag{4.92}$$

$$i_3 = i_3' + i_3'' = 5 + 6 = 11 \text{ A}, \tag{4.93}$$

$$i_4 = i_4' + i_4'' = 5 - 6 = -1 \text{ A}. \tag{4.94}$$

You should verify that the currents given by Eqs. 4.91–4.94 are the correct values for the branch currents in the circuit shown in Fig. 4.62.

When applying superposition to linear circuits containing both independent and dependent sources, you must recognize that the dependent sources are never deactivated. Example 4.13 illustrates the application of superposition when a circuit contains both dependent and independent sources.

Example 4.13   Using Superposition to Solve a Circuit

Use the principle of superposition to find v_o in the circuit shown in Fig. 4.66.

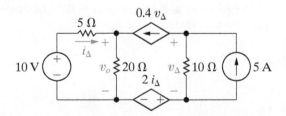

Figure 4.66 ▲ The circuit for Example 4.13.

Solution

We begin by finding the component of v_o resulting from the 10 V source. Figure 4.67 shows the circuit. With the 5 A source deactivated, v_Δ' must equal

$(-0.4v_\Delta')(10)$. Hence, v_Δ' must be zero, the branch containing the two dependent sources is open, and

$$v_o' = \frac{20}{25}(10) = 8 \text{ V}.$$

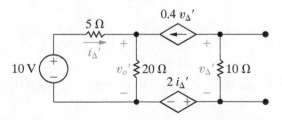

Figure 4.67 ▲ The circuit shown in Fig. 4.66 with the 5 A source deactivated.

When the 10 V source is deactivated, the circuit reduces to the one shown in Fig. 4.68. We have added a reference node and the node designations a, b, and c to aid the discussion. Summing the currents away from node a yields

$$\frac{v_o''}{20} + \frac{v_o''}{5} - 0.4v_\Delta'' = 0, \quad \text{or} \quad 5v_o'' - 8v_\Delta'' = 0.$$

Summing the currents away from node b gives

$$0.4v_\Delta'' + \frac{v_b - 2i_\Delta''}{10} - 5 = 0, \quad \text{or}$$

$$4v_\Delta'' + v_b - 2i_\Delta'' = 50.$$

We now use

$$v_b = 2i_\Delta'' + v_\Delta''$$

to find the value for v_Δ''. Thus,

$$5v_\Delta'' = 50, \quad \text{or} \quad v_\Delta'' = 10 \text{ V}.$$

From the node a equation,

$$5v_0'' = 80, \quad \text{or} \quad v_0'' = 16 \text{ V}.$$

The value of v_o is the sum of v_o' and v_o'', or 24 V.

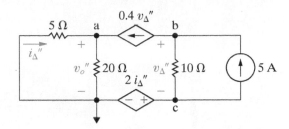

Figure 4.68 ▲ The circuit shown in Fig. 4.66 with the 10 V source deactivated.

NOTE: Assess your understanding of this material by trying Chapter Problems 4.93 and 4.98.

Practical Perspective

Circuits with Realistic Resistors
It is not possible to fabricate identical electrical components. For example, resistors produced from the same manufacturing process can vary in value by as much as 20%. Therefore, in creating an electrical system the designer must consider the impact that component variation will have on the performance of the system. One way to evaluate this impact is by performing sensitivity analysis. Sensitivity analysis permits the designer to calculate the impact of variations in the component values on the output of the system. We will see how this information enables a designer to specify an acceptable component value tolerance for each of the system's components.

Consider the circuit shown in Fig. 4.69. To illustrate sensitivity analysis, we will investigate the sensitivity of the node voltages v_1 and v_2 to changes in the resistor R_1. Using nodal analysis we can derive the expressions for v_1 and v_2 as functions of the circuit resistors and source currents. The results are given in Eqs. 4.95 and 4.96:

$$v_1 = \frac{R_1\{R_3R_4I_{g2} - [R_2(R_3 + R_4) + R_3R_4]I_{g1}\}}{(R_1 + R_2)(R_3 + R_4) + R_3R_4}, \tag{4.95}$$

$$v_2 = \frac{R_3R_4[(R_1 + R_2)I_{g2} - R_1I_{g1}]}{(R_1 + R_2)(R_3 + R_4) + R_3R_4}. \tag{4.96}$$

The sensitivity of v_1 with respect to R_1 is found by differentiating Eq. 4.95 with respect to R_1, and similarly the sensitivity of v_2 with respect to R_1 is found by differentiating Eq. 4.96 with respect to R_1. We get

$$\frac{dv_1}{dR_1} = \frac{[R_3R_4 + R_2(R_3 + R_4)]\{R_3R_4I_{g2} - [R_3R_4 + R_2(R_3 + R_4)]I_{g1}\}}{[(R_1 + R_2)(R_3 + R_4) + R_3R_4]^2}, \tag{4.97}$$

$$\frac{dv_2}{dR_1} = \frac{R_3R_4\{R_3R_4I_{g2} - [R_2(R_3 + R_4) + R_3R_4]I_{g1}\}}{[(R_1 + R_2)(R_3 + R_4) + R_3R_4]^2}. \tag{4.98}$$

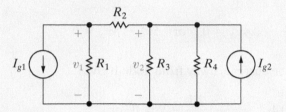

Figure 4.69 ▲ Circuit used to introduce sensitivity analysis.

We now consider an example with actual component values to illustrate the use of Eqs. 4.97 and 4.98.

EXAMPLE

Assume the nominal values of the components in the circuit in Fig. 4.69 are: $R_1 = 25\ \Omega$; $R_2 = 5\ \Omega$; $R_3 = 50\ \Omega$; $R_4 = 75\ \Omega$; $I_{g1} = 12$ A and $I_{g2} = 16$ A. Use sensitivity analysis to predict the values of v_1 and v_2 if the value of R_1 is different by 10% from its nominal value.

Solution

From Eqs. 4.95 and 4.96 we find the nominal values of v_1 and v_2. Thus

$$v_1 = \frac{25\{3750(16) - [5(125) + 3750]12\}}{30(125) + 3750} = 25\text{ V}, \tag{4.99}$$

and

$$v_2 = \frac{3750[30(16) - 25(12)]}{30(125) + 3750} = 90\text{ V}. \tag{4.100}$$

Now from Eqs. 4.97 and 4.98 we can find the sensitivity of v_1 and v_2 to changes in R_1. Hence

$$\frac{dv_1}{dR_1} = \frac{[3750 + 5(125)] - \{3750(16) - [3750 + 5(125)]12\}}{[(30)(125) + 3750]^2}$$

$$= \frac{7}{12}\text{ V}/\Omega, \tag{4.101}$$

and

$$\frac{dv_2}{dR_1} = \frac{3750\{3750(16) - [5(125) + 3750]12\}]}{(7500)^2}$$

$$= 0.5\text{ V}/\Omega. \tag{4.102}$$

How do we use the results given by Eqs. 4.101 and 4.102? Assume that R_1 is 10% less than its nominal value, that is, $R_1 = 22.5 \, \Omega$. Then $\Delta R_1 = -2.5 \, \Omega$ and Eq. 4.101 predicts Δv_1 will be

$$\Delta v_1 = \left(\frac{7}{12}\right)(-2.5) = -1.4583 \text{ V}.$$

Therefore, if R_1 is 10% less than its nominal value, our analysis predicts that v_1 will be

$$v_1 = 25 - 1.4583 = 23.5417 \text{ V}. \tag{4.103}$$

Similarly for Eq. 4.102 we have

$$\Delta v_2 = 0.5(-2.5) = -1.25 \text{ V},$$

$$v_2 = 90 - 1.25 = 88.75 \text{ V}. \tag{4.104}$$

We attempt to confirm the results in Eqs. 4.103 and 4.104 by substituting the value $R_1 = 22.5 \, \Omega$ into Eqs. 4.95 and 4.96. When we do, the results are

$$v_1 = 23.4780 \text{ V}, \tag{4.105}$$

$$v_2 = 88.6960 \text{ V}. \tag{4.106}$$

Why is there a difference between the values predicted from the sensitivity analysis and the exact values computed by substituting for R_1 in the equations for v_1 and v_2? We can see from Eqs. 4.97 and 4.98 that the sensitivity of v_1 and v_2 with respect to R_1 is a function of R_1, because R_1 appears in the denominator of both Eqs. 4.97 and 4.98. This means that as R_1 changes, the sensitivities change and hence we cannot expect Eqs. 4.97 and 4.98 to give exact results for large changes in R_1. Note that for a 10% change in R_1, the percent error between the predicted and exact values of v_1 and v_2 is small. Specifically, the percent error in $v_1 = 0.2713\%$ and the percent error in $v_2 = 0.0676\%$.

From this example, we can see that a tremendous amount of work is involved if we are to determine the sensitivity of v_1 and v_2 to changes in the remaining component values, namely R_2, R_3, R_4, I_{g1}, and I_{g2}. Fortunately, PSpice has a sensitivity function that will perform sensitivity analysis for us. The sensitivity function in PSpice calculates two types of sensitivity. The first is known as the one-unit sensitivity, and the second is known as the 1% sensitivity. In the example circuit, a one-unit change in a resistor would change its value by $1 \, \Omega$ and a one-unit change in a current source would change its value by $1 \, A$. In contrast, 1% sensitivity analysis determines the effect of changing resistors or sources by 1% of their nominal values.

The result of PSpice sensitivity analysis of the circuit in Fig. 4.69 is shown in Table 4.2. Because we are analyzing a linear circuit, we can use superposition to predict values of v_1 and v_2 if more than one component's value changes. For example, let us assume R_1 decreases to $24 \, \Omega$ and R_2 decreases to $4 \, \Omega$. From Table 4.2 we can combine the unit sensitivity of v_1 to changes in R_1 and R_2 to get

$$\frac{\Delta v_1}{\Delta R_1} + \frac{\Delta v_1}{\Delta R_2} = 0.5833 - 5.417 = -4.8337 \text{ V}/\Omega.$$

Similarly,

$$\frac{\Delta v_2}{\Delta R_1} + \frac{\Delta v_2}{\Delta R_2} = 0.5 + 6.5 = 7.0 \text{ V}/\Omega.$$

Thus if both R_1 and R_2 decreased by 1 Ω we would predict

$$v_1 = 25 + 4.8227 = 29.8337 \text{ V},$$

$$v_2 = 90 - 7 = 83 \text{ V}.$$

TABLE 4.2   PSpice Sensitivity Analysis Results

Element Name	Element Value	Element Sensitivity (Volts/Unit)	Normalized Sensitivity (Volts/Percent)
(a) DC Sensitivities of Node Voltage V1			
R1	25	0.5833	0.1458
R2	5	−5.417	−0.2708
R3	50	0.45	0.225
R4	75	0.2	0.15
IG1	12	−14.58	−1.75
IG2	16	12.5	2
(b) Sensitivities of Output V2			
R1	25	0.5	0.125
R2	5	6.5	0.325
R3	50	0.54	0.27
R4	75	0.24	0.18
IG1	12	−12.5	−1.5
IG2	16	15	2.4

If we substitute $R_1 = 24 \ \Omega$ and $R_2 = 4 \ \Omega$ into Eqs. 4.95 and 4.96 we get

$$v_1 = 29.793 \text{ V},$$

$$v_2 = 82.759 \text{ V}.$$

In both cases our predictions are within a fraction of a volt of the actual node voltage values.

Circuit designers use the results of sensitivity analysis to determine which component value variation has the greatest impact on the output of the circuit. As we can see from the PSpice sensitivity analysis in Table 4.2, the node voltages v_1 and v_2 are much more sensitive to changes in R_2 than to changes in R_1. Specifically, v_1 is (5.417/0.5833) or approximately 9 times more sensitive to changes in R_2 than to changes in R_1 and v_2 is (6.5/0.5) or 13 times more sensitive to changes in R_2 than to changes in R_1. Hence in the example circuit, the tolerance on R_2 must be more stringent than the tolerance on R_1 if it is important to keep v_1 and v_2 close to their nominal values.

NOTE: Assess your understanding of this Practical Perspective by trying Chapter Problems 4.105–4.107.

Summary

- For the topics in this chapter, mastery of some basic terms, and the concepts they represent, is necessary. Those terms are **node**, **essential node**, **path**, **branch**, **essential branch**, **mesh**, and **planar circuit**. Table 4.1 provides definitions and examples of these terms. (See page 91.)

- Two new circuit analysis techniques were introduced in this chapter:

  - The **node-voltage method** works with both planar and nonplanar circuits. A reference node is chosen from among the essential nodes. Voltage variables are assigned at the remaining essential nodes, and Kirchhoff's current law is used to write one equation per voltage variable. The number of equations is $n_e - 1$, where n_e is the number of essential nodes. (See page 93.)

  - The **mesh-current method** works only with planar circuits. Mesh currents are assigned to each mesh, and Kirchhoff's voltage law is used to write one equation per mesh. The number of equations is $b - (n - 1)$, where b is the number of branches in which the current is unknown, and n is the number of nodes. The mesh currents are used to find the branch currents. (See page 99.)

- Several new circuit simplification techniques were introduced in this chapter:

  - **Source transformations** allow us to exchange a voltage source (v_s) and a series resistor (R) for a current source (i_s) and a parallel resistor (R) and vice versa. The combinations must be equivalent in terms of their terminal voltage and current. Terminal equivalence holds provided that

    $$i_s = \frac{v_s}{R}.$$

    (See page 109.)

- **Thévenin equivalents** and **Norton equivalents** allow us to simplify a circuit comprised of sources and resistors into an equivalent circuit consisting of a voltage source and a series resistor (Thévenin) or a current source and a parallel resistor (Norton). The simplified circuit and the original circuit must be equivalent in terms of their terminal voltage and current. Thus keep in mind that (1) the Thévenin voltage (V_{Th}) is the open-circuit voltage across the terminals of the original circuit, (2) the Thévenin resistance (R_{Th}) is the ratio of the Thévenin voltage to the short-circuit current across the terminals of the original circuit; and (3) the Norton equivalent is obtained by performing a source transformation on a Thévenin equivalent. (See page 113.)

- **Maximum power transfer** is a technique for calculating the maximum value of p that can be delivered to a load, R_L. Maximum power transfer occurs when $R_L = R_{Th}$, the Thévenin resistance as seen from the resistor R_L. The equation for the maximum power transferred is

  $$p = \frac{V_{Th}^2}{4R_L}.$$

  (See page 120.)

- In a circuit with multiple independent sources, **superposition** allows us to activate one source at a time and sum the resulting voltages and currents to determine the voltages and currents that exist when all independent sources are active. Dependent sources are never deactivated when applying superposition. (See page 122.)

Problems

Section 4.1

4.1 For the circuit shown in Fig. P4.1, state the numerical value of the number of (a) branches, (b) branches where the current is unknown, (c) essential branches, (d) essential branches where the current is unknown, (e) nodes, (f) essential nodes, and (g) meshes.

Figure P4.1

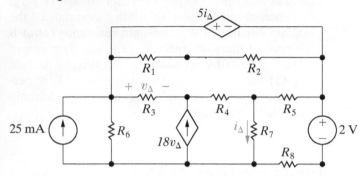

4.2 a) If only the essential nodes and branches are identified in the circuit in Fig. P4.1, how many simultaneous equations are needed to describe the circuit?

b) How many of these equations can be derived using Kirchhoff's current law?

c) How many must be derived using Kirchhoff's voltage law?

d) What two meshes should be avoided in applying the voltage law?

4.3 Assume the voltage v_s in the circuit in Fig. P4.3 is known. The resistors $R_1 - R_7$ are also known.

a) How many unknown currents are there?

b) How many independent equations can be written using Kirchhoff's current law (KCL)?

c) Write an independent set of KCL equations.

d) How many independent equations can be derived from Kirchhoff's voltage law (KVL)?

e) Write a set of independent KVL equations.

Figure P4.3

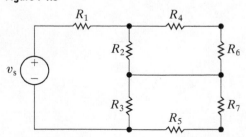

4.4 A current leaving a node is defined as positive.

a) Sum the currents at each node in the circuit shown in Fig. P4.3.

b) Show that any one of the equations in (a) can be derived from the remaining three equations.

4.5 a) How many separate parts does the circuit in Fig. P4.5 have?

b) How many nodes?

c) How many branches are there?

d) Assume that the lower node in each part of the circuit is joined by a single conductor. Repeat the calculations in (a)–(c).

Figure P4.5

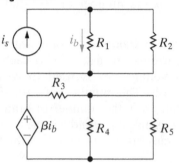

Section 4.2

4.6 Use the node-voltage method to find v_o in the circuit in Fig. P4.6.

PSPICE
MULTISIM

Figure P4.6

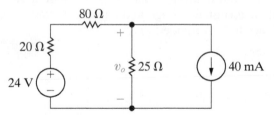

4.7 a) Find the power developed by the 40 mA current source in the circuit in Fig. P4.6.

PSPICE
MULTISIM

b) Find the power developed by the 24 V voltage source in the circuit in Fig. P4.6.

c) Verify that the total power developed equals the total power dissipated.

4.8 A 50 Ω resistor is connected in series with the 40 mA current source in the circuit in Fig. P4.6.

PSPICE
MULTISIM

a) Find v_o.

b) Find the power developed by the 40 mA current source.

c) Find the power developed by the 24 V voltage source.

d) Verify that the total power developed equals the total power dissipated.

e) What effect will any finite resistance connected in series with the 40 mA current source have on the value of v_o?

4.9 Use the node-voltage method to find how much power the 2 A source extracts from the circuit in Fig. P4.9.

PSPICE
MULTISIM

Figure P4.9

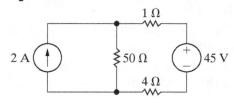

4.10 a) Use the node-voltage method to show that the output voltage v_o in the circuit in Fig. P4.10 is equal to the average value of the source voltages.

PSPICE
MULTISIM

b) Find v_o if $v_1 = 100$ V, $v_2 = 80$ V, and $v_3 = -60$ V.

Figure P4.10

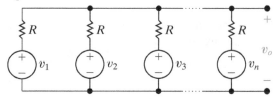

4.11 a) Use the node-voltage method to find the branch currents $i_a - i_c$ in the circuit shown in Fig. P4.11.

PSPICE
MULTISIM

b) Find the total power developed in the circuit.

Figure P4.11

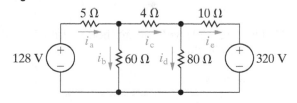

4.12 Use the node-voltage method to find v_1 and v_2 in the circuit in Fig. P4.12.

PSPICE
MULTISIM

Figure P4.12

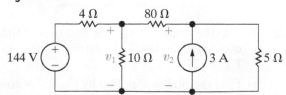

4.13 Use the node-voltage method to find v_1 and v_2 in the circuit shown in Fig. P4.13.

PSPICE
MULTISIM

Figure P4.13

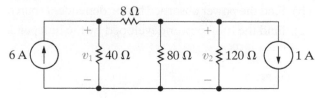

4.14 a) Use the node-voltage method to find v_1, v_2, and v_3 in the circuit in Fig. P4.14.

PSPICE
MULTISIM

b) How much power does the 40 V voltage source deliver to the circuit?

Figure P4.14

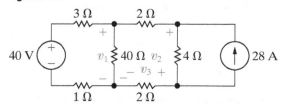

4.15 The circuit shown in Fig. P4.15 is a dc model of a residential power distribution circuit.

PSPICE
MULTISIM

a) Use the node-voltage method to find the branch currents $i_1 - i_6$.

b) Test your solution for the branch currents by showing that the total power dissipated equals the total power developed.

Figure P4.15

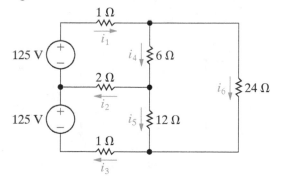

4.16 Use the node-voltage method to find the total power dissipated in the circuit in Fig. P4.16.

PSPICE
MULTISIM

Figure P4.16

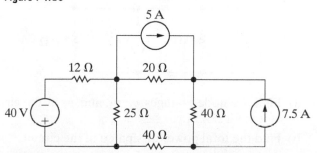

Section 4.3

4.17 a) Use the node-voltage method to find v_o in the circuit in Fig. P4.17.

PSPICE
MULTISIM

b) Find the power absorbed by the dependent source.

c) Find the total power developed by the independent sources.

Figure P4.17

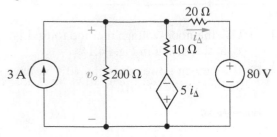

4.18 Use the node-voltage method to calculate the power delivered by the dependent voltage source in the circuit in Fig. P4.18.

PSPICE
MULTISIM

Figure P4.18

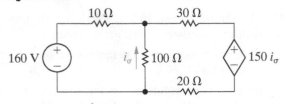

4.19 a) Use the node-voltage method to find the total power developed in the circuit in Fig. P4.19.

PSPICE
MULTISIM

b) Check your answer by finding the total power absorbed in the circuit.

Figure P4.19

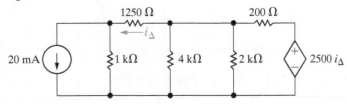

4.20 a) Use the node voltage method to find v_o for the circuit in Fig. P4.20.

b) Find the total power supplied in the circuit.

Figure P4.20

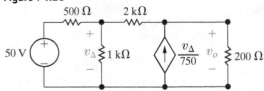

4.21 a) Find the node voltages v_1, v_2, and v_3 in the circuit in Fig. P4.21.

PSPICE
MULTISIM

b) Find the total power dissipated in the circuit.

Figure P4.21

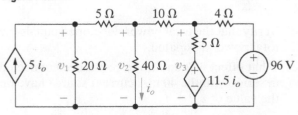

Section 4.4

4.22 a) Use the node-voltage method to find v_o and the power delivered by the 2 A current source in the circuit in Fig. P4.22. Use node a as the reference node.

PSPICE
MULTISIM

b) Repeat part (a), but use node b as the reference node.

c) Compare the choice of reference node in (a) and (b). Which is better, and why?

Figure P4.22

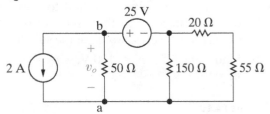

4.23 Use the node-voltage method to find the value of v_o in the circuit in Fig. P4.23.

PSPICE
MULTISIM

Figure P4.23

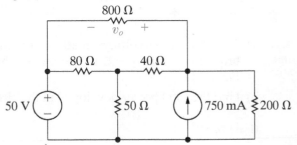

4.24 Use the node-voltage method to find i_o in the circuit in Fig. P4.24.

PSPICE
MULTISIM

Figure P4.24

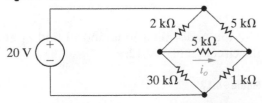

4.25 a) Use the node-voltage method to find the power dissipated in the 2 Ω resistor in the circuit in Fig. P4.25.

b) Find the power supplied by the 230 V source.

Figure P4.25

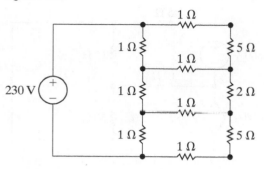

4.26 Use the node-voltage method to find v_o in the cir-
PSPICE cuit in Fig. P4.26.
MULTISIM

Figure P4.26

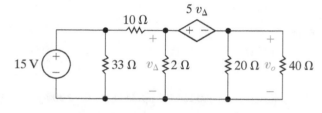

4.27 a) Use the node-voltage method to find the
PSPICE branch currents i_1, i_2, and i_3 in the circuit in
MULTISIM Fig. P4.27.

b) Check your solution for i_1, i_2, and i_3 by showing
that the power dissipated in the circuit equals
the power developed.

Figure P4.27

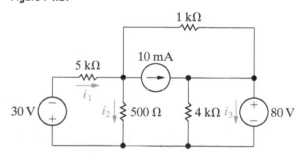

4.28 Use the node-voltage method to find the value of v_o
PSPICE in the circuit in Fig. P4.28.
MULTISIM

Figure P4.28

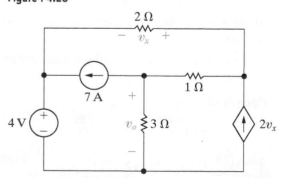

4.29 Assume you are a project engineer and one of
your staff is assigned to analyze the circuit shown
in Fig. P4.29. The reference node and node numbers given on the figure were assigned by the analyst. Her solution gives the values of v_1 and v_2 as
105 V and 85 V, respectively.

a) What values did the analyst use for the left-most
and right-most node voltages when writing KCL
equations at nodes 1 and 2?

b) Use the values supplied by the analyst to calculate the total power developed in the circuit
and the total power dissipated in the circuit.

c) Do you agree with the solution submitted by the
analyst?

Figure P4.29

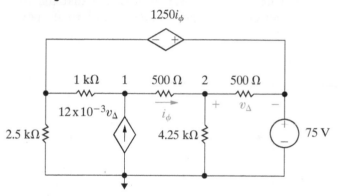

4.30 Use the node-voltage method to find the power
PSPICE developed by the 20 V source in the circuit in
MULTISIM Fig. P4.30.

Figure P4.30

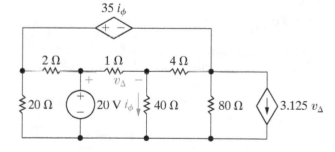

4.31 Show that when Eqs. 4.16, 4.17, and 4.19 are solved
for i_B, the result is identical to Eq. 2.25.

4.32 a) Use the mesh-current method to find the branch
PSPICE currents i_a, i_b, and i_c in the circuit in Fig. P4.32.
MULTISIM

b) Repeat (a) if the polarity of the 140 V source is
reversed.

Figure P4.32

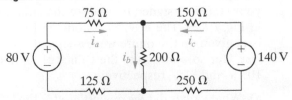

Section 4.5

4.33 Solve Problem 4.11 using the mesh-current method.

4.34 Solve Problem 4.15 using the mesh-current method.

4.35 Solve Problem 4.24 using the mesh-current method.

4.36 a) Use the mesh-current method to find the total power developed in the circuit in Fig. P4.36.

PSPICE
MULTISIM

b) Check your answer by showing that the total power developed equals the total power dissipated.

Figure P4.36

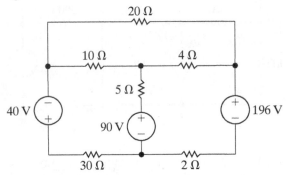

4.37 Solve Problem 4.25 using the mesh-current method.

Section 4.6

4.38 Solve Problem 4.18 using the mesh-current method.

4.39 Use the mesh-current method to find the power dissipated in the 15 Ω resistor in the circuit in Fig. P4.39.

PSPICE
MULTISIM

Figure P4.39

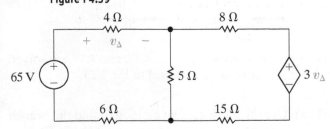

4.40 Use the mesh-current method to find the power delivered by the dependent voltage source in the circuit seen in Fig. P4.40.

PSPICE
MULTISIM

Figure P4.40

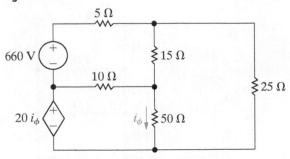

4.41 a) Use the mesh-current method to find v_o in the circuit in Fig. P4.41.

PSPICE
MULTISIM

b) Find the power delivered by the dependent source.

Figure P4.41

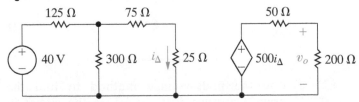

4.42 Use the mesh-current method to find the power developed in the dependent voltage source in the circuit in Fig. P4.42.

PSPICE
MULTISIM

Figure P4.42

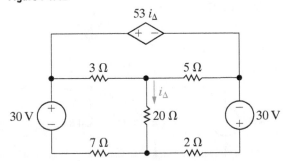

Section 4.7

4.43 a) Use the mesh-current method to solve for i_Δ in the circuit in Fig. P4.43.

PSPICE
MULTISIM

b) Find the power delivered by the independent current source.

c) Find the power delivered by the dependent voltage source.

Figure P4.43

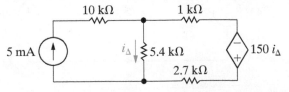

4.44 Solve Problem 4.13 using the mesh-current method.

4.45 Solve Problem 4.21 using the mesh-current method.

4.46 Use the mesh-current method to find the total power

PSPICE
MULTISIM
developed in the circuit in Fig. P4.46.

Figure P4.46

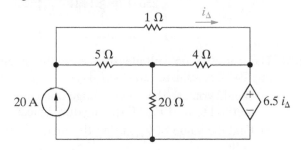

4.47 a) Use the mesh-current method to find how much power the 5 A current source delivers to the circuit in Fig. P4.47.

b) Find the total power delivered to the circuit.

c) Check your calculations by showing that the total power developed in the circuit equals the total power dissipated

Figure P4.47

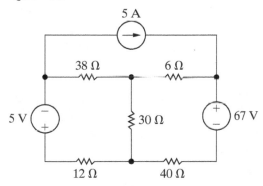

4.48 a) Use the mesh-current method to determine

PSPICE
MULTISIM
which sources in the circuit in Fig. P4.48 are generating power.

b) Find the total power dissipated in the circuit.

Figure P4.48

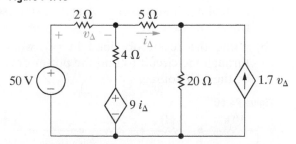

4.49 Use the mesh-current method to find the total

PSPICE
MULTISIM
power dissipated in the circuit in Fig. P4.49.

Figure P4.49

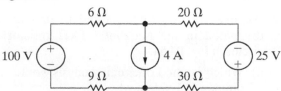

4.50 a) Assume the 100 V source in the circuit in Fig. P4.49 is changed to 67.5 V. Find the total power dissipated in the circuit.

b) Repeat (a) with the 4 A current source replaced by a short circuit.

c) Explain why the answers to (a) and (b) are the same.

c) Now assume you wish to change the value of the 25 V source, instead of the 100 V source, in the circuit in Fig. P4.49 to get the same power dissipated by the current source that you found in (a) and (b). Use the results in part (c) to calculate the new value of this voltage source.

4.51 Solve Problem 4.27 using the mesh-current method.

4.52 a) Use the mesh-current method to find the branch

PSPICE
MULTISIM
currents in $i_a - i_e$ in the circuit in Fig. P4.52.

b) Check your solution by showing that the total power developed in the circuit equals the total power dissipated.

Figure P4.52

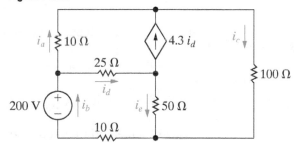

4.53 a) Find the branch currents $i_a - i_e$ for the circuit

PSPICE
MULTISIM
shown in Fig. P4.53.

b) Check your answers by showing that the total power generated equals the total power dissipated.

Figure P4.53

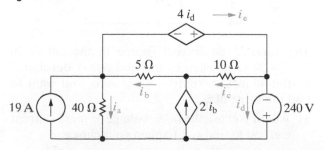

Section 4.8

4.54 Assume you have been asked to find the power
dissipated in the horizontal 1 kΩ resistor in the
circuit in Fig. P4.54.

PSPICE
MULTISIM

a) Which method of circuit analysis would you recommend? Explain why.

b) Use your recommended method of analysis to
find the power dissipated in the horizontal 1 kΩ
resistor.

c) Would you change your recommendation if the
problem had been to find the power developed
by the 10 mA current source? Explain.

d) Find the power delivered by the 10 mA current source.

Figure P4.54

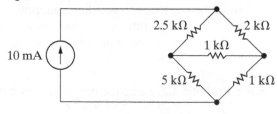

4.55 A 4 kΩ resistor is placed in parallel with the 10 mA
current source in the circuit in Fig. P4.54. Assume
you have been asked to calculate the power developed by the current source.

PSPICE
MULTISIM

a) Which method of circuit analysis would you recommend? Explain why.

b) Find the power developed by the current source.

4.56 a) Would you use the node-voltage or mesh-current
method to find the power absorbed by the
20 V source in the circuit in Fig. P4.56? Explain
your choice.

PSPICE
MULTISIM

b) Use the method you selected in (a) to find
the power.

Figure P4.56

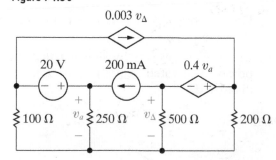

4.57 The variable dc current source in the circuit in
Fig. P4.57 is adjusted so that the power developed
by the 40 mA current source is zero. You want to
find the value of i_{dc}.

PSPICE
MULTISIM

a) Would you use the node-voltage or mesh-current
method to find i_{dc}? Explain your choice.

b) Use the method selected in (a) to find i_{dc}.

Figure P4.57

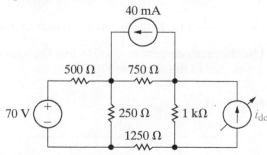

4.58 The variable dc voltage source in the circuit in
Fig. P4.58 is adjusted so that i_o is zero.

PSPICE
MULTISIM

a) Would you use the node-voltage or mesh-current
method to find V_{dc}? Explain your choice.

b) Find the value of V_{dc}, using the method selected
in (a).

c) Check your solution by showing the power
developed equals the power dissipated.

Figure P4.58

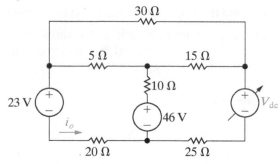

Section 4.9

4.59 a) Make a series of source transformations to find
the voltage v_0 in the circuit in Fig. P4.59.

b) Verify your solution using the mesh-current
method.

Figure P4.59

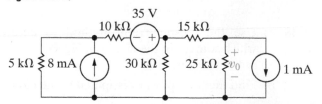

4.60 a) Find the current i_o in the circuit in Fig. P4.60
by making a succession of appropriate source
transformations.

PSPICE
MULTISIM

b) Using the result obtained in (a), work back
through the circuit to find the power developed
by the 50 V source.

Figure P4.60

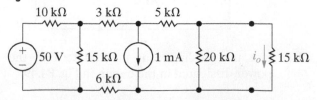

4.61 a) Use source transformations to find the current i_o in the circuit in Fig. P4.61.

PSPICE

MULTISIM

b) Verify your solution by using the node-voltage method to find i_o.

Figure P4.61

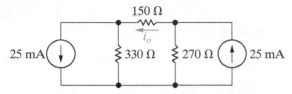

4.62 a) Use a series of source transformations to find i_o in the circuit in Fig. P4.62.

PSPICE

MULTISIM

b) Verify your solution by using the mesh-current method to find i_o.

Figure P4.62

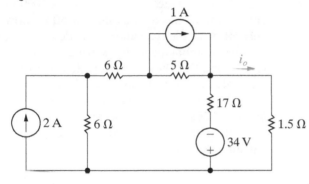

4.63 a) Use source transformations to find v_o in the circuit in Fig. P4.63.

PSPICE

MULTISIM

b) Find the power developed by the 520 V source.

c) Find the power developed by the 1 A current source.

d) Verify that the total power developed equals the total power dissipated.

Figure P4.63

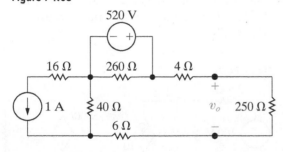

Section 4.10

4.64 Find the Thévenin equivalent with respect to the terminals a,b for the circuit in Fig. P4.64.

PSPICE

MULTISIM

Figure P4.64

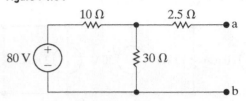

4.65 Find the Norton equivalent with respect to the terminals a,b for the circuit in Fig. P4.65.

Figure P4.65

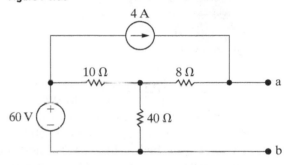

4.66 Find the Norton equivalent with respect to the terminals a,b for the circuit in Fig. P4.66.

PSPICE

MULTISIM

Figure P4.66

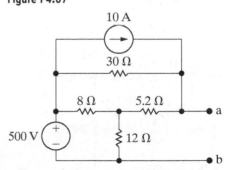

4.67 Find the Thévenin equivalent with respect to the terminals a,b for the circuit in Fig. P4.67.

PSPICE

MULTISIM

Figure P4.67

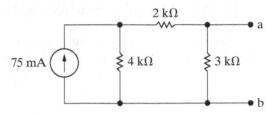

4.68 Find the Norton equivalent with respect to the terminals a,b in the circuit in Fig. P4.68.

PSPICE

MULTISIM

Figure P4.68

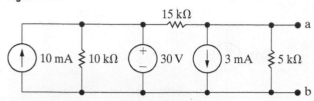

4.69 A Thévenin equivalent can also be determined from measurements made at the pair of terminals of interest. Assume the following measurements were made at the terminals a,b in the circuit in Fig. P4.69.

When a 20 Ω resistor is connected to the terminals a,b, the voltage v_{ab} is measured and found to be 100 V.

When a 50 Ω resistor is connected to the terminals a,b, the voltage is measured and found to be 200 V.

Find the Thévenin equivalent of the network with respect to the terminals a,b.

Figure P4.69

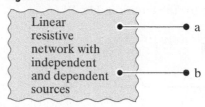

4.70 An automobile battery, when connected to a car radio, provides 12.5 V to the radio. When connected to a set of headlights, it provides 11.7 V to the headlights. Assume the radio can be modeled as a 6.25 Ω resistor and the headlights can be modeled as a 0.65 Ω resistor. What are the Thévenin and Norton equivalents for the battery?

4.71 Determine i_o and v_o in the circuit shown in Fig. P4.71 when R_o is a resistor from Appendix H such that $100 \Omega \leq R_o < 200 \Omega$.

Figure P4.71

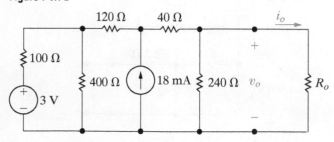

4.72 A voltmeter with a resistance of 85.5 kΩ is used to measure the voltage v_{ab} in the circuit in Fig. P4.72.
a) What is the voltmeter reading?
b) What is the percentage of error in the voltmeter reading if the percentage of error is defined as $[(\text{measured} - \text{actual})/\text{actual}] \times 100$?

Figure P4.72

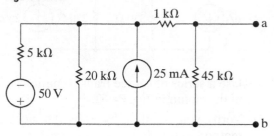

4.73 The Wheatstone bridge in the circuit shown in Fig. P4.73 is balanced when R_3 equals 3000 Ω. If the galvanometer has a resistance of 50 Ω, how much current will the galvanometer detect, when the bridge is unbalanced by setting R_3 to 3003 Ω? (*Hint:* Find the Thévenin equivalent with respect to the galvanometer terminals when $R_3 = 3003 \Omega$. Note that once we have found this Thévenin equivalent, it is easy to find the amount of unbalanced current in the galvanometer branch for different galvanometer movements.)

Figure P4.73

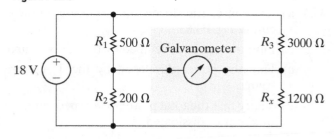

4.74 Determine the Thévenin equivalent with respect to the terminals a,b for the circuit shown in Fig. P4.74.

Figure P4.74

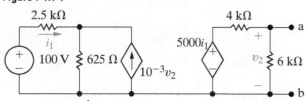

4.75 Find the Norton equivalent with respect to the terminals a,b for the circuit seen in Fig. P4.75.

PSPICE

MULTISIM

Figure P4.75

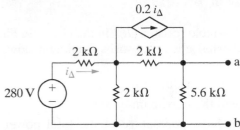

4.76 When an ammeter is used to measure the current i_ϕ in the circuit shown in Fig. P4.76, it reads 6 A.

PSPICE

MULTISIM

a) What is the resistance of the ammeter?

b) What is the percentage of error in the current measurement?

Figure P4.76

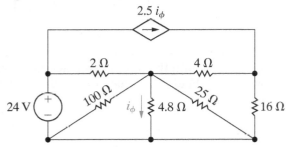

Section 4.11

4.77 a) Find the Thévenin equivalent resistance with respect to the terminals a,b in the circuit in Fig. P4.64 without finding either the open circuit voltage or the short circuit current.

b) Find the Norton equivalent resistance with respect to the terminals a,b in the circuit in Fig. P4.66 without finding either the open circuit voltage or the short circuit current.

4.78 a) Find the Thévenin equivalent with respect to the terminals a,b for the circuit in Fig. P4.78 by finding the open-circuit voltage and the short-circuit current.

PSPICE

MULTISIM

b) Solve for the Thévenin resistance by removing the independent sources. Compare your result to the Thévenin resistance found in (a).

Figure P4.78

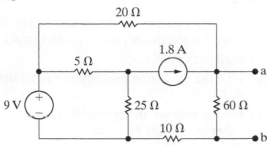

4.79 Find the Thévenin equivalent with respect to the terminals a,b in the circuit in Fig. P4.79.

Figure P4.79

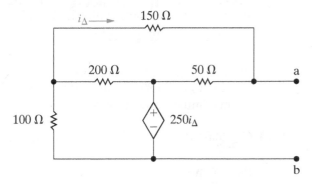

4.80 Find the Thévenin equivalent with respect to the terminals a,b in the circuit in Fig. P4.80.

Figure P4.80

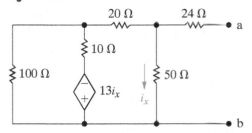

4.81 Find the Norton equivalent with respect to the terminals a,b for the circuit seen in Fig. P4.81.

Figure P4.81

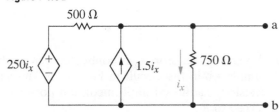

Section 4.12

4.82 The variable resistor in the circuit in Fig. P4.82 is
adjusted for maximum power transfer to R_o.

PSPICE

MULTISIM

a) Find the value of R_o.

b) Find the maximum power that can be delivered
to R_o.

c) Find a resistor in Appendix H closest to the
value in part (a). How much power is delivered
to this resistor?

Figure P4.82

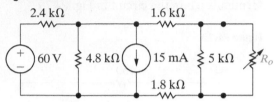

4.83 What percentage of the total power developed in
the circuit in Fig. P4.82 is delivered to R_o when R_o is
set for maximum power transfer?

PSPICE

MULTISIM

4.84 a) Calculate the power delivered for each value of
R_o used in Problem 4.71.

b) Plot the power delivered to R_o versus the resistance R_o.

c) At what value of R_o is the power delivered to R_o
a maximum?

4.85 a) Find the value of the variable resistor R_o in the
circuit in Fig. P4.85 that will result in maximum
power dissipation in the 6 Ω resistor. (*Hint:*
Hasty conclusions could be hazardous to
your career.)

b) What is the maximum power that can be delivered to the 6 Ω resistor?

Figure P4.85

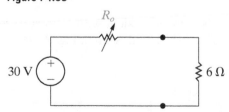

4.86 A variable resistor R_o is connected across the terminals a,b in the circuit in Fig. P4.75. The variable
resistor is adjusted until maximum power is transferred to R_o.

PSPICE

MULTISIM

a) Find the value of R_o.

b) Find the maximum power delivered to R_o.

c) Find the percentage of the total power developed in the circuit that is delivered to R_o.

d) Find the resistor from Appendix H closest in
value to the R_o. from part (a).

e) Find the percentage of the total power developed in the circuit that is delivered to the resistor in part (d).

4.87 The variable resistor (R_o) in the circuit in Fig. P4.87
is adjusted until it absorbs maximum power from
the circuit.

PSPICE

MULTISIM

a) Find the value of R_o.

b) Find the maximum power.

c) Find the percentage of the total power developed in the circuit that is delivered to R_o.

Figure P4.87

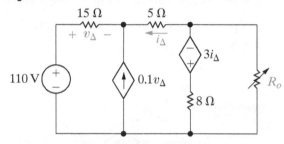

4.88 The variable resistor (R_o) in the circuit in Fig. P4.88
is adjusted until the power dissipated in the resistor
is 250 W. Find the values of R_o that satisfy this
condition.

PSPICE

MULTISIM

Figure P4.88

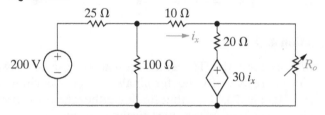

4.89 The variable resistor in the circuit in Fig. P4.89 is
adjusted for maximum power transfer to R_o.

PSPICE

MULTISIM

a) Find the numerical value of R_o.

b) Find the maximum power delivered to R_o.

c) How much power does the 180 V source deliver
to the circuit when R_o is adjusted to the value
found in (a)?

Figure P4.89

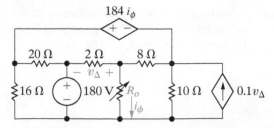

4.90 The variable resistor (R_L) in the circuit in Fig. P4.90 is adjusted for maximum power transfer to R_L.

PSPICE
MULTISIM

a) Find the numerical value of R_L.

b) Find the maximum power transferred to R_L.

Figure P4.90

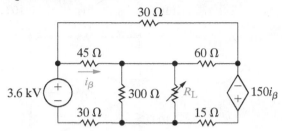

4.91 The variable resistor (R_o) in the circuit in Fig. P4.91 is adjusted for maximum power transfer to R_o.

PSPICE
MULTISIM

a) Find the value of R_o.

b) Find the maximum power that can be delivered to R_o.

c) What percentage of the total power developed in the circuit is delivered to R_o found in part(a)?

d) If R_o is selected from Appendix H, which resistor value will result in the greatest amount of power delivered to R_o?

Figure P4.91

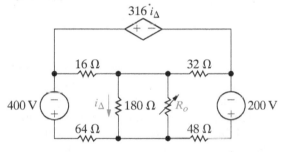

Section 4.13

4.92 a) In the circuit in Fig. P4.92, before the 5 mA current source is attached to the terminals a,b, the current i_o is calculated and found to be 3.5 mA. Use superposition to find the value of i_o after the current source is attached.

PSPICE
MULTISIM

b) Verify your solution by finding i_o when all three sources are acting simultaneously.

Figure P4.92

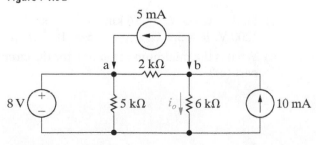

4.93 a) Use the principle of superposition to find the voltage v in the circuit of Fig. P4.93.

PSPICE
MULTISIM

b) Find the power dissipated in the 10 Ω resistor.

Figure P4.93

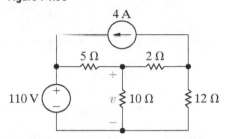

4.94 Use superposition to solve for i_o and v_o in the circuit in Fig. P4.94.

Figure P4.94

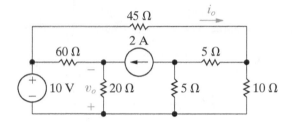

4.95 Use the principle of superposition to find the current i_o in the circuit shown in Fig. P4.95.

PSPICE
MULTISIM

Figure P4.95

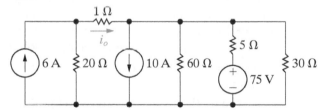

4.96 Use the principle of superposition to find the voltage v_o in the circuit in Fig. P4.96.

PSPICE
MULTISIM

Figure P4.96

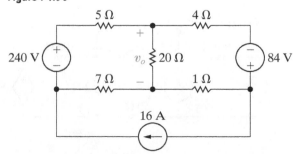

4.97 Use the principle of superposition to find v_o in the circuit in Fig. P4.97.

PSPICE
MULTISIM

Figure P4.97

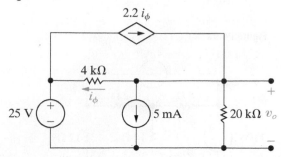

4.98 Use the principle of superposition to find the current i in the circuit of Fig. P4.98.

PSPICE
MULTISIM

Figure P4.98

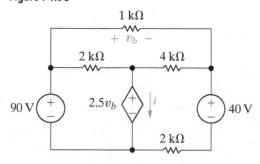

Sections 4.1–4.13

4.99 Assume your supervisor has asked you to determine the power developed by the 50 V source in the circuit in Fig. P4.99. Before calculating the power developed by the 50 V source, the supervisor asks you to submit a proposal describing how you plan to attack the problem. Furthermore, he asks you to explain why you have chosen your proposed method of solution.

a) Describe your plan of attack, explaining your reasoning.

b) Use the method you have outlined in (a) to find the power developed by the 50 V source.

Figure P4.99

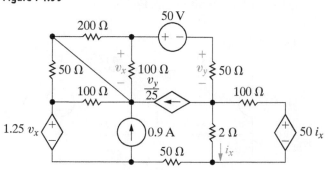

4.100 Find i_1 and i_2 in the circuit in Fig. P4.100.

PSPICE
MULTISIM

Figure P4.100

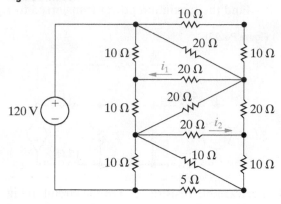

4.101 Find v_1, v_2, and v_3 in the circuit in Fig. P4.101.

PSPICE
MULTISIM

Figure P4.101

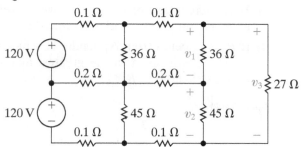

4.102 Two ideal dc voltage sources are connected by electrical conductors that have a resistance of r Ω/m, as shown in Fig. P4.102. A load having a resistance of R Ω moves between the two voltage sources. Let x equal the distance between the load and the source v_1, and let L equal the distance between the sources.

a) Show that

$$v = \frac{v_1 RL + R(v_2 - v_1)x}{RL + 2rLx - 2rx^2}.$$

b) Show that the voltage v will be minimum when

$$x = \frac{L}{v_2 - v_1}\left[-v_1 \pm \sqrt{v_1 v_2 - \frac{R}{2rL}(v_1 - v_2)^2}\right].$$

c) Find x when $L = 16$ km, $v_1 = 1000$ V, $v_2 = 1200$ V, $R = 3.9$ Ω, and $r = 5 \times 10^{-5}$ Ω/m.

d) What is the minimum value of v for the circuit of part (c)?

Figure P4.102

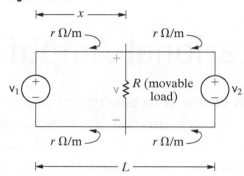

4.103 Laboratory measurements on a dc voltage source
PSPICE yield a terminal voltage of 75 V with no load con-
MULTISIM nected to the source and 60 V when loaded with a
20 Ω resistor.

a) What is the Thévenin equivalent with respect to
   the terminals of the dc voltage source?

b) Show that the Thévenin resistance of the source
   is given by the expression

$$R_{Th} = \left(\frac{v_{Th}}{v_o} - 1 \right) R_L,$$

where

v_{Th} = the Thévenin voltage,

v_o = the terminal voltage corresponding
    to the load resistance R_L.

4.104 For the circuit in Fig. 4.69 derive the expressions for
DESIGN the sensitivity of v_1 and v_2 to changes in the source
PROBLEM currents I_{g1} and I_{g2}.

4.105 Assume the nominal values for the components in
PRACTICAL the circuit in Fig. 4.69 are: $R_1 = 25 \ \Omega$; $R_2 = 5 \ \Omega$;
PERSPECTIVE $R_3 = 50 \ \Omega$; $R_4 = 75 \ \Omega$; $I_{g1} = 12$ A; and $I_{g2} = 16$ A.
PSPICE Predict the values of v_1 and v_2 if I_{g1} decreases to
MULTISIM 11 A and all other components stay at their nominal
values. Check your predictions using a tool like
PSpice or MATLAB.

4.106 Repeat Problem 4.105 if I_{g2} increases to 17 A, and
PRACTICAL all other components stay at their nominal values.
PERSPECTIVE Check your predictions using a tool like PSpice or
MATLAB.

4.107 Repeat Problem 4.105 if I_{g1} decreases to 11 A and
PRACTICAL I_{g2} increases to 17 A. Check your predictions using
PERSPECTIVE a tool like PSpice or MATLAB.
PSPICE
MULTISIM

4.108 Use the results given in Table 4.2 to predict the val-
PRACTICAL ues of v_1 and v_2 if R_1 and R_3 increase to 10% above
PERSPECTIVE their nominal values and R_2 and R_4 decrease to
10% below their nominal values. I_{g1} and I_{g2} remain
at their nominal values. Compare your predicted
values of v_1 and v_2 with their actual values.

The Operational Amplifier

✓ CHAPTER OBJECTIVES

1 Be able to name the five op amp terminals and describe and use the voltage and current constraints and the resulting simplifications they lead to in an ideal op amp.

2 Be able to analyze simple circuits containing ideal op amps, and recognize the following op amp circuits: inverting amplifier, summing amplifier, noninverting amplifier, and difference amplifier.

3 Understand the more realistic model for an op amp and be able to use this model to analyze simple circuits containing op amps.

The electronic circuit known as an operational amplifier has become increasingly important. However, a detailed analysis of this circuit requires an understanding of electronic devices such as diodes and transistors. You may wonder, then, why we are introducing the circuit before discussing the circuit's electronic components. There are several reasons. First, you can develop an appreciation for how the operational amplifier can be used as a circuit building block by focusing on its terminal behavior. At an introductory level, you need not fully understand the operation of the electronic components that govern terminal behavior. Second, the circuit model of the operational amplifier requires the use of a dependent source. Thus you have a chance to use this type of source in a practical circuit rather than as an abstract circuit component. Third, you can combine the operational amplifier with resistors to perform some very useful functions, such as scaling, summing, sign changing, and subtracting. Finally, after introducing inductors and capacitors in Chapter 6, we can show you how to use the operational amplifier to design integrating and differentiating circuits.

Our focus on the terminal behavior of the operational amplifier implies taking a black box approach to its operation; that is, we are not interested in the internal structure of the amplifier nor in the currents and voltages that exist in this structure. The important thing to remember is that the internal behavior of the amplifier accounts for the voltage and current constraints imposed at the terminals. (For now, we ask that you accept these constraints on faith.)

Practical Perspective

Strain Gages

How could you measure the amount of bending in a metal bar such as the one shown in the figure without physically contacting the bar? One method would be to use a strain gage. A strain gage is a type of **transducer**. A transducer is a device that measures a quantity by converting it into a more convenient form. The quantity we wish to measure in the metal bar is the bending angle, but measuring the angle directly is quite difficult and could even be dangerous. Instead, we attach a strain gage (shown in the line drawing here) to the metal bar. A strain gage is a grid of thin wires whose resistance changes when the wires are lengthened or shortened:

$$\Delta R = 2R\frac{\Delta L}{L}$$

where R is the resistance of the gage at rest, $\Delta L/L$ is the fractional lengthening of the gage (which is the definition of "strain"), the constant 2 is typical of the manufacturer's gage factor, and ΔR is the change in resistance due to the bending of the bar. Typically, pairs of strain gages are attached to opposite sides of a bar. When the bar is bent, the wires in one pair of gages get longer and thinner, increasing the resistance, while the wires in the other pair of gages get shorter and thicker, decreasing the resistance.

But how can the change in resistance be measured? One way would be to use an ohmmeter. However, the change in resistance experienced by the strain gage is typically much smaller than could be accurately measured by an ohmmeter. Usually the pairs of strain gages are connected to form a Wheatstone bridge, and the voltage difference between two legs of the bridge is measured. In order to make an accurate measurement of the voltage difference, we use an operational amplifier circuit to amplify, or increase, the voltage difference. After we introduce the operational amplifier and some of the important circuits that employ these devices, we will present the circuit used together with the strain gages for measuring the amount of bending in a metal bar.

The operational amplifier circuit first came into existence as a basic building block in analog computers. It was referred to as *operational* because it was used to implement the mathematical operations of integration, differentiation, addition, sign changing, and scaling. In recent years, the range of application has broadened beyond implementing mathematical operations; however, the original name for the circuit persists. Engineers and technicians have a penchant for creating technical jargon; hence the operational amplifier is widely known as the **op amp**.

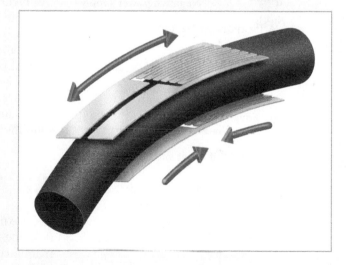

Ron Chapple/Corbis

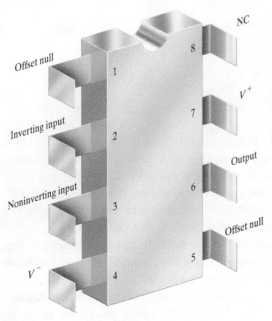

Figure 5.1 ▲ The eight-lead DIP package (top view).

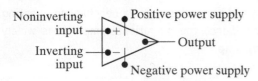

Figure 5.2 ▲ The circuit symbol for an operational amplifier (op amp).

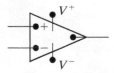

Figure 5.3 ▲ A simplified circuit symbol for an op amp.

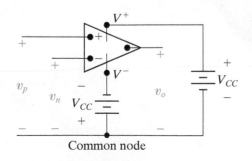

Figure 5.4 ▲ Terminal voltage variables.

5.1 Operational Amplifier Terminals

Because we are stressing the terminal behavior of the operational amplifier (op amp), we begin by discussing the terminals on a commercially available device. In 1968, Fairchild Semiconductor introduced an op amp that has found widespread acceptance: the μA741. (The μA prefix is used by Fairchild to indicate a microcircuit fabrication of the amplifier.) This amplifier is available in several different packages. For our discussion, we assume an eight-lead DIP.[1] Figure 5.1 shows a top view of the package, with the terminal designations given alongside the terminals. The terminals of primary interest are

- inverting input,
- noninverting input,
- output,
- positive power supply (V^+),
- negative power supply (V^-).

The remaining three terminals are of little or no concern. The offset null terminals may be used in an auxiliary circuit to compensate for a degradation in performance because of aging and imperfections. However, the degradation in most cases is negligible, so the offset terminals often are unused and play a secondary role in circuit analysis. Terminal 8 is of no interest simply because it is an unused terminal; NC stands for no connection, which means that the terminal is not connected to the amplifier circuit.

Figure 5.2 shows a widely used circuit symbol for an op amp that contains the five terminals of primary interest. Using word labels for the terminals is inconvenient in circuit diagrams, so we simplify the terminal designations in the following way. The noninverting input terminal is labeled plus ($+$), and the inverting input terminal is labeled minus ($-$). The power supply terminals, which are always drawn outside the triangle, are marked V^+ and V^-. The terminal at the apex of the triangular box is always understood to be the output terminal. Figure 5.3 summarizes these simplified designations.

5.2 Terminal Voltages and Currents

We are now ready to introduce the terminal voltages and currents used to describe the behavior of the op amp. The voltage variables are measured from a common reference node.[2] Figure 5.4 shows the voltage variables with their reference polarities.

All voltages are considered as voltage rises from the common node. This convention is the same as that used in the node-voltage method of analysis. A positive supply voltage (V_{CC}) is connected between V^+ and the common node. A negative supply voltage ($-V_{CC}$) is connected between V^- and the common node. The voltage between the inverting input terminal and the common node is denoted v_n. The voltage between the noninverting input terminal and the common node is designated as v_p. The voltage between the output terminal and the common node is denoted v_o.

---

[1] DIP is an abbreviation for *dual in-line package*. This means that the terminals on each side of the package are in line, and that the terminals on opposite sides of the package also line up.

[2] The common node is external to the op amp. It is the reference terminal of the circuit in which the op amp is embedded.

Figure 5.5 shows the current variables with their reference directions. Note that all the current reference directions are into the terminals of the operational amplifier: i_n is the current into the inverting input terminal; i_p is the current into the noninverting input terminal; i_o is the current into the output terminal; i_{c^+} is the current into the positive power supply terminal; and i_{c^-} is the current into the negative power supply terminal.

The terminal behavior of the op amp as a linear circuit element is characterized by constraints on the input voltages and the input currents. The voltage constraint is derived from the voltage transfer characteristic of the op amp integrated circuit and is pictured in Fig. 5.6.

The voltage transfer characteristic describes how the output voltage varies as a function of the input voltages; that is, how voltage is transferred from the input to the output. Note that for the op amp, the output voltage is a function of the difference between the input voltages, $v_p - v_n$. The equation for the voltage transfer characteristic is

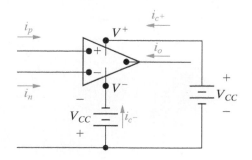

Figure 5.5 ▲ Terminal current variables.

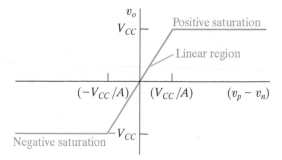

Figure 5.6 ▲ The voltage transfer characteristic of an op amp.

$$v_o = \begin{cases} -V_{CC} & A(v_p - v_n) < -V_{CC}, \\ A(v_p - v_n) & -V_{CC} \le A(v_p - v_n) \le +V_{CC}, \\ +V_{CC} & A(v_p - v_n) > +V_{CC}. \end{cases} \qquad (5.1)$$

We see from Fig. 5.6 and Eq. 5.1 that the op amp has three distinct regions of operation. When the magnitude of the input voltage difference ($|v_p - v_n|$) is small, the op amp behaves as a linear device, as the output voltage is a linear function of the input voltages. Outside this linear region, the output of the op amp saturates, and the op amp behaves as a nonlinear device, because the output voltage is no longer a linear function of the input voltages. When it is operating linearly, the op amp's output voltage is equal to the difference in its input voltages times the multiplying constant, or **gain**, A.

When we confine the op amp to its linear operating region, a constraint is imposed on the input voltages, v_p and v_n. The constraint is based on typical numerical values for V_{CC} and A in Eq. 5.1. For most op amps, the recommended dc power supply voltages seldom exceed 20 V, and the gain, A, is rarely less than 10,000, or 10^4. We see from both Fig. 5.6 and Eq. 5.1 that in the linear region, the magnitude of the input voltage difference ($|v_p - v_n|$) must be less than $20/10^4$, or 2 mV.

Typically, node voltages in the circuits we study are much larger than 2 mV, so a voltage difference of less than 2 mV means the two voltages are essentially equal. Thus, when an op amp is constrained to its linear operating region and the node voltages are much larger than 2 mV, the constraint on the input voltages of the op amp is

$$v_p = v_n. \qquad (5.2)$$

◀ **Input voltage constraint for ideal op amp**

Note that Eq. 5.2 characterizes the relationship between the input voltages for an ideal op amp; that is, an op amp whose value of A is infinite.

The input voltage constraint in Eq. 5.2 is called the *virtual short* condition at the input of the op amp. It is natural to ask how the virtual short is maintained at the input of the op amp when the op amp is embedded in a circuit, thus ensuring linear operation. The answer is that a signal is fed back from the output terminal to the inverting input terminal. This configuration is known as **negative feedback** because the signal fed back from the output subtracts from the input signal. The negative feedback causes the input voltage difference to decrease. Because the output voltage is proportional to the input voltage difference, the output voltage is also decreased, and the op amp operates in its linear region.

If a circuit containing an op amp does not provide a negative feedback path from the op amp output to the inverting input, then the op amp will normally saturate. The difference in the input signals must be extremely small to prevent saturation with no negative feedback. But even if the circuit provides a negative feedback path for the op amp, linear operation is not ensured. So how do we know whether the op amp is operating in its linear region?

The answer is, we don't! We deal with this dilemma by assuming linear operation, performing the circuit analysis, and then checking our results for contradictions. For example, suppose we assume that an op amp in a circuit is operating in its linear region, and we compute the output voltage of the op amp to be 10 V. On examining the circuit, we discover that V_{CC} is 6 V, resulting in a contradiction, because the op amp's output voltage can be no larger than V_{CC}. Thus our assumption of linear operation was invalid, and the op amp output must be saturated at 6 V.

We have identified a constraint on the input voltages that is based on the voltage transfer characteristic of the op amp integrated circuit, the assumption that the op amp is restricted to its linear operating region and to typical values for V_{CC} and A. Equation 5.2 represents the voltage constraint for an ideal op amp, that is, with a value of A that is infinite.

We now turn our attention to the constraint on the input currents. Analysis of the op amp integrated circuit reveals that the equivalent resistance seen by the input terminals of the op amp is very large, typically 1 MΩ or more. Ideally, the equivalent input resistance is infinite, resulting in the current constraint

Input current constraint for ideal op amp ▶

$$i_p = i_n = 0. \tag{5.3}$$

Note that the current constraint is not based on assuming the op amp is confined to its linear operating region as was the voltage constraint. Together, Eqs. 5.2 and 5.3 form the constraints on terminal behavior that define our ideal op amp model.

From Kirchhoff's current law we know that the sum of the currents entering the operational amplifier is zero, or

$$i_p + i_n + i_o + i_{c^+} + i_{c^-} = 0. \tag{5.4}$$

Substituting the constraint given by Eq. 5.3 into Eq. 5.4 gives

$$i_o = -(i_{c^+} + i_{c^-}). \tag{5.5}$$

The significance of Eq. 5.5 is that, even though the current at the input terminals is negligible, there may still be appreciable current at the output terminal.

Before we start analyzing circuits containing op amps, let's further simplify the circuit symbol. When we know that the amplifier is operating within its linear region, the dc voltages $\pm V_{CC}$ do not enter into the circuit equations.

In this case, we can remove the power supply terminals from the symbol and the dc power supplies from the circuit, as shown in Fig. 5.7. A word of caution: Because the power supply terminals have been omitted, there is a danger of inferring from the symbol that $i_p + i_n + i_o = 0$. We have already noted that such is not the case; that is, $i_p + i_n + i_o + i_{c^+} + i_{c^-} = 0$. In other words, the ideal op amp model constraint that $i_p = i_n = 0$ does not imply that $i_o = 0$.

Note that the positive and negative power supply voltages do not have to be equal in magnitude. In the linear operating region, v_o must lie between the two supply voltages. For example, if $V^+ = 15$ V and $V^- = -10$ V, then -10 V $\leq v_o \leq 15$ V. Be aware also that the value of A is not constant under all operating conditions. For now, however, we assume that it is. A discussion of how and why the value of A can change must be delayed until after you have studied the electronic devices and components used to fabricate an amplifier.

Example 5.1 illustrates the judicious application of Eqs. 5.2 and 5.3. When we use these equations to predict the behavior of a circuit containing an op amp, in effect we are using an ideal model of the device.

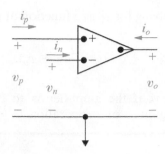

Figure 5.7 ▲ The op amp symbol with the power supply terminals removed.

Example 5.1   Analyzing an Op Amp Circuit

The op amp in the circuit shown in Fig. 5.8 is ideal.

a) Calculate v_o if $v_a = 1$ V and $v_b = 0$ V.

b) Repeat (a) for $v_a = 1$ V and $v_b = 2$ V.

c) If $v_a = 1.5$ V, specify the range of v_b that avoids amplifier saturation.

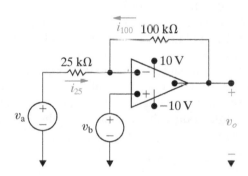

Figure 5.8 ▲ The circuit for Example 5.1.

Solution

a) Because a negative feedback path exists from the op amp's output to its inverting input through the 100 kΩ resistor, let's assume the op amp is confined to its linear operating region. We can write a node-voltage equation at the inverting input terminal. The voltage at the inverting input terminal is 0, as $v_p = v_b = 0$ from the connected voltage source, and $v_n = v_p$ from the voltage constraint Eq. 5.2. The node-voltage equation at v_n is thus

$$i_{25} = i_{100} - i_n.$$

From Ohm's law,

$$i_{25} = (v_a - v_n)/25 = \frac{1}{25} \text{ mA},$$

$$i_{100} = (v_o - v_n)/100 = v_o/100 \text{ mA}.$$

The current constraint requires $i_n = 0$. Substituting the values for the three currents into the node-voltage equation, we obtain

$$\frac{1}{25} + \frac{v_o}{100} = 0.$$

Hence, v_o is -4 V. Note that because v_o lies between ± 10 V, the op amp is in its linear region of operation.

b) Using the same process as in (a), we get

$$v_p = v_b = v_n = 2 \text{ V},$$

$$i_{25} = \frac{v_a - v_n}{25} = \frac{1-2}{25} = -\frac{1}{25} \text{ mA},$$

$$i_{100} = \frac{v_o - v_n}{100} = \frac{v_o - 2}{100} \text{ mA},$$

$$i_{25} = -i_{100}.$$

Therefore, $v_o = 6$ V. Again, v_o lies within ± 10 V.

c) As before, $v_n = v_p = v_b$, and $i_{25} = -i_{100}$. Because $v_a = 1.5$ V,

$$\frac{1.5 - v_b}{25} = -\frac{v_o - v_b}{100}.$$

Solving for v_b as a function of v_o gives

$$v_b = \frac{1}{5}(6 + v_o).$$

Now, if the amplifier is to be within the linear region of operation, $-10 \text{ V} \leq v_o \leq 10 \text{ V}$.

Substituting these limits on v_o into the expression for v_b, we see that v_b is limited to

$$-0.8 \text{ V} \leq v_b \leq 3.2 \text{ V}.$$

✓ ASSESSMENT PROBLEM

Objective 1—Use voltage and current constraints in an ideal op amp

5.1 Assume that the op amp in the circuit shown is ideal.

  a) Calculate v_o for the following values of v_s: 0.4, 2.0, 3.5, −0.6, −1.6, and −2.4 V.

  b) Specify the range of v_s required to avoid amplifier saturation.

Answer: (a) −2, −10, −15, 3, 8, and 10 V;

  (b) −2 V $\leq v_s \leq$ 3 V.

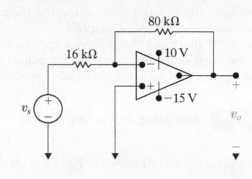

NOTE: Also try Chapter Problems 5.1, 5.4, and 5.5.

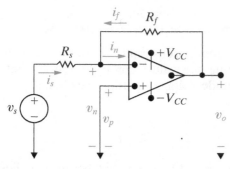

Figure 5.9 ▲ An inverting-amplifier circuit.

Inverting-amplifier equation ▶

5.3 The Inverting-Amplifier Circuit

We are now ready to discuss the operation of some important op amp circuits, using Eqs. 5.2 and 5.3 to model the behavior of the device itself. Figure 5.9 shows an inverting-amplifier circuit. We assume that the op amp is operating in its linear region. Note that, in addition to the op amp, the circuit consists of two resistors (R_f and R_s), a voltage signal source (v_s), and a short circuit connected between the noninverting input terminal and the common node.

We now analyze this circuit, assuming an ideal op amp. The goal is to obtain an expression for the output voltage, v_o, as a function of the source voltage, v_s. We employ a single node-voltage equation at the inverting terminal of the op amp, given as

$$i_s + i_f = i_n. \tag{5.6}$$

The voltage constraint of Eq. 5.2 sets the voltage at $v_n = 0$, because the voltage at $v_p = 0$. Therefore,

$$i_s = \frac{v_s}{R_s}, \tag{5.7}$$

$$i_f = \frac{v_o}{R_f}. \tag{5.8}$$

Now we invoke the constraint stated in Eq. 5.3, namely,

$$i_n = 0. \tag{5.9}$$

Substituting Eqs. 5.7–5.9 into Eq. 5.6 yields the sought-after result:

$$v_o = \frac{-R_f}{R_s} v_s. \tag{5.10}$$

Note that the output voltage is an inverted, scaled replica of the input. The sign reversal from input to output is, of course, the reason for referring to the circuit as an *inverting* amplifier. The scaling factor, or gain, is the ratio R_f/R_s.

The result given by Eq. 5.10 is valid only if the op amp shown in the circuit in Fig. 5.9 is ideal; that is, if A is infinite and the input resistance is infinite. For a practical op amp, Eq. 5.10 is an approximation, usually a good one. (We say more about this later.) Equation 5.10 is important because it tells us that if the op amp gain A is large, we can specify the gain of the inverting amplifier with the external resistors R_f and R_s. The upper limit on the gain, R_f/R_s, is determined by the power supply voltages and the value of the signal voltage v_s. If we assume equal power supply voltages, that is, $V^+ = -V^- = V_{CC}$, we get

$$|v_o| \le V_{CC}, \qquad \left|\frac{R_f}{R_s}v_s\right| \le V_{CC}, \qquad \frac{R_f}{R_s} \le \left|\frac{V_{CC}}{v_s}\right|. \qquad (5.11)$$

For example, if $V_{CC} = 15$ V and $v_s = 10$ mV, the ratio R_f/R_s must be less than 1500.

In the inverting amplifier circuit shown in Fig. 5.9, the resistor R_f provides the negative feedback connection. That is, it connects the output terminal to the inverting input terminal. If R_f is removed, the feedback path is opened and the amplifier is said to be operating *open loop*. Figure 5.10 shows the open-loop operation.

Opening the feedback path drastically changes the behavior of the circuit. First, the output voltage is now

$$v_o = -Av_n, \qquad (5.12)$$

assuming as before that $V^+ = -V^- = V_{CC}$; then $|v_n| < V_{CC}/A$ for linear operation. Because the inverting input current is almost zero, the voltage drop across R_s is almost zero, and the inverting input voltage nearly equals the signal voltage, v_s; that is, $v_n \approx v_s$. Hence, the op amp can operate open loop in the linear mode only if $|v_s| < V_{CC}/A$. If $|v_s| > V_{CC}/A$, the op amp simply saturates. In particular, if $v_s < -V_{CC}/A$, the op amp saturates at $+V_{CC}$, and if $v_s > V_{CC}/A$, the op amp saturates at $-V_{CC}$. Because the relationship shown in Eq. 5.12 occurs when there is no feedback path, the value of A is often called the **open-loop gain** of the op amp.

Example 5.2 uses the inverting-amplifier equation to design an inverting amplifier using realistic resistor values.

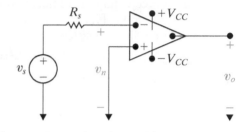

Figure 5.10 ▲ An inverting amplifier operating open loop.

| Example 5.2 | **Designing an Inverting Amplifier** |

a) Design an inverting amplifier (see Fig. 5.9) with a gain of 12. Use ±15 V power supplies and an ideal op amp.

b) What range of input voltages, v_s, allows the op amp in this design to remain in its linear operating region?

Solution

a) We need to find two resistors whose ratio is 12 from the realistic resistor values listed in

Appendix H. There are lots of different possibilities, but let's choose $R_s = 1$ kΩ and $R_f = 12$ kΩ. Use the inverting-amplifier equation (Eq. 5.10) to verify the design:

$$v_o = -\frac{R_f}{R_s}v_s = -\frac{12{,}000}{1000}v_s = -12v_s.$$

Thus, we have an inverting-amplifier with a gain of 12, as shown in Fig. 5.11.

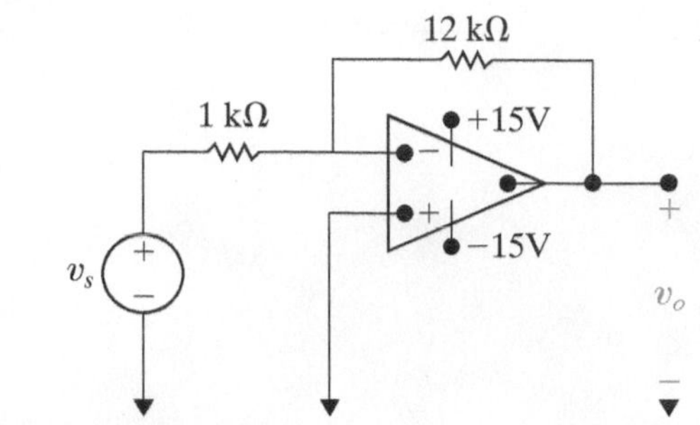

Figure 5.11 ▲ Inverting amplifier for Example 5.2.

b) Solve two different versions of the inverting-amplifier equation for v_s—first using $v_o = +15$ V and then using $v_o = -15$ V:

$$15 = -12v_s \quad \text{so} \quad v_s = -1.25 \text{ V};$$

$$-15 = -12v_s \quad \text{so} \quad v_s = 1.25 \text{ V}.$$

Thus, if the input voltage is greater than or equal to -1.25 V and less than or equal to $+1.25$ V, the op amp in the inverting-amplifier will remain in its linear operating region.

✓ ASSESSMENT PROBLEM

Objective 2—Be able to analyze simple circuits containing ideal op amps

5.2 The source voltage v_s in the circuit in Assessment Problem 5.1 is -640 mV. The 80 kΩ feedback resistor is replaced by a variable resistor R_x. What range of R_x allows the inverting amplifier to operate in its linear region?

Answer: $0 \leq R_x \leq 250 \text{ k}\Omega$.

NOTE: Also try Chapter Problems 5.9 and 5.11.

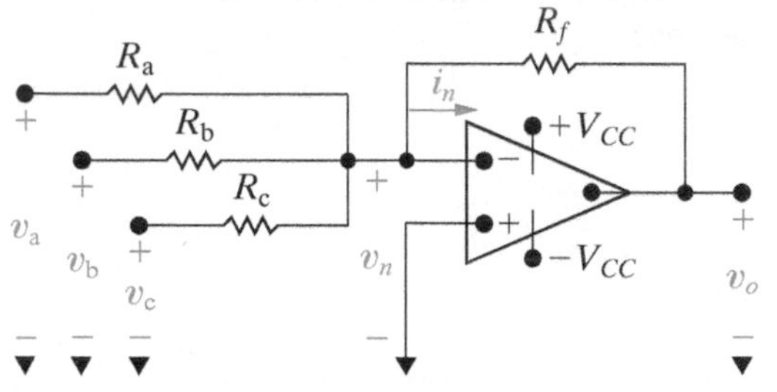

Figure 5.12 ▲ A summing amplifier.

5.4 The Summing-Amplifier Circuit

The output voltage of a summing amplifier is an inverted, scaled sum of the voltages applied to the input of the amplifier. Figure 5.12 shows a summing amplifier with three input voltages.

We obtain the relationship between the output voltage v_o and the three input voltages, v_a, v_b, and v_c, by summing the currents away from the inverting input terminal:

$$\frac{v_n - v_a}{R_a} + \frac{v_n - v_b}{R_b} + \frac{v_n - v_c}{R_c} + \frac{v_n - v_o}{R_f} + i_n = 0. \tag{5.13}$$

Assuming an ideal op amp, we can use the voltage and current constraints together with the ground imposed at v_p by the circuit to see that $v_n = v_p = 0$ and $i_n = 0$. This reduces Eq. 5.13 to

Inverting-summing amplifier equation ▶

$$v_o = -\left(\frac{R_f}{R_a}v_a + \frac{R_f}{R_b}v_b + \frac{R_f}{R_c}v_c\right). \tag{5.14}$$

Equation 5.14 states that the output voltage is an inverted, scaled sum of the three input voltages.

If $R_a = R_b = R_c = R_s$, then Eq. 5.14 reduces to

$$v_o = -\frac{R_f}{R_s}(v_a + v_b + v_c). \tag{5.15}$$

Finally, if we make $R_f = R_s$, the output voltage is just the inverted sum of the input voltages. That is,

$$v_o = -(v_a + v_b + v_c).$$

(5.16)

Although we illustrated the summing amplifier with just three input signals, the number of input voltages can be increased as needed. For example, you might wish to sum 16 individually recorded audio signals to form a single audio signal. The summing amplifier configuration in Fig. 5.12 could include 16 different input resistor values so that each of the input audio tracks appears in the output signal with a different amplification factor. The summing amplifier thus plays the role of an audio mixer. As with inverting-amplifier circuits, the scaling factors in summing-amplifier circuits are determined by the external resistors $R_f, R_a, R_b, R_c, \ldots, R_n$.

✓ ASSESSMENT PROBLEM

Objective 2—Be able to analyze simple circuits containing ideal op amps

5.3   a) Find v_o in the circuit shown if $v_a = 0.1$ V and $v_b = 0.25$ V.

   b) If $v_b = 0.25$ V, how large can v_a be before the op amp saturates?

   c) If $v_a = 0.10$ V, how large can v_b be before the op amp saturates?

   d) Repeat (a), (b), and (c) with the polarity of v_b reversed.

(c) 0.5 V;

(d) −2.5, 0.25, and 2 V.

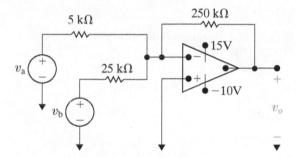

Answer: (a) −7.5 V;

   (b) 0.15 V;

NOTE: Also try Chapter Problems 5.12–5.14.

5.5 The Noninverting-Amplifier Circuit

Figure 5.13 depicts a noninverting-amplifier circuit. The signal source is represented by v_g in series with the resistor R_g. In deriving the expression for the output voltage as a function of the source voltage, we assume an ideal op amp operating within its linear region. Thus, as before, we use Eqs. 5.2 and 5.3 as the basis for the derivation. Because the op amp input current is zero, we can write $v_p = v_g$ and, from Eq. 5.2, $v_n = v_g$ as well. Now, because the input current is zero ($i_n = i_p = 0$), the resistors R_f and R_s form an unloaded voltage divider across v_o. Therefore,

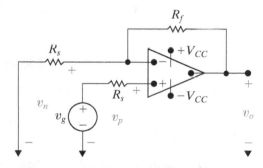

Figure 5.13 ▲ A noninverting amplifier.

$$v_n = v_g = \frac{v_o R_s}{R_s + R_f}.$$

(5.17)

Solving Eq. 5.17 for v_o gives us the sought-after expression:

$$v_o = \frac{R_s + R_f}{R_s} v_g.$$

(5.18)   ◀ **Noninverting-amplifier equation**

Operation in the linear region requires that

$$\frac{R_s + R_f}{R_s} < \left| \frac{V_{CC}}{v_g} \right|.$$

Note again that, because of the ideal op amp assumption, we can express the output voltage as a function of the input voltage and the external resistors—in this case, R_s and R_f.

Example 5.3 illustrates the design of a noninverting amplifier using realistic resistor values.

Example 5.3 **Designing a Noninverting Amplifier**

a) Design a noninverting amplifier (see Fig. 5.13) with a gain of 6. Assume the op amp is ideal.

b) Suppose we wish to amplify a voltage v_g, such that $-1.5\,V \le v_g \le +1.5\,V$. What are the smallest power supply voltages that could be used with the resistors selected in part (a) and still have the op amp in this design remain in its linear operating region?

Solution

a) Using the noninverting amplifier equation (Eq. 5.18),

$$v_o = \frac{R_s + R_f}{R_s} v_g = 6v_g \quad \text{so} \quad \frac{R_s + R_f}{R_s} = 6.$$

Therefore,

$$R_s + R_f = 6R_s, \quad \text{so} \quad R_f = 5R_s.$$

We want two resistors whose ratio is 5. Look at the realistic resistor values listed in Appendix H. Let's choose $R_f = 10\,k\Omega$, so $R_s = 2\,k\Omega$. But there is not a 2 kΩ resistor in Appendix H. We can create an equivalent 2 kΩ resistor by combining two 1 kΩ resistors in series. We can use a third 1 kΩ resistor as the value of the resistor R_g.

b) Solve two different versions of the noninverting amplifier equation for v_o—first using $v_g = +1.5\,V$ and then using $v_g = -1.5\,V$:

$$v_o = 6(1.5) = 9\,V;$$

$$v_o = 6(-1.5) = -9\,V.$$

Thus, if we use $\pm 9\,V$ power supplies for the noninverting amplifier designed in part (a) and $-1.5\,V \le v_g \le +1.5\,V$, the op amp will remain in its linear operating region. The circuit resulting from the analysis in parts (a) and (b) is shown in Fig. 5.14.

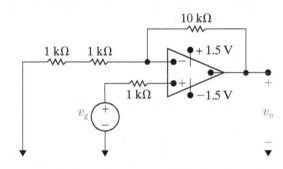

Figure 5.14 ▲ The noninverting amplifier design of Example 5.3.

✓ ASSESSMENT PROBLEM

Objective 2—Be able to analyze simple circuits containing ideal op amps

5.4 Assume that the op amp in the circuit shown is ideal.

a) Find the output voltage when the variable resistor is set to 60 kΩ.

b) How large can R_x be before the amplifier saturates?

Answer: (a) 4.8 V;

(b) 75 kΩ.

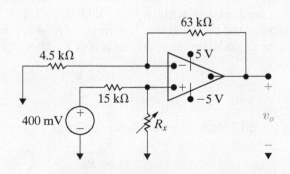

NOTE: Also try Chapter Problems 5.19 and 5.20.

5.6 The Difference-Amplifier Circuit

The output voltage of a difference amplifier is proportional to the difference between the two input voltages. To demonstrate, we analyze the difference-amplifier circuit shown in Fig. 5.15, assuming an ideal op amp operating in its linear region. We derive the relationship between v_o and the two input voltages v_a and v_b by summing the currents away from the inverting input node:

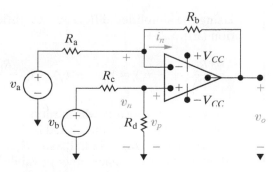

Figure 5.15 ▲ A difference amplifier.

$$\frac{v_n - v_a}{R_a} + \frac{v_n - v_o}{R_b} + i_n = 0. \qquad (5.19)$$

Because the op amp is ideal, we use the voltage and current constraints to see that

$$i_n = i_p = 0, \qquad (5.20)$$

$$v_n = v_p = \frac{R_d}{R_c + R_d}\, v_b. \qquad (5.21)$$

Combining Eqs. 5.19, 5.20, and 5.21 gives the desired relationship:

$$v_o = \frac{R_d(R_a + R_b)}{R_a(R_c + R_d)}\, v_b - \frac{R_b}{R_a}\, v_a. \qquad (5.22)$$

Equation 5.22 shows that the output voltage is proportional to the difference between a scaled replica of v_b and a scaled replica of v_a. In general the scaling factor applied to v_b is not the same as that applied to v_a. However, the scaling factor applied to each input voltage can be made equal by setting

$$\frac{R_a}{R_b} = \frac{R_c}{R_d}. \qquad (5.23)$$

When Eq. 5.23 is satisfied, the expression for the output voltage reduces to

$$v_o = \frac{R_b}{R_a}(v_b - v_a). \qquad (5.24)$$ ◀ **Simplified difference-amplifier equation**

Equation 5.24 indicates that the output voltage can be made a scaled replica of the difference between the input voltages v_b and v_a. As in the previous ideal amplifier circuits, the scaling is controlled by the external resistors. Furthermore, the relationship between the output voltage and the input voltages is not affected by connecting a nonzero load resistance across the output of the amplifier.

Example 5.4 describes the design of a difference amplifier using realistic resistor values.

Example 5.4   **Designing a Difference Amplifier**

a) Design a difference amplifier (see Fig. 5.15) that amplifies the difference between two input voltages by a gain of 8, using an ideal op amp and ±8 V power supplies.

b) Suppose $v_a = 1$ V in the difference amplifier designed in part (a). What range of input voltages for v_b will allow the op amp to remain in its linear operating region?

Solution

a) Using the simplified difference-amplifier equation (Eq. 5.24),

$$v_o = \frac{R_b}{R_a}(v_b - v_a) = 8(v_b - v_a) \quad \text{so} \quad \frac{R_b}{R_a} = 8.$$

We want two resistors whose ratio is 8. Look at the realistic resistor values listed in Appendix H. Let's choose $R_b = 12\,\text{k}\Omega$, so $R_a = 1.5\,\text{k}\Omega$, although there are many other possibilities. Note that the simplified difference-amplifier equation requires that

$$\frac{R_a}{R_b} = \frac{R_c}{R_d}.$$

A simple choice for R_c and R_d is $R_c = R_a = 1.5\,\text{k}\Omega$ and $R_d = R_b = 12\,\text{k}\Omega$. The resulting circuit is shown in Fig. 5.16.

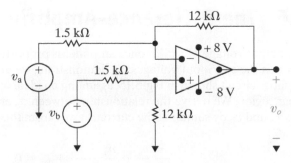

Figure 5.16 ▲ The difference amplifier designed in Example 5.4.

b) Solve two different versions of the simplified difference-amplifier equation for v_o in terms of v_b—first using $v_o = +8\,\text{V}$ and then using $v_o = -8\,\text{V}$:

$$v_o = 8(v_b - 1) = 8\,\text{V} \quad \text{so } v_b = 2\,\text{V};$$

$$v_o = 8(v_b - 1) = -8\,\text{V} \quad \text{so } v_b = 0\,\text{V}.$$

Thus, if $v_a = 1\,\text{V}$ in the difference amplifier from part (a), the op amp will remain in its linear region of operation if $0\,\text{V} \le v_b \le +2\,\text{V}$.

✓ ASSESSMENT PROBLEM

Objective 2—Be able to analyze simple circuits containing ideal op amps

5.5 a) In the difference amplifier shown, $v_b = 4.0\,\text{V}$. What range of values for v_a will result in linear operation?

  b) Repeat (a) with the 20 kΩ resistor decreased to 8 kΩ.

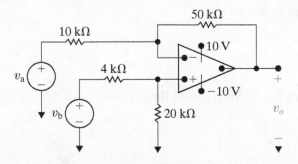

Answer: (a) $2\,\text{V} \le v_a \le 6\,\text{V}$;

  (b) $1.2\,\text{V} \le v_a \le 5.2\,\text{V}$.

NOTE: Also try Chapter Problems 5.26, 5.27, and 5.30.

The Difference Amplifier—Another Perspective

We can examine the behavior of a difference amplifier more closely if we redefine its inputs in terms of two other voltages. The first is the **differential mode** input, which is the difference between the two input voltages in Fig. 5.15:

$$v_{dm} = v_b - v_a. \tag{5.25}$$

The second is the **common mode** input, which is the average of the two input voltages in Fig. 5.15:

$$v_{cm} = (v_a + v_b)/2. \tag{5.26}$$

Using Eqs. 5.25 and 5.26, we can now represent the original input voltages, v_a and v_b, in terms of the differential mode and common mode voltages, v_{dm} and v_{cm}:

$$v_a = v_{cm} - \frac{1}{2}v_{dm}, \tag{5.27}$$

$$v_b = v_{cm} + \frac{1}{2}v_{dm}. \tag{5.28}$$

Substituting Eqs. 5.27 and 5.28 into Eq. 5.22 gives the output of the difference amplifier in terms of the differential mode and common mode voltages:

$$v_o = \left[\frac{R_aR_d - R_bR_c}{R_a(R_c + R_d)}\right]v_{cm}$$

$$+ \left[\frac{R_d(R_a + R_b) + R_b(R_c + R_d)}{2R_a(R_c + R_d)}\right]v_{dm} \tag{5.29}$$

$$= A_{cm}v_{cm} + A_{dm}v_{dm}, \tag{5.30}$$

where A_{cm} is the common mode gain and A_{dm} is the differential mode gain. Now, substitute $R_c = R_a$ and $R_d = R_b$, which are possible values for R_c and R_d that satisfy Eq. 5.23, into Eq. 5.29:

$$v_o = (0)v_{cm} + \left(\frac{R_b}{R_a}\right)v_{dm}. \tag{5.31}$$

Thus, an ideal difference amplifier has $A_{cm} = 0$, amplifies only the differential mode portion of the input voltage, and eliminates the common mode portion of the input voltage. Figure 5.17 shows a difference-amplifier circuit with differential mode and common mode input voltages in place of v_a and v_b.

Equation 5.30 provides an important perspective on the function of the difference amplifier, since in many applications it is the differential mode signal that contains the information of interest, whereas the common mode signal is the noise found in all electric signals. For example, an electrocardiograph electrode measures the voltages produced by your body to regulate your heartbeat. These voltages have very small magnitudes compared with the electrical noise that the electrode picks up from sources such as lights and electrical equipment. The noise appears as the common mode portion of the measured voltage, whereas the heart rate voltages comprise the differential mode portion. Thus an ideal difference amplifier would amplify only the voltage of interest and would suppress the noise.

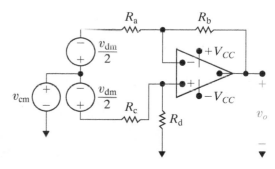

Figure 5.17 ▲ A difference amplifier with common mode and differential mode input voltages.

Measuring Difference-Amplifier Performance—The Common Mode Rejection Ratio

An ideal difference amplifier has zero common mode gain and nonzero (and usually large) differential mode gain. Two factors have an influence on the ideal common mode gain—resistance mismatches (that is, Eq. [5.23] is not satisfied) or a nonideal op amp (that is, Eq. [5.20] is not satisfied). We focus here on the effect of resistance mismatches on the performance of a difference amplifier.

Suppose that resistor values are chosen that do not precisely satisfy Eq. 5.23. Instead, the relationship among the resistors R_a, R_b, R_c, and R_d is

$$\frac{R_a}{R_b} = (1 - \epsilon)\frac{R_c}{R_d},$$

so

$$R_a = (1 - \epsilon)R_c \quad \text{and} \quad R_b = R_d, \tag{5.32}$$

or

$$R_d = (1 - \epsilon)R_b \quad \text{and} \quad R_a = R_c, \tag{5.33}$$

where ϵ is a very small number. We can see the effect of this resistance mismatch on the common mode gain of the difference amplifier by substituting Eq. 5.33 into Eq. 5.29 and simplifying the expression for A_{cm}:

$$A_{cm} = \frac{R_a(1 - \epsilon)R_b - R_aR_b}{R_a[R_a + (1 - \epsilon)R_b]} \tag{5.34}$$

$$= \frac{-\epsilon R_b}{R_a + (1 - \epsilon)R_b} \tag{5.35}$$

$$\approx \frac{-\epsilon R_b}{R_a + R_b}. \tag{5.36}$$

We can make the approximation to give Eq. 5.36 because ϵ is very small, and therefore $(1 - \epsilon)$ is approximately 1 in the denominator of Eq. 5.35. Note that, when the resistors in the difference amplifier satisfy Eq. 5.23, $\epsilon = 0$ and Eq. 5.36 gives $A_{cm} = 0$.

Now calculate the effect of the resistance mismatch on the differential mode gain by substituting Eq. 5.33 into Eq. 5.29 and simplifying the expression for A_{dm}:

$$A_{dm} = \frac{(1 - \epsilon)R_b(R_a + R_b) + R_b[R_a + (1 - \epsilon)R_b]}{2R_a[R_a + (1 - \epsilon)R_b]} \tag{5.37}$$

$$= \frac{R_b}{R_a}\left[1 - \frac{(\epsilon/2)R_a}{R_a + (1 - \epsilon)R_b}\right] \tag{5.38}$$

$$\approx \frac{R_b}{R_a}\left[1 - \frac{(\epsilon/2)R_a}{R_a + R_b}\right]. \tag{5.39}$$

We use the same rationale for the approximation in Eq. 5.39 as in the computation of A_{cm}. When the resistors in the difference amplifier satisfy Eq. 5.23, $\epsilon = 0$ and Eq. 5.39 gives $A_{dm} = R_b/R_a$.

The **common mode rejection ratio (CMRR)** can be used to measure how nearly ideal a difference amplifier is. It is defined as the ratio of the differential mode gain to the common mode gain:

$$\text{CMRR} = \left|\frac{A_{dm}}{A_{cm}}\right|. \tag{5.40}$$

The higher the CMRR, the more nearly ideal the difference amplifier. We can see the effect of resistance mismatch on the CMRR by substituting Eqs. 5.36 and 5.39 into Eq. 5.40:

$$\text{CMRR} \approx \left| \frac{\dfrac{R_{\text{b}}}{R_{\text{a}}}[1 - (R_{\text{a}}\epsilon/2)/(R_{\text{a}} + R_{\text{b}})]}{-\epsilon R_{\text{b}}/(R_{\text{a}} + R_{\text{b}})} \right| \qquad (5.41)$$

$$\approx \left| \frac{R_{\text{a}}(1 - \epsilon/2) + R_{\text{b}}}{-\epsilon R_{\text{a}}} \right| \qquad (5.42)$$

$$\approx \left| \frac{1 + R_{\text{b}}/R_{\text{a}}}{-\epsilon} \right|. \qquad (5.43)$$

From Eq. 5.43, if the resistors in the difference amplifier are matched, $\epsilon = 0$ and $\text{CMRR} = \infty$. Even if the resistors are mismatched, we can minimize the impact of the mismatch by making the differential mode gain $(R_{\text{b}}/R_{\text{a}})$ very large, thereby making the CMRR large.

We said at the outset that another reason for nonzero common mode gain is a nonideal op amp. Note that the op amp is itself a difference amplifier, because in the linear operating region, its output is proportional to the difference of its inputs; that is, $v_o = A(v_p - v_n)$. The output of a nonideal op amp is not strictly proportional to the difference between the inputs (the differential mode input) but also is comprised of a common mode signal. Internal mismatches in the components of the integrated circuit make the behavior of the op amp nonideal, in the same way that the resistor mismatches in the difference-amplifier circuit make its behavior nonideal. Even though a discussion of nonideal op amps is beyond the scope of this text, you may note that the CMRR is often used in assessing how nearly ideal an op amp's behavior is. In fact, it is one of the main ways of rating op amps in practice.

NOTE: Assess your understanding of this material by trying Chapter Problems 5.33 and 5.34.

5.7 A More Realistic Model for the Operational Amplifier

We now consider a more realistic model that predicts the performance of an op amp in its linear region of operation. Such a model includes three modifications to the ideal op amp: (1) a finite input resistance, R_i; (2) a finite open-loop gain, A; and (3) a nonzero output resistance, R_o. The circuit shown in Fig. 5.18 illustrates the more realistic model.

Whenever we use the equivalent circuit shown in Fig. 5.18, we disregard the assumptions that $v_n = v_p$ (Eq. 5.2) and $i_n = i_p = 0$ (Eq. 5.3). Furthermore, Eq. 5.1 is no longer valid because of the presence of the nonzero output resistance, R_o. Another way to understand the circuit shown in Fig. 5.18 is to reverse our thought process. That is, we can see that the circuit reduces to the ideal model when $R_i \rightarrow \infty$, $A \rightarrow \infty$, and $R_o \rightarrow 0$. For the μA741 op amp, the typical values of R_i, A, and R_o are 2 MΩ, 10^5, and 75 Ω, respectively.

Although the presence of R_i and R_o makes the analysis of circuits containing op amps more cumbersome, such analysis remains straightforward.

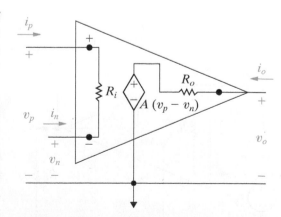

Figure 5.18 ▲ An equivalent circuit for an operational amplifier.

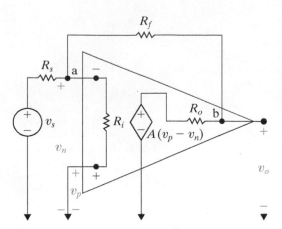

Figure 5.19 ▲ An inverting-amplifier circuit.

To illustrate, we analyze both an inverting and a noninverting amplifier, using the equivalent circuit shown in Fig. 5.18. We begin with the inverting amplifier.

Analysis of an Inverting-Amplifier Circuit Using the More Realistic Op Amp Model

If we use the op amp circuit shown in Fig. 5.18, the circuit for the inverting amplifier is the one depicted in Fig. 5.19. As before, our goal is to express the output voltage, v_o, as a function of the source voltage, v_s. We obtain the desired expression by writing the two node-voltage equations that describe the circuit and then solving the resulting set of equations for v_o. In Fig. 5.19, the two nodes are labeled a and b. Also note that $v_p = 0$ by virtue of the external short-circuit connection at the noninverting input terminal. The two node-voltage equations are as follows:

$$\text{node a:} \quad \frac{v_n - v_s}{R_s} + \frac{v_n}{R_i} + \frac{v_n - v_o}{R_f} = 0, \tag{5.44}$$

$$\text{node b:} \quad \frac{v_o - v_n}{R_f} + \frac{v_o - A(-v_n)}{R_o} = 0. \tag{5.45}$$

We rearrange Eqs. 5.44 and 5.45 so that the solution for v_o by Cramer's method becomes apparent:

$$\left(\frac{1}{R_s} + \frac{1}{R_i} + \frac{1}{R_f} \right) v_n - \frac{1}{R_f} v_o = \frac{1}{R_s} v_s, \tag{5.46}$$

$$\left(\frac{A}{R_o} - \frac{1}{R_f} \right) v_n + \left(\frac{1}{R_f} + \frac{1}{R_o} \right) v_o = 0. \tag{5.47}$$

Solving for v_o yields

$$v_o = \frac{-A + (R_o/R_f)}{\dfrac{R_s}{R_f}\left(1 + A + \dfrac{R_o}{R_i}\right) + \left(\dfrac{R_s}{R_i} + 1\right) + \dfrac{R_o}{R_f}} v_s. \tag{5.48}$$

Note that Eq. 5.48 reduces to Eq. 5.10 as $R_o \to 0$, $R_i \to \infty$, and $A \to \infty$.

If the inverting amplifier shown in Fig. 5.19 were loaded at its output terminals with a load resistance of R_L ohms, the relationship between v_o and v_s would become

$$v_o = \frac{-A + (R_o/R_f)}{\dfrac{R_s}{R_f}\left(1 + A + \dfrac{R_o}{R_i} + \dfrac{R_o}{R_L}\right) + \left(1 + \dfrac{R_o}{R_L}\right)\left(1 + \dfrac{R_s}{R_i}\right) + \dfrac{R_o}{R_f}} v_s. \tag{5.49}$$

Analysis of a Noninverting-Amplifier Circuit Using the More Realistic Op Amp Model

When we use the equivalent circuit shown in Fig. 5.18 to analyze a noninverting amplifier, we obtain the circuit depicted in Fig. 5.20. Here, the voltage source v_g, in series with the resistance R_g, represents the signal source. The resistor R_L denotes the load on the amplifier. Our analysis

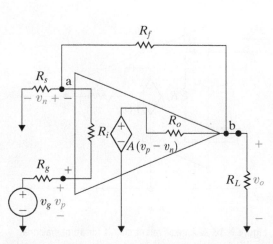

Figure 5.20 ▲ A noninverting-amplifier circuit.

consists of deriving an expression for v_o as a function of v_g. We do so by writing the node-voltage equations at nodes a and b. At node a,

$$\frac{v_n}{R_s} + \frac{v_n - v_g}{R_g + R_i} + \frac{v_n - v_o}{R_f} = 0, \qquad (5.50)$$

and at node b,

$$\frac{v_o - v_n}{R_f} + \frac{v_o}{R_L} + \frac{v_o - A(v_p - v_n)}{R_o} = 0. \qquad (5.51)$$

Because the current in R_g is the same as in R_i, we have

$$\frac{v_p - v_g}{R_g} = \frac{v_n - v_g}{R_i + R_g}. \qquad (5.52)$$

We use Eq. 5.52 to eliminate v_p from Eq. 5.51, giving a pair of equations involving the unknown voltages v_n and v_o. This algebraic manipulation leads to

$$v_n\left(\frac{1}{R_s} + \frac{1}{R_g + R_i} + \frac{1}{R_f}\right) - v_o\left(\frac{1}{R_f}\right) = v_g\left(\frac{1}{R_g + R_i}\right), \qquad (5.53)$$

$$v_n\left[\frac{AR_i}{R_o(R_i + R_g)} - \frac{1}{R_f}\right] + v_o\left(\frac{1}{R_f} + \frac{1}{R_o} + \frac{1}{R_L}\right)$$

$$= v_g\left[\frac{AR_i}{R_o(R_i + R_g)}\right]. \qquad (5.54)$$

Solving for v_o yields

$$v_o = \frac{[(R_f + R_s) + (R_sR_o/AR_i)]v_g}{R_s + \dfrac{R_o}{A}(1 + K_r) + \dfrac{R_fR_s + (R_f + R_s)(R_i + R_g)}{AR_i}}, \qquad (5.55)$$

where

$$K_r = \frac{R_s + R_g}{R_i} + \frac{R_f + R_s}{R_L} + \frac{R_fR_s + R_fR_g + R_gR_s}{R_iR_L}.$$

Note that Eq. 5.55 reduces to Eq. 5.18 when $R_o \to 0$, $A \to \infty$, and $R_i \to \infty$. For the unloaded ($R_L = \infty$) noninverting amplifier, Eq. 5.55 simplifies to

$$v_o = \frac{[(R_f + R_s) + R_sR_o/AR_i]v_g}{R_s + \dfrac{R_o}{A}\left(1 + \dfrac{R_s + R_g}{R_i}\right) + \dfrac{1}{AR_i}[R_fR_s + (R_f + R_s)(R_i + R_g)]}. \qquad (5.56)$$

Note that, in the derivation of Eq. 5.56 from Eq. 5.55, K_r reduces to $(R_s + R_g)/R_i$.

✓**ASSESSMENT PROBLEM**

Objective 3—Understand the more realistic model for an op amp

5.6 The inverting amplifier in the circuit shown has an input resistance of 500 kΩ, an output resistance of 5 kΩ, and an open-loop gain of 300,000. Assume that the amplifier is operating in its linear region.

a) Calculate the voltage gain (v_o/v_g) of the amplifier.

b) Calculate the value of v_n in microvolts when $v_g = 1$ V.

c) Calculate the resistance seen by the signal source (v_g).

d) Repeat (a)–(c) using the ideal model for the op amp.

NOTE: Also try Chapter Problems 5.44 and 5.48.

Answer: (a) −19.9985;

(b) 69.995 μV;

(c) 5000.35 Ω;

(d) −20, 0 μV, 5 kΩ.

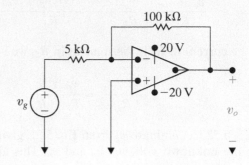

Practical Perspective

Strain Gages

Changes in the shape of elastic solids are of great importance to engineers who design structures that twist, stretch, or bend when subjected to external forces. An aircraft frame is a prime example of a structure in which engineers must take into consideration elastic strain. The intelligent application of strain gages requires information about the physical structure of the gage, methods of bonding the gage to the surface of the structure, and the orientation of the gage relative to the forces exerted on the structure. Our purpose here is to point out that strain gage measurements are important in engineering applications, and a knowledge of electric circuits is germane to their proper use.

The circuit shown in Fig. 5.21 provides one way to measure the change in resistance experienced by strain gages in applications like the one

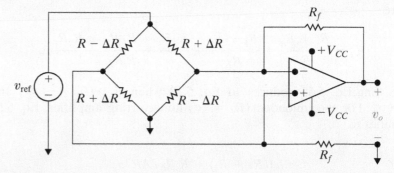

Figure 5.21 ▲ An op amp circuit used for measuring the change in strain gage resistance.

described in the beginning of this chapter. As we will see, this circuit is the familiar difference amplifier, with the strain gage bridge providing the two voltages whose difference is amplified. The pair of strain gages that are lengthened once the bar is bent have the values $R + \Delta R$ in the bridge feeding the difference amplifier, whereas the pair of strain gages that are shortened have the values $R - \Delta R$. We will analyze this circuit to discover the relationship between the output voltage, v_o and the change in resistance, ΔR experienced by the strain gages.

To begin, assume that the op amp is ideal. Writing the KCL equations at the inverting and noninverting input terminals of the op amp we see

$$\frac{v_{\text{ref}} - v_n}{R + \Delta R} = \frac{v_n}{R - \Delta R} + \frac{v_n - v_o}{R_f}, \tag{5.57}$$

$$\frac{v_{\text{ref}} - v_p}{R - \Delta R} = \frac{v_p}{R + \Delta R} + \frac{v_p}{R_f}. \tag{5.58}$$

Now rearrange Eq. 5.58 to get an expression for the voltage at the noninverting terminal of the op amp:

$$v_p = \frac{v_{\text{ref}}}{(R - \Delta R)\left(\dfrac{1}{R + \Delta R} + \dfrac{1}{R - \Delta R} + \dfrac{1}{R_f}\right)}. \tag{5.59}$$

As usual, we will assume that the op amp is operating in its linear region, so $v_p = v_n$ and the expression for v_p in Eq. 5.59 must also be the expression for v_n. We can thus substitute the right-hand side of Eq. 5.59 in place of v_n in Eq. 5.57 and solve for v_o. After some algebraic manipulation,

$$v_o = \frac{R_f(2\Delta R)}{R^2 - (\Delta R)^2}v_{\text{ref}}. \tag{5.60}$$

Because the change in resistance experienced by strain gages is very small, $(\Delta R)^2 \ll R^2$, so $R^2 - (\Delta R)^2 \approx R^2$ and Eq. 5.60 becomes

$$v_o \approx \frac{R_f}{R}2\delta v_{\text{ref}}, \tag{5.61}$$

where $\delta = \Delta R/R$.

NOTE: Assess your understanding of this Practical Perspective by trying Chapter Problem 5.49.

Summary

- The equation that defines the voltage transfer characteristic of an ideal op amp is

$$v_o = \begin{cases} -V_{CC}, & A(v_p - v_n) < -V_{CC}, \\ A(v_p - v_n), & -V_{CC} \leq A(v_p - v_n) \leq +V_{CC}, \\ +V_{CC}, & A(v_p - v_n) > +V_{CC}, \end{cases}$$

  where A is a proportionality constant known as the open-loop gain, and V_{CC} represents the power supply voltages. (See page 147.)

- A feedback path between an op amp's output and its inverting input can constrain the op amp to its linear operating region where $v_o = A(v_p - v_n)$. (See page 147.)

- A voltage constraint exists when the op amp is confined to its linear operating region due to typical values of V_{CC} and A. If the ideal modeling assumptions are made—meaning A is assumed to be infinite—the ideal op amp model is characterized by the voltage constraint

$$v_p = v_n.$$

  (See page 147.)

- A current constraint further characterizes the ideal op amp model, because the ideal input resistance of the op amp integrated circuit is infinite. This current constraint is given by

$$i_p = i_n = 0.$$

  (See page 148.)

- We considered both a simple, ideal op amp model and a more realistic model in this chapter. The differences between the two models are as follows:

Simplified Model	More Realistic Model
Infinite input resistance	Finite input resistance
Infinite open-loop gain	Finite open-loop gain
Zero output resistance	Nonzero output resistance

  (See page 159.)

- An inverting amplifier is an op amp circuit producing an output voltage that is an inverted, scaled replica of the input. (See page 150.)

- A summing amplifier is an op amp circuit producing an output voltage that is a scaled sum of the input voltages. (See page 152.)

- A noninverting amplifier is an op amp circuit producing an output voltage that is a scaled replica of the input voltage. (See page 153.)

- A difference amplifier is an op amp circuit producing an output voltage that is a scaled replica of the input voltage difference. (See page 155.)

- The two voltage inputs to a difference amplifier can be used to calculate the common mode and difference mode voltage inputs, v_{cm} and v_{dm}. The output from the difference amplifier can be written in the form

$$v_o = A_{cm}v_{cm} + A_{dm}v_{dm},$$

  where A_{cm} is the common mode gain, and A_{dm} is the differential mode gain. (See page 157.)

- In an ideal difference amplifier, $A_{cm} = 0$. To measure how nearly ideal a difference amplifier is, we use the common mode rejection ratio:

$$CMRR = \left| \frac{A_{dm}}{A_{cm}} \right|.$$

  An ideal difference amplifier has an infinite CMRR. (See page 159.)

Problems

Sections 5.1–5.2

5.1 The op amp in the circuit in Fig. P5.1 is ideal.

PSPICE
MULTISIM
  a) Label the five op amp terminals with their names.

  b) What ideal op amp constraint determines the value of i_n? What is this value?

  c) What ideal op amp constraint determines the value of $(v_p - v_n)$? What is this value?

  d) Calculate v_o.

Figure P5.1

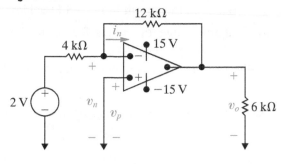

5.2 a) Replace the 2 V source in the circuit in Fig. P5.1 and calculate v_o for each of the following source values: −6 V, −3.5 V, −1.25 V, 2.4 V, 4.5 V, 5.4 V.

  b) Specify the range of voltage source values that will not cause the op amp to saturate.

5.3 Find i_L (in milliamperes) in the circuit in Fig. P5.3.

PSPICE
MULTISIM
Figure P5.3

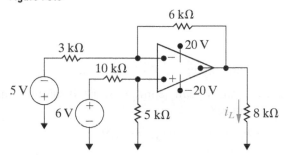

5.4 The op amp in the circuit in Fig. P5.4 is ideal.

PSPICE
MULTISIM
  a) Calculate v_o if $v_a = 1.5$ V and $v_b = 0$ V.

  b) Calculate v_o if $v_a = -0.5$ V and $v_b = 0$ V.

  c) Calculate v_o if $v_a = 1$ V and $v_b = 2.5$ V.

  d) Calculate v_o if $v_a = 2.5$ V and $v_b = 1$ V.

  e) Calculate v_o if $v_a = 2.5$ V and $v_b = 0$ V.

  f) If $v_b = 2$ V, specify the range of v_a such that the amplifier does not saturate.

Figure P5.4

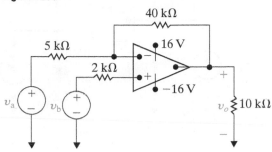

5.5 Find i_o in the circuit in Fig. P5.5 if the op amp is ideal.

PSPICE
MULTISIM
Figure P5.5

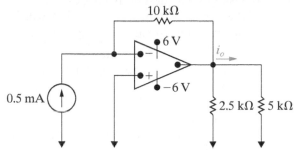

5.6 The op amp in the circuit in Fig. P5.6 is ideal. Calculate the following:

PSPICE
MULTISIM
  a) i_a

  b) v_a

  c) v_o

  d) i_o

Figure P5.6

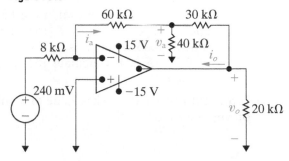

5.7 A voltmeter with a full-scale reading of 10 V is used

to measure the output voltage in the circuit in Fig. P5.7. What is the reading of the voltmeter? Assume the op amp is ideal.

Figure P5.7

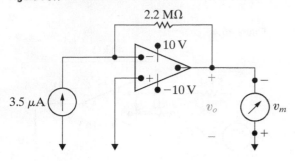

Figure P5.10

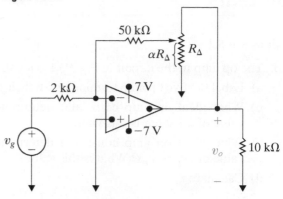

Section 5.3

5.8 a) Design an inverting amplifier with a gain of 4. Use an ideal op amp, a 30 kΩ resistor in the feedback path, and ±12 V power supplies.

b) Using your design from part (a), determine the range of input voltages that will keep the op amp in its linear operating region.

c) Suppose you wish to amplify a 2 V signal, using your design from part (a) with a variable feedback resistor. What is the largest value of feedback resistance that keeps the op amp in its linear operation region? Using this resistor value, what is the new gain of the inverting amplifier?

5.9 a) Design an inverting amplifier using an ideal

op amp that has a gain of 2.5. Use a set of identical resistors from Appendix H.

b) If you wish to amplify signals between −2 V and +3 V using the circuit you designed in part (a), what are the smallest power supply voltages you can use?

5.10 a) The op amp in the circuit shown in Fig. P5.10 is

ideal. The adjustable resistor R_Δ has a maximum value of 100 kΩ, and α is restricted to the range of $0.2 \leq \alpha \leq 1$. Calculate the range of v_o if $v_g = 40$ mV.

b) If α is not restricted, at what value of α will the op amp saturate?

5.11 The op amp in the circuit in Fig. P5.11 is ideal.

a) Find the range of values for σ in which the op amp does not saturate.

b) Find i_o (in microamperes) when $\sigma = 0.272$.

Figure P5.11

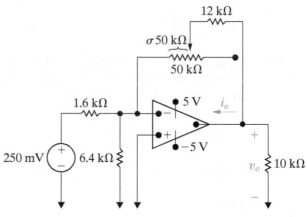

Section 5.4

5.12 The op amp in Fig. P5.12 is ideal.

a) What circuit configuration is shown in this figure?

b) Find v_o if $v_a = 1$ V, $v_b = 1.5$ V, and $v_c = -4$ V.

c) The voltages v_a and v_c remain at 1 V and −4 V, respectively. What are the limits on v_b if the op amp operates within its linear region?

Figure P5.12

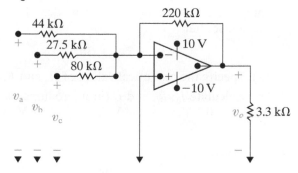

5.13 Refer to the circuit in Fig. 5.12, where the op amp is assumed to be ideal. Given that $R_a = 4\,k\Omega$, $R_b = 5\,k\Omega$, $R_c = 20\,k\Omega$, $v_a = 200\,mV$, $v_b = 150\,mV$, $v_c = 400\,mV$, and $V_{CC} = \pm 6\,V$, specify the range of R_f for which the op amp operates within its linear region.

5.14 a) The op amp in Fig. P5.14 is ideal. Find v_o if $v_a = 3\,V$, $v_b = 9\,V$, $v_c = 5\,V$, and $v_d = 6\,V$.

b) Assume v_a v_b, and v_d retain their values as given in (a). Specify the range of v_c such that the op amp operates within its linear region.

Figure P5.14

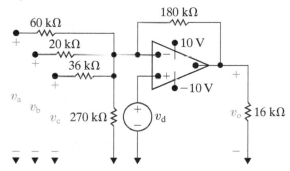

5.15 The 180 kΩ feedback resistor in the circuit in Fig. P5.14 is replaced by a variable resistor R_f. The voltages $v_a - v_d$ have the same values as given in Problem 5.14(a).

a) What value of R_f will cause the op amp to saturate? Note that $0 \leq R_f \leq \infty$.

b) When R_f has the value found in (a), what is the current (in microamperes) into the output terminal of the op amp?

5.16 a) Design an inverting-summing amplifier using a 120 kΩ resistor in the feedback path so that

$$v_o = -(8v_a + 5v_b + 12v_c).$$

Use ±15 V power supplies.

b) Suppose $v_a = 2\,V$ and $v_c = -1\,V$. What range of values for v_b will keep the op amp in its linear operating region?

5.17 Design an inverting-summing amplifier so that

$$v_o = -(8v_a + 4v_b + 10v_c + 6v_d).$$

DESIGN
PROBLEM

PSPICE
MULTISIM

Start by choosing a feedback resistor (R_f) from Appendix H. Then choose single resistors from Appendix H or construct resistor neworks from resistors in Appendix H to satisfy the design values for R_a, R_b, R_c, and R_d. Draw your final circuit diagram.

Section 5.5

5.18 The op amp in the circuit of Fig. P5.18 is ideal.

a) What op amp circuit configuration is this?

b) Calculate v_o.

Figure P5.18

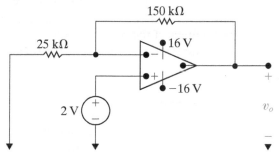

5.19 The op amp in the circuit of Fig. P5.19 is ideal.

a) What op amp circuit configuration is this?

b) Find v_o in terms of v_s.

c) Find the range of values for v_s such that v_o does not saturate and the op amp remains in its linear region of operation.

Figure P5.19

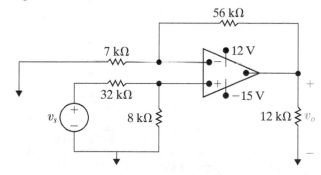

5.20 The op amp in the circuit shown in Fig. P5.20 is ideal,

a) Calculate v_o when v_g equals 4 V.

b) Specify the range of values of v_g so that the op amp operates in a linear mode.

c) Assume that v_g equals 2 V and that the 63 kΩ resistor is replaced with a variable resistor. What value of the variable resistor will cause the op amp to saturate?

Figure P5.20

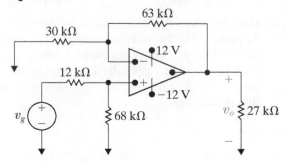

5.21 a) Design a non-inverting amplifier (see Fig. 5.13) with a gain of 6, using a 75 kΩ resistor in the feedback path. Draw your final circuit diagram.

b) Suppose you wish to amplify input signals in the range $-2.5 \text{ V} \leq v_g \leq 1.5 \text{ V}$. What are the minimum values of the power supplies that will keep the op amp in its linear operating region?

5.22 a) Design a non-inverting amplifier (see Fig. 5.13) with a gain of 2.5. Use resistors from Appendix H. You might need to combine resistors in series and in parallel to get the desired resistance. Draw your final circuit.

b) If you use ±16 V power supplies for the op amp, what range of input values will allow the op amp to stay in its linear operating region?

5.23 The op amp in the circuit of Fig. P5.23 is ideal.
PSPICE
MULTISIM
a) What op amp circuit configuration is this?

b) Find v_o in terms of v_s.

c) Find the range of values for v_s such that v_o does not saturate and the op amp remains in its linear region of operation.

Figure P5.23

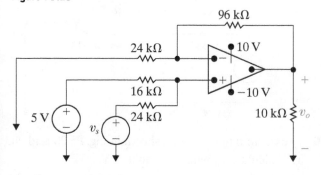

5.24 The circuit in Fig. P5.24 is a noninverting summing
DESIGN
PROBLEM
amplifier. Assume the op amp is ideal. Design the
PSPICE
circuit so that
MULTISIM

$$v_o = v_a + 2v_b + 3v_c.$$

a) Specify the numerical values of R_a and R_c.

b) Calculate i_a, i_b, and i_c (in microamperes) when $v_a = 0.7 \text{ V}$, $v_b = 0.4 \text{ V}$, and $v_c = 1.1 \text{ V}$.

Figure P5.24

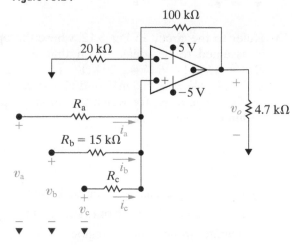

Section 5.6

5.25 a) Use the principle of superposition to derive Eq. 5.22.

b) Derive Eqs. 5.23 and 5.24.

5.26 The op amp in the circuit of Fig. P5.26 is ideal.

a) What op amp circuit configuration is this?

b) Find an expression for the output voltage v_o in terms of the input voltage v_a.

c) Suppose $v_a = 2 \text{ V}$. What value of R_f will cause the op amp to saturate?

Figure P5.26

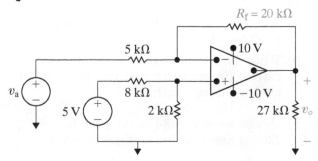

5.27 The resistors in the difference amplifier shown in Fig. 5.15 are $R_a = 24\,\text{k}\Omega$, $R_b = 75\,\text{k}\Omega$, $R_c = 130\,\text{k}\Omega$ and $R_d = 120\,\text{k}\Omega$. The signal voltages v_a and v_b are 8 and 5 V, respectively, and $V_{CC} = \pm 20\,\text{V}$.

PSPICE
MULTISIM

a) Find v_o.

b) What is the resistance seen by the signal source v_a?

c) What is the resistance seen by the signal source v_b?

5.28 The resistor R_f in the circuit in Fig. P5.28 is adjusted until the ideal op amp saturates. Specify R_f in kilohms.

Figure P5.28

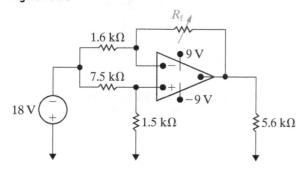

5.29 Design a difference amplifier (Fig. 5.15) to meet the following criteria: $v_o = 3v_b - 4v_a$. The resistance seen by the signal source v_b is $470\,\text{k}\Omega$, and the resistance seen by the signal source v_a is $22\,\text{k}\Omega$ when the output voltage v_o is zero. Specify the values of R_a, R_b, R_c, and R_d using single resistors or combinations of resistors from Appendix H.

DESIGN
PROBLEM

PSPICE
MULTISIM

5.30 The op amp in the adder-subtracter circuit shown in Fig. P5.30 is ideal.

PSPICE
MULTISIM

a) Find v_o when $v_a = 1\,\text{V}$, $v_b = 2\,\text{V}$, $v_c = 3\,\text{V}$, and $v_d = 4\,\text{V}$.

b) If v_a, v_b, and v_d are held constant, what values of v_c will not saturate the op amp?

Figure P5.30

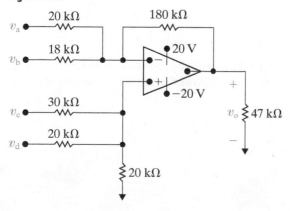

5.31 Select the values of R_a and R_f in the circuit in Fig. P5.31 so that

DESIGN
PROBLEM

PSPICE
MULTISIM

$$v_o = 8000(i_b - i_a).$$

Use single resistors or combinations of resistors from Appendix H. The op amp is ideal.

Figure P5.31

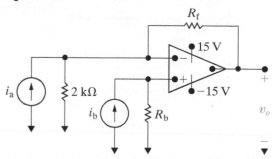

5.32 The op amp in the circuit of Fig. P5.32 is ideal.

a) Plot v_o versus α when $R_f = 4R_1$ and $v_g = 2\,\text{V}$. Use increments of 0.1 and note by hypothesis that $0 \le \alpha \le 1.0$.

b) Write an equation for the straight line you plotted in (a). How are the slope and intercept of the line related to v_g and the ratio R_f/R_1?

c) Using the results from (b), choose values for v_g and the ratio R_f/R_1 such that $v_o = -6\alpha + 4$.

Figure P5.32

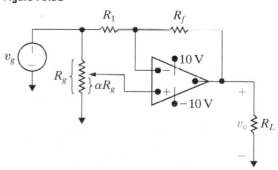

5.33 In the difference amplifier shown in Fig. P5.33, compute (a) the differential mode gain, (b) the common mode gain, and (c) the CMRR.

Figure P5.33

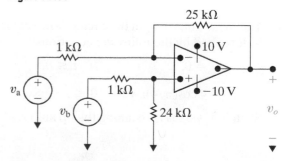

5.34 In the difference amplifier shown in Fig. P5.34, what range of values of R_x yields a CMRR ≥ 1500?

Figure P5.34

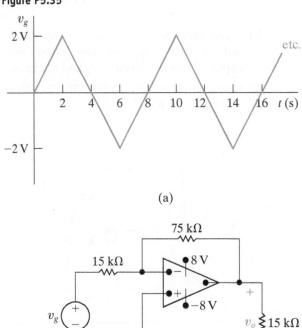

Figure P5.36

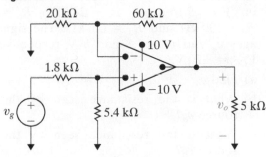

Sections 5.1–5.6

5.35 The voltage v_g shown in Fig. P5.35(a) is applied to
PSPICE   the inverting amplifier shown in Fig. P5.35(b).
MULTISIM Sketch v_o versus t, assuming the op amp is ideal.

Figure P5.35

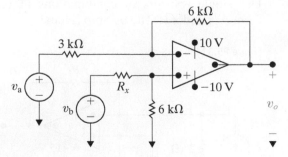

(a)

(b)

5.36 The signal voltage v_g in the circuit shown in Fig. P5.36
PSPICE   is described by the following equations:
MULTISIM

$$v_g = 0, \qquad\qquad t \leq 0,$$

$$v_g = 4\cos(\pi/4)t \text{ V}, \qquad 0 \leq t \leq \infty.$$

Sketch v_o versus t, assuming the op amp is ideal.

5.37 a) Show that when the ideal op amp in Fig. P5.37 is operating in its linear region,

$$i_a = \frac{3v_g}{R}.$$

b) Show that the ideal op amp will saturate when

$$R_a = \frac{R(\pm V_{CC} - 2v_g)}{3v_g}.$$

Figure P5.37

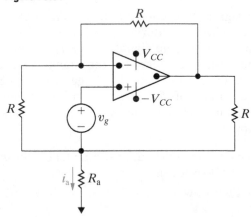

5.38 Assume that the ideal op amp in the circuit seen in Fig. P5.38 is operating in its linear region.

a) Show that $v_o = [(R_1 + R_2)/R_1]v_s$.

b) What happens if $R_1 \rightarrow \infty$ and $R_2 \rightarrow 0$?

c) Explain why this circuit is referred to as a voltage follower when $R_1 = \infty$ and $R_2 = 0$.

Figure P5.38

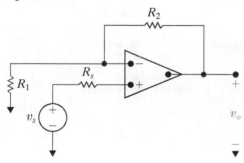

5.39 The two op amps in the circuit in Fig. P5.39 are ideal. Calculate v_{o1} and v_{o2}.

PSPICE
MULTISIM

Figure P5.39

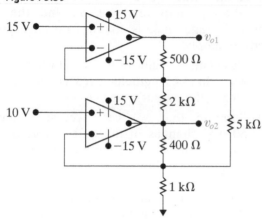

5.40 Assume that the ideal op amp in the circuit in Fig. P5.40 is operating in its linear region.

PSPICE
MULTISIM

a) Calculate the power delivered to the 16 kΩ resistor.

b) Repeat (a) with the op amp removed from the circuit, that is, with the 16 kΩ resistor connected in the series with the voltage source and the 48 kΩ resistor.

c) Find the ratio of the power found in (a) to that found in (b).

d) Does the insertion of the op amp between the source and the load serve a useful purpose? Explain.

Figure P5.40

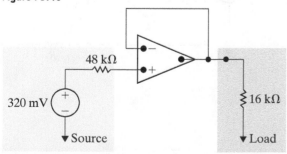

5.41 The op amps in the circuit in Fig. P5.41 are ideal.

PSPICE
MULTISIM

a) Find i_a.

b) Find the value of the left source voltage for which $i_a = 0$.

Figure P5.41

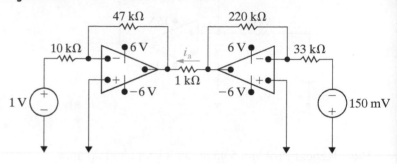

5.42 The circuit inside the shaded area in Fig. P5.42 is a constant current source for a limited range of values of R_L.

PSPICE
MULTISIM

a) Find the value of i_L for $R_L = 4$ kΩ.

b) Find the maximum value for R_L for which i_L will have the value in (a).

c) Assume that $R_L = 16$ kΩ. Explain the operation of the circuit. You can assume that $i_n = i_p \approx 0$ under all operating conditions.

d) Sketch i_L versus R_L for $0 \le R_L \le 16$ kΩ.

Figure P5.42

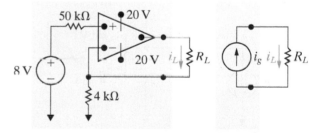

Section 5.7

5.43 Derive Eq. 5.60.

5.44 Repeat Assessment Problem 5.6, given that the inverting amplifier is loaded with a 500 Ω resistor.

PSPICE
MULTISIM

5.45 a) Find the Thévenin equivalent circuit with respect to the output terminals a, b for the inverting amplifier of Fig. P5.45. The dc signal source has a value of 880 mV. The op amp has an input resistance of 500 kΩ, an output resistance of 2 kΩ and an open-loop gain of 100,000.

PSPICE
MULTISIM

b) What is the output resistance of the inverting amplifier?

c) What is the resistance (in ohms) seen by the signal source v_s when the load at the terminals a, b is 330 Ω?

Figure P5.45

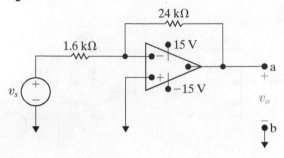

5.46 Repeat Problem 5.45 assuming an ideal op amp.

PSPICE
MULTISIM

5.47 Assume the input resistance of the op amp in Fig. P5.47 is infinite and its output resistance is zero.

PSPICE
MULTISIM

a) Find v_o as a function of v_g and the open-loop gain A.

b) What is the value of v_o if $v_g = 1$ V and $A = 150$?

c) What is the value of v_o if $v_g = 1$ V and $A = \infty$?

d) How large does A have to be so that v_o is 99% of its value in (c)?

Figure P5.47

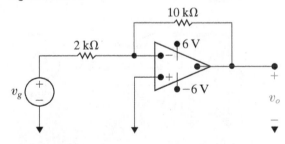

5.48 The op amp in the noninverting amplifier circuit of Fig. P5.48 has an input resistance of 560 kΩ, an output resistance of 8 kΩ, and an open-loop gain of 50,000. Assume that the op amp is operating in its linear region.

PSPICE
MULTISIM

a) Calculate the voltage gain (v_o/v_g).

b) Find the inverting and noninverting input voltages v_n and v_p (in millivolts) if $v_g = 1$ V.

c) Calculate the difference $(v_p - v_n)$ in microvolts when $v_g = 1$ V.

d) Find the current drain in picoamperes on the signal source v_g when $v_g = 1$ V.

e) Repeat (a)–(d) assuming an ideal op amp.

Figure P5.48

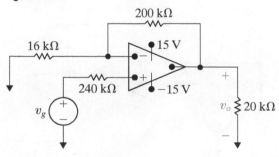

Sections 5.1–5.7

5.49 Suppose the strain gages in the bridge in Fig. 5.21 have the value 120 Ω ± 1%. The power supplies to the op amp are ±15 V, and the reference voltage, v_{ref}, is taken from the positive power supply.

PRACTICAL
PERSPECTIVE

a) Calculate the value of R_f so that when the strain gage that is lengthening reaches its maximum length, the output voltage is 5 V.

b) Suppose that we can accurately measure 50 mV changes in the output voltage. What change in strain gage resistance can be detected in milliohms?

5.50 a) For the circuit shown in Fig. P5.50, show that if $\Delta R \ll R$, the output voltage of the op amp is approximately

PRACTICAL
PERSPECTIVE

PSPICE
MULTISIM

$$v_o \approx \frac{R_f}{R^2} \frac{(R + R_f)}{(R + 2R_f)}(-\Delta R)v_{in}.$$

b) Find v_o if $R_f = 470$ kΩ, $R = 10$ kΩ, $\Delta R = 95$ Ω, and $v_{in} = 15$ V.

c) Find the actual value of v_o in (b).

Figure P5.50

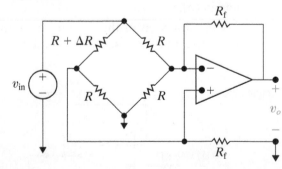

5.51 a) If percent error is defined as

PRACTICAL
PERSPECTIVE

PSPICE

MULTISIM

$$\% \text{ error} = \left[\frac{\text{approximate value}}{\text{true value}} - 1 \right] \times 100,$$

show that the percent error in the approximation of v_o in Problem 5.50 is

$$\% \text{ error} = \frac{\Delta R}{R} \frac{(R + R_f)}{(R + 2R_f)} \times 100.$$

b) Calculate the percent error in v_o for Problem 5.50.

5.52 Assume the percent error in the approximation of v_o in the circuit in Fig. P5.50 is not to exceed 1%. What is the largest percent change in R that can be tolerated?

PRACTICAL
PERSPECTIVE

PSPICE

MULTISIM

5.53 Assume the resistor in the variable branch of the bridge circuit in Fig. P5.50 is $R - \Delta R$ instead of $R + \Delta R$.

PRACTICAL
PERSPECTIVE

PSPICE

MULTISIM

a) What is the expression for v_o if $\Delta R \ll R$?

b) What is the expression for the percent error in v_o as a function of R, R_f, and ΔR?

c) Assume the resistance in the variable arm of the bridge circuit in Fig. P5.50 is 9810 Ω and the values of R, R_f, and v_{in} are the same as in Problem 5.50(b). What is the approximate value of v_o?

d) What is the percent error in the approximation of v_o when the variable arm resistance is 9810 Ω?

Inductance, Capacitance, and Mutual Inductance

✓ CHAPTER OBJECTIVES

1 Know and be able to use the equations for voltage, current, power, and energy in an inductor; understand how an inductor behaves in the presence of constant current, and the requirement that the current be continuous in an inductor.

2 Know and be able to use the equations for voltage, current, power, and energy in a capacitor; understand how a capacitor behaves in the presence of constant voltage, and the requirement that the voltage be continuous in a capacitor.

3 Be able to combine inductors with initial conditions in series and in parallel to form a single equivalent inductor with an initial condition; be able to combine capacitors with initial conditions in series and in parallel to form a single equivalent capacitor with an initial condition.

4 Understand the basic concept of mutual inductance and be able to write mesh-current equations for a circuit containing magnetically coupled coils using the dot convention correctly.

We begin this chapter by introducing the last two ideal circuit elements mentioned in Chapter 2, namely, inductors and capacitors. Be assured that the circuit analysis techniques introduced in Chapters 3 and 4 apply to circuits containing inductors and capacitors. Therefore, once you understand the terminal behavior of these elements in terms of current and voltage, you can use Kirchhoff's laws to describe any interconnections with the other basic elements. Like other components, inductors and capacitors are easier to describe in terms of circuit variables rather than electromagnetic field variables. However, before we focus on the circuit descriptions, a brief review of the field concepts underlying these basic elements is in order.

An inductor is an electrical component that opposes any change in electrical current. It is composed of a coil of wire wound around a supporting core whose material may be magnetic or nonmagnetic. The behavior of inductors is based on phenomena associated with magnetic fields. The source of the magnetic field is charge in motion, or current. If the current is varying with time, the magnetic field is varying with time. A time-varying magnetic field induces a voltage in any conductor linked by the field. The circuit parameter of **inductance** relates the induced voltage to the current. We discuss this quantitative relationship in Section 6.1.

A capacitor is an electrical component that consists of two conductors separated by an insulator or dielectric material. The capacitor is the only device other than a battery that can store electrical charge. The behavior of capacitors is based on phenomena associated with electric fields. The source of the electric field is separation of charge, or voltage. If the voltage is varying with time, the electric field is varying with time. A time-varying electric field produces a displacement current in the space occupied by the field. The circuit parameter of **capacitance** relates the displacement current to the voltage, where the displacement current is equal to the conduction current at the terminals of the capacitor. We discuss this quantitative relationship in Section 6.2.

Practical Perspective

Capacitive Touch Screens

The Practical Perspective in Chapter 3 showed how a grid of resistors is used to create a touch screen for a phone or computer monitor. But resistive touch screens have some limitations, the most important of which is that the screen can only process a single touch at any instant in time (see Problem 3.75). For example, a resistive touch screen cannot process the "pinch" gesture used by many devices to enlarge or shrink the image on the screen.

Multi-touch screens use a different component within a grid below the screen – capacitors. As you are about to discover in this chapter, a capacitor is a circuit element whose terminal characteristics are determined by electric fields. When you touch a capacitive touch screen, you produce a change in the value of a capacitor, causing a voltage change. Once you have learned the basic behavior of capacitors and have learned how they combine in series and in parallel, we will present two possible designs for a multi-touch screen using a grid of capacitors. These designs are presented in the Practical Perspective example at the end of this chapter.

cobalt88 / Shutterstock

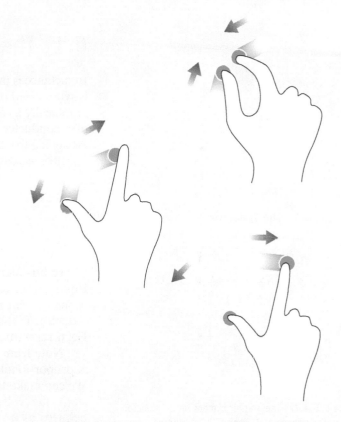

Section 6.3 describes techniques used to simplify circuits with series or parallel combinations of capacitors or inductors.

Energy can be stored in both magnetic and electric fields. Hence you should not be too surprised to learn that inductors and capacitors are capable of storing energy. For example, energy can be stored in an inductor and then released to fire a spark plug. Energy can be stored in a capacitor and then released to fire a flashbulb. In ideal inductors and capacitors, only as much energy can be extracted as has been stored. Because inductors and capacitors cannot generate energy, they are classified as **passive elements**.

In Sections 6.4 and 6.5 we consider the situation in which two circuits are linked by a magnetic field and thus are said to be magnetically coupled. In this case, the voltage induced in the second circuit can be related to the time-varying current in the first circuit by a parameter known as **mutual inductance**. The practical significance of magnetic coupling unfolds as we study the relationships between current, voltage, power, and several new parameters specific to mutual inductance. We introduce these relationships here and then describe their utility in a device called a transformer in Chapters 9 and 10.

6.1 The Inductor

Inductance is the circuit parameter used to describe an inductor. Inductance is symbolized by the letter L, is measured in henrys (H), and is represented graphically as a coiled wire—a reminder that inductance is a consequence of a conductor linking a magnetic field. Figure 6.1(a) shows an inductor. Assigning the reference direction of the current in the direction of the voltage drop across the terminals of the inductor, as shown in Fig. 6.1(b), yields

The inductor $v - i$ equation ▶

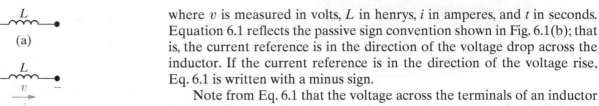

$$v = L\frac{di}{dt}, \qquad\qquad (6.1)$$

where v is measured in volts, L in henrys, i in amperes, and t in seconds. Equation 6.1 reflects the passive sign convention shown in Fig. 6.1(b); that is, the current reference is in the direction of the voltage drop across the inductor. If the current reference is in the direction of the voltage rise, Eq. 6.1 is written with a minus sign.

Note from Eq. 6.1 that the voltage across the terminals of an inductor is proportional to the time rate of change of the current in the inductor. We can make two important observations here. First, if the current is constant, the voltage across the ideal inductor is zero. Thus the inductor behaves as a short circuit in the presence of a constant, or dc, current. Second, current cannot change instantaneously in an inductor; that is, the current cannot change by a finite amount in zero time. Equation 6.1 tells us that this change would require an infinite voltage, and infinite voltages are not possible. For example, when someone opens the switch on an inductive circuit in an actual system, the current initially continues to flow in the air across the switch, a phenomenon called *arcing*. The arc across the switch prevents the current from dropping to zero instantaneously. Switching inductive circuits is an important engineering problem, because arcing and voltage surges must be controlled to prevent equipment damage. The first step to understanding the nature of this problem is to master the introductory material presented in this and the following two chapters. Example 6.1 illustrates the application of Eq. 6.1 to a simple circuit.

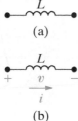

Figure 6.1 ▲ (a) The graphic symbol for an inductor with an inductance of L henrys. (b) Assigning reference voltage and current to the inductor, following the passive sign convention.

Example 6.1   **Determining the Voltage, Given the Current, at the Terminals of an Inductor**

The independent current source in the circuit shown in Fig. 6.2 generates zero current for $t < 0$ and a pulse $10te^{-5t}$ A, for $t > 0$.

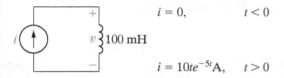

$$i = 0, \qquad t < 0$$

$$i = 10te^{-5t} \text{A}, \qquad t > 0$$

Figure 6.2 ▲ The circuit for Example 6.1.

a) Sketch the current waveform.

b) At what instant of time is the current maximum?

c) Express the voltage across the terminals of the 100 mH inductor as a function of time.

d) Sketch the voltage waveform.

e) Are the voltage and the current at a maximum at the same time?

f) At what instant of time does the voltage change polarity?

g) Is there ever an instantaneous change in voltage across the inductor? If so, at what time?

Solution

a) Figure 6.3 shows the current waveform.

b) $di/dt = 10(-5te^{-5t} + e^{-5t}) = 10e^{-5t}$ $(1 - 5t)$ A/s; $di/dt = 0$ when $t = \frac{1}{5}$ s. (See Fig. 6.3.)

c) $v = L di/dt = (0.1)10e^{-5t}(1 - 5t) = e^{-5t}$ $(1 - 5t)$ V, $t > 0$; $v = 0, t < 0$.

d) Figure 6.4 shows the voltage waveform.

e) No; the voltage is proportional to di/dt, not i.

f) At 0.2 s, which corresponds to the moment when di/dt is passing through zero and changing sign.

g) Yes, at $t = 0$. Note that the voltage can change instantaneously across the terminals of an inductor.

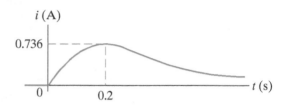

Figure 6.3 ▲ The current waveform for Example 6.1.

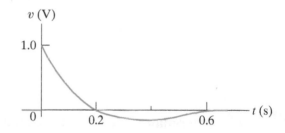

Figure 6.4 ▲ The voltage waveform for Example 6.1.

Current in an Inductor in Terms of the Voltage Across the Inductor

Equation 6.1 expresses the voltage across the terminals of an inductor as a function of the current in the inductor. Also desirable is the ability to express the current as a function of the voltage. To find i as a function of v, we start by multiplying both sides of Eq. 6.1 by a differential time dt:

$$v \, dt = L \left(\frac{di}{dt} \right) dt. \qquad (6.2)$$

Multiplying the rate at which i varies with t by a differential change in time generates a differential change in i, so we write Eq. 6.2 as

$$v \, dt = L \, di. \qquad (6.3)$$

We next integrate both sides of Eq. 6.3. For convenience, we interchange the two sides of the equation and write

$$L \int_{i(t_0)}^{i(t)} dx = \int_{t_0}^{t} v \, d\tau. \qquad (6.4)$$

Note that we use x and τ as the variables of integration, whereas i and t become limits on the integrals. Then, from Eq. 6.4,

The inductor $i - v$ equation ▶

$$i(t) = \frac{1}{L} \int_{t_0}^{t} v \, d\tau + i(t_0), \qquad (6.5)$$

where $i(t)$ is the current corresponding to t, and $i(t_0)$ is the value of the inductor current when we initiate the integration, namely, t_0. In many practical applications, t_0 is zero and Eq. 6.5 becomes

$$i(t) = \frac{1}{L} \int_{0}^{t} v \, d\tau + i(0). \qquad (6.6)$$

Equations 6.1 and 6.5 both give the relationship between the voltage and current at the terminals of an inductor. Equation 6.1 expresses the voltage as a function of current, whereas Eq. 6.5 expresses the current as a function of voltage. In both equations the reference direction for the current is in the direction of the voltage drop across the terminals. Note that $i(t_0)$ carries its own algebraic sign. If the initial current is in the same direction as the reference direction for i, it is a positive quantity. If the initial current is in the opposite direction, it is a negative quantity. Example 6.2 illustrates the application of Eq. 6.5.

Example 6.2   Determining the Current, Given the Voltage, at the Terminals of an Inductor

The voltage pulse applied to the 100 mH inductor shown in Fig. 6.5 is 0 for $t < 0$ and is given by the expression

$$v(t) = 20te^{-10t} \text{ V}$$

for $t > 0$. Also assume $i = 0$ for $t \le 0$.

a) Sketch the voltage as a function of time.

b) Find the inductor current as a function of time.

c) Sketch the current as a function of time.

Solution

a) The voltage as a function of time is shown in Fig. 6.6.

b) The current in the inductor is 0 at $t = 0$. Therefore, the current for $t > 0$ is

$$i = \frac{1}{0.1} \int_{0}^{t} 20\tau e^{-10\tau} d\tau + 0$$

$$= 200 \left[\frac{-e^{-10\tau}}{100} (10\tau + 1) \right] \Bigg|_{0}^{t},$$

$$= 2(1 - 10te^{-10t} - e^{-10t}) \text{ A}, \qquad t > 0.$$

c) Figure 6.7 shows the current as a function of time.

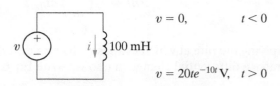

$$v = 0, \qquad t < 0$$

$$v = 20te^{-10t} \text{ V}, \quad t > 0$$

Figure 6.5 ▲ The circuit for Example 6.2.

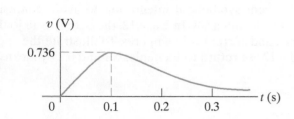

Figure 6.6 ▲ The voltage waveform for Example 6.2.

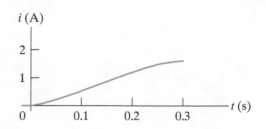

Figure 6.7 ▲ The current waveform for Example 6.2.

Note in Example 6.2 that i approaches a constant value of 2 A as t increases. We say more about this result after discussing the energy stored in an inductor.

Power and Energy in the Inductor

The power and energy relationships for an inductor can be derived directly from the current and voltage relationships. If the current reference is in the direction of the voltage drop across the terminals of the inductor, the power is

$$p = vi. \qquad (6.7)$$

Remember that power is in watts, voltage is in volts, and current is in amperes. If we express the inductor voltage as a function of the inductor current, Eq. 6.7 becomes

$$p = Li\frac{di}{dt}. \qquad (6.8) \qquad \blacktriangleleft \text{ Power in an inductor}$$

We can also express the current in terms of the voltage:

$$p = v\left[\frac{1}{L}\int_{t_0}^{t} v\, d\tau + i(t_0)\right]. \qquad (6.9)$$

Equation 6.8 is useful in expressing the energy stored in the inductor. Power is the time rate of expending energy, so

$$p = \frac{dw}{dt} = Li\frac{di}{dt}. \qquad (6.10)$$

Multiplying both sides of Eq. 6.10 by a differential time gives the differential relationship

$$dw = Li\, di. \qquad (6.11)$$

Both sides of Eq. 6.11 are integrated with the understanding that the reference for zero energy corresponds to zero current in the inductor. Thus

$$\int_{0}^{w} dx = L\int_{0}^{i} y\, dy,$$

$$w = \frac{1}{2}Li^2. \qquad (6.12) \qquad \blacktriangleleft \text{ Energy in an inductor}$$

As before, we use different symbols of integration to avoid confusion with the limits placed on the integrals. In Eq. 6.12, the energy is in joules, inductance is in henrys, and current is in amperes. To illustrate the application of Eqs. 6.7 and 6.12, we return to Examples 6.1 and 6.2 by means of Example 6.3.

Example 6.3   Determining the Current, Voltage, Power, and Energy for an Inductor

a) For Example 6.1, plot i, v, p, and w versus time. Line up the plots vertically to allow easy assessment of each variable's behavior.

b) In what time interval is energy being stored in the inductor?

c) In what time interval is energy being extracted from the inductor?

d) What is the maximum energy stored in the inductor?

e) Evaluate the integrals

$$\int_0^{0.2} p \, dt \quad \text{and} \quad \int_{0.2}^{\infty} p \, dt,$$

and comment on their significance.

f) Repeat (a)–(c) for Example 6.2.

g) In Example 6.2, why is there a sustained current in the inductor as the voltage approaches zero?

Solution

a) The plots of i, v, p, and w follow directly from the expressions for i and v obtained in Example 6.1 and are shown in Fig. 6.8. In particular, $p = vi$, and $w = (\frac{1}{2})Li^2$.

b) An increasing energy curve indicates that energy is being stored. Thus energy is being stored in the time interval 0 to 0.2 s. Note that this corresponds to the interval when $p > 0$.

c) A decreasing energy curve indicates that energy is being extracted. Thus energy is being extracted in the time interval 0.2 s to ∞. Note that this corresponds to the interval when $p < 0$.

d) From Eq. 6.12 we see that energy is at a maximum when current is at a maximum; glancing at the graphs confirms this. From Example 6.1, maximum current = 0.736 A. Therefore, $w_{max} = 27.07$ mJ.

e) From Example 6.1,

$$i = 10te^{-5t} \text{ A} \quad \text{and} \quad v = e^{-5t}(1 - 5t) \text{ V}.$$

Therefore,

$$p = vi = 10te^{-10t} - 50t^2e^{-10t} \text{ W}.$$

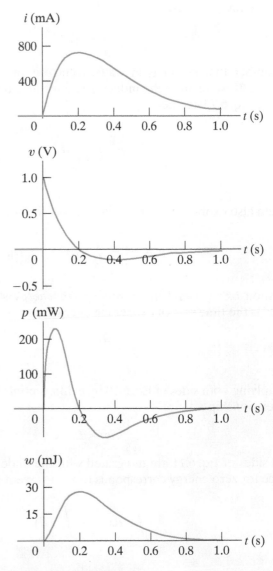

Figure 6.8 ▲ The variables i, v, p, and w versus t for Example 6.1.

Thus

$$\int_0^{0.2} p \, dt = 10 \left[\frac{e^{-10t}}{100}(-10t - 1) \right]_0^{0.2}$$

$$- 50 \left\{ \frac{t^2 e^{-10t}}{-10} + \frac{2}{10} \left[\frac{e^{-10t}}{100}(-10t - 1) \right] \right\}_0^{0.2}$$

$$= 0.2e^{-2} = 27.07 \text{ mJ},$$

$$\int_{0.2}^{\infty} p \, dt = 10 \left[\frac{e^{-10t}}{100}(-10t - 1) \right]_{0.2}^{\infty}$$

$$- 50 \left\{ \frac{t^2 e^{-10t}}{-10} + \frac{2}{10} \left[\frac{e^{-10t}}{100}(-10t - 1) \right] \right\}_{0.2}^{\infty}$$

$$= -0.2e^{-2} = -27.07 \text{ mJ}.$$

Based on the definition of p, the area under the plot of p versus t represents the energy expended over the interval of integration. Hence the integration of the power between 0 and 0.2 s represents the energy stored in the inductor during this time interval. The integral of p over the interval 0.2 s $- \infty$ is the energy extracted. Note that in this time interval, all the energy originally stored is removed; that is, after the current peak has passed, no energy is stored in the inductor.

f) The plots of v, i, p, and w follow directly from the expressions for v and i given in Example 6.2 and are shown in Fig. 6.9. Note that in this case the power is always positive, and hence energy is always being stored during the voltage pulse.

g) The application of the voltage pulse stores energy in the inductor. Because the inductor is ideal, this energy cannot dissipate after the voltage subsides to zero. Therefore, a sustained current circulates in the circuit. A lossless inductor obviously is an ideal circuit element. Practical inductors require a resistor in the circuit model. (More about this later.)

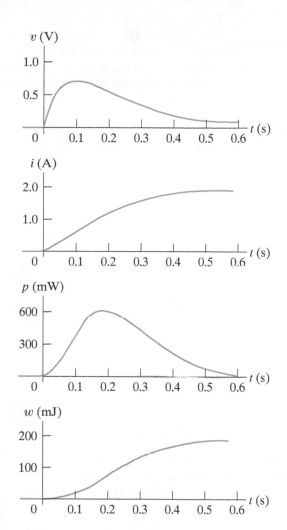

Figure 6.9 ▲ The variables v, i, p, and w versus t for Example 6.2.

✓ ASSESSMENT PROBLEM

Objective 1—Know and be able to use the equations for voltage, current, power, and energy in an inductor

6.1   The current source in the circuit shown generates the current pulse

$$i_g(t) = 0, \qquad\qquad t < 0,$$

$$i_g(t) = 8e^{-300t} - 8e^{-1200t} \text{ A}, \qquad t \geq 0.$$

Find (a) $v(0)$; (b) the instant of time, greater than zero, when the voltage v passes through zero; (c) the expression for the power delivered to the inductor; (d) the instant when the power delivered to the inductor is maximum; (e) the maximum power; (f) the instant of time when the stored energy is maximum; and (g) the maximum energy stored in the inductor.

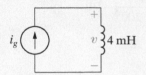

Answer: (a) 28.8 V;
(b) 1.54 ms;
(c) $-76.8e^{-600t} + 384e^{-1500t}$
$\quad - 307.2e^{-2400t}$ W, $t \geq 0$;
(d) 411.05 μs;
(e) 32.72 W;
(f) 1.54 ms;
(g) 28.57 mJ.

NOTE: Also try Chapter Problems 6.2 and 6.8.

6.2 The Capacitor

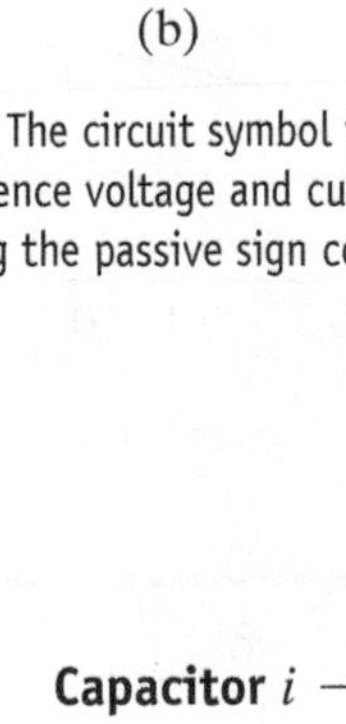

The circuit parameter of capacitance is represented by the letter C, is measured in farads (F), and is symbolized graphically by two short parallel conductive plates, as shown in Fig. 6.10(a). Because the farad is an extremely large quantity of capacitance, practical capacitor values usually lie in the picofarad (pF) to microfarad (μF) range.

The graphic symbol for a capacitor is a reminder that capacitance occurs whenever electrical conductors are separated by a dielectric, or insulating, material. This condition implies that electric charge is not transported through the capacitor. Although applying a voltage to the terminals of the capacitor cannot move a charge through the dielectric, it can displace a charge within the dielectric. As the voltage varies with time, the displacement of charge also varies with time, causing what is known as the **displacement current**.

At the terminals, the displacement current is indistinguishable from a conduction current. The current is proportional to the rate at which the voltage across the capacitor varies with time, or, mathematically,

Capacitor $i - v$ equation ▶

$$i = C\frac{dv}{dt}, \qquad\qquad (6.13)$$

where i is measured in amperes, C in farads, v in volts, and t in seconds.

Equation 6.13 reflects the passive sign convention shown in Fig. 6.10(b); that is, the current reference is in the direction of the voltage drop across the capacitor. If the current reference is in the direction of the voltage rise, Eq. 6.13 is written with a minus sign.

Figure 6.10 ▲ (a) The circuit symbol for a capacitor. (b) Assigning reference voltage and current to the capacitor, following the passive sign convention.

(a)

(b)

Two important observations follow from Eq. 6.13. First, voltage cannot change instantaneously across the terminals of a capacitor. Equation 6.13 indicates that such a change would produce infinite current, a physical impossibility. Second, if the voltage across the terminals is constant, the capacitor current is zero. The reason is that a conduction current cannot be established in the dielectric material of the capacitor. Only a time-varying voltage can produce a displacement current. Thus a capacitor behaves as an open circuit in the presence of a constant voltage.

Equation 6.13 gives the capacitor current as a function of the capacitor voltage. Expressing the voltage as a function of the current is also useful. To do so, we multiply both sides of Eq. 6.13 by a differential time dt and then integrate the resulting differentials:

$$i\,dt = C\,dv \quad \text{or} \quad \int_{v(t_0)}^{v(t)} dx = \frac{1}{C}\int_{t_0}^{t} i\,d\tau.$$

Carrying out the integration of the left-hand side of the second equation gives

$$v(t) = \frac{1}{C}\int_{t_0}^{t} i\,d\tau + v(t_0).$$

(6.14)   ◀ **Capacitor $v-i$ equation**

In many practical applications of Eq. 6.14, the initial time is zero; that is, $t_0 = 0$. Thus Eq. 6.14 becomes

$$v(t) = \frac{1}{C}\int_{0}^{t} i\,d\tau + v(0).$$

(6.15)

We can easily derive the power and energy relationships for the capacitor. From the definition of power,

$$p = vi = Cv\frac{dv}{dt},$$

(6.16)   ◀ **Capacitor power equation**

or

$$p = i\left[\frac{1}{C}\int_{t_0}^{t} i\,d\tau + v(t_0)\right].$$

(6.17)

Combining the definition of energy with Eq. 6.16 yields

$$dw = Cv\, dv,$$

from which

$$\int_0^w dx = C \int_0^v y\, dy,$$

or

Capacitor energy equation ▶

$$w = \frac{1}{2}Cv^2.\qquad (6.18)$$

In the derivation of Eq. 6.18, the reference for zero energy corresponds to zero voltage.

Examples 6.4 and 6.5 illustrate the application of the current, voltage, power, and energy relationships for a capacitor.

Example 6.4   Determining Current, Voltage, Power, and Energy for a Capacitor

The voltage pulse described by the following equations is impressed across the terminals of a 0.5 μF capacitor:

$$v(t) = \begin{cases} 0, & t \le 0\text{ s}; \\ 4t\text{ V}, & 0\text{ s} \le t \le 1\text{ s}; \\ 4e^{-(t-1)}\text{ V}, & t \ge 1\text{ s}. \end{cases}$$

a) Derive the expressions for the capacitor current, power, and energy.

b) Sketch the voltage, current, power, and energy as functions of time. Line up the plots vertically.

c) Specify the interval of time when energy is being stored in the capacitor.

d) Specify the interval of time when energy is being delivered by the capacitor.

e) Evaluate the integrals

$$\int_0^1 p\, dt \quad \text{and} \quad \int_1^\infty p\, dt$$

and comment on their significance.

Solution

a) From Eq. 6.13,

$$i = \begin{cases} (0.5 \times 10^{-6})(0) = 0, & t < 0\text{s}; \\ (0.5 \times 10^{-6})(4) = 2\ \mu\text{A}, & 0\text{ s} < t < 1\text{ s}; \\ (0.5 \times 10^{-6})(-4e^{-(t-1)}) = -2e^{-(t-1)}\ \mu\text{A}, & t > 1\text{ s}. \end{cases}$$

The expression for the power is derived from Eq. 6.16:

$$p = \begin{cases} 0, & t \le 0\text{ s}; \\ (4t)(2) = 8t\ \mu\text{W}, & 0\text{ s} \le t < 1\text{ s}; \\ (4e^{-(t-1)})(-2e^{-(t-1)}) = -8e^{-2(t-1)}\ \mu\text{W}, & t > 1\text{ s}. \end{cases}$$

The energy expression follows directly from Eq. 6.18:

$$w = \begin{cases} 0, & t \le 0\text{ s}; \\ \frac{1}{2}(0.5)16t^2 = 4t^2\mu\text{J}, & 0\text{ s} \le t \le 1\text{ s}; \\ \frac{1}{2}(0.5)16e^{-2(t-1)} = 4e^{-2(t-1)}\ \mu\text{J}, & t \ge 1\text{ s}. \end{cases}$$

b) Figure 6.11 shows the voltage, current, power, and energy as functions of time.

c) Energy is being stored in the capacitor whenever the power is positive. Hence energy is being stored in the interval 0–1 s.

d) Energy is being delivered by the capacitor whenever the power is negative. Thus energy is being delivered for all t greater than 1 s.

e) The integral of $p\,dt$ is the energy associated with the time interval corresponding to the limits on the integral. Thus the first integral represents the energy stored in the capacitor between 0 and 1 s, whereas the second integral represents the energy returned, or delivered, by the capacitor in the interval 1 s to ∞:

$$\int_0^1 p\,dt = \int_0^1 8t\,dt = 4t^2\Big|_0^1 = 4\,\mu J,$$

$$\int_1^\infty p\,dt = \int_1^\infty (-8e^{-2(t-1)})dt = (-8)\frac{e^{-2(t-1)}}{-2}\Big|_1^\infty = -4\,\mu J.$$

The voltage applied to the capacitor returns to zero as time increases without limit, so the energy returned by this ideal capacitor must equal the energy stored.

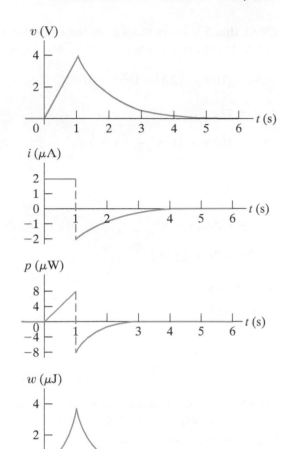

Figure 6.11 ▲ The variables v, i, p, and w versus t for Example 6.4.

Example 6.5   Finding v, p, and w Induced by a Triangular Current Pulse for a Capacitor

An uncharged 0.2 μF capacitor is driven by a triangular current pulse. The current pulse is described by

$$i(t) = \begin{cases} 0, & t \le 0; \\ 5000t \text{ A}, & 0 \le t \le 20\,\mu s; \\ 0.2 - 5000t \text{ A}, & 20 \le t \le 40\,\mu s; \\ 0, & t \ge 40\,\mu s. \end{cases}$$

a) Derive the expressions for the capacitor voltage, power, and energy for each of the four time intervals needed to describe the current.

b) Plot i, v, p, and w versus t. Align the plots as specified in the previous examples.

c) Why does a voltage remain on the capacitor after the current returns to zero?

Solution

a) For $t \le 0$, v, p, and w all are zero.
For $0 \le t \le 20\,\mu s$,

$$v = 5 \times 10^6 \int_0^t (5000\tau)\,d\tau + 0 = 12.5 \times 10^9 t^2 \text{ V},$$

$$p = vi = 62.5 \times 10^{12}t^3 \text{ W},$$

$$w = \frac{1}{2}Cv^2 = 15.625 \times 10^{12}t^4 \text{ J}.$$

For $20\,\mu s \le t \le 40\,\mu s$,

$$v = 5 \times 10^6 \int_{20\mu s}^t (0.2 - 5000\tau)\,d\tau + 5.$$

(Note that 5 V is the voltage on the capacitor at the end of the preceding interval.) Then,

$$v = (10^6 t - 12.5 \times 10^9 t^2 - 10) \text{ V},$$

$$p = vi,$$

$$= (62.5 \times 10^{12} t^3 - 7.5 \times 10^9 t^2 + 2.5 \times 10^5 t - 2) \text{ W},$$

$$w = \frac{1}{2} C v^2,$$

$$= (15.625 \times 10^{12} t^4 - 2.5 \times 10^9 t^3 + 0.125 \times 10^6 t^2$$

$$-2t + 10^{-5}) \text{ J}.$$

For $t \geq 40 \,\mu s$,

$$v = 10 \text{ V},$$

$$p = vi = 0,$$

$$w = \frac{1}{2} C v^2 = 10 \,\mu J.$$

b) The excitation current and the resulting voltage, power, and energy are plotted in Fig. 6.12.

c) Note that the power is always positive for the duration of the current pulse, which means that energy is continuously being stored in the capacitor. When the current returns to zero, the stored energy is trapped because the ideal capacitor offers no means for dissipating energy. Thus a voltage remains on the capacitor after i returns to zero.

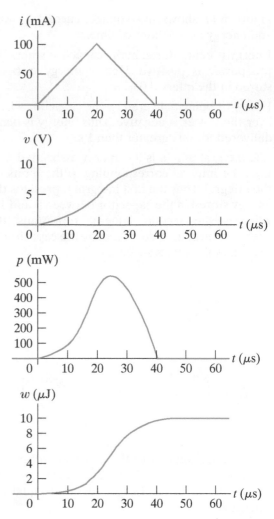

Figure 6.12 ▲ The variables i, v, p, and w versus t for Example 6.5.

✓ ASSESSMENT PROBLEMS

Objective 2—Know and be able to use the equations for voltage, current, power, and energy in a capacitor

6.2   The voltage at the terminals of the 0.6 μF capacitor shown in the figure is 0 for $t < 0$ and $40e^{-15,000t} \sin 30,000t$ V for $t \geq 0$. Find (a) $i(0)$; (b) the power delivered to the capacitor at $t = \pi/80$ ms; and (c) the energy stored in the capacitor at $t = \pi/80$ ms.

0.6 μF

$$\circ\!\!-\!\!|\!(\!-\!\!\circ$$
$$+ \quad v \quad -$$
$$\xrightarrow{\ i\ }$$

Answer: (a) 0.72 A;
(b) −649.2 mW;
(c) 126.13 μJ.

6.3   The current in the capacitor of Assessment Problem 6.2 is 0 for $t < 0$ and $3 \cos 50,000t$ A for $t \geq 0$. Find (a) $v(t)$; (b) the maximum power delivered to the capacitor at any one instant of time; and (c) the maximum energy stored in the capacitor at any one instant of time.

Answer: (a) $100 \sin 50,000t$ V, $t \geq 0$;
(b) 150 W; (c) 3 mJ.

NOTE: Also try Chapter Problems 6.16 and 6.21.

6.3 Series-Parallel Combinations of Inductance and Capacitance

Just as series-parallel combinations of resistors can be reduced to a single equivalent resistor, series-parallel combinations of inductors or capacitors can be reduced to a single inductor or capacitor. Figure 6.13 shows inductors in series. Here, the inductors are forced to carry the same current; thus we define only one current for the series combination. The voltage drops across the individual inductors are

$$v_1 = L_1 \frac{di}{dt}, \qquad v_2 = L_2 \frac{di}{dt}, \qquad \text{and} \qquad v_3 = L_3 \frac{di}{dt}.$$

The voltage across the series connection is

$$v = v_1 + v_2 + v_3 = (L_1 + L_2 + L_3)\frac{di}{dt},$$

from which it should be apparent that the equivalent inductance of series-connected inductors is the sum of the individual inductances. For n inductors in series,

$$L_{eq} = L_1 + L_2 + L_3 + \cdots + L_n. \tag{6.19}$$

◀ **Combining inductors in series**

If the original inductors carry an initial current of $i(t_0)$, the equivalent inductor carries the same initial current. Figure 6.14 shows the equivalent circuit for series inductors carrying an initial current.

Inductors in parallel have the same terminal voltage. In the equivalent circuit, the current in each inductor is a function of the terminal voltage and the initial current in the inductor. For the three inductors in parallel shown in Fig. 6.15, the currents for the individual inductors are

$$i_1 = \frac{1}{L_1}\int_{t_0}^t v\,d\tau + i_1(t_0),$$

$$i_2 = \frac{1}{L_2}\int_{t_0}^t v\,d\tau + i_2(t_0),$$

$$i_3 = \frac{1}{L_3}\int_{t_0}^t v\,d\tau + i_3(t_0). \tag{6.20}$$

The current at the terminals of the three parallel inductors is the sum of the inductor currents:

$$i = i_1 + i_2 + i_3. \tag{6.21}$$

Substituting Eq. 6.20 into Eq. 6.21 yields

$$i = \left(\frac{1}{L_1} + \frac{1}{L_2} + \frac{1}{L_3}\right)\int_{t_0}^t v\,d\tau + i_1(t_0) + i_2(t_0) + i_3(t_0). \tag{6.22}$$

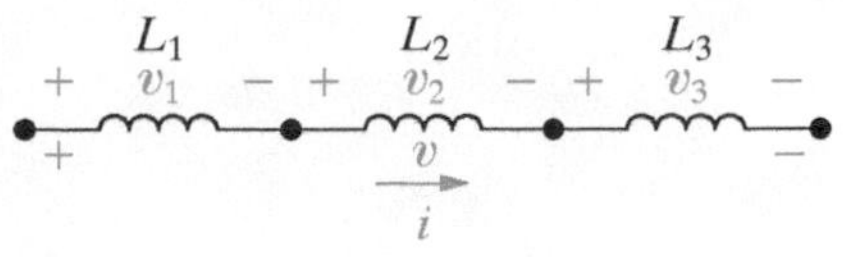

Figure 6.13 ▲ Inductors in series.

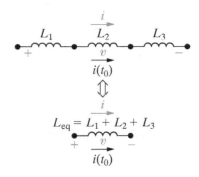

Figure 6.14 ▲ An equivalent circuit for inductors in series carrying an initial current $i(t_0)$.

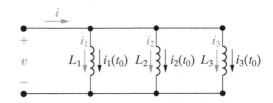

Figure 6.15 ▲ Three inductors in parallel.

Now we can interpret Eq. 6.22 in terms of a single inductor; that is,

$$i = \frac{1}{L_{eq}} \int_{t_0}^{t} v \, d\tau + i(t_0). \tag{6.23}$$

Comparing Eq. 6.23 with (6.22) yields

$$\frac{1}{L_{eq}} = \frac{1}{L_1} + \frac{1}{L_2} + \frac{1}{L_3} \tag{6.24}$$

$$i(t_0) = i_1(t_0) + i_2(t_0) + i_3(t_0). \tag{6.25}$$

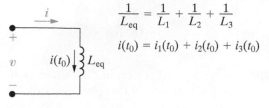

Figure 6.16 shows the equivalent circuit for the three parallel inductors in Fig. 6.15.

The results expressed in Eqs. 6.24 and 6.25 can be extended to n inductors in parallel:

Figure 6.16 ▲ An equivalent circuit for three inductors in parallel.

Combining inductors in parallel ▶

$$\frac{1}{L_{eq}} = \frac{1}{L_1} + \frac{1}{L_2} + \cdots + \frac{1}{L_n} \tag{6.26}$$

Equivalent inductance initial current ▶

$$i(t_0) = i_1(t_0) + i_2(t_0) + \cdots + i_n(t_0). \tag{6.27}$$

Capacitors connected in series can be reduced to a single equivalent capacitor. The reciprocal of the equivalent capacitance is equal to the sum of the reciprocals of the individual capacitances. If each capacitor carries its own initial voltage, the initial voltage on the equivalent capacitor is the algebraic sum of the initial voltages on the individual capacitors. Figure 6.17 and the following equations summarize these observations:

Combining capacitors in series ▶

$$\frac{1}{C_{eq}} = \frac{1}{C_1} + \frac{1}{C_2} + \cdots + \frac{1}{C_n}, \tag{6.28}$$

Equivalent capacitance initial voltage ▶

$$v(t_0) = v_1(t_0) + v_2(t_0) + \cdots + v_n(t_0). \tag{6.29}$$

We leave the derivation of the equivalent circuit for series-connected capacitors as an exercise. (See Problem 6.32.)

The equivalent capacitance of capacitors connected in parallel is simply the sum of the capacitances of the individual capacitors, as Fig. 6.18 and the following equation show:

Combining capacitors in parallel ▶

$$C_{eq} = C_1 + C_2 + \cdots + C_n. \tag{6.30}$$

Capacitors connected in parallel must carry the same voltage. Therefore, if there is an initial voltage across the original parallel capacitors, this same initial voltage appears across the equivalent capacitance C_{eq}. The derivation of the equivalent circuit for parallel capacitors is left as an exercise. (See Problem 6.33.)

We say more about series-parallel equivalent circuits of inductors and capacitors in Chapter 7, where we interpret results based on their use.

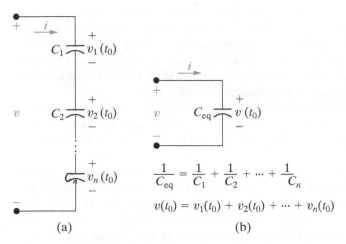

$$\frac{1}{C_{eq}} = \frac{1}{C_1} + \frac{1}{C_2} + \cdots + \frac{1}{C_n}$$

$$v(t_0) = v_1(t_0) + v_2(t_0) + \cdots + v_n(t_0)$$

(a)   (b)

Figure 6.17 ▲ An equivalent circuit for capacitors connected in series. (a) The series capacitors. (b) The equivalent circuit.

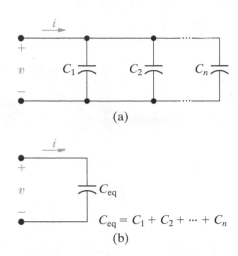

$$C_{eq} = C_1 + C_2 + \cdots + C_n$$

(b)

Figure 6.18 ▲ An equivalent circuit for capacitors connected in parallel. (a) Capacitors in parallel. (b) The equivalent circuit.

✓ ASSESSMENT PROBLEMS

Objective 3—Be able to combine inductors or capacitors in series and in parallel to form a single equivalent inductor

6.4 The initial values of i_1 and i_2 in the circuit shown are $+3$ A and -5 A, respectively. The voltage at the terminals of the parallel inductors for $t \geq 0$ is $-30e^{-5t}$ mV.

   a) If the parallel inductors are replaced by a single inductor, what is its inductance?

   b) What is the initial current and its reference direction in the equivalent inductor?

   c) Use the equivalent inductor to find $i(t)$.

   d) Find $i_1(t)$ and $i_2(t)$. Verify that the solutions for $i_1(t)$, $i_2(t)$, and $i(t)$ satisfy Kirchhoff's current law.

Answer: (a) 48 mH;

        (b) 2 A, up;

        (c) $0.125e^{-5t} - 2.125$ A, $t \geq 0$;

        (d) $i_1(t) = 0.1e^{-5t} + 2.9$ A, $t \geq 0$, $i_2(t) = 0.025e^{-5t} - 5.025$ A, $t \geq 0$.

6.5 The current at the terminals of the two capacitors shown is $240e^{-10t} \mu$A for $t \geq 0$. The initial values of v_1 and v_2 are -10 V and -5 V, respectively. Calculate the total energy trapped in the capacitors as $t \to \infty$. (*Hint:* Don't combine the capacitors in series—find the energy trapped in each, and then add.)

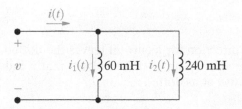

Answer: 20 μJ.

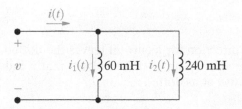

NOTE: Also try Chapter Problems 6.22, 6.24, 6.27, and 6.31.

6.4 Mutual Inductance

The magnetic field we considered in our study of inductors in Section 6.1 was restricted to a single circuit. We said that inductance is the parameter that relates a voltage to a time-varying current in the same circuit; thus, inductance is more precisely referred to as self-inductance.

We now consider the situation in which two circuits are linked by a magnetic field. In this case, the voltage induced in the second circuit can be related to the time-varying current in the first circuit by a parameter

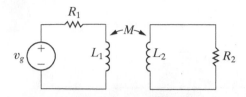

Figure 6.19 ▲ Two magnetically coupled coils.

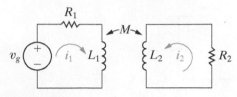

Figure 6.20 ▲ Coil currents i_1 and i_2 used to describe the circuit shown in Fig. 6.19.

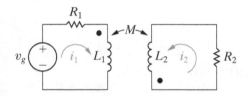

Figure 6.21 ▲ The circuit of Fig. 6.20 with dots added to the coils indicating the polarity of the mutually induced voltages.

Dot convention for mutually coupled coils ▶

Dot convention for mutually coupled coils (alternate) ▶

known as mutual inductance. The circuit shown in Fig. 6.19 represents two magnetically coupled coils. The self-inductances of the two coils are labeled L_1 and L_2, and the mutual inductance is labeled M. The double-headed arrow adjacent to M indicates the pair of coils with this value of mutual inductance. This notation is needed particularly in circuits containing more than one pair of magnetically coupled coils.

The easiest way to analyze circuits containing mutual inductance is to use mesh currents. The problem is to write the circuit equations that describe the circuit in terms of the coil currents. First, choose the reference direction for each coil current. Figure 6.20 shows arbitrarily selected reference currents. After choosing the reference directions for i_1 and i_2, sum the voltages around each closed path. Because of the mutual inductance M, there will be two voltages across each coil, namely, a self-induced voltage and a mutually induced voltage. The self-induced voltage is the product of the self-inductance of the coil and the first derivative of the current in that coil. The mutually induced voltage is the product of the mutual inductance of the coils and the first derivative of the current in the other coil. Consider the coil on the left in Fig. 6.20 whose self-inductance has the value L_1. The self-induced voltage across this coil is $L_1(di_1/dt)$ and the mutually induced voltage across this coil is $M(di_2/dt)$. But what about the polarities of these two voltages?

Using the passive sign convention, the self-induced voltage is a voltage drop in the direction of the current producing the voltage. But the polarity of the mutually induced voltage depends on the way the coils are wound in relation to the reference direction of coil currents. In general, showing the details of mutually coupled windings is very cumbersome. Instead, we keep track of the polarities by a method known as the **dot convention**, in which a dot is placed on one terminal of each winding, as shown in Fig. 6.21. These dots carry the sign information and allow us to draw the coils schematically rather than showing how they wrap around a core structure.

The rule for using the dot convention to determine the polarity of mutually induced voltage can be summarized as follows:

When the reference direction for a current enters the dotted terminal of a coil, the reference polarity of the voltage that it induces in the other coil is positive at its dotted terminal.

Or, stated alternatively,

When the reference direction for a current leaves the dotted terminal of a coil, the reference polarity of the voltage that it induces in the other coil is negative at its dotted terminal.

For the most part, dot markings will be provided for you in the circuit diagrams in this text. The important skill is to be able to write the appropriate circuit equations given your understanding of mutual inductance and the dot convention. Figuring out where to place the polarity dots if they are not given may be possible by examining the physical configuration of an actual circuit or by testing it in the laboratory. We will discuss these procedures after we discuss the use of dot markings.

In Fig. 6.21, the dot convention rule indicates that the reference polarity for the voltage induced in coil 1 by the current i_2 is negative at the dotted terminal of coil 1. This voltage (Mdi_2/dt) is a voltage rise with respect to i_1. The voltage induced in coil 2 by the current i_1 is Mdi_1/dt, and its reference polarity is positive at the dotted terminal of coil 2. This voltage is a voltage rise in the direction of i_2. Figure 6.22 shows the self- and mutually induced voltages across coils 1 and 2 along with their polarity marks.

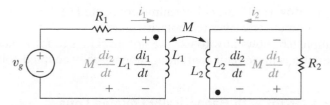

Figure 6.22 ▲ The self- and mutually induced voltages appearing across the coils shown in Fig. 6.21.

Now let's look at the sum of the voltages around each closed loop. In Eqs. 6.31 and 6.32, voltage rises in the reference direction of a current are negative:

$$-v_g + i_1 R_1 + L_1 \frac{di_1}{dt} - M\frac{di_2}{dt} = 0, \tag{6.31}$$

$$i_2 R_2 + L_2 \frac{di_2}{dt} - M\frac{di_1}{dt} = 0. \tag{6.32}$$

The Procedure for Determining Dot Markings

We shift now to two methods of determining dot markings. The first assumes that we know the physical arrangement of the two coils and the mode of each winding in a magnetically coupled circuit. The following six steps, applied here to Fig. 6.23, determine a set of dot markings:

a) Arbitrarily select one terminal—say, the D terminal—of one coil and mark it with a dot.

b) Assign a current into the dotted terminal and label it i_D.

c) Use the right-hand rule[1] to determine the direction of the magnetic field established by i_D *inside* the coupled coils and label this field ϕ_D.

d) Arbitrarily pick one terminal of the second coil—say, terminal A—and assign a current into this terminal, showing the current as i_A.

e) Use the right-hand rule to determine the direction of the flux established by i_A *inside* the coupled coils and label this flux ϕ_A.

f) Compare the directions of the two fluxes ϕ_D and ϕ_A. If the fluxes have the same reference direction, place a dot on the terminal of the second coil where the test current (i_A) enters. (In Fig. 6.23, the fluxes ϕ_D and ϕ_A have the same reference direction, and therefore a dot goes on terminal A.) If the fluxes have different reference directions, place a dot on the terminal of the second coil where the test current leaves.

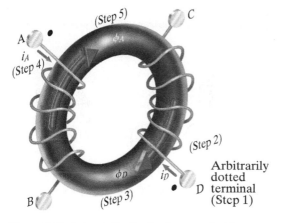

Figure 6.23 ▲ A set of coils showing a method for determining a set of dot markings.

The relative polarities of magnetically coupled coils can also be determined experimentally. This capability is important because in some situations, determining how the coils are wound on the core is impossible. One experimental method is to connect a dc voltage source, a resistor, a switch, and a dc voltmeter to the pair of coils, as shown in Fig. 6.24. The shaded box covering the coils implies that physical inspection of the coils is not possible. The resistor R limits the magnitude of the current supplied by the dc voltage source.

The coil terminal connected to the positive terminal of the dc source via the switch and limiting resistor receives a polarity mark, as shown in Fig. 6.24. When the switch is closed, the voltmeter deflection is observed. If the momentary deflection is upscale, the coil terminal connected to the positive terminal of the voltmeter receives the polarity mark. If the

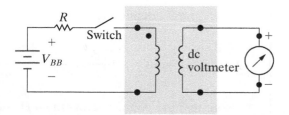

Figure 6.24 ▲ An experimental setup for determining polarity marks.

---

[1] See discussion of Faraday's law on page 193.

deflection is downscale, the coil terminal connected to the negative terminal of the voltmeter receives the polarity mark.

Example 6.6 shows how to use the dot markings to formulate a set of circuit equations in a circuit containing magnetically coupled coils.

Example 6.6   Finding Mesh-Current Equations for a Circuit with Magnetically Coupled Coils

a) Write a set of mesh-current equations that describe the circuit in Fig. 6.25 in terms of the currents i_1 and i_2.

b) Verify that if there is no energy stored in the circuit at $t = 0$ and if $i_g = 16 - 16e^{-5t}$ A, the solutions for i_1 and i_2 are

$$i_1 = 4 + 64e^{-5t} - 68e^{-4t} \text{ A},$$

$$i_2 = 1 - 52e^{-5t} + 51e^{-4t} \text{ A}.$$

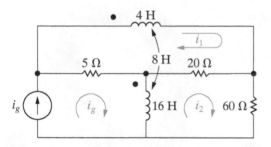

Figure 6.25 ▲ The circuit for Example 6.6.

Solution

a) Summing the voltages around the i_1 mesh yields

$$4\frac{di_1}{dt} + 8\frac{d}{dt}(i_g - i_2) + 20(i_1 - i_2) + 5(i_1 - i_g) = 0.$$

The i_2 mesh equation is

$$20(i_2 - i_1) + 60i_2 + 16\frac{d}{dt}(i_2 - i_g) - 8\frac{di_1}{dt} = 0.$$

Note that the voltage across the 4 H coil due to the current $(i_g - i_2)$, that is, $8d(i_g - i_2)/dt$, is a voltage drop in the direction of i_1. The voltage induced in the 16 H coil by the current i_1, that is, $8di_1/dt$, is a voltage rise in the direction of i_2.

b) To check the validity of i_1 and i_2, we begin by testing the initial and final values of i_1 and i_2. We know by hypothesis that $i_1(0) = i_2(0) = 0$. From the given solutions we have

$$i_1(0) = 4 + 64 - 68 = 0,$$

$$i_2(0) = 1 - 52 + 51 = 0.$$

Now we observe that as t approaches infinity the source current (i_g) approaches a constant value of 16 A, and therefore the magnetically coupled coils behave as short circuits. Hence at $t = \infty$ the circuit reduces to that shown in Fig. 6.26. From Fig. 6.26 we see that at $t = \infty$ the three resistors are in parallel across the 16 A source. The equivalent resistance is 3.75 Ω and thus the voltage across the 16 A current source is 60 V. It follows that

$$i_1(\infty) = \frac{60}{20} + \frac{60}{60} = 4 \text{ A},$$

$$i_2(\infty) = \frac{60}{60} = 1 \text{ A}.$$

These values agree with the final values predicted by the solutions for i_1 and i_2.

Finally we check the solutions by seeing if they satisfy the differential equations derived in (a). We will leave this final check to the reader via Problem 6.37.

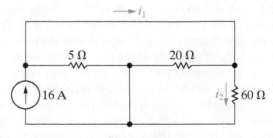

Figure 6.26 ▲ The circuit of Example 6.6 when $t = \infty$.

Objective 4—Use the dot convention to write mesh-current equations for mutually coupled coils

6.6   a) Write a set of mesh-current equations for the circuit in Example 6.6 if the dot on the 4 H inductor is at the right-hand terminal, the reference direction of i_g is reversed, and the 60 Ω resistor is increased to 780 Ω.

b) Verify that if there is no energy stored in the circuit at $t = 0$, and if $i_g = 1.96 - 1.96e^{-4t}$ A, the solutions to the differential equations derived in (a) of this Assessment Problem are

$$i_1 = -0.4 - 11.6e^{-4t} + 12e^{-5t} \text{ A},$$
$$i_2 = -0.01 - 0.99e^{-4t} + e^{-5t} \text{ A}.$$

Answer: (a) $4(di_1/dt) + 25i_1 + 8(di_2/dt) - 20i_2$
$= -5i_g - 8(di_g/dt)$
and

$8(di_1/dt) - 20i_1 + 16(di_2/dt) + 800i_2$
$= -16(di_g/dt);$

(b) verification.

NOTE: Also try Chapter Problem 6.39.

6.5 A Closer Look at Mutual Inductance

In order to fully explain the circuit parameter mutual inductance, and to examine the limitations and assumptions made in the qualitative discussion presented in Section 6.4, we begin with a more quantitative description of self-inductance than was previously provided.

A Review of Self-Inductance

The concept of inductance can be traced to Michael Faraday, who did pioneering work in this area in the early 1800s. Faraday postulated that a magnetic field consists of lines of force surrounding the current-carrying conductor. Visualize these lines of force as energy-storing elastic bands that close on themselves. As the current increases and decreases, the elastic bands (that is, the lines of force) spread and collapse about the conductor. The voltage induced in the conductor is proportional to the number of lines that collapse into, or cut, the conductor. This image of induced voltage is expressed by what is called Faraday's law; that is,

$$v = \frac{d\lambda}{dt}, \tag{6.33}$$

where λ is referred to as the flux linkage and is measured in weber-turns.

How do we get from Faraday's law to the definition of inductance presented in Section 6.1? We can begin to draw this connection using Fig. 6.27 as a reference.

The lines threading the N turns and labeled ϕ represent the magnetic lines of force that make up the magnetic field. The strength of the magnetic field depends on the strength of the current, and the spatial orientation of the field depends on the direction of the current. The right-hand rule relates the orientation of the field to the direction of the current: When the fingers of the right hand are wrapped around the coil so that the fingers point in the direction of the current, the thumb points in the direction of that portion of the magnetic field inside the coil. The flux linkage is the product of the magnetic field (ϕ), measured in webers (Wb), and the number of turns linked by the field (N):

$$\lambda = N\phi. \tag{6.34}$$

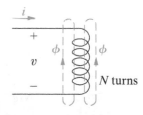

Figure 6.27 ▲ Representation of a magnetic field linking an N-turn coil.

The magnitude of the flux, ϕ, is related to the magnitude of the coil current by the relationship

$$\phi = \mathscr{P}Ni, \tag{6.35}$$

where N is the number of turns on the coil, and $\mathscr{P}$ is the permeance of the space occupied by the flux. Permeance is a quantity that describes the magnetic properties of this space, and as such, a detailed discussion of permeance is outside the scope of this text. Here, we need only observe that, when the space containing the flux is made up of magnetic materials (such as iron, nickel, and cobalt), the permeance varies with the flux, giving a nonlinear relationship between ϕ and i. But when the space containing the flux is comprised of nonmagnetic materials, the permeance is constant, giving a linear relationship between ϕ and i. Note from Eq. 6.35 that the flux is also proportional to the number of turns on the coil.

Here, we assume that the core material—the space containing the flux—is nonmagnetic. Then, substituting Eqs. 6.34 and 6.35 into Eq. 6.33 yields

$$v = \frac{d\lambda}{dt} = \frac{d(N\phi)}{dt}$$

$$= N\frac{d\phi}{dt} = N\frac{d}{dt}(\mathscr{P}Ni)$$

$$= N^2\mathscr{P}\frac{di}{dt} = L\frac{di}{dt}, \tag{6.36}$$

which shows that self-inductance is proportional to the square of the number of turns on the coil. We make use of this observation later.

The polarity of the induced voltage in the circuit in Fig. 6.27 reflects the reaction of the field to the current creating the field. For example, when i is increasing, di/dt is positive and v is positive. Thus energy is required to establish the magnetic field. The product vi gives the rate at which energy is stored in the field. When the field collapses, di/dt is negative, and again the polarity of the induced voltage is in opposition to the change. As the field collapses about the coil, energy is returned to the circuit.

Keeping in mind this further insight into the concept of self-inductance, we now turn back to mutual inductance.

The Concept of Mutual Inductance

Figure 6.28 shows two magnetically coupled coils. You should verify that the dot markings on the two coils agree with the direction of the coil windings and currents shown. The number of turns on each coil are N_1 and N_2, respectively. Coil 1 is energized by a time-varying current source that establishes the current i_1 in the N_1 turns. Coil 2 is not energized and is open. The coils are wound on a nonmagnetic core. The flux produced by the current i_1 can be divided into two components, labeled ϕ_{11} and ϕ_{21}. The flux component ϕ_{11} is the flux produced by i_1 that links only the N_1 turns. The component ϕ_{21} is the flux produced by i_1 that links the N_2 turns and the N_1 turns. The first digit in the subscript to the flux gives the coil number, and the second digit refers to the coil current. Thus ϕ_{11} is a flux linking coil 1 and produced by a current in coil 1, whereas ϕ_{21} is a flux linking coil 2 and produced by a current in coil 1.

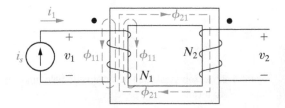

Figure 6.28 ▲ Two magnetically coupled coils.

The total flux linking coil 1 is ϕ_1, the sum of ϕ_{11} and ϕ_{21}:

$$\phi_1 = \phi_{11} + \phi_{21}. \tag{6.37}$$

The flux ϕ_1 and its components ϕ_{11} and ϕ_{21} are related to the coil current i_1 as follows:

$$\phi_1 = \mathscr{P}_1 N_1 i_1, \tag{6.38}$$

$$\phi_{11} = \mathscr{P}_{11} N_1 i_1, \tag{6.39}$$

$$\phi_{21} = \mathscr{P}_{21} N_1 i_1, \tag{6.40}$$

where $\mathscr{P}_1$ is the permeance of the space occupied by the flux ϕ_1, $\mathscr{P}_{11}$ is the permeance of the space occupied by the flux ϕ_{11}, and $\mathscr{P}_{21}$ is the permeance of the space occupied by the flux ϕ_{21}. Substituting Eqs. 6.38, 6.39, and 6.40 into Eq. 6.37 yields the relationship between the permeance of the space occupied by the total flux ϕ_1 and the permeances of the spaces occupied by its components ϕ_{11} and ϕ_{21}:

$$\mathscr{P}_1 = \mathscr{P}_{11} + \mathscr{P}_{21}. \tag{6.41}$$

We use Faraday's law to derive expressions for v_1 and v_2:

$$v_1 = \frac{d\lambda_1}{dt} = \frac{d(N_1\phi_1)}{dt} = N_1 \frac{d}{dt}(\phi_{11} + \phi_{21})$$

$$= N_1^2(\mathscr{P}_{11} + \mathscr{P}_{21})\frac{di_1}{dt} = N_1^2 \mathscr{P}_1 \frac{di_1}{dt} = L_1 \frac{di_1}{dt}, \tag{6.42}$$

and

$$v_2 = \frac{d\lambda_2}{dt} = \frac{d(N_2\phi_{21})}{dt} = N_2 \frac{d}{dt}(\mathscr{P}_{21} N_1 i_1)$$

$$= N_2 N_1 \mathscr{P}_{21} \frac{di_1}{dt}. \tag{6.43}$$

The coefficient of di_1/dt in Eq. 6.42 is the self-inductance of coil 1. The coefficient of di_1/dt in Eq. 6.43 is the mutual inductance between coils 1 and 2. Thus

$$M_{21} = N_2 N_1 \mathscr{P}_{21}. \tag{6.44}$$

The subscript on M specifies an inductance that relates the voltage induced in coil 2 to the current in coil 1.

The coefficient of mutual inductance gives

$$v_2 = M_{21} \frac{di_1}{dt}. \tag{6.45}$$

Note that the dot convention is used to assign the polarity reference to v_2 in Fig. 6.28.

For the coupled coils in Fig. 6.28, exciting coil 2 from a time-varying current source (i_2) and leaving coil 1 open produces the circuit arrangement

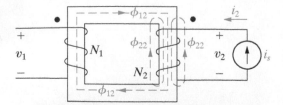

Figure 6.29 ▲ The magnetically coupled coils of Fig. 6.28, with coil 2 excited and coil 1 open.

shown in Fig. 6.29. Again, the polarity reference assigned to v_1 is based on the dot convention.

The total flux linking coil 2 is

$$\phi_2 = \phi_{22} + \phi_{12}. \tag{6.46}$$

The flux ϕ_2 and its components ϕ_{22} and ϕ_{12} are related to the coil current i_2 as follows:

$$\phi_2 = \mathscr{P}_2 N_2 i_2, \tag{6.47}$$

$$\phi_{22} = \mathscr{P}_{22} N_2 i_2, \tag{6.48}$$

$$\phi_{12} = \mathscr{P}_{12} N_2 i_2. \tag{6.49}$$

The voltages v_2 and v_1 are

$$v_2 = \frac{d\lambda_2}{dt} = N_2^2 \mathscr{P}_2 \frac{di_2}{dt} = L_2 \frac{di_2}{dt}, \tag{6.50}$$

$$v_1 = \frac{d\lambda_1}{dt} = \frac{d}{dt}(N_1 \phi_{12}) = N_1 N_2 \mathscr{P}_{12} \frac{di_2}{dt}. \tag{6.51}$$

The coefficient of mutual inductance that relates the voltage induced in coil 1 to the time-varying current in coil 2 is the coefficient of di_2/dt in Eq. 6.51:

$$M_{12} = N_1 N_2 \mathscr{P}_{12}. \tag{6.52}$$

For nonmagnetic materials, the permeances $\mathscr{P}_{12}$ and $\mathscr{P}_{21}$ are equal, and therefore

$$M_{12} = M_{21} = M. \tag{6.53}$$

Hence for linear circuits with just two magnetically coupled coils, attaching subscripts to the coefficient of mutual inductance is not necessary.

Mutual Inductance in Terms of Self-Inductance

The value of mutual inductance is a function of the self-inductances. We derive this relationship as follows. From Eqs. 6.42 and 6.50,

$$L_1 = N_1^2 \mathscr{P}_1, \tag{6.54}$$

$$L_2 = N_2^2 \mathscr{P}_2, \tag{6.55}$$

respectively. From Eqs. 6.54 and 6.55,

$$L_1 L_2 = N_1^2 N_2^2 \mathscr{P}_1 \mathscr{P}_2. \tag{6.56}$$

We now use Eq. 6.41 and the corresponding expression for $\mathcal{P}_2$ to write

$$L_1 L_2 = N_1^2 N_2^2 (\mathcal{P}_{11} + \mathcal{P}_{21})(\mathcal{P}_{22} + \mathcal{P}_{12}). \tag{6.57}$$

But for a linear system, $\mathcal{P}_{21} = \mathcal{P}_{12}$, so Eq. 6.57 becomes

$$L_1 L_2 = (N_1 N_2 \mathcal{P}_{12})^2 \left(1 + \frac{\mathcal{P}_{11}}{\mathcal{P}_{12}} \right) \left(1 + \frac{\mathcal{P}_{22}}{\mathcal{P}_{12}} \right)$$

$$= M^2 \left(1 + \frac{\mathcal{P}_{11}}{\mathcal{P}_{12}} \right) \left(1 + \frac{\mathcal{P}_{22}}{\mathcal{P}_{12}} \right). \tag{6.58}$$

Replacing the two terms involving permeances by a single constant expresses Eq. 6.58 in a more meaningful form:

$$\frac{1}{k^2} = \left(1 + \frac{\mathcal{P}_{11}}{\mathcal{P}_{12}} \right) \left(1 + \frac{\mathcal{P}_{22}}{\mathcal{P}_{12}} \right). \tag{6.59}$$

Substituting Eq. 6.59 into Eq. 6.58 yields

$$M^2 = k^2 L_1 L_2$$

or

$$M = k\sqrt{L_1 L_2}, \tag{6.60}$$

◀ **Relating self-inductances and mutual inductance using coupling coefficient**

where the constant k is called the **coefficient of coupling**. According to Eq. 6.59, $1/k^2$ must be greater than 1, which means that k must be less than 1. In fact, the coefficient of coupling must lie between 0 and 1, or

$$0 \le k \le 1. \tag{6.61}$$

The coefficient of coupling is 0 when the two coils have no common flux; that is, when $\phi_{12} = \phi_{21} = 0$. This condition implies that $\mathcal{P}_{12} = 0$, and Eq. 6.59 indicates that $1/k^2 = \infty$, or $k = 0$. If there is no flux linkage between the coils, obviously M is 0.

The coefficient of coupling is equal to 1 when ϕ_{11} and ϕ_{22} are 0. This condition implies that all the flux that links coil 1 also links coil 2. In terms of Eq. 6.59, $\mathcal{P}_{11} = \mathcal{P}_{22} = 0$, which obviously represents an ideal state; in reality, winding two coils so that they share precisely the same flux is physically impossible. Magnetic materials (such as alloys of iron, cobalt, and nickel) create a space with high permeance and are used to establish coefficients of coupling that approach unity. (We say more about this important quality of magnetic materials in Chapter 9.)

NOTE: Assess your understanding of this material by trying Chapter Problems 6.46 and 6.50.

Energy Calculations

We conclude our first look at mutual inductance with a discussion of the total energy stored in magnetically coupled coils. In doing so, we will confirm two observations made earlier: For linear magnetic coupling, (1) $M_{12} = M_{21} = M$, and (2) $M = k\sqrt{L_1 L_2}$, where $0 \le k \le 1$.

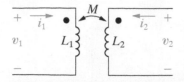

Figure 6.30 ▲ The circuit used to derive the basic energy relationships.

We use the circuit shown in Fig. 6.30 to derive the expression for the total energy stored in the magnetic fields associated with a pair of linearly coupled coils. We begin by assuming that the currents i_1 and i_2 are zero and that this zero-current state corresponds to zero energy stored in the coils. Then we let i_1 increase from zero to some arbitrary value I_1 and compute the energy stored when $i_1 = I_1$. Because $i_2 = 0$, the total power input into the pair of coils is $v_1 i_1$, and the energy stored is

$$\int_0^{W_1} dw = L_1 \int_0^{I_1} i_1 di_1,$$

$$W_1 = \frac{1}{2}L_1 I_1^2. \tag{6.62}$$

Now we hold i_1 constant at I_1 and increase i_2 from zero to some arbitrary value I_2. During this time interval, the voltage induced in coil 2 by i_1 is zero because I_1 is constant. The voltage induced in coil 1 by i_2 is $M_{12}di_2/dt$. Therefore, the power input to the pair of coils is

$$p = I_1 M_{12}\frac{di_2}{dt} + i_2 v_2.$$

The total energy stored in the pair of coils when $i_2 = I_2$ is

$$\int_{W_1}^{W} dw = \int_0^{I_2} I_1 M_{12} di_2 + \int_0^{I_2} L_2 i_2 di_2,$$

or

$$W = W_1 + I_1 I_2 M_{12} + \frac{1}{2}L_2 I_2^2,$$

$$= \frac{1}{2}L_1 I_1^2 + \frac{1}{2}L_2 I_2^2 + I_1 I_2 M_{12}. \tag{6.63}$$

If we reverse the procedure—that is, if we first increase i_2 from zero to I_2 and then increase i_1 from zero to I_1—the total energy stored is

$$W = \frac{1}{2}L_1 I_1^2 + \frac{1}{2}L_2 I_2^2 + I_1 I_2 M_{21}. \tag{6.64}$$

Equations 6.63 and 6.64 express the total energy stored in a pair of linearly coupled coils as a function of the coil currents, the self-inductances, and the mutual inductance. Note that the only difference between these equations is the coefficient of the current product $I_1 I_2$. We use Eq. 6.63 if i_1 is established first and Eq. 6.64 if i_2 is established first.

When the coupling medium is linear, the total energy stored is the same regardless of the order used to establish I_1 and I_2. The reason is that in a linear coupling, the resultant magnetic flux depends only on the final values of i_1 and i_2, not on how the currents reached their final values. If the resultant flux is the same, the stored energy is the same. Therefore, for linear coupling, $M_{12} = M_{21}$. Also, because I_1 and I_2 are arbitrary values of i_1 and i_2, respectively, we represent the coil currents by their instantaneous values i_1 and i_2. Thus, at any instant of time, the total energy stored in the coupled coils is

$$w(t) = \frac{1}{2}L_1 i_1^2 + \frac{1}{2}L_2 i_2^2 + M i_1 i_2. \tag{6.65}$$

We derived Eq. 6.65 by assuming that both coil currents entered polarity-marked terminals. We leave it to you to verify that, if one current enters a polarity-marked terminal while the other leaves such a terminal, the algebraic sign of the term $M i_1 i_2$ reverses. Thus, in general,

$$w(t) = \frac{1}{2}L_1 i_1^2 + \frac{1}{2}L_2 i_2^2 \pm M i_1 i_2. \tag{6.66}$$

◄ **Energy stored in magnetically-coupled coils**

We use Eq. 6.66 to show that M cannot exceed $\sqrt{L_1 L_2}$. The magnetically coupled coils are passive elements, so the total energy stored can never be negative. If $w(t)$ can never be negative, Eq. 6.66 indicates that the quantity

$$\frac{1}{2}L_1 i_1^2 + \frac{1}{2}L_2 i_2^2 - M i_1 i_2$$

must be greater than or equal to zero when i_1 and i_2 are either both positive or both negative. The limiting value of M corresponds to setting the quantity equal to zero:

$$\frac{1}{2}L_1 i_1^2 + \frac{1}{2}L_2 i_2^2 - M i_1 i_2 = 0. \tag{6.67}$$

To find the limiting value of M we add and subtract the term $i_1 i_2 \sqrt{L_1 L_2}$ to the left-hand side of Eq. 6.67. Doing so generates a term that is a perfect square:

$$\left(\sqrt{\frac{L_1}{2}} i_1 - \sqrt{\frac{L_2}{2}} i_2 \right)^2 + i_1 i_2 \left(\sqrt{L_1 L_2} - M \right) = 0. \tag{6.68}$$

The squared term in Eq. 6.68 can never be negative, but it can be zero. Therefore $w(t) \geq 0$ only if

$$\sqrt{L_1 L_2} \geq M, \tag{6.69}$$

which is another way of saying that

$$M = k\sqrt{L_1 L_2} \qquad (0 \le k \le 1).$$

We derived Eq. 6.69 by assuming that i_1 and i_2 are either both positive or both negative. However, we get the same result if i_1 and i_2 are of opposite sign, because in this case we obtain the limiting value of M by selecting the plus sign in Eq. 6.66.

NOTE: Assess your understanding of this material by trying Chapter Problems 6.47 and 6.48.

Practical Perspective

Capacitive Touch Screens

Capacitive touch screens are often used in applications where two or more simultaneous touch points must be detected. We will discuss two designs for a multi-touch screen. The first design employs a grid of electrodes, as shown in Fig. 6.31. When energized, a small parasitic capacitance, C_p, exists between each electrode strip and ground, as shown in Fig. 6.32(a). When the screen is touched, say at the position x, y on the screen, a second capacitance exists due to the transfer of a small amount of charge from the screen to the human body, which acts like a conductor. The effect is to introduce a second capacitance at the point of touch with respect to ground, as shown in Fig. 6.32(b).

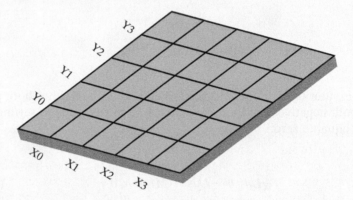

Figure 6.31 ▲ Multi-touch screen with grid of electrodes.

The touchscreen controller is continually monitoring the capacitance between the electrodes in the grid and ground. If the screen is not being touched, the capacitance between every electrode in the x-grid and ground is C_p; the same is true for the capacitance between every electrode in the y-grid and ground.

When the screen is touched at a single point, C_t and C_p combine in parallel. The equivalent capacitance between the x-grid electrode closest to the touch point and ground is now

$$C_{tx} = C_t + C_p.$$

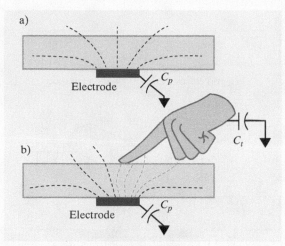

Figure 6.32 ▲ (a) Parasitic capacitance between electrode and ground with no touch; (b) Additional capacitance introduced by a touch.

Likewise, the equivalent capacitance between the y-grid electrode closest to the touch point and ground is now

$$C_{ty} = C_t + C_p.$$

Thus, a screen touch increases the capacitance between the electrodes and ground for the x- and y-grid electrodes closest to the touch point.

Now consider what happens when there are two simultaneous points where the screen is touched. Assume that the first touch point has coordinates x_1, y_1 and the second touch point has coordinates x_2, y_2. Now there are four screen locations that correspond to an increase in capacitance: x_1, y_1; x_1, y_2; x_2, y_1; and x_2, y_2. Two of those screen locations match the two touch points, and the other two points are called "ghost" points, because the screen was not touched at those points. Therefore, this method for implementing a capacitive touch screen cannot accurately identify more than a single touch point.

Most modern capacitive touch screens do not use the "self-capacitance" design discussed above. Instead of measuring the capacitance between each x-grid electrode and ground, and each y-grid electrode and ground, the capacitance between each x-grid electrode and each y-grid electrode is measured. This capacitance is known as "mutual" capacitance and is shown in Fig. 6.33(a).

When the screen is touched, say at the position x, y on the screen, a second capacitance again exists due to the transfer of a small amount of charge from the screen to the human body. A second capacitance exists at the point of touch with respect to ground, as shown in Fig. 6.33(b). Therefore, whenever there is a change in the mutual capacitance, C_{mxy}, the screen touch point can be uniquely identified as x, y. If the screen is touched at the points x_1, y_1 and x_2, y_2 then there will be precisely two mutual capacitances that change: $C_{mx_1y_1}$ and $C_{mx_2y_2}$. There are no "ghost"

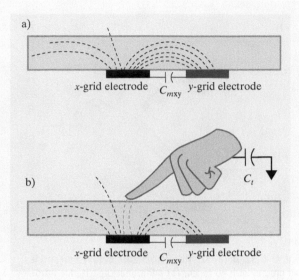

Figure 6.33 ▲ (a) Mutual capacitance between an *x*-grid and a *y*-grid electrode; (b) Additional capacitance introduced by a touch.

points identified, as there were in the self-capacitance design, so the mutual capacitance design truly produces a multi-touch screen capable of identifying two or more touch points uniquely and accurately.

NOTE: Assess your understanding of the Practical Perspective by solving Chapter Problems 6.51–6.53.

Summary

- **Inductance** is a linear circuit parameter that relates the voltage induced by a time-varying magnetic field to the current producing the field. (See page 176.)

- **Capacitance** is a linear circuit parameter that relates the current induced by a time-varying electric field to the voltage producing the field. (See page 182.)

- Inductors and capacitors are passive elements; they can store and release energy, but they cannot generate or dissipate energy. (See page 176.)

- The instantaneous power at the terminals of an inductor or capacitor can be positive or negative, depending on whether energy is being delivered to or extracted from the element.

- An inductor:
  - does not permit an instantaneous change in its terminal current,
  - does permit an instantaneous change in its teminal voltage, and
  - behaves as a short circuit in the presence of a constant terminal current. (See page 188.)

- A capacitor:
  - does not permit an instantaneous change in its terminal voltage,
  - does permit an instantaneous change in its terminal current, and
  - behaves as an open circuit in the presence of a constant terminal voltage. (See page 183.)

- Equations for voltage, current, power, and energy in ideal inductors and capacitors are given in Table 6.1.

- Inductors in series or in parallel can be replaced by an equivalent inductor. Capacitors in series or in parallel can be replaced by an equivalent capacitor. The equations arc summarized in Table 6.2. See Section 6.3 for a discussion on how to handle the initial conditions for series and parallel equivalent circuits involving inductors and capacitors.

- **Mutual inductance**, M, is the circuit parameter relating the voltage induced in one circuit to a time-varying current in another circuit. Specifically,

$$v_1 = L_1 \frac{di_1}{dt} + M_{12} \frac{di_2}{dt}$$

$$v_2 = M_{21} \frac{di_1}{dt} + L_2 \frac{di_2}{dt},$$

where v_1 and i_1 are the voltage and current in circuit 1, and v_2 and i_2 are the voltage and current in circuit 2. For coils wound on nonmagnetic cores, $M_{12} = M_{21} = \text{M}$. (See page 190.)

- The **dot convention** establishes the polarity of mutually induced voltages:

  When the reference direction for a current enters the dotted terminal of a coil, the reference polarity of the voltage that it induces in the other coil is positive at its dotted terminal.

  Or, alternatively,

  When the reference direction for a current leaves the dotted terminal of a coil, the reference polarity of the voltage that it induces in the other coil is negative at its dotted terminal.

(See page 190.)

- The relationship between the self-inductance of each winding and the mutual inductance bctween windings is

$$M = k\sqrt{L_1 L_2}.$$

The **coefficient of coupling**, k, is a measure of the degree of magnetic coupling. By definition, $0 \le k \le 1$. (See page 197.)

TABLE 6.1 Terminal Equations for Ideal Inductors and Capacitors

Inductors

$v = L\frac{di}{dt}$	(V)
$i = \frac{1}{L}\int_{t_0}^{t} v \, d\tau + i(t_0)$	(A)
$p = vi = Li\frac{di}{dt}$	(W)
$w = \frac{1}{2}Li^2$	(J)

Capacitors

$v = \frac{1}{C}\int_{t_0}^{t} i \, d\tau + v(t_0)$	(V)
$i = C\frac{dv}{dt}$	(A)
$p = vi = Cv\frac{dv}{dt}$	(W)
$w = \frac{1}{2}Cv^2$	(J)

TABLE 6.2 Equations for Series- and Parallel-Connected Inductors and Capacitors

Series-Connected

$$L_{eq} = L_1 + L_2 + \cdots + L_n$$

$$\frac{1}{C_{eq}} = \frac{1}{C_1} + \frac{1}{C_2} + \cdots + \frac{1}{C_n}$$

Parallel-Conncctcd

$$\frac{1}{L_{eq}} = \frac{1}{L_1} + \frac{1}{L_2} + \cdots + \frac{1}{L_n}$$

$$C_{eq} = C_1 + C_2 + \cdots + C_n$$

- The energy stored in magnetically coupled coils in a linear medium is related to the coil currents and inductances by the relationship

$$w = \frac{1}{2}L_1 i_1^2 + \frac{1}{2}L_2 i_2^2 \pm M i_1 i_2.$$

(See page 199.)

Problems

Section 6.1

6.1 The current in a 150 μH inductor is known to be

$$i_L = 25te^{-500t}\,\text{A} \quad \text{for } t \geq 0.$$

a) Find the voltage across the inductor for $t > 0$. (Assume the passive sign convention.)

b) Find the power (in microwatts) at the terminals of the inductor when $t = 5$ ms.

c) Is the inductor absorbing or delivering power at 5 ms?

d) Find the energy (in microjoules) stored in the inductor at 5 ms.

e) Find the maximum energy (in microjoules) stored in the inductor and the time (in milliseconds) when it occurs.

6.2 The triangular current pulse shown in Fig. P6.2 is applied to a 500 mH inductor.

a) Write the expressions that describe $i(t)$ in the four intervals $t < 0$, $0 \leq t \leq 25$ ms, 25 ms $\leq t \leq 50$ ms, and $t > 50$ ms.

b) Derive the expressions for the inductor voltage, power, and energy. Use the passive sign convention.

Figure P6.2

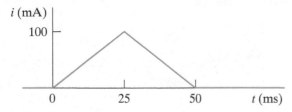

6.3 The current in a 50 mH inductor is known to be

$$i = 120\,\text{mA}, \qquad\qquad t \leq 0;$$

$$i = A_1 e^{-500t} + A_2 e^{-2000t}\,\text{A}, \qquad t \geq 0.$$

The voltage across the inductor (passive sign convention) is 3 V at $t = 0$.

a) Find the expression for the voltage across the inductor for $t > 0$.

b) Find the time, greater than zero, when the power at the terminals of the inductor is zero.

6.4 Assume in Problem 6.3 that the value of the voltage across the inductor at $t = 0$ is -18 V instead of 3 V.

a) Find the numerical expressions for i and v for $t \geq 0$.

b) Specify the time intervals when the inductor is storing energy and the time intervals when the inductor is delivering energy.

c) Show that the total energy extracted from the inductor is equal to the total energy stored.

6.5 The current in a 200 mH inductor is

$$i = 75\,\text{mA}, \qquad\qquad t \leq 0;$$

$$i = (B_1 \cos 200t + B_2 \sin 200t)e^{-50t}\,\text{A}, \quad t \geq 0.$$

The voltage across the inductor (passive sign convention) is 4.25 V at $t = 0$. Calculate the power at the terminals of the inductor at $t = 25$ ms. State whether the inductor is absorbing or delivering power.

6.6 Evaluate the integral

$$\int_0^\infty p\, dt$$

for Example 6.2. Comment on the significance of the result.

6.7 The voltage at the terminals of the 750 μH inductor in Fig. P6.7(a) is shown in Fig. P6.7(b). The inductor current i is known to be zero for $t \leq 0$.

a) Derive the expressions for i for $t \geq 0$.

b) Sketch i versus t for $0 \leq t \leq \infty$.

Figure P6.7

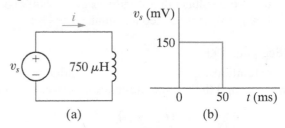

6.8 The current in the 50 mH inductor in Fig. P6.8 is known to be 100 mA for $t < 0$. The inductor voltage for $t \geq 0$ is given by the expression

$$v_L(t) = 2e^{-100t}\,\text{V}, \qquad\qquad 0^+ \leq t \leq 100\,\text{ms}$$

$$v_L(t) = -2e^{-100(t-0.1)}\,\text{V}, \qquad 100\,\text{ms} \leq t < \infty$$

Sketch $v_L(t)$ and $i_L(t)$ for $0 \leq t < \infty$.

Figure P6.8

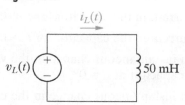

6.9 The current in and the voltage across a 10 H inductor are known to be zero for $t \leq 0$. The voltage across the inductor is given by the graph in Fig. P6.9 for $t \geq 0$.

a) Derive the expression for the current as a function of time in the intervals $0 \leq t \leq 25$ ms, 25 ms $\leq t \leq 75$ ms, 75 ms $\leq t \leq 125$ ms, 125 ms $\leq t \leq 150$ ms, and 150 ms $\leq t < \infty$.

b) For $t > 0$, what is the current in the inductor when the voltage is zero?

c) Sketch i versus t for $0 \leq t < \infty$.

Figure P6.9

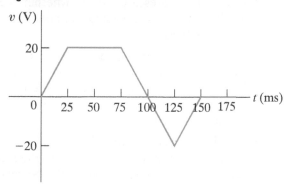

6.10 a) Find the inductor current in the circuit in Fig. P6.10 if $v = 20 \cos 80t$ V, L = 100 mH, and $i(0) = 0$ A.

b) Sketch v, i, p, and w versus t. In making these sketches, use the format used in Fig. 6.8. Plot over one complete cycle of the voltage waveform.

c) Describe the subintervals in the time interval between 0 and 8π ms when power is being absorbed by the inductor. Repeat for the subintervals when power is being delivered by the inductor.

Figure P6.10

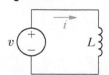

6.11 The current in a 25 mH inductor is known to be -10 A for $t \leq 0$ and $(-10 \cos 400t - 5 \sin 400t)\, e^{-200t}$ A for $t \geq 0$. Assume the passive sign convention.

a) At what instant of time is the voltage across the inductor maximum?

b) What is the maximum voltage?

6.12 Initially there was no energy stored in the 5 H inductor in the circuit in Fig. P6.12 when it was placed across the terminals of the voltmeter. At $t = 0$ the inductor was switched instantaneously to position b where it remained for 1.6 s before returning instantaneously to position a. The d'Arsonval voltmeter has a full-scale reading of 20 V and a sensitivity of 1000 Ω/V. What will the reading of the voltmeter be at the instant the switch returns to position a if the inertia of the d'Arsonval movement is negligible?

Figure P6.12

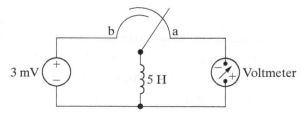

Section 6.2

6.13 The voltage across a 5 μF capacitor is known to be

$$v_c = 500te^{-2500t} \text{ V} \quad \text{for} \quad t \geq 0.$$

a) Find the current through the capacitor for $t > 0$. Assume the passive sign convention.

b) Find the power at the terminals of the capacitor when $t = 100\ \mu$s.

c) Is the capacitor absorbing or delivering power at $t = 100\ \mu$s ?

d) Find the energy stored in the capacitor at $t = 100\ \mu$s.

e) Find the maximum energy stored in the capacitors and the time when the maximum occurs.

6.14 The triangular voltage pulse shown in Fig. P6.14 is applied to a 200 μF capacitor.

a) Write the expressions that describe $v(t)$ in the five time intervals $t < 0, 0 \leq t \leq 2$ s, 2 s $\leq t \leq 6$ s, 6 s $\leq t \leq 8$ s, and $t > 8$ s.

b) Derive the expressions for the capacitor current, power, and energy for the time intervals in part (a). Use the passive sign convention.

c) Identify the time intervals between 0 and 8 s when power is being delivered by the capacitor. Repeat for the time intervals when power is being absorbed by the capacitor.

Figure P6.14

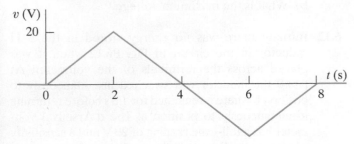

6.15 The voltage across the terminals of a 5 μF capacitor is

PSPICE
MULTISIM

$$v = \begin{cases} 60 \text{ V}, & t \leq 0; \\ (A_1 e^{-1500t} + A_2 t e^{-1500t}) \text{ V}, & t \geq 0. \end{cases}$$

The initial current in the capacitor is 100 mA. Assume the passive sign convention.

a) What is the initial energy stored in the capacitor?

b) Evaluate the coefficients A_1 and A_2.

c) What is the expression for the capacitor current?

6.16 A 100 μF capacitor is subjected to a voltage pulse having a duration of 4 s. The pulse is described by the following equations:

$$v_c(t) = \begin{cases} 5t^3 \text{ V}, & 0 \leq t \leq 2 \text{ s}; \\ -5(t-4)^3 \text{ V}, & 2 \text{ s} \leq t \leq 4 \text{ s}; \\ 0 & \text{elsewhere}. \end{cases}$$

Sketch the current pulse that exists in the capacitor during the 4 s interval.

6.17 The voltage at the terminals of the capacitor in Fig. 6.10 is known to be

PSPICE
MULTISIM

$$v = \begin{cases} 60 \text{ V}, & t \leq 0; \\ 30 + 5e^{-500t} (6 \cos 2000t + \sin 2000\ t) \text{ V}, & t \geq 0. \end{cases}$$

Assume $C = 120\ \mu$F.

a) Find the current in the capacitor for $t < 0$.

b) Find the current in the capacitor for $t > 0$.

c) Is there an instantaneous change in the voltage across the capacitor at $t = 0$?

d) Is there an instantaneous change in the current in the capacitor at $t = 0$?

e) How much energy (in millijoules) is stored in the capacitor at $t = \infty$?

6.18 The expressions for voltage, power, and energy derived in Example 6.5 involved both integration and manipulation of algebraic expressions. As an engineer, you cannot accept such results on faith alone. That is, you should develop the habit of asking yourself, "Do these results make sense in terms of the known behavior of the circuit they purport to describe?" With these thoughts in mind, test the expressions of Example 6.5 by performing the following checks:

a) Check the expressions to see whether the voltage is continuous in passing from one time interval to the next.

b) Check the power expression in each interval by selecting a time within the interval and seeing whether it gives the same result as the corresponding product of v and i. For example, test at 10 and 30 μs.

c) Check the energy expression within each interval by selecting a time within the interval and seeing whether the energy equation gives the same result as $\frac{1}{2}Cv^2$. Use 10 and 30 μs as test points.

6.19 The initial voltage on the 0.5 μF capacitor shown in Fig. P6.19(a) is -20 V. The capacitor current has the waveform shown in Fig. P6.19(b).

PSPICE
MULTISIM

a) How much energy, in microjoules, is stored in the capacitor at $t = 500\ \mu$s?

b) Repeat (a) for $t = \infty$.

Figure P6.19

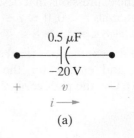

(a)

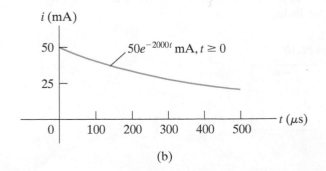

(b)

6.20 The current shown in Fig. 6.20 is applied to a 2 μF capacitor. The initial voltage on the capacitor is zero.

PSPICE
MULTISIM

a) Find the charge on the capacitor at $t = 6$ ms.

b) Find the voltage on the capacitor at $t = 10$ ms.

c) How much energy is stored in the capacitor by this current?

Figure P6.20

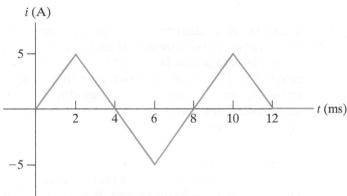

6.21 The rectangular-shaped current pulse shown in Fig. P6.21 is applied to a 0.1 μF capacitor. The initial voltage on the capacitor is a 15 V drop in the reference direction of the current. Derive the expression for the capacitor voltage for the time intervals in (a)–(d).

PSPICE
MULTISIM

a) $0 \le t \le 10 \mu s$;

b) $10 \mu s \le t \le 20 \mu s$;

c) $20 \mu s \le t \le 40 \mu s$

d) $40 \mu s \le t < \infty$

e) Sketch $v(t)$ over the interval $-10 \mu s \le t \le 50 \mu s$.

Figure P6.21

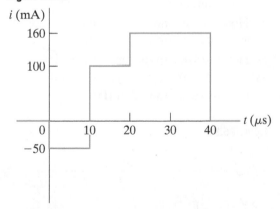

Section 6.3

6.22 Assume that the initial energy stored in the inductors of Figs. P6.22(a) and (b) is zero. Find the equivalent inductance with respect to the terminals a, b.

PSPICE
MULTISIM

Figure P6.22

(a)

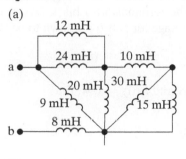

(b)

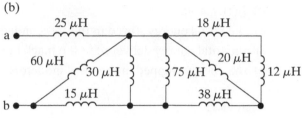

6.23 Use realistic inductor values from Appendix H to construct series and parallel combinations of inductors to yield the equivalent inductances specified below. Try to minimize the number of inductors used. Assume that no initial energy is stored in any of the inductors.

a) 8 mH

b) 45 μH

c) 180 μH

6.24 The two parallel inductors in Fig. P6.24 are connected across the terminals of a black box at $t = 0$. The resulting voltage v for $t > 0$ is known to be $64e^{-4t}$ V. It is also known that $i_1(0) = -10$ A and $i_2(0) = 5$ A.

a) Replace the original inductors with an equivalent inductor and find $i(t)$ for $t \ge 0$.

b) Find $i_1(t)$ for $t \ge 0$.

c) Find $i_2(t)$ for $t \ge 0$.

d) How much energy is delivered to the black box in the time interval $0 \le t < \infty$?

e) How much energy was initially stored in the parallel inductors?

f) How much energy is trapped in the ideal inductors?

g) Show that your solutions for i_1 and i_2 agree with the answer obtained in (f).

Figure P6.24

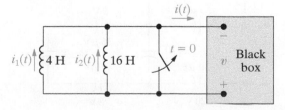

6.25 The three inductors in the circuit in Fig. P6.25 are con-
PSPICE   nected across the terminals of a black box at $t = 0$.
MULTISIM The resulting voltage for $t > 0$ is known to be

$$v_o = 2000e^{-100t} \text{ V}.$$

If $i_1(0) = -6$ A and $i_2(0) = 1$ A, find

a) $i_o(0)$;

b) $i_o(t), t \geq 0$;

c) $i_1(t), t \geq 0$;

d) $i_2(t), t \geq 0$;

e) the initial energy stored in the three inductors;

f) the total energy delivered to the black box; and

g) the energy trapped in the ideal inductors.

Figure P6.25

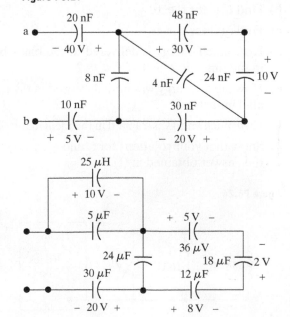

6.26 For the circuit shown in Fig. P6.25, how many milliseconds after the switch is opened is the energy
delivered to the black box 80% of the total energy
delivered?

6.27 Find the equivalent capacitance with respect to the
terminals a, b for the circuits shown in Fig. P6.27.

Figure P6.27

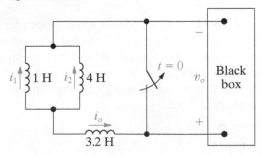

6.28 Use realistic capacitor values from Appendix H to
construct series and parallel combinations of capacitors to yield the equivalent capacitances specified
below. Try to minimize the number of capacitors
used. Assume that no initial energy is stored in any
of the capacitors.

a) 480 pF

b) 600 nF

c) 120 μF

6.29 Derive the equivalent circuit for a series connection
of ideal capacitors. Assume that each capacitor has
its own initial voltage. Denote these initial voltages
as $v_1(t_0)$, $v_2(t_0)$, and so on. (*Hint:* Sum the voltages
across the string of capacitors, recognizing that the
series connection forces the current in each capacitor to be the same.)

6.30 Derive the equivalent circuit for a parallel connection of ideal capacitors. Assume that the initial voltage across the paralleled capacitors is $v(t_0)$. (*Hint:*
Sum the currents into the string of capacitors, recognizing that the parallel connection forces the
voltage across each capacitor to be the same.)

6.31 The two series-connected capacitors in Fig. P6.31
are connected to the terminals of a black box at
$t = 0$. The resulting current $i(t)$ for $t > 0$ is known
to be $800e^{-25t}$ μA.

a) Replace the original capacitors with an equivalent capacitor and find $v_o(t)$ for $t \geq 0$.

b) Find $v_1(t)$ for $t \geq 0$.

c) Find $v_2(t)$ for $t \geq 0$.

d) How much energy is delivered to the black box
in the time interval $0 \leq t < \infty$?

e) How much energy was initially stored in the
series capacitors?

f) How much energy is trapped in the ideal capacitors?

g) Show that the solutions for v_1 and v_2 agree with
the answer obtained in (f).

Figure P6.31

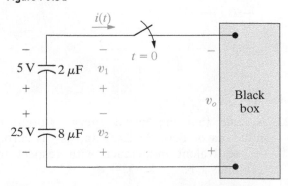

6.32 The four capacitors in the circuit in Fig. P6.32 are connected across the terminals of a black box at $t = 0$. The resulting current i_b for $t > 0$ is known to be

$$i_b = -5e^{-50t} \text{ mA}.$$

If $v_a(0) = -20$ V, $v_c(0) = -30$ V, and $v_d(0) = 250$ V, find the following for $t \geq 0$: (a) $v_b(t)$, (b) $v_a(t)$, (c) $v_c(t)$, (d) $v_d(t)$, (e) $i_1(t)$, and (f) $i_2(t)$.

Figure P6.32

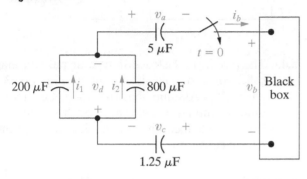

6.33 For the circuit in Fig. P6.32, calculate

a) the initial energy stored in the capacitors;

b) the final energy stored in the capacitors;

c) the total energy delivered to the black box;

d) the percentage of the initial energy stored that is delivered to the black box; and

e) the time, in milliseconds, it takes to deliver 7.5 mJ to the black box.

6.34 At $t = 0$, a series-connected capacitor and inductor are placed across the terminals of a black box, as shown in Fig. P6.34. For $t > 0$, it is known that

$$i_o = 200e^{-800t} - 40e^{-200t} \text{ mA}.$$

If $v_c(0) = 5$ V find v_o for $t \geq 0$.

Figure P6.34

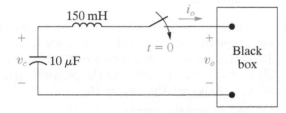

6.35 The current in the circuit in Fig. P6.35 is known to be
$$i_o = 2e^{-5000t}(\cos 1000t + 5 \sin 1000t) \text{ A}$$
for $t \geq 0^+$. Find $v_1(0^+)$ and $v_2(0^+)$.

Figure P6.35

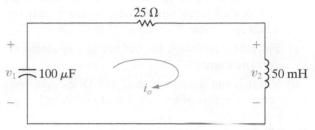

Section 6.4

6.36 a) Show that the differential equations derived in (a) of Example 6.6 can be rearranged as follows:

$$4\frac{di_1}{dt} + 25i_1 - 8\frac{di_2}{dt} - 20i_2 = 5i_g - 8\frac{di_g}{dt};$$

$$-8\frac{di_1}{dt} - 20i_1 + 16\frac{di_2}{dt} + 80i_2 = 16\frac{di_g}{dt}.$$

b) Show that the solutions for i_1, and i_2 given in (b) of Example 6.6 satisfy the differential equations given in part (a) of this problem.

6.37 Let v_o represent the voltage across the 16 H inductor in the circuit in Fig. 6.25. Assume v_o is positive at the dot. As in Example 6.6, $i_g = 16 - 16e^{-5t}$ A.

a) Can you find v_o without having to differentiate the expressions for the currents? Explain.

b) Derive the expression for v_o.

c) Check your answer in (b) using the appropriate current derivatives and inductances.

6.38 Let v_g represent the voltage across the current source in the circuit in Fig. 6.25. The reference for v_g is positive at the upper terminal of the current source.

a) Find v_g as a function of time when $i_g = 16 - 16e^{-5t}$ A.

b) What is the initial value of v_g?

c) Find the expression for the power developed by the current source.

d) How much power is the current source developing when t is infinite?

e) Calculate the power dissipated in each resistor when t is infinite.

6.39 There is no energy stored in the circuit in Fig. P6.39 at the time the switch is opened.

a) Derive the differential equation that governs the behavior of i_2 if $L_1 = 5$ H, $L_2 = 0.2$ H, $M = 0.5$ H, and $R_o = 10 \Omega$.

b) Show that when $i_g = e^{-10t} - 10$ A, $t \geq 0$, the differential equation derived in (a) is satisfied when $i_2 = 625e^{-10t} - 250e^{-50t}$ mA, $t \geq 0$.

c) Find the expression for the voltage v_1 across the current source.

d) What is the initial value of v_1? Does this make sense in terms of known circuit behavior?

Figure P6.39

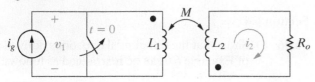

6.40 a) Show that the two coupled coils in Fig. P6.40 can be replaced by a single coil having an inductance of $L_{ab} = L_1 + L_2 + 2M$. (*Hint:* Express v_{ab} as a function of i_{ab}.)

b) Show that if the connections to the terminals of the coil labeled L_2 are reversed, $L_{ab} = L_1 + L_2 - 2M$.

Figure P6.40

6.41 a) Show that the two magnetically coupled coils in Fig. P6.41 (see page 210) can be replaced by a single coil having an inductance of

$$L_{ab} = \frac{L_1 L_2 - M^2}{L_1 + L_2 - 2M}.$$

(*Hint:* Let i_1 and i_2 be clockwise mesh currents in the left and right "windows" of Fig. P6.41, respectively. Sum the voltages around the two meshes. In mesh 1 let v_{ab} be the unspecified applied voltage. Solve for di_1/dt as a function of v_{ab}.)

b) Show that if the magnetic polarity of coil 2 is reversed, then

$$L_{ab} = \frac{L_1 L_2 - M^2}{L_1 + L_2 + 2M}.$$

Figure P6.41

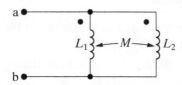

6.42 The polarity markings on two coils are to be determined experimentally. The experimental setup is shown in Fig. P6.42. Assume that the terminal connected to the positive terminal of the battery has been given a polarity mark as shown. When the switch is *opened*, the dc voltmeter kicks downscale. Where should the polarity mark be placed on the coil connected to the voltmeter?

Figure P6.42

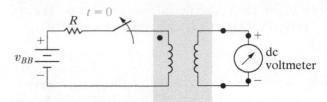

6.43 The physical construction of four pairs of magnetically coupled coils is shown in Fig. P6.43. (See page 211.) Assume that the magnetic flux is confined to the core material in each structure. Show two possible locations for the dot markings on each pair of coils.

Section 6.5

6.44 a) Starting with Eq. 6.59, show that the coefficient of coupling can also be expressed as

$$k = \sqrt{\left(\frac{\phi_{21}}{\phi_1}\right)\left(\frac{\phi_{12}}{\phi_2}\right)}.$$

b) On the basis of the fractions ϕ_{21}/ϕ_1 and ϕ_{12}/ϕ_2, explain why k is less than 1.0.

6.45 Two magnetically coupled coils have self-inductances of 60 mH and 9.6 mH, respectively. The mutual inductance between the coils is 22.8 mH.

a) What is the coefficient of coupling?

b) For these two coils, what is the largest value that M can have?

c) Assume that the physical structure of these coupled coils is such that $\mathcal{P}_1 = \mathcal{P}_2$. What is the turns ratio N_1/N_2 if N_1 is the number of turns on the 60 mH coil?

6.46 Two magnetically coupled coils are wound on a nonmagnetic core. The self-inductance of coil 1 is 288 mH, the mutual inductance is 90 mH, the coefficient of coupling is 0.75, and the physical structure of the coils is such that $\mathcal{P}_{11} = \mathcal{P}_{22}$.

a) Find L_2 and the turns ratio N_1/N_2.

b) If $N_1 = 1200$, what is the value of $\mathcal{P}_1$ and $\mathcal{P}_2$?

6.47 The self-inductances of the coils in Fig. 6.30 are $L_1 = 18$ mH and $L_2 = 32$ mH. If the coefficient of coupling is 0.85, calculate the energy stored in the system in millijoules when (a) $i_1 = 6$ A, $i_2 = 9$ A; (b) $i_1 = -6$ A, $i_2 = -9$ A; (c) $i_1 = -6$ A, $i_2 = 9$ A; and (d) $i_1 = 6$ A, $i_2 = -9$A.

6.48 The coefficient of coupling in Problem 6.47 is increased to 1.0.

a) If i_1 equals 6 A, what value of i_2 results in zero stored energy?

b) Is there any physically realizable value of i_2 that can make the stored energy negative?

6.49 The self-inductances of two magnetically coupled coils are 72 mH and 40.5 mH, respectively. The 72 mH coil has 250 turns, and the coefficient of coupling between the coils is ⅔. The coupling medium is nonmagnetic. When coil 1 is excited with coil 2 open, the flux linking only coil 1 is 0.2 as large as the flux linking coil 2.

a) How many turns does coil 2 have?

b) What is the value of $\mathcal{P}_2$ in nanowebers per ampere?

c) What is the value of $\mathcal{P}_{11}$ in nanowebers per ampere?

d) What is the ratio (ϕ_{22}/ϕ_{12})?

6.50 The self-inductances of two magnetically coupled coils are $L_1 = 180\ \mu H$ and $L_2 = 500\ \mu H$. The coupling medium is nonmagnetic. If coil 1 has 300 turns and coil 2 has 500 turns, find $\mathcal{P}_{11}$ and $\mathcal{P}_{21}$ (in nanowebers per ampere) when the coefficient of coupling is 0.6.

Sections 6.1–6.5

6.51 Suppose a capacitive touch screen that uses the mutual-capacitance design, as shown in Fig. 6.33, is touched at the point x, y. Determine the mutual capacitance at that point, C'_{mxy}, in terms of the mutual capacitance at the point without a touch, C_{mxy}, and the capacitance introduced by the touch, C_t.

6.52 a) Assume the parasitic capacitance in the self-capacitance design, $C_p = 30$ pF, and the capacitance introduced by a touch is 15 pF (see Fig. 6.32[b]). What is the capacitance at the touch point with respect to ground for the x-grid and y-grid electrodes closest to the touch point?

b) Assume the mutual capacitance in the mutual-capacitance design, $C_{mxy} = 30$ pF, and the capacitance introduced by a touch is 15 pF (see Fig. 6.33[b]). What is the mutual capacitance between the x- and y-grid electrodes closest to the touch point?

c) Compare your results in parts (a) and (b) – does touching the screen increase or decrease the capacitance in these two different capacitive touch screen designs?

6.53 a) As shown in the Practical Perspective, the self-capacitance design does not permit a true multi-touch screen – if the screen is touched at two difference points, a total of four touch points are identified, the two actual touch points and two ghost points. If a self-capacitance touch screen is touched at the x, y coordinates (2.1, 4.3) and (3.2, 2.5), what are the four touch locations that will be identified? (Assume the touch coordinates are measured in inches from the upper left corner of the screen.)

b) A self-capacitance touch screen can still function as a multi-touch screen for several common gestures. For example, suppose at time t_1 the two touch points are those identified in part (a), and at time t_2 four touch points associated with the x, y coordinates (1.8, 4.9) and (3.9, 1.8) are identified. Comparing the four points at t_1 with the four points at t_2, software can recognize a pinch gesture – should the screen be zoomed in or zoomed out?

c) Repeat part (b), assuming that at time t_2 four touch points associated with the x, y coordinates (2.8, 3.9) and (3.0, 2.8) are identified.

Response of First-Order
RL and *RC* Circuits

✓ CHAPTER OBJECTIVES

1 Be able to determine the natural response of both *RL* and *RC* circuits.

2 Be able to determine the step response of both *RL* and *RC* circuits.

3 Know how to analyze circuits with sequential switching.

4 Be able to analyze op amp circuits containing resistors and a single capacitor.

In Chapter 6, we noted that an important attribute of inductors and capacitors is their ability to store energy. We are now in a position to determine the currents and voltages that arise when energy is either released or acquired by an inductor or capacitor in response to an abrupt change in a dc voltage or current source. In this chapter, we will focus on circuits that consist only of sources, resistors, and either (but not both) inductors or capacitors. For brevity, such configurations are called **RL** (resistor-inductor) and **RC** (resistor-capacitor) **circuits**.

Our analysis of *RL* and *RC* circuits will be divided into three phases. In the first phase, we consider the currents and voltages that arise when stored energy in an inductor or capacitor is suddenly released to a resistive network. This happens when the inductor or capacitor is abruptly disconnected from its dc source. Thus we can reduce the circuit to one of the two equivalent forms shown in Fig. 7.1 on page 214. The currents and voltages that arise in this configuration are referred to as the **natural response** of the circuit, to emphasize that the nature of the circuit itself, not external sources of excitation, determines its behavior.

In the second phase of our analysis, we consider the currents and voltages that arise when energy is being acquired by an inductor or capacitor due to the sudden application of a dc voltage or current source. This response is referred to as the **step response**. The process for finding both the natural and step responses is the same; thus, in the third phase of our analysis, we develop a general method that can be used to find the response of *RL* and *RC* circuits to any abrupt change in a dc voltage or current source.

Figure 7.2 on page 214 shows the four possibilities for the general configuration of *RL* and *RC* circuits. Note that when there are no independent sources in the circuit, the Thévenin voltage or Norton current is zero, and the circuit reduces to one of those shown in Fig. 7.1; that is, we have a natural-response problem.

Practical Perspective

Artificial Pacemaker

The muscle that makes up the heart contracts due to rhythmical electrical impulses. The frequency of the impulses is controlled by pacemaker cells. In adults, the pacemaker cells establish a resting heart rate of about 72 beats per minutes. But sometimes the pacemaker cells are damaged and may produce a very low resting heart rate (a condition known as bradycardia) or a very high resting heart rate (a condition known as tachycardia). A normal heart rhythm can be restored by implanting an artificial pacemaker that delivers electrical impulses to the heart, mimicking the pacemaker cells. An example of an artificial pacemaker both outside and inside the body is shown in the figures below.

Artificial pacemakers are very small and lightweight. They have a programmable microprocessor that monitors a few parameters and adjusts the heart rate, an efficient battery with a life of up to 15 years, and circuitry that generates the pulse. The simplest circuit consists of a resistor and a capacitor. Once we have introduced the first-order RC circuit, we will look at an RC circuit design for artificial pacemakers.

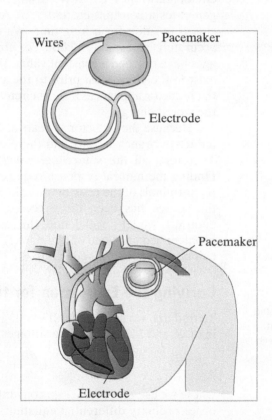

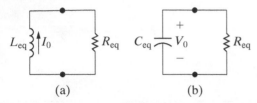

Figure 7.1 ▲ The two forms of the circuits for natural response. (a) *RL* circuit. (b) *RC* circuit.

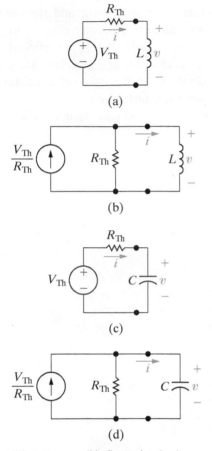

Figure 7.2 ▲ Four possible first-order circuits.
(a) An inductor connected to a Thévenin equivalent.
(b) An inductor connected to a Norton equivalent.
(c) A capacitor connected to a Thévenin equivalent.
(d) A capacitor connected to a Norton equivalent.

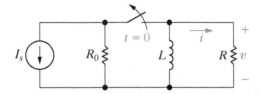

Figure 7.3 ▲ An *RL* circuit.

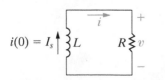

Figure 7.4 ▲ The circuit shown in Fig. 7.3, for $t \geq 0$.

RL and *RC* circuits are also known as **first-order circuits**, because their voltages and currents are described by first-order differential equations. No matter how complex a circuit may appear, if it can be reduced to a Thévenin or Norton equivalent connected to the terminals of an equivalent inductor or capacitor, it is a first-order circuit. (Note that if multiple inductors or capacitors exist in the original circuit, they must be interconnected so that they can be replaced by a single equivalent element.)

After introducing the techniques for analyzing the natural and step responses of first-order circuits, we discuss some special cases of interest. The first is that of sequential switching, involving circuits in which switching can take place at two or more instants in time. Next is the unbounded response. Finally, we analyze a useful circuit called the integrating amplifier.

7.1 The Natural Response of an *RL* Circuit

The natural response of an *RL* circuit can best be described in terms of the circuit shown in Fig. 7.3. We assume that the independent current source generates a constant current of I_s A, and that the switch has been in a closed position for a long time. We define the phrase *a long time* more accurately later in this section. For now it means that all currents and voltages have reached a constant value. Thus only constant, or dc, currents can exist in the circuit just prior to the switch's being opened, and therefore the inductor appears as a short circuit ($L \, di/dt = 0$) prior to the release of the stored energy.

Because the inductor appears as a short circuit, the voltage across the inductive branch is zero, and there can be no current in either R_0 or R. Therefore, all the source current I_s appears in the inductive branch. Finding the natural response requires finding the voltage and current at the terminals of the resistor after the switch has been opened, that is, after the source has been disconnected and the inductor begins releasing energy. If we let $t = 0$ denote the instant when the switch is opened, the problem becomes one of finding $v(t)$ and $i(t)$ for $t \geq 0$. For $t \geq 0$, the circuit shown in Fig. 7.3 reduces to the one shown in Fig. 7.4.

Deriving the Expression for the Current

To find $i(t)$, we use Kirchhoff's voltage law to obtain an expression involving i, R, and L. Summing the voltages around the closed loop gives

$$L\frac{di}{dt} + Ri = 0, \qquad (7.1)$$

where we use the passive sign convention. Equation 7.1 is known as a first-order ordinary differential equation, because it contains terms involving the ordinary derivative of the unknown, that is, di/dt. The highest order derivative appearing in the equation is 1; hence the term **first-order**.

We can go one step further in describing this equation. The coefficients in the equation, R and L, are constants; that is, they are not functions of either the dependent variable i or the independent variable t. Thus the equation can also be described as an ordinary differential equation with constant coefficients.

To solve Eq. 7.1, we divide by L, transpose the term involving i to the right-hand side, and then multiply both sides by a differential time dt. The result is

$$\frac{di}{dt}dt = -\frac{R}{L}i \, dt. \qquad (7.2)$$

Next, we recognize the left-hand side of Eq. 7.2 as a differential change in the current i, that is, di. We now divide through by i, getting

$$\frac{di}{i} = -\frac{R}{L}dt. \qquad (7.3)$$

We obtain an explicit expression for i as a function of t by integrating both sides of Eq. 7.3. Using x and y as variables of integration yields

$$\int_{i(t_0)}^{i(t)} \frac{dx}{x} = -\frac{R}{L} \int_{t_0}^{t} dy, \qquad (7.4)$$

in which $i(t_0)$ is the current corresponding to time t_0, and $i(t)$ is the current corresponding to time t. Here, $t_0 = 0$. Therefore, carrying out the indicated integration gives

$$\ln \frac{i(t)}{i(0)} = -\frac{R}{L}t. \qquad (7.5)$$

Based on the definition of the natural logarithm,

$$i(t) = i(0)e^{-(R/L)t}. \qquad (7.6)$$

Recall from Chapter 6 that an instantaneous change of current cannot occur in an inductor. Therefore, in the first instant after the switch has been opened, the current in the inductor remains unchanged. If we use 0^- to denote the time just prior to switching, and 0^+ for the time immediately following switching, then

$$i(0^-) = i(0^+) = I_0, $$

◀ **Initial inductor current**

where, as in Fig. 7.1, I_0 denotes the initial current in the inductor. The initial current in the inductor is oriented in the same direction as the reference direction of i. Hence Eq. 7.6 becomes

$$i(t) = I_0 e^{-(R/L)t}, \quad t \geq 0, \qquad (7.7)$$

◀ **Natural response of an *RL* circuit**

which shows that the current starts from an initial value I_0 and decreases exponentially toward zero as t increases. Figure 7.5 shows this response.

We derive the voltage across the resistor in Fig. 7.4 from a direct application of Ohm's law:

$$v = iR = I_0 R e^{-(R/L)t}, \quad t \geq 0^+. \qquad (7.8)$$

Note that in contrast to the expression for the current shown in Eq. 7.7, the voltage is defined only for $t > 0$, not at $t = 0$. The reason is that a step change occurs in the voltage at zero. Note that for $t < 0$, the derivative of the current is zero, so the voltage is also zero. (This result follows from $v = L di/dt = 0$.) Thus

$$v(0^-) = 0, \qquad (7.9)$$

$$v(0^+) = I_0 R, \qquad (7.10)$$

where $v(0^+)$ is obtained from Eq. 7.8 with $t = 0^+$.[1] With this step change at an instant in time, the value of the voltage at $t = 0$ is unknown. Thus we use $t \geq 0^+$ in defining the region of validity for these solutions.

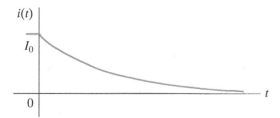

Figure 7.5 ▲ The current response for the circuit shown in Fig. 7.4.

---

[1] We can define the expressions 0^- and 0^+ more formally. The expression $x(0^-)$ refers to the limit of the variable x as $t \to 0$ from the left, or from negative time. The expression $x(0^+)$ refers to the limit of the variable x as $t \to 0$ from the right, or from positive time.

We derive the power dissipated in the resistor from any of the following expressions:

$$p = vi, \quad p = i^2R, \quad \text{or} \quad p = \frac{v^2}{R}. \tag{7.11}$$

Whichever form is used, the resulting expression can be reduced to

$$p = I_0^2 R e^{-2(R/L)t}, \quad t \geq 0^+. \tag{7.12}$$

The energy delivered to the resistor during any interval of time after the switch has been opened is

$$w = \int_0^t p\,dx = \int_0^t I_0^2 R e^{-2(R/L)x}\,dx$$

$$= \frac{1}{2(R/L)} I_0^2 R (1 - e^{-2(R/L)t})$$

$$= \frac{1}{2} L I_0^2 (1 - e^{-2(R/L)t}), \quad t \geq 0. \tag{7.13}$$

Note from Eq. 7.13 that as *t* becomes infinite, the energy dissipated in the resistor approaches the initial energy stored in the inductor.

The Significance of the Time Constant

The expressions for $i(t)$ (Eq. 7.7) and $v(t)$ (Eq. 7.8) include a term of the form $e^{-(R/L)t}$. The coefficient of *t*—namely, R/L—determines the rate at which the current or voltage approaches zero. The reciprocal of this ratio is the **time constant** of the circuit, denoted

Time constant for *RL* circuit ▶

$$\tau = \text{time constant} = \frac{L}{R}. \tag{7.14}$$

Using the time-constant concept, we write the expressions for current, voltage, power, and energy as

$$i(t) = I_0 e^{-t/\tau}, \quad t \geq 0, \tag{7.15}$$

$$v(t) = I_0 R e^{-t/\tau}, \quad t \geq 0^+, \tag{7.16}$$

$$p = I_0^2 R e^{-2t/\tau}, \quad t \geq 0^+, \tag{7.17}$$

$$w = \frac{1}{2} L I_0^2 (1 - e^{-2t/\tau}), \quad t \geq 0. \tag{7.18}$$

The time constant is an important parameter for first-order circuits, so mentioning several of its characteristics is worthwhile. First, it is convenient to think of the time elapsed after switching in terms of integral multiples of τ. Thus one time constant after the inductor has begun to release its stored energy to the resistor, the current has been reduced to e^{-1}, or approximately 0.37 of its initial value.

Table 7.1 gives the value of $e^{-t/\tau}$ for integral multiples of τ from 1 to 10. Note that when the elapsed time exceeds five time constants, the current is less than 1% of its initial value. Thus we sometimes say that five time constants after switching has occurred, the currents and voltages have, for most practical purposes, reached their final values. For single time-constant circuits (first-order circuits) with 1% accuracy, the phrase *a long time* implies that five or more time constants have elapsed. Thus the existence of current in the *RL* circuit shown in Fig. 7.1(a) is a momentary event and is referred to as the **transient response** of the circuit. The response that exists a long time after the switching has taken place is called the **steady-state response**. The phrase *a long time* then also means the time it takes the circuit to reach its steady-state value.

Any first-order circuit is characterized, in part, by the value of its time constant. If we have no method for calculating the time constant of such a circuit (perhaps because we don't know the values of its components), we can determine its value from a plot of the circuit's natural response. That's because another important characteristic of the time constant is that it gives the time required for the current to reach its final value if the current continues to change at its initial rate. To illustrate, we evaluate di/dt at 0^+ and assume that the current continues to change at this rate:

$$\frac{di}{dt}(0^+) = -\frac{R}{L}I_0 = -\frac{I_0}{\tau}. \tag{7.19}$$

Now, if i starts as I_0 and decreases at a constant rate of I_0/τ amperes per second, the expression for i becomes

$$i = I_0 - \frac{I_0}{\tau}t. \tag{7.20}$$

Equation 7.20 indicates that i would reach its final value of zero in τ seconds. Figure 7.6 shows how this graphic interpretation is useful in estimating the' time constant of a circuit from a plot of its natural response. Such a plot could be generated on an oscilloscope measuring output current. Drawing the tangent to the natural response plot at $t = 0$ and reading the value at which the tangent intersects the time axis gives the value of τ.

Calculating the natural response of an *RL* circuit can be summarized as follows:

1. Find the initial current, I_0, through the inductor.
2. Find the time constant of the circuit, $\tau = L/R$.
3. Use Eq. 7.15, $I_0 e^{-t/\tau}$, to generate $i(t)$ from I_0 and τ.

All other calculations of interest follow from knowing $i(t)$. Examples 7.1 and 7.2 illustrate the numerical calculations associated with the natural response of an *RL* circuit.

TABLE 7.1   Value of $e^{-t/\tau}$ For t Equal to Integral Multiples of τ

t	$e^{-t/\tau}$	t	$e^{-t/\tau}$
τ	3.6788×10^{-1}	6τ	2.4788×10^{-3}
2τ	1.3534×10^{-1}	7τ	9.1188×10^{-4}
3τ	4.9787×10^{-2}	8τ	3.3546×10^{-4}
4τ	1.8316×10^{-2}	9τ	1.2341×10^{-4}
5τ	6.7379×10^{-3}	10τ	4.5400×10^{-5}

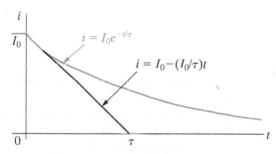

Figure 7.6 ▲ A graphic interpretation of the time constant of the *RL* circuit shown in Fig. 7.4.

◀ **Calculating the natural response of *RL* circuit**

Example 7.1 | **Determining the Natural Response of an *RL* Circuit**

The switch in the circuit shown in Fig. 7.7 has been closed for a long time before it is opened at $t = 0$. Find

a) $i_L(t)$ for $t \geq 0$,
b) $i_o(t)$ for $t \geq 0^+$,
c) $v_o(t)$ for $t \geq 0^+$,
d) the percentage of the total energy stored in the 2 H inductor that is dissipated in the 10 Ω resistor.

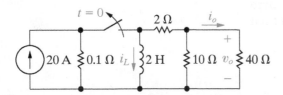

Figure 7.7 ▲ The circuit for Example 7.1.

Solution

a) The switch has been closed for a long time prior to $t = 0$, so we know the voltage across the inductor must be zero at $t = 0^-$. Therefore the initial current in the inductor is 20 A at $t = 0^-$. Hence, $i_L(0^+)$ also is 20 A, because an instantaneous change in the current cannot occur in an inductor. We replace the resistive circuit connected to the terminals of the inductor with a single resistor of 10 Ω:

$$R_{eq} = 2 + (40 \parallel 10) = 10\,\Omega.$$

The time constant of the circuit is L/R_{eq}, or 0.2 s, giving the expression for the inductor current as

$$i_L(t) = 20e^{-5t}\,\text{A}, \quad t \geq 0.$$

b) We find the current in the 40 Ω resistor most easily by using current division; that is,

$$i_o = -i_L\frac{10}{10 + 40}.$$

Note that this expression is valid for $t \geq 0^+$ because $i_o = 0$ at $t = 0^-$. The inductor behaves as a short circuit prior to the switch being opened, producing an instantaneous change in the current i_o. Then,

$$i_o(t) = -4e^{-5t}\,\text{A}, \quad t \geq 0^+.$$

c) We find the voltage v_o by direct application of Ohm's law:

$$v_o(t) = 40i_o = -160e^{-5t}\,\text{V}, \quad t \geq 0^+.$$

d) The power dissipated in the 10 Ω resistor is

$$p_{10\Omega}(t) = \frac{v_o^2}{10} = 2560e^{-10t}\,\text{W}, \quad t \geq 0^+.$$

The total energy dissipated in the 10 Ω resistor is

$$w_{10\Omega}(t) = \int_0^\infty 2560e^{-10t}\,dt = 256\,\text{J}.$$

The initial energy stored in the 2 H inductor is

$$w(0) = \frac{1}{2}Li^2(0) = \frac{1}{2}(2)(400) = 400\,\text{J}.$$

Therefore the percentage of energy dissipated in the 10 Ω resistor is

$$\frac{256}{400}(100) = 64\%.$$

Example 7.2   **Determining the Natural Response of an *RL* Circuit with Parallel Inductors**

In the circuit shown in Fig. 7.8, the initial currents in inductors L_1 and L_2 have been established by sources not shown. The switch is opened at $t = 0$.

a) Find i_1, i_2, and i_3 for $t \geq 0$.

b) Calculate the initial energy stored in the parallel inductors.

c) Determine how much energy is stored in the inductors as $t \to \infty$.

d) Show that the total energy delivered to the resistive network equals the difference between the results obtained in (b) and (c).

Solution

a) The key to finding currents i_1, i_2, and i_3 lies in knowing the voltage $v(t)$. We can easily find $v(t)$ if we reduce the circuit shown in Fig. 7.8 to the equivalent form shown in Fig. 7.9. The parallel inductors simplify to an equivalent inductance of 4 H, carrying an initial current of 12 A. The resistive network reduces to a single resistance of 8 Ω. Hence the initial value of $i(t)$ is 12 A and the time constant is 4/8, or 0.5 s. Therefore

$$i(t) = 12e^{-2t} \text{ A}, \quad t \geq 0.$$

Now $v(t)$ is simply the product $8i$, so

$$v(t) = 96e^{-2t} \text{ V}, \quad t \geq 0^+.$$

The circuit shows that $v(t) = 0$ at $t = 0^-$, so the expression for $v(t)$ is valid for $t \geq 0^+$. After obtaining $v(t)$, we can calculate i_1, i_2, and i_3:

$$i_1 = \frac{1}{5} \int_0^t 96e^{-2x} dx - 8$$

$$= 1.6 - 9.6e^{-2t} \text{ A}, \quad t \geq 0,$$

$$i_2 = \frac{1}{20} \int_0^t 96e^{-2x} dx - 4$$

$$= -1.6 - 2.4e^{-2t} \text{ A}, \quad t \geq 0,$$

$$i_3 = \frac{v(t)}{10} \frac{15}{25} = 5.76e^{-2t} \text{ A}, \quad t \geq 0^+.$$

Note that the expressions for the inductor currents i_1 and i_2 are valid for $t \geq 0$, whereas the expression for the resistor current i_3 is valid for $t \geq 0^+$.

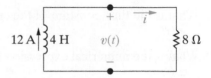

12 A   4 H $v(t)$ 8 Ω

Figure 7.9 ▲ A simplification of the circuit shown in Fig. 7.8.

b) The initial energy stored in the inductors is

$$w = \frac{1}{2}(5)(64) + \frac{1}{2}(20)(16) = 320 \text{ J}.$$

c) As $t \to \infty$, $i_1 \to 1.6 \text{ A}$ and $i_2 \to -1.6 \text{ A}$. Therefore, a long time after the switch has been opened, the energy stored in the two inductors is

$$w = \frac{1}{2}(5)(1.6)^2 + \frac{1}{2}(20)(-1.6)^2 = 32 \text{ J}.$$

d) We obtain the total energy delivered to the resistive network by integrating the expression for the instantaneous power from zero to infinity:

$$w = \int_0^\infty p \, dt = \int_0^\infty 1152e^{-4t} dt$$

$$= 1152 \frac{e^{-4t}}{-4} \Big|_0^\infty = 288 \text{ J}.$$

This result is the difference between the initially stored energy (320 J) and the energy trapped in the parallel inductors (32 J). The equivalent inductor for the parallel inductors (which predicts the terminal behavior of the parallel combination) has an initial energy of 288 J; that is, the energy stored in the equivalent inductor represents the amount of energy that will be delivered to the resistive network at the terminals of the original inductors.

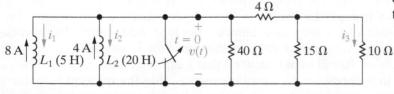

8 A i_1 4 A i_2 $t = 0$ 4 Ω i_3
L_1 (5 H) L_2 (20 H) $v(t)$ 40 Ω   15 Ω   10 Ω

Figure 7.8 ▲ The circuit for Example 7.2.

✓ ASSESSMENT PROBLEMS

Objective 1—Be able to determine the natural response of both *RL* and *RC* circuits

7.1 The switch in the circuit shown has been closed for a long time and is opened at $t = 0$.

    a) Calculate the initial value of i.

    b) Calculate the initial energy stored in the inductor.

    c) What is the time constant of the circuit for $t > 0$?

    d) What is the numerical expression for $i(t)$ for $t \geq 0$?

    e) What percentage of the initial energy stored has been dissipated in the 2 Ω resistor 5 ms after the switch has been opened?

Answer: (a) -12.5 A;

        (b) 625 mJ;

        (c) 4 ms;

        (d) $-12.5e^{-250t}$ A, $t \geq 0$;

        (e) 91.8%.

7.2 At $t = 0$, the switch in the circuit shown moves instantaneously from position a to position b.

    a) Calculate v_o for $t \geq 0^+$.

    b) What percentage of the initial energy stored in the inductor is eventually dissipated in the 4 Ω resistor?

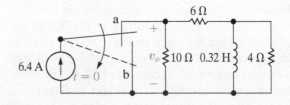

Answer: (a) $-8e^{-10t}$ V, $t \geq 0$;

        (b) 80%.

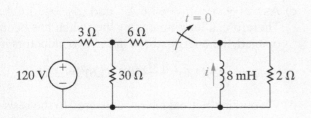

NOTE: Also try Chapter Problems 7.3, 7.8, and 7.9.

7.2 The Natural Response of an *RC* Circuit

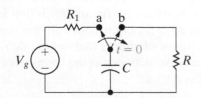

Figure 7.10 ▲ An *RC* circuit.

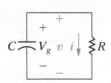

Figure 7.11 ▲ The circuit shown in Fig. 7.10, after switching.

As mentioned in Section 7.1, the natural response of an *RC* circuit is analogous to that of an *RL* circuit. Consequently, we don't treat the *RC* circuit in the same detail as we did the *RL* circuit.

The natural response of an *RC* circuit is developed from the circuit shown in Fig. 7.10. We begin by assuming that the switch has been in position a for a long time, allowing the loop made up of the dc voltage source V_g, the resistor R_1, and the capacitor C to reach a steady-state condition. Recall from Chapter 6 that a capacitor behaves as an open circuit in the presence of a constant voltage. Thus the voltage source cannot sustain a current, and so the source voltage appears across the capacitor terminals. In Section 7.3, we will discuss how the capacitor voltage actually builds to the steady-state value of the dc voltage source, but for now the important point is that when the switch is moved from position a to position b (at $t = 0$), the voltage on the capacitor is V_g. Because there can be no instantaneous change in the voltage at the terminals of a capacitor, the problem reduces to solving the circuit shown in Fig. 7.11.

Deriving the Expression for the Voltage

We can easily find the voltage $v(t)$ by thinking in terms of node voltages. Using the lower junction between R and C as the reference node and summing the currents away from the upper junction between R and C gives

$$C\frac{dv}{dt} + \frac{v}{R} = 0. \tag{7.21}$$

Comparing Eq. 7.21 with Eq. 7.1 shows that the same mathematical techniques can be used to obtain the solution for $v(t)$. We leave it to you to show that

$$v(t) = v(0)e^{-t/RC}, \quad t \geq 0. \tag{7.22}$$

As we have already noted, the initial voltage on the capacitor equals the voltage source voltage V_g, or

$$v(0^-) = v(0) = v(0^+) = V_g = V_0, \tag{7.23}$$ ◀ **Initial capacitor voltage**

where V_0 denotes the initial voltage on the capacitor. The time constant for the RC circuit equals the product of the resistance and capacitance, namely,

$$\tau = RC. \tag{7.24}$$ ◀ **Time constant for *RC* circuit**

Substituting Eqs. 7.23 and 7.24 into Eq. 7.22 yields

$$v(t) = V_0 e^{-t/\tau}, \quad t \geq 0, \tag{7.25}$$ ◀ **Natural response of an *RC* circuit**

which indicates that the natural response of an RC circuit is an exponential decay of the initial voltage. The time constant RC governs the rate of decay. Figure 7.12 shows the plot of Eq. 7.25 and the graphic interpretation of the time constant.

After determining $v(t)$, we can easily derive the expressions for $i, p,$ and w:

$$i(t) = \frac{v(t)}{R} = \frac{V_0}{R}e^{-t/\tau}, \quad t \geq 0^+, \tag{7.26}$$

$$p = vi = \frac{V_0^2}{R}e^{-2t/\tau}, \quad t \geq 0^+, \tag{7.27}$$

$$w = \int_0^t p \, dx = \int_0^t \frac{V_0^2}{R}e^{-2x/\tau}\, dx$$

$$= \frac{1}{2}CV_0^2(1 - e^{-2t/\tau}), \quad t \geq 0. \tag{7.28}$$

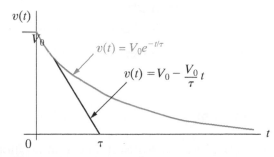

Figure 7.12 ▲ The natural response of an *RC* circuit.

Calculating the natural response of an *RC* circuit can be summarized as follows:

Calculating the natural response of an *RC* circuit ▶

1. Find the initial voltage, V_0, across the capacitor.
2. Find the time constant of the circuit, $\tau = RC$.
3. Use Eq. 7.25, $v(t) = V_0 e^{-t/\tau}$, to generate $v(t)$ from V_0 and τ.

All other calculations of interest follow from knowing $v(t)$. Examples 7.3 and 7.4 illustrate the numerical calculations associated with the natural response of an *RC* circuit.

Example 7.3   Determining the Natural Response of an *RC* Circuit

The switch in the circuit shown in Fig. 7.13 has been in position *x* for a long time. At $t = 0$, the switch moves instantaneously to position *y*. Find

a) $v_C(t)$ for $t \geq 0$,
b) $v_o(t)$ for $t \geq 0^+$,
c) $i_o(t)$ for $t \geq 0^+$, and
d) the total energy dissipated in the 60 kΩ resistor.

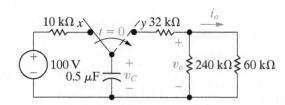

Figure 7.13 ▲ The circuit for Example 7.3.

Solution

a) Because the switch has been in position *x* for a long time, the 0.5 mF capacitor will charge to 100 V and be positive at the upper terminal. We can replace the resistive network connected to the capacitor at $t = 0^+$ with an equivalent resistance of 80 kΩ. Hence the time constant of the circuit is $(0.5 \times 10^{-6})(80 \times 10^3)$ or 40 ms. Then,

$$v_C(t) = 100e^{-25t} \text{ V}, \quad t \geq 0.$$

b) The easiest way to find $v_o(t)$ is to note that the resistive circuit forms a voltage divider across the terminals of the capacitor. Thus

$$v_o(t) = \frac{48}{80}v_C(t) = 60e^{-25t} \text{ V}, \quad t \geq 0^+.$$

This expression for $v_o(t)$ is valid for $t \geq 0^+$ because $v_o(0^-)$ is zero. Thus we have an instantaneous change in the voltage across the 240 kΩ resistor.

c) We find the current $i_o(t)$ from Ohm's law:

$$i_o(t) = \frac{v_o(t)}{60 \times 10^3} = e^{-25t} \text{ mA}, \quad t \geq 0^+.$$

d) The power dissipated in the 60 kΩ resistor is

$$p_{60k\Omega}(t) = i_o^2(t)(60 \times 10^3) = 60e^{-50t} \text{ mW}, \quad t \geq 0^+.$$

The total energy dissipated is

$$w_{60k\Omega} = \int_0^\infty i_o^2(t)(60 \times 10^3)\, dt = 1.2 \text{ mJ}.$$

Example 7.4   Determining the Natural Response of an *RC* Circuit with Series Capacitors

The initial voltages on capacitors C_1 and C_2 in the circuit shown in Fig. 7.14 have been established by sources not shown. The switch is closed at $t = 0$.

a) Find $v_1(t)$, $v_2(t)$, and $v(t)$ for $t \geq 0$ and $i(t)$ for $t \geq 0^+$.

b) Calculate the initial energy stored in the capacitors C_1 and C_2.

c) Determine how much energy is stored in the capacitors as $t \to \infty$.

d) Show that the total energy delivered to the 250 kΩ resistor is the difference between the results obtained in (b) and (c).

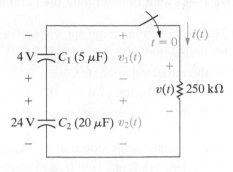

Figure 7.14 ▲ The circuit for Example 7.4.

Solution

a) Once we know $v(t)$, we can obtain the current $i(t)$ from Ohm's law. After determining $i(t)$, we can calculate $v_1(t)$ and $v_2(t)$ because the voltage across a capacitor is a function of the capacitor current. To find $v(t)$, we replace the series-connected capacitors with an equivalent capacitor. It has a capacitance of 4 μF and is charged to a voltage of 20 V. Therefore, the circuit shown in Fig. 7.14 reduces to the one shown in Fig. 7.15, which reveals that the initial value of $v(t)$ is 20 V, and that the time constant of the circuit is $(4)(250) \times 10^{-3}$, or 1 s. Thus the expression for $v(t)$ is

$$v(t) = 20e^{-t} \text{ V}, \quad t \geq 0.$$

The current $i(t)$ is

$$i(t) = \frac{v(t)}{250,000} = 80e^{-t} \,\mu\text{A}, \quad t \geq 0^+.$$

Knowing $i(t)$, we calculate the expressions for $v_1(t)$ and $v_2(t)$:

$$v_1(t) = -\frac{10^6}{5} \int_0^t 80 \times 10^{-6} e^{-x} \, dx - 4$$

$$= (16e^{-t} - 20) \text{ V}, \quad t \geq 0,$$

$$v_2(t) = -\frac{10^6}{20} \int_0^t 80 \times 10^{-6} e^{-x} \, dx + 24$$

$$= (4e^{-t} + 20) \text{ V}, \quad t \geq 0.$$

b) The initial energy stored in C_1 is

$$w_1 = \frac{1}{2}(5 \times 10^{-6})(16) = 40 \,\mu\text{J}.$$

The initial energy stored in C_2 is

$$w_2 = \frac{1}{2}(20 \times 10^{-6})(576) = 5760 \,\mu\text{J}.$$

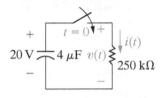

Figure 7.15 ▲ A simplification of the circuit shown in Fig. 7.14.

The total energy stored in the two capacitors is

$$w_o = 40 + 5760 = 5800 \,\mu\text{J}.$$

c) As $t \to \infty$,

$$v_1 \to -20 \text{ V} \quad \text{and} \quad v_2 \to +20 \text{ V}.$$

Therefore the energy stored in the two capacitors is

$$w_\infty = \frac{1}{2}(5 + 20) \times 10^{-6}(400) = 5000 \,\mu\text{J}.$$

d) The total energy delivered to the 250 kΩ resistor is

$$w = \int_0^\infty p \, dt = \int_0^\infty \frac{400e^{-2t}}{250,000} \, dt = 800 \,\mu\text{J}.$$

Comparing the results obtained in (b) and (c) shows that

$$800 \,\mu\text{J} = (5800 - 5000) \,\mu\text{J}.$$

The energy stored in the equivalent capacitor in Fig. 7.15 is $\frac{1}{2}(4 \times 10^{-6})(400)$, or 800 μJ. Because this capacitor predicts the terminal behavior of the original series-connected capacitors, the energy stored in the equivalent capacitor is the energy delivered to the 250 kΩ resistor.

✓ ASSESSMENT PROBLEMS

Objective 1—Be able to determine the natural response of both *RL* and *RC* circuits

7.3 The switch in the circuit shown has been closed for a long time and is opened at $t = 0$. Find

   a) the initial value of $v(t)$,

   b) the time constant for $t > 0$,

   c) the numerical expression for $v(t)$ after the switch has been opened,

   d) the initial energy stored in the capacitor, and

   e) the length of time required to dissipate 75% of the initially stored energy.

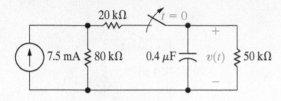

Answer: (a) 200 V;

       (b) 20 ms;

       (c) $200e^{-50t}$ V, $t \geq 0$;

       (d) 8 mJ;

       (e) 13.86 ms.

NOTE: Also try Chapter Problems 7.23 and 7.25.

7.4 The switch in the circuit shown has been closed for a long time before being opened at $t = 0$.

   a) Find $v_o(t)$ for $t \geq 0$.

   b) What percentage of the initial energy stored in the circuit has been dissipated after the switch has been open for 60 ms?

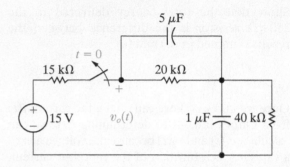

Answer: (a) $8e^{-25t} + 4e^{-10t}$ V, $t \geq 0$;

       (b) 81.05%.

7.3 The Step Response of *RL* and *RC* Circuits

We are now ready to discuss the problem of finding the currents and voltages generated in first-order *RL* or *RC* circuits when either dc voltage or current sources are suddenly applied. The response of a circuit to the sudden application of a constant voltage or current source is referred to as the step response of the circuit. In presenting the step response, we show how the circuit responds when energy is being stored in the inductor or capacitor. We begin with the step response of an *RL* circuit.

The Step Response of an RL Circuit

To begin, we modify the first-order circuit shown in Fig. 7.2(a) by adding a switch. We use the resulting circuit, shown in Fig. 7.16, in developing the step response of an *RL* circuit. Energy stored in the inductor at the time the switch is closed is given in terms of a nonzero initial current $i(0)$. The task is to find the expressions for the current in the circuit and for the voltage across the inductor after the switch has been closed. The procedure is the same as that used in Section 7.1; we use circuit analysis to derive the

Figure 7.16 ▲ A circuit used to illustrate the step response of a first-order *RL* circuit.

differential equation that describes the circuit in terms of the variable of interest, and then we use elementary calculus to solve the equation.

After the switch in Fig. 7.16 has been closed, Kirchhoff's voltage law requires that

$$V_s = Ri + L\frac{di}{dt}, \tag{7.29}$$

which can be solved for the current by separating the variables i and t and then integrating. The first step in this approach is to solve Eq. 7.29 for the derivative di/dt:

$$\frac{di}{dt} = \frac{-Ri + V_s}{L} = \frac{-R}{L}\left(i - \frac{V_s}{R}\right). \tag{7.30}$$

Next, we multiply both sides of Eq. 7.30 by a differential time dt. This step reduces the left-hand side of the equation to a differential change in the current. Thus

$$\frac{di}{dt}dt = \frac{-R}{L}\left(i - \frac{V_s}{R}\right)dt, \tag{7.31}$$

or

$$di = \frac{-R}{L}\left(i - \frac{V_s}{R}\right)dt.$$

We now separate the variables in Eq. 7.31 to get

$$\frac{di}{i - (V_s/R)} = \frac{-R}{L}dt, \tag{7.32}$$

and then integrate both sides of Eq. 7.32. Using x and y as variables for the integration, we obtain

$$\int_{I_0}^{i(t)} \frac{dx}{x - (V_s/R)} = \frac{-R}{L}\int_0^t dy, \tag{7.33}$$

where I_0 is the current at $t = 0$ and $i(t)$ is the current at any $t > 0$. Performing the integration called for in Eq. 7.33 generates the expression

$$\ln\frac{i(t) - (V_s/R)}{I_0 - (V_s/R)} = \frac{-R}{L}t, \tag{7.34}$$

from which

$$\frac{i(t) - (V_s/R)}{I_0 - (V_s/R)} = e^{-(R/L)t},$$

or

$$i(t) = \frac{V_s}{R} + \left(I_0 - \frac{V_s}{R}\right)e^{-(R/L)t}. \tag{7.35}$$

◀ **Step response of *RL* circuit**

When the initial energy in the inductor is zero, I_0 is zero. Thus Eq. 7.35 reduces to

$$i(t) = \frac{V_s}{R} - \frac{V_s}{R}e^{-(R/L)t}. \tag{7.36}$$

Equation 7.36 indicates that after the switch has been closed, the current increases exponentially from zero to a final value of V_s/R. The time constant of the circuit, L/R, determines the rate of increase. One time constant after the switch has been closed, the current will have reached approximately 63% of its final value, or

$$i(\tau) = \frac{V_s}{R} - \frac{V_s}{R}e^{-1} \approx 0.6321\frac{V_s}{R}. \qquad (7.37)$$

If the current were to continue to increase at its initial rate, it would reach its final value at $t = \tau$; that is, because

$$\frac{di}{dt} = \frac{-V_s}{R}\left(\frac{-1}{\tau}\right)e^{-t/\tau} = \frac{V_s}{L}e^{-t/\tau}, \qquad (7.38)$$

the initial rate at which $i(t)$ increases is

$$\frac{di}{dt}(0) = \frac{V_s}{L}. \qquad (7.39)$$

If the current were to continue to increase at this rate, the expression for i would be

$$i = \frac{V_s}{L}t, \qquad (7.40)$$

from which, at $t = \tau$,

$$i = \frac{V_s}{L}\frac{L}{R} = \frac{V_s}{R}. \qquad (7.41)$$

Equations 7.36 and 7.40 are plotted in Fig. 7.17. The values given by Eqs. 7.37 and 7.41 are also shown in this figure.

The voltage across an inductor is $L\,di/dt$, so from Eq. 7.35, for $t \geq 0^+$,

$$v = L\left(\frac{-R}{L}\right)\left(I_0 - \frac{V_s}{R}\right)e^{-(R/L)t} = (V_s - I_0R)e^{-(R/L)t}. \qquad (7.42)$$

The voltage across the inductor is zero before the switch is closed. Equation 7.42 indicates that the inductor voltage jumps to $V_s - I_0R$ at the instant the switch is closed and then decays exponentially to zero.

Does the value of v at $t = 0^+$ make sense? Because the initial current is I_0 and the inductor prevents an instantaneous change in current, the current is I_0 in the instant after the switch has been closed. The voltage drop across the resistor is I_0R, and the voltage impressed across the inductor is the source voltage minus the voltage drop, that is, $V_s - I_0R$.

When the initial inductor current is zero, Eq. 7.42 simplifies to

$$v = V_s e^{-(R/L)t}. \qquad (7.43)$$

If the initial current is zero, the voltage across the inductor jumps to V_s. We also expect the inductor voltage to approach zero as t increases, because the current in the circuit is approaching the constant value of V_s/R. Figure 7.18 shows the plot of Eq. 7.43 and the relationship between the time constant and the initial rate at which the inductor voltage is decreasing.

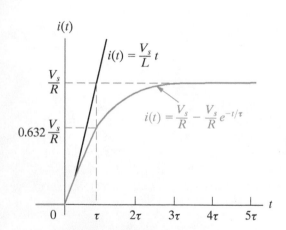

Figure 7.17 ▲ The step response of the *RL* circuit shown in Fig. 7.16 when $I_0 = 0$.

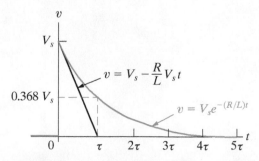

Figure 7.18 ▲ Inductor voltage versus time.

If there is an initial current in the inductor, Eq. 7.35 gives the solution for it. The algebraic sign of I_0 is positive if the initial current is in the same direction as i; otherwise, I_0 carries a negative sign. Example 7.5 illustrates the application of Eq. 7.35 to a specific circuit.

Example 7.5   Determining the Step Response of an *RL* Circuit

The switch in the circuit shown in Fig. 7.19 has been in position a for a long time. At $t = 0$, the switch moves from position a to position b. The switch is a make-before-break type; that is, the connection at position b is established before the connection at position a is broken, so there is no interruption of current through the inductor.

a) Find the expression for $i(t)$ for $t \geq 0$.

b) What is the initial voltage across the inductor just after the switch has been moved to position b?

c) How many milliseconds after the switch has been moved does the inductor voltage equal 24 V?

d) Does this initial voltage make sense in terms of circuit behavior?

e) Plot both $i(t)$ and $v(t)$ versus t.

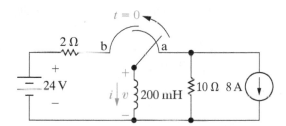

Figure 7.19 ▲ The circuit for Example 7.5.

Solution

a) The switch has been in position a for a long time, so the 200 mH inductor is a short circuit across the 8 A current source. Therefore, the inductor carries an initial current of 8 A. This current is oriented opposite to the reference direction for i; thus I_0 is -8 A. When the switch is in position b, the final value of i will be 24/2, or 12 A. The time constant of the circuit is 200/2, or 100 ms. Substituting these values into Eq. 7.35 gives

$$i = 12 + (-8 - 12)e^{-t/0.1}$$

$$= 12 - 20e^{-10t} \text{ A}, \quad t \geq 0.$$

b) The voltage across the inductor is

$$v = L\frac{di}{dt}$$

$$= 0.2(200e^{-10t})$$

$$= 40e^{-10t} \text{ V}, \quad t \geq 0^+.$$

The initial inductor voltage is

$$v(0^+) = 40 \text{ V}.$$

c) Yes; in the instant after the switch has been moved to position b, the inductor sustains a current of 8 A counterclockwise around the newly formed closed path. This current causes a 16 V drop across the 2 Ω resistor. This voltage drop adds to the drop across the source, producing a 40 V drop across the inductor.

d) We find the time at which the inductor voltage equals 24 V by solving the expression

$$24 = 40e^{-10t}$$

for t:

$$t = \frac{1}{10}\ln\frac{40}{24}$$

$$= 51.08 \times 10^{-3}$$

$$= 51.08 \text{ ms}.$$

e) Figure 7.20 shows the graphs of $i(t)$ and $v(t)$ versus t. Note that the instant of time when the current equals zero corresponds to the instant of time when the inductor voltage equals the source voltage of 24 V, as predicted by Kirchhoff's voltage law.

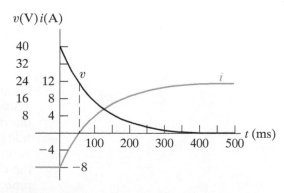

Figure 7.20 ▲ The current and voltage waveforms for Example 7.5.

Objective 2—Be able to determine the step response of both *RL* and *RC* circuits

7.5   Assume that the switch in the circuit shown in Fig. 7.19 has been in position b for a long time, and at $t = 0$ it moves to position a. Find (a) $i(0^+)$; (b) $v(0^+)$; (c) $\tau, t > 0$; (d) $i(t), t \geq 0$; and (e) $v(t), t \geq 0^+$.

Answer: (a) 12 A;
(b) −200 V;
(c) 20 ms;
(d) $-8 + 20e^{-50t}$ A, $t \geq 0$;
(e) $-200e^{-50t}$ V, $t \geq 0^+$.

NOTE: Also try Chapter Problems 7.35–7.37.

We can also describe the voltage $v(t)$ across the inductor in Fig. 7.16 directly, not just in terms of the circuit current. We begin by noting that the voltage across the resistor is the difference between the source voltage and the inductor voltage. We write

$$i(t) = \frac{V_s}{R} - \frac{v(t)}{R}, \tag{7.44}$$

where V_s is a constant. Differentiating both sides with respect to time yields

$$\frac{di}{dt} = -\frac{1}{R}\frac{dv}{dt}. \tag{7.45}$$

Then, if we multiply each side of Eq. 7.45 by the inductance L, we get an expression for the voltage across the inductor on the left-hand side, or

$$v = -\frac{L}{R}\frac{dv}{dt}. \tag{7.46}$$

Putting Eq. 7.46 into standard form yields

$$\frac{dv}{dt} + \frac{R}{L}v = 0. \tag{7.47}$$

You should verify (in Problem 7.38) that the solution to Eq. 7.47 is identical to that given in Eq. 7.42.

At this point, a general observation about the step response of an *RL* circuit is pertinent. (This observation will prove helpful later.) When we derived the differential equation for the inductor current, we obtained Eq. 7.29. We now rewrite Eq. 7.29 as

$$\frac{di}{dt} + \frac{R}{L}i = \frac{V_s}{L}. \tag{7.48}$$

Observe that Eqs. 7.47 and 7.48 have the same form. Specifically, each equates the sum of the first derivative of the variable and a constant times the variable to a constant value. In Eq. 7.47, the constant on the right-hand side happens to be zero; hence this equation takes on the same form as the natural response equations in Section 7.1. In both Eq. 7.47 and Eq. 7.48, the constant multiplying the dependent variable is the reciprocal of the time constant, that is, $R/L = 1/\tau$. We encounter a similar situation in the derivations for the step response of an *RC* circuit. In Section 7.4, we will use these observations to develop a general approach to finding the natural and step responses of *RL* and *RC* circuits.

The Step Response of an *RC* Circuit

We can find the step response of a first-order *RC* circuit by analyzing the circuit shown in Fig. 7.21. For mathematical convenience, we choose the Norton equivalent of the network connected to the equivalent capacitor. Summing the currents away from the top node in Fig. 7.21 generates the differential equation

$$C\frac{dv_C}{dt} + \frac{v_C}{R} = I_s. \tag{7.49}$$

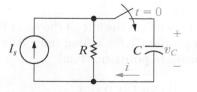

Figure 7.21 ▲ A circuit used to illustrate the step response of a first-order *RC* circuit.

Division of Eq. 7.49 by *C* gives

$$\frac{dv_C}{dt} + \frac{v_C}{RC} = \frac{I_s}{C}. \tag{7.50}$$

Comparing Eq. 7.50 with Eq. 7.48 reveals that the form of the solution for v_C is the same as that for the current in the inductive circuit, namely, Eq. 7.35. Therefore, by simply substituting the appropriate variables and coefficients, we can write the solution for v_C directly. The translation requires that I_s replace V_s, *C* replace *L*, $1/R$ replace *R*, and V_0 replace I_0. We get

$$v_C = I_sR + (V_0 - I_sR)e^{-t/RC}, \quad t \geq 0. \tag{7.51}$$

◀ **Step response of an *RC* circuit**

A similar derivation for the current in the capacitor yields the differential equation

$$\frac{di}{dt} + \frac{1}{RC}i = 0. \tag{7.52}$$

Equation 7.52 has the same form as Eq. 7.47, hence the solution for *i* is obtained by using the same translations used for the solution of Eq. 7.50. Thus

$$i = \left(I_s - \frac{V_0}{R}\right)e^{-t/RC}, \quad t \geq 0^+, \tag{7.53}$$

where V_0 is the initial value of v_C, the voltage across the capacitor.

We obtained Eqs. 7.51 and 7.53 by using a mathematical analogy to the solution for the step response of the inductive circuit. Let's see whether these solutions for the *RC* circuit make sense in terms of known circuit behavior. From Eq. 7.51, note that the initial voltage across the capacitor is V_0, the final voltage across the capacitor is I_sR, and the time constant of the circuit is *RC*. Also note that the solution for v_C is valid for $t \geq 0$. These observations are consistent with the behavior of a capacitor in parallel with a resistor when driven by a constant current source.

Equation 7.53 predicts that the current in the capacitor at $t = 0^+$ is $I_s - V_0/R$. This prediction makes sense because the capacitor voltage cannot change instantaneously, and therefore the initial current in the resistor is V_0/R. The capacitor branch current changes instantaneously from zero at $t = 0^-$ to $I_s - V_0/R$ at $t = 0^+$. The capacitor current is zero at $t = \infty$. Also note that the final value of $v = I_sR$.

Example 7.6 illustrates how to use Eqs. 7.51 and 7.53 to find the step response of a first-order *RC* circuit.

Example 7.6 Determining the Step Response of an *RC* Circuit

The switch in the circuit shown in Fig. 7.22 has been in position 1 for a long time. At $t = 0$, the switch moves to position 2. Find

a) $v_o(t)$ for $t \geq 0$ and

b) $i_o(t)$ for $t \geq 0^+$.

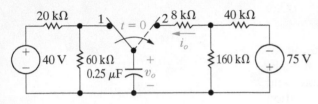

Figure 7.22 ▲ The circuit for Example 7.6.

Solution

a) The switch has been in position 1 for a long time, so the initial value of v_o is $40(60/80)$, or 30 V. To take advantage of Eqs. 7.51 and 7.53, we find the Norton equivalent with respect to the terminals of the capacitor for $t \geq 0$. To do this, we begin by computing the open-circuit voltage, which is given by the −75 V source divided across the 40 kΩ and 160 kΩ resistors:

$$V_{oc} = \frac{160 \times 10^3}{(40 + 160) \times 10^3}(-75) = -60 \text{ V}.$$

Next, we calculate the Thévenin resistance, as seen to the right of the capacitor, by shorting the −75 V source and making series and parallel combinations of the resistors:

$$R_{Th} = 8000 + 40{,}000 \parallel 160{,}000 = 40 \text{ k}\Omega$$

The value of the Norton current source is the ratio of the open-circuit voltage to the Thévenin resistance, or $-60/(40 \times 10^3) = -1.5$ mA. The resulting Norton equivalent circuit is shown in Fig. 7.23. From Fig. 7.23, $I_s R = -60$ V and $RC = 10$ ms. We have already noted that $v_o(0) = 30$ V, so the solution for v_o is

$$v_o = -60 + [30 - (-60)]e^{-100t}$$

$$= -60 + 90e^{-100t} \text{ V}, \quad t \geq 0.$$

b) We write the solution for i_o directly from Eq. 7.53 by noting that $I_s = -1.5$ mA and $V_o/R = (30/40) \times 10^{-3}$, or 0.75 mA:

$$i_o = -2.25e^{-100t} \text{ mA}, \quad t \geq 0^+.$$

We check the consistency of the solutions for v_o and i_o by noting that

$$i_o = C\frac{dv_o}{dt} = (0.25 \times 10^{-6})(-9000e^{-100t})$$

$$= -2.25e^{-100t} \text{ mA}.$$

Because $dv_o(0^-)/dt = 0$, the expression for i_o clearly is valid only for $t \geq 0^+$.

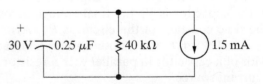

Figure 7.23 ▲ The equivalent circuit for $t > 0$ for the circuit shown in Fig. 7.22.

Objective 2—Be able to determine the step response of both *RL* and *RC* circuits

7.6   a) Find the expression for the voltage across
the 160 kΩ resistor in the circuit shown in
Fig. 7.22. Let this voltage be denoted v_A, and
assume that the reference polarity for the
voltage is positive at the upper terminal of
the 160 kΩ resistor.

b) Specify the interval of time for which the
expression obtained in (a) is valid.

Answer: (a) $-60 + 72e^{-100t}$ V;
    (b) $t \geq 0^+$.

NOTE: Also try Chapter Problems 7.53 and 7.54.

7.4 A General Solution for Step and Natural Responses

The general approach to finding either the natural response or the step
response of the first-order *RL* and *RC* circuits shown in Fig. 7.24 is based
on their differential equations having the same form (compare Eq. 7.48
and Eq. 7.50). To generalize the solution of these four possible circuits, we
let $x(t)$ represent the unknown quantity, giving $x(t)$ four possible values. It
can represent the current or voltage at the terminals of an inductor or the
current or voltage at the terminals of a capacitor. From Eqs. 7.47, 7.48,
7.50, and 7.52, we know that the differential equation describing any one
of the four circuits in Fig. 7.24 takes the form

$$\frac{dx}{dt} + \frac{x}{\tau} = K, \tag{7.54}$$

where the value of the constant K can be zero. Because the sources in the
circuit are constant voltages and/or currents, the final value of x will be
constant; that is, the final value must satisfy Eq. 7.54, and, when x reaches
its final value, the derivative dx/dt must be zero. Hence

$$x_f = K\tau, \tag{7.55}$$

where x_f represents the final value of the variable.

   We solve Eq. 7.54 by separating the variables, beginning by solving for
the first derivative:

$$\frac{dx}{dt} = \frac{-x}{\tau} + K = \frac{-(x - K\tau)}{\tau} = \frac{-(x - x_f)}{\tau}. \tag{7.56}$$

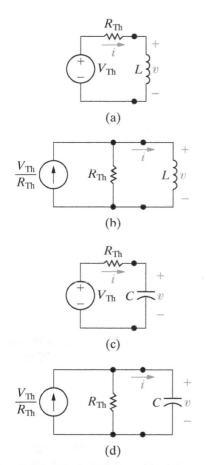

(a)

(b)

(c)

(d)

Figure 7.24 ▲ Four possible first-order circuits.
(a) An inductor connected to a Thévenin equivalent.
(b) An inductor connected to a Norton equivalent.
(c) A capacitor connected to a Thévenin equivalent.
(d) A capacitor connected to a Norton equivalent.

In writing Eq. 7.56, we used Eq. 7.55 to substitute x_f for $K\tau$. We now multiply both sides of Eq. 7.56 by dt and divide by $x - x_f$ to obtain

$$\frac{dx}{x - x_f} = \frac{-1}{\tau}dt. \tag{7.57}$$

Next, we integrate Eq. 7.57. To obtain as general a solution as possible, we use time t_0 as the lower limit and t as the upper limit. Time t_0 corresponds to the time of the switching or other change. Previously we assumed that $t_0 = 0$, but this change allows the switching to take place at any time. Using u and v as symbols of integration, we get

$$\int_{x(t_0)}^{x(t)} \frac{du}{u - x_f} = -\frac{1}{\tau}\int_{t_0}^{t} dv. \tag{7.58}$$

Carrying out the integration called for in Eq. 7.58 gives

◀ **General solution for natural and step responses of *RL* and *RC* circuits**

$$x(t) = x_f + [x(t_0) - x_f]e^{-(t-t_0)/\tau}. \tag{7.59}$$

The importance of Eq. 7.59 becomes apparent if we write it out in words:

$$\begin{matrix} \text{the unknown} \\ \text{variable as a} \\ \text{function of time} \end{matrix} = \begin{matrix} \text{the final} \\ \text{value of the} \\ \text{variable} \end{matrix}$$

$$+ \begin{bmatrix} \text{the initial} & & \text{the final} \\ \text{value of the} & - & \text{value of the} \\ \text{variable} & & \text{variable} \end{bmatrix} \times e^{\frac{-[t-(\text{time of switching})]}{(\text{time constant})}} \tag{7.60}$$

In many cases, the time of switching—that is, t_0—is zero.

When computing the step and natural responses of circuits, it may help to follow these steps:

◀ **Calculating the natural or step response of *RL* or *RC* circuits**

1. Identify the variable of interest for the circuit. For *RC* circuits, it is most convenient to choose the capacitive voltage; for *RL* circuits, it is best to choose the inductive current.
2. Determine the initial value of the variable, which is its value at t_0. Note that if you choose capacitive voltage or inductive current as your variable of interest, it is not necessary to distinguish between $t = t_0^-$ and $t = t_0^+$.[2] This is because they both are continuous variables. If you choose another variable, you need to remember that its initial value is defined at $t = t_0^+$.
3. Calculate the final value of the variable, which is its value as $t \to \infty$.
4. Calculate the time constant for the circuit.

With these quantities, you can use Eq. 7.60 to produce an equation describing the variable of interest as a function of time. You can then find equations for other circuit variables using the circuit analysis techniques introduced in Chapters 3 and 4 or by repeating the preceding steps for the other variables.

Examples 7.7–7.9 illustrate how to use Eq. 7.60 to find the step response of an *RC* or *RL* circuit.

---

[2] The expressions t_0^- and t_0^+ are analogous to 0^- and 0^+. Thus $x(t_0^-)$ is the limit of $x(t)$ as $t \to t_0$ from the left, and $x(t_0^+)$ is the limit of $x(t)$ as $t \to t_0$ from the right.

Example 7.7   **Using the General Solution Method to Find an *RC* Circuit's Step Response**

The switch in the circuit shown in Fig. 7.25 has been in position a for a long time. At $t = 0$ the switch is moved to position b.

a) What is the initial value of v_C?

b) What is the final value of v_C?

c) What is the time constant of the circuit when the switch is in position b?

d) What is the expression for $v_C(t)$ when $t \geq 0$?

e) What is the expression for $i(t)$ when $t \geq 0^+$?

f) How long after the switch is in position b does the capacitor voltage equal zero?

g) Plot $v_C(t)$ and $i(t)$ versus t.

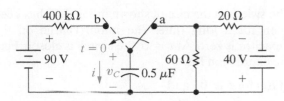

Figure 7.25 ▲ The circuit for Example 7.7.

Solution

a) The switch has been in position a for a long time, so the capacitor looks like an open circuit. Therefore the voltage across the capacitor is the voltage across the 60 Ω resistor. From the voltage-divider rule, the voltage across the 60 Ω resistor is $40 \times [60/(60 + 20)]$, or 30 V. As the reference for v_C is positive at the upper terminal of the capacitor, we have $v_C(0) = -30$ V.

b) After the switch has been in position b for a long time, the capacitor will look like an open circuit in terms of the 90 V source. Thus the final value of the capacitor voltage is $+90$ V.

c) The time constant is

$$\tau = RC$$
$$= (400 \times 10^3)(0.5 \times 10^{-6})$$
$$= 0.2 \text{ s.}$$

d) Substituting the appropriate values for v_f, $v(0)$, and t into Eq. 7.60 yields

$$v_C(t) = 90 + (-30 - 90)e^{-5t}$$
$$= 90 - 120e^{-5t} \text{ V}, \quad t \geq 0.$$

e) Here the value for τ doesn't change. Thus we need to find only the initial and final values for the current in the capacitor. When obtaining the initial value, we must get the value of $i(0^+)$, because the current in the capacitor can change instantaneously. This current is equal to the current in the resistor, which from Ohm's law is $[90 - (-30)]/(400 \times 10^3) = 300 \ \mu A$. Note that when applying Ohm's law we recognized that the

capacitor voltage cannot change instantaneously. The final value of $i(t) = 0$, so

$$i(t) = 0 + (300 - 0)e^{-5t}$$
$$= 300e^{-5t} \ \mu A, \quad t \geq 0^+.$$

We could have obtained this solution by differentiating the solution in (d) and multiplying by the capacitance. You may want to do so for yourself. Note that this alternative approach to finding $i(t)$ also predicts the discontinuity at $t = 0$.

f) To find how long the switch must be in position b before the capacitor voltage becomes zero, we solve the equation derived in (d) for the time when $v_C(t) = 0$:

$$120e^{-5t} = 90 \quad \text{or} \quad e^{5t} = \frac{120}{90},$$

so

$$t = \frac{1}{5}\ln\left(\frac{4}{3}\right)$$
$$= 57.54 \text{ ms.}$$

Note that when $v_C = 0$, $i = 225 \ \mu A$ and the voltage drop across the 400 kΩ resistor is 90 V.

g) Figure 7.26 shows the graphs of $v_C(t)$ and $i(t)$ versus t.

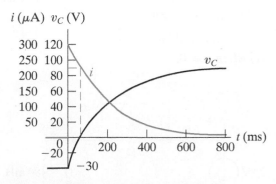

Figure 7.26 ▲ The current and voltage waveforms for Example 7.7.

Example 7.8   Using the General Solution Method with Zero Initial Conditions

The switch in the circuit shown in Fig. 7.27 has been open for a long time. The initial charge on the capacitor is zero. At $t = 0$, the switch is closed. Find the expression for

a) $i(t)$ for $t \geq 0^+$ and

b) $v(t)$ when $t \geq 0^+$.

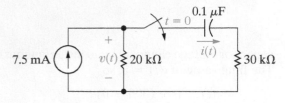

Figure 7.27 ▲ The circuit for Example 7.8.

Solution

a) Because the initial voltage on the capacitor is zero, at the instant when the switch is closed the current in the 30 kΩ branch will be

$$i(0^+) = \frac{(7.5)(20)}{50}$$

$$= 3 \text{ mA}.$$

The final value of the capacitor current will be zero because the capacitor eventually will appear as an open circuit in terms of dc current. Thus $i_f = 0$. The time constant of the circuit will equal the product of the Thévenin resistance (as seen from the capacitor) and the capacitance.

Therefore $\tau = (20 + 30)10^3(0.1) \times 10^{-6} = 5$ ms. Substituting these values into Eq. 7.60 generates the expression

$$i(t) = 0 + (3 - 0)e^{-t/5 \times 10^{-3}}$$

$$= 3e^{-200t} \text{ mA}, \quad t \geq 0^+.$$

b) To find $v(t)$, we note from the circuit that it equals the sum of the voltage across the capacitor and the voltage across the 30 kΩ resistor. To find the capacitor voltage (which is a drop in the direction of the current), we note that its initial value is zero and its final value is (7.5)(20), or 150 V. The time constant is the same as before, or 5 ms. Therefore we use Eq. 7.60 to write

$$v_C(t) = 150 + (0 - 150)e^{-200t}$$

$$= (150 - 150e^{-200t}) \text{ V}, \quad t \geq 0.$$

Hence the expression for the voltage $v(t)$ is

$$v(t) = 150 - 150e^{-200t} + (30)(3)e^{-200t}$$

$$= (150 - 60e^{-200t}) \text{ V}, \quad t \geq 0^+.$$

As one check on this expression, note that it predicts the initial value of the voltage across the 20 Ω resistor as $150 - 60$, or 90 V. The instant the switch is closed, the current in the 20 kΩ resistor is (7.5)(30/50), or 4.5 mA. This current produces a 90 V drop across the 20 kΩ resistor, confirming the value predicted by the solution.

Example 7.9   Using the General Solution Method to Find an *RL* Circuit's Step Response

The switch in the circuit shown in Fig. 7.28 has been open for a long time. At $t = 0$ the switch is closed. Find the expression for

a) $v(t)$ when $t \geq 0^+$ and

b) $i(t)$ when $t \geq 0$.

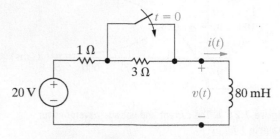

Figure 7.28 ▲ The circuit for Example 7.9.

Solution

a) The switch has been open for a long time, so the initial current in the inductor is 5 A, oriented from top to bottom. Immediately after the switch closes, the current still is 5 A, and therefore the initial voltage across the inductor becomes $20 - 5(1)$, or 15 V. The final value of the inductor voltage is 0 V. With the switch closed, the time constant is 80/1, or 80 ms. We use Eq. 7.60 to write the expression for $v(t)$:

$$v(t) = 0 + (15 - 0)e^{-t/80 \times 10^{-3}}$$

$$= 15e^{-12.5t} \text{ V}, \quad t \geq 0^+.$$

b) We have already noted that the initial value of the inductor current is 5 A. After the switch has been closed for a long time, the inductor current reaches 20/1, or 20 A. The circuit time constant is 80 ms, so the expression for $i(t)$ is

$$i(t) = 20 + (5 - 20)e^{-12.5t}$$
$$= (20 - 15e^{-12.5t}) \text{ A}, \quad t \geq 0.$$

We determine that the solutions for $v(t)$ and $i(t)$ agree by noting that

$$v(t) = L\frac{di}{dt}$$
$$= 80 \times 10^{-3}[15(12.5)e^{-12.5t}]$$
$$= 15e^{-12.5t} \text{ V}, \quad t \geq 0^+.$$

NOTE: Assess your understanding of the general solution method by trying Chapter Problems 7.51 and 7.53.

Example 7.10 shows that Eq. 7.60 can even be used to find the step response of some circuits containing magnetically coupled coils.

Example 7.10   Determining Step Response of a Circuit with Magnetically Coupled Coils

There is no energy stored in the circuit in Fig. 7.29 at the time the switch is closed.

a) Find the solutions for i_o, v_o, i_1, and i_2.

b) Show that the solutions obtained in (a) make sense in terms of known circuit behavior.

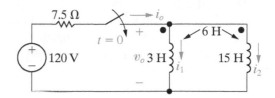

Figure 7.29 ▲ The circuit for Example 7.10.

Solution

a) For the circuit in Fig. 7.29, the magnetically coupled coils can be replaced by a single inductor having an inductance of

$$L_{eq} = \frac{L_1 L_2 - M^2}{L_1 + L_2 - 2M} = \frac{45 - 36}{18 - 12} = 1.5 \text{ H}.$$

(See Problem 6.41.) It follows that the circuit in Fig. 7.29 can be simplified as shown in Fig. 7.30.

By hypothesis the initial value of i_o is zero. From Fig. 7.30 we see that the final value of i_o will be 120/7.5 or 16 A. The time constant of the circuit is 1.5/7.5 or 0.2 s. It follows directly from Eq. 7.60 that

$$i_o = 16 - 16e^{-5t} \text{ A}, \quad t \geq 0.$$

The voltage v_o follows from Kirchhoff's voltage law. Thus,

$$v_o = 120 - 7.5i_o$$
$$= 120e^{-5t} \text{ V}, \quad t \geq 0^+.$$

To find i_1 and i_2 we first note from Fig. 7.29 that

$$3\frac{di_1}{dt} + 6\frac{di_2}{dt} = 6\frac{di_1}{dt} + 15\frac{di_2}{dt}$$

or

$$\frac{di_1}{dt} = -3\frac{di_2}{dt}.$$

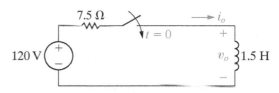

Figure 7.30 ▲ The circuit in Fig. 7.29 with the magnetically coupled coils replaced by an equivalent coil.

It also follows from Fig. 7.29 that because $i_o = i_1 + i_2$,

$$\frac{di_o}{dt} = \frac{di_1}{dt} + \frac{di_2}{dt}.$$

Therefore

$$80e^{-5t} = -2\frac{di_2}{dt}.$$

Because $i_2(0)$ is zero we have

$$i_2 = \int_0^t -40e^{-5x} dx$$
$$= -8 + 8e^{-5t} \text{ A}, \quad t \geq 0.$$

Using Kirchhoff's current law we get

$$i_1 = 24 - 24e^{-5t} \text{ A}, \quad t \geq 0.$$

b) First we observe that $i_o(0)$, $i_1(0)$, and $i_2(0)$ are all zero, which is consistent with the statement that no energy is stored in the circuit at the instant the switch is closed.

Next we observe $v_o(0^+) = 120$ V, which is consistent with the fact that $i_o(0) = 0$.

Now we observe the solutions for i_1 and i_2 are consistent with the solution for v_o by observing

$$v_o = 3\frac{di_1}{dt} + 6\frac{di_2}{dt}$$

$$= 360e^{-5t} - 240e^{-5t}$$

$$= 120e^{-5t} \text{ V}, \quad t \geq 0^+,$$

or

$$v_o = 6\frac{di_1}{dt} + 15\frac{di_2}{dt}$$

$$= 720e^{-5t} - 600e^{-5t}$$

$$= 120e^{-5t} \text{ V}, \quad t \geq 0^+.$$

The final values of i_1 and i_2 can be checked using flux linkages. The flux linking the 3 H coil (λ_1) must be equal to the flux linking the 15 H coil (λ_2), because

$$v_o = \frac{d\lambda_1}{dt}$$

$$= \frac{d\lambda_2}{dt}.$$

Now

$$\lambda_1 = 3i_1 + 6i_2 \text{ Wb-turns}$$

and

$$\lambda_2 = 6i_1 + 15i_2 \text{ Wb-turns}.$$

Regardless of which expression we use, we obtain

$$\lambda_1 = \lambda_2 = 24 - 24e^{-5t} \text{ Wb-turns}.$$

Note the solution for λ_1 or λ_2 is consistent with the solution for v_o.

The final value of the flux linking either coil 1 or coil 2 is 24 Wb-turns, that is,

$$\lambda_1(\infty) = \lambda_2(\infty) = 24 \text{ Wb-turns}.$$

The final value of i_1 is

$$i_1(\infty) = 24 \text{ A}$$

and the final value of i_2 is

$$i_2(\infty) = -8 \text{ A}.$$

The consistency between these final values for i_1 and i_2 and the final value of the flux linkage can be seen from the expressions:

$$\lambda_1(\infty) = 3i_1(\infty) + 6i_2(\infty)$$

$$= 3(24) + 6(-8) = 24 \text{ Wb-turns},$$

$$\lambda_2(\infty) = 6i_1(\infty) + 15i_2(\infty)$$

$$= 6(24) + 15(-8) = 24 \text{ Wb-turns}.$$

It is worth noting that the final values of i_1 and i_2 can only be checked via flux linkage because at $t = \infty$ the two coils are ideal short circuits. The division of current between ideal short circuits cannot be found from Ohm's law.

NOTE: Assess your understanding of this material by using the general solution method to solve Chapter Problems 7.68 and 7.71.

7.5 Sequential Switching

Whenever switching occurs more than once in a circuit, we have **sequential switching**. For example, a single, two-position switch may be switched back and forth, or multiple switches may be opened or closed in sequence. The time reference for all switchings cannot be $t = 0$. We determine the voltages and currents generated by a switching sequence by using the techniques described previously in this chapter. We derive the expressions for $v(t)$ and $i(t)$ for a given position of the switch or switches and then use these solutions to determine the initial conditions for the next position of the switch or switches.

With sequential switching problems, a premium is placed on obtaining the initial value $x(t_0)$. Recall that anything but inductive currents and capacitive voltages can change instantaneously at the time of switching. Thus solving first for inductive currents and capacitive voltages is even more pertinent in sequential switching problems. Drawing the circuit that pertains to each time interval in such a problem is often helpful in the solution process.

Examples 7.11 and 7.12 illustrate the analysis techniques for circuits with sequential switching. The first is a natural response problem with two switching times, and the second is a step response problem.

Example 7.11   **Analyzing an *RL* Circuit that has Sequential Switching**

The two switches in the circuit shown in Fig. 7.31 have been closed for a long time. At $t = 0$, switch 1 is opened. Then, 35 ms later, switch 2 is opened.

a) Find $i_L(t)$ for $0 \le t \le 35$ ms.

b) Find i_L for $t \ge 35$ ms.

c) What percentage of the initial energy stored in the 150 mH inductor is dissipated in the 18 Ω resistor?

d) Repeat (c) for the 3 Ω resistor.

e) Repeat (c) for the 6 Ω resistor.

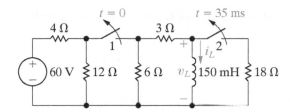

Figure 7.31 ▲ The circuit for Example 7.11.

Solution

a) For $t < 0$ both switches are closed, causing the 150 mH inductor to short-circuit the 18 Ω resistor. The equivalent circuit is shown in Fig. 7.32. We determine the initial current in the inductor by solving for $i_L(0^-)$ in the circuit shown in Fig. 7.32. After making several source transformations, we find $i_L(0^-)$ to be 6 A. For $0 \le t \le 35$ ms, switch 1 is open (switch 2 is closed), which disconnects the 60 V voltage source and the 4 Ω and 12 Ω resistors from the circuit. The inductor is no longer behaving as a short circuit (because the dc source is no longer in the circuit), so the 18 Ω resistor is no longer short-circuited. The equivalent circuit is shown in Fig. 7.33. Note that the equivalent resistance across the terminals of the inductor is the parallel combination of 9 Ω and 18 Ω, or 6 Ω. The time constant of the circuit is $(150/6) \times 10^{-3}$, or 25 ms. Therefore the expression for i_L is

$$i_L = 6e^{-40t} \text{ A}, \quad 0 \le t \le 35 \text{ ms}.$$

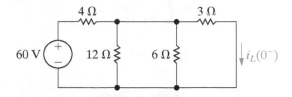

Figure 7.32 ▲ The circuit shown in Fig. 7.31, for $t < 0$.

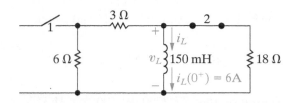

Figure 7.33 ▲ The circuit shown in Fig. 7.31, for $0 \le t \le 35$ ms.

b) When $t = 35$ ms, the value of the inductor current is

$$i_L = 6e^{-1.4} = 1.48 \text{ A}.$$

Thus, when switch 2 is opened, the circuit reduces to the one shown in Fig. 7.34, and the time constant changes to $(150/9) \times 10^{-3}$, or 16.67 ms. The expression for i_L becomes

$$i_L = 1.48e^{-60(t-0.035)} \text{ A}, \quad t \ge 35 \text{ ms}.$$

Note that the exponential function is shifted in time by 35 ms.

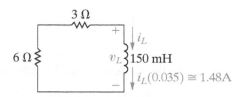

Figure 7.34 ▲ The circuit shown in Fig. 7.31, for $t \ge 35$ ms.

c) The 18 Ω resistor is in the circuit only during the first 35 ms of the switching sequence. During this interval, the voltage across the resistor is

$$v_L = 0.15 \frac{d}{dt}(6e^{-40t})$$

$$= -36e^{-40t} \text{ V}, \quad 0 < t < 35 \text{ ms}.$$

The power dissipated in the 18 Ω resistor is

$$p = \frac{v_L^2}{18} = 72e^{-80t} \text{ W}, \quad 0 < t < 35 \text{ ms}.$$

Hence the energy dissipated is

$$w = \int_0^{0.035} 72e^{-80t}\, dt$$

$$= \frac{72}{-80}e^{-80t}\Big|_0^{0.035}$$

$$= 0.9(1 - e^{-2.8})$$

$$= 845.27 \text{ mJ}.$$

The initial energy stored in the 150 mH inductor is

$$w_i = \frac{1}{2}(0.15)(36) = 2.7 \text{ J} = 2700 \text{ mJ}.$$

Therefore $(845.27/2700) \times 100$, or 31.31% of the initial energy stored in the 150 mH inductor is dissipated in the 18 Ω resistor.

d) For $0 < t < 35$ ms, the voltage across the 3 Ω resistor is

$$v_{3\Omega} = \left(\frac{v_L}{9}\right)(3)$$

$$= \frac{1}{3}v_L$$

$$= -12e^{-40t} \text{ V}.$$

Therefore the energy dissipated in the 3 Ω resistor in the first 35 ms is

$$w_{3\Omega} = \int_0^{0.035} \frac{144e^{-80t}}{3}\, dt$$

$$= 0.6(1 - e^{-2.8})$$

$$= 563.51 \text{ mJ}.$$

For $t > 35$ ms, the current in the 3 Ω resistor is

$$i_{3\Omega} = i_L = (6e^{-1.4})e^{-60(t-0.035)} \text{ A}.$$

Hence the energy dissipated in the 3 Ω resistor for $t > 35$ ms is

$$w_{3\Omega} = \int_{0.035}^{\infty} i_{3\Omega}^2 \times 3\, dt$$

$$= \int_{0.035}^{\infty} 3(36)e^{-2.8}e^{-120(t-0.035)}\, dt$$

$$= 108e^{-2.8} \times \frac{e^{-120(t-0.035)}}{-120}\Big|_{0.035}^{\infty}$$

$$= \frac{108}{120}e^{-2.8} = 54.73 \text{ mJ}.$$

The total energy dissipated in the 3 Ω resistor is

$$w_{3\Omega}(\text{total}) = 563.51 + 54.73$$

$$= 618.24 \text{ mJ}.$$

The percentage of the initial energy stored is

$$\frac{618.24}{2700} \times 100 = 22.90\%.$$

e) Because the 6 Ω resistor is in series with the 3 Ω resistor, the energy dissipated and the percentage of the initial energy stored will be twice that of the 3 Ω resistor:

$$w_{6\Omega}(\text{total}) = 1236.48 \text{ mJ},$$

and the percentage of the initial energy stored is 45.80%. We check these calculations by observing that

$$1236.48 + 618.24 + 845.27 = 2699.99 \text{ mJ}$$

and

$$31.31 + 22.90 + 45.80 = 100.01\%.$$

The small discrepancies in the summations are the result of roundoff errors.

Example 7.12   Analyzing an *RC* Circuit that has Sequential Switching

The uncharged capacitor in the circuit shown in Fig. 7.35 is initially switched to terminal a of the three-position switch. At $t = 0$, the switch is moved to position b, where it remains for 15 ms. After the 15 ms delay, the switch is moved to position c, where it remains indefinitely.

a) Derive the numerical expression for the voltage across the capacitor.

b) Plot the capacitor voltage versus time.

c) When will the voltage on the capacitor equal 200 V?

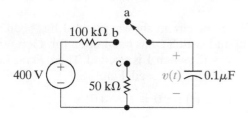

Figure 7.35 ▲ The circuit for Example 7.12.

Solution

a) At the instant the switch is moved to position b, the initial voltage on the capacitor is zero. If the switch were to remain in position b, the capacitor would eventually charge to 400 V. The time constant of the circuit when the switch is in position b is 10 ms. Therefore we can use Eq. 7.59 with $t_0 = 0$ to write the expression for the capacitor voltage:

$$v = 400 + (0 - 400)e^{-100t}$$

$$= (400 - 400e^{-100t}) \text{ V}, \quad 0 \leq t \leq 15 \text{ ms}.$$

Note that, because the switch remains in position b for only 15 ms, this expression is valid only for the time interval from 0 to 15 ms. After the switch has been in this position for 15 ms, the voltage on the capacitor will be

$$v(15 \text{ ms}) = 400 - 400e^{-1.5} = 310.75 \text{ V}.$$

Therefore, when the switch is moved to position c, the initial voltage on the capacitor is 310.75 V. With the switch in position c, the final value of the capacitor voltage is zero, and the time constant is 5 ms. Again, we use Eq. 7.59 to write the expression for the capacitor voltage:

$$v = 0 + (310.75 - 0)e^{-200(t-0.015)}$$

$$= 310.75e^{-200(t-0.015)} \text{ V}, \quad 15 \text{ ms} \leq t.$$

In writing the expression for v, we recognized that $t_0 = 15$ ms and that this expression is valid only for $t \geq 15$ ms.

b) Figure 7.36 shows the plot of v versus t.

c) The plot in Fig. 7.36 reveals that the capacitor voltage will equal 200 V at two different times: once in the interval between 0 and 15 ms and once after 15 ms. We find the first time by solving the expression

$$200 = 400 - 400e^{-100t_1},$$

which yields $t_1 = 6.93$ ms. We find the second time by solving the expression

$$200 = 310.75e^{-200(t_2-0.015)}.$$

In this case, $t_2 = 17.20$ ms.

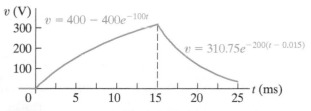

Figure 7.36 ▲ The capacitor voltage for Example 7.12.

✓ ASSESSMENT PROBLEMS

Objective 3—Know how to analyze circuits with sequential switching

7.7 In the circuit shown, switch 1 has been closed and switch 2 has been open for a long time. At $t = 0$, switch 1 is opened. Then 10 ms later, switch 2 is closed. Find

a) $v_c(t)$ for $0 \leq t \leq 0.01$ s,

b) $v_c(t)$ for $t \geq 0.01$ s,

c) the total energy dissipated in the 25 kΩ resistor, and

d) the total energy dissipated in the 100 kΩ resistor.

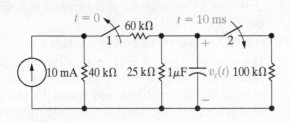

Answer: (a) $80e^{-40t}$ V;

(b) $53.63e^{-50(t-0.01)}$ V;

(c) 2.91 mJ;

(d) 0.29 mJ.

NOTE: Also try Chapter Problems 7.72 and 7.80.

7.8 Switch a in the circuit shown has been open for a long time, and switch b has been closed for a long time. Switch a is closed at $t = 0$ and, after remaining closed for 1 s, is opened again. Switch b is opened simultaneously, and both switches remain open indefinitely. Determine the expression for the inductor current i that is valid when (a) $0 \leq t \leq 1$ s and (b) $t \geq 1$ s.

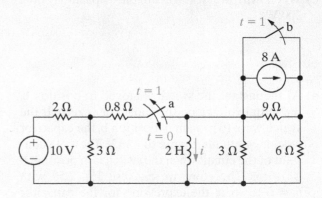

Answer: (a) $(3 - 3e^{-0.5t})$ A, $0 \leq t \leq 1$ s;

(b) $(-4.8 + 5.98e^{-1.25(t-1)})$ A, $t \geq 1$ s.

7.6 Unbounded Response

A circuit response may grow, rather than decay, exponentially with time. This type of response, called an **unbounded response**, is possible if the circuit contains dependent sources. In that case, the Thévenin equivalent resistance with respect to the terminals of either an inductor or a capacitor may be negative. This negative resistance generates a negative time constant, and the resulting currents and voltages increase without limit. In an actual circuit, the response eventually reaches a limiting value when a component breaks down or goes into a saturation state, prohibiting further increases in voltage or current.

When we consider unbounded responses, the concept of a final value is confusing. Hence, rather than using the step response solution given in Eq. 7.59, we derive the differential equation that describes the circuit containing the negative resistance and then solve it using the separation of variables technique. Example 7.13 presents an exponentially growing response in terms of the voltage across a capacitor.

Example 7.13   Finding the Unbounded Response in an *RC* Circuit

a) When the switch is closed in the circuit shown in Fig. 7.37, the voltage on the capacitor is 10 V. Find the expression for v_o for $t \geq 0$.

b) Assume that the capacitor short-circuits when its terminal voltage reaches 150 V. How many milliseconds elapse before the capacitor short-circuits?

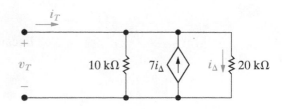

i_T

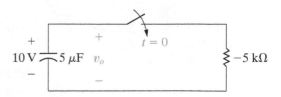

v_T 10 kΩ $7i_\Delta$ i_Δ 20 kΩ

Figure 7.38 ▲ The test-source method used to find R_{Th}.

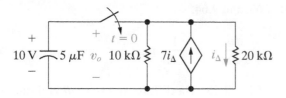

$t = 0$

10 V   5 μF v_o 10 kΩ $7i_\Delta$ i_Δ 20 kΩ

Figure 7.37 ▲ The circuit for Example 7.13.

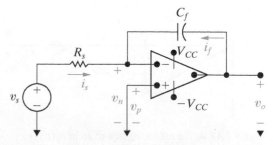

$t = 0$

10 V   5 μF v_o −5 kΩ

Figure 7.39 ▲ A simplification of the circuit shown in Fig. 7.37.

Solution

a) To find the Thévenin equivalent resistance with respect to the capacitor terminals, we use the test-source method described in Chapter 4. Figure 7.38 shows the resulting circuit, where v_T is the test voltage and i_T is the test current. For v_T expressed in volts, we obtain

$$i_T = \frac{v_T}{10} - 7\left(\frac{v_T}{20}\right) + \frac{v_T}{20} \text{ mA}.$$

Solving for the ratio v_T/i_T yields the Thévenin resistance:

$$R_{Th} = \frac{v_T}{i_T} = -5 \text{ kΩ}.$$

With this Thévenin resistance, we can simplify the circuit shown in Fig. 7.37 to the one shown in Fig. 7.39.

For $t \geq 0$, the differential equation describing the circuit shown in Fig. 7.39 is

$$(5 \times 10^{-6})\frac{dv_o}{dt} - \frac{v_o}{5} \times 10^{-3} = 0.$$

Dividing by the coefficient of the first derivative yields

$$\frac{dv_o}{dt} - 40v_o = 0.$$

We now use the separation of variables technique to find $v_o(t)$:

$$v_o(t) = 10e^{40t} \text{ V}, \quad t \geq 0.$$

b) $v_o = 150$ V when $e^{40t} = 15$. Therefore, $40t = \ln 15$, and $t = 67.70$ ms.

NOTE: Assess your understanding of this material by trying Chapter Problems 7.86 and 7.88.

The fact that interconnected circuit elements may lead to ever-increasing currents and voltages is important to engineers. If such interconnections are unintended, the resulting circuit may experience unexpected, and potentially dangerous, component failures.

7.7 The Integrating Amplifier

Recall from the introduction to Chapter 5 that one reason for our interest in the operational amplifier is its use as an integrating amplifier. We are now ready to analyze an integrating-amplifier circuit, which is shown in Fig. 7.40. The purpose of such a circuit is to generate an output voltage proportional to the integral of the input voltage. In Fig. 7.40, we added the branch currents i_f and i_s, along with the node voltages v_n and v_p, to aid our analysis.

C_f

R_s V_{CC} i_f

v_s i_s v_n v_p $-V_{CC}$ v_o

Figure 7.40 ▲ An integrating amplifier.

We assume that the operational amplifier is ideal. Thus we take advantage of the constraints

$$i_f + i_s = 0, \tag{7.61}$$
$$v_n = v_p. \tag{7.62}$$

Because $v_p = 0$,

$$i_s = \frac{v_s}{R_s}, \tag{7.63}$$

$$i_f = C_f \frac{dv_o}{dt}. \tag{7.64}$$

Hence, from Eqs. 7.61, 7.63, and 7.64,

$$\frac{dv_o}{dt} = -\frac{1}{R_s C_f} v_s. \tag{7.65}$$

Multiplying both sides of Eq. 7.65 by a differential time dt and then integrating from t_0 to t generates the equation

$$v_o(t) = -\frac{1}{R_s C_f} \int_{t_0}^{t} v_s \, dy + v_o(t_0). \tag{7.66}$$

In Eq. 7.66, t_0 represents the instant in time when we begin the integration. Thus $v_o(t_0)$ is the value of the output voltage at that time. Also, because $v_n = v_p = 0$, $v_o(t_0)$ is identical to the initial voltage on the feedback capacitor C_f.

Equation 7.66 states that the output voltage of an integrating amplifier equals the initial value of the voltage on the capacitor plus an inverted (minus sign), scaled $(1/R_s C_f)$ replica of the integral of the input voltage. If no energy is stored in the capacitor when integration commences, Eq. 7.66 reduces to

$$v_o(t) = -\frac{1}{R_s C_f} \int_{t_0}^{t} v_s \, dy. \tag{7.67}$$

If v_s is a step change in a dc voltage level, the output voltage will vary linearly with time. For example, assume that the input voltage is the rectangular voltage pulse shown in Fig. 7.41. Assume also that the initial value of $v_o(t)$ is zero at the instant v_s steps from 0 to V_m. A direct application of Eq. 7.66 yields

$$v_o = -\frac{1}{R_s C_f} V_m t + 0, \quad 0 \le t \le t_1. \tag{7.68}$$

When t lies between t_1 and $2t_1$,

$$v_o = -\frac{1}{R_s C_f} \int_{t_1}^{t} (-V_m) \, dy - \frac{1}{R_s C_f} V_m t_1$$

$$= \frac{V_m}{R_s C_f} t - \frac{2V_m}{R_s C_f} t_1, \quad t_1 \le t \le 2t_1. \tag{7.69}$$

Figure 7.42 shows a sketch of $v_o(t)$ versus t. Clearly, the output voltage is an inverted, scaled replica of the integral of the input voltage.

The output voltage is proportional to the integral of the input voltage only if the op amp operates within its linear range, that is, if it doesn't saturate. Examples 7.14 and 7.15 further illustrate the analysis of the integrating amplifier.

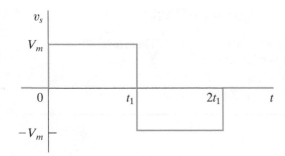

Figure 7.41 ▲ An input voltage signal.

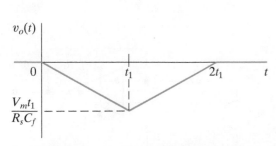

Figure 7.42 ▲ The output voltage of an integrating amplifier.

Example 7.14   **Analyzing an Integrating Amplifier**

Assume that the numerical values for the signal voltage shown in Fig. 7.41 are $V_m = 50$ mV and $t_1 = 1$ s. This signal voltage is applied to the integrating-amplifier circuit shown in Fig. 7.40. The circuit parameters of the amplifier are $R_s = 100$ kΩ, $C_f = 0.1$ μF, and $V_{CC} = 6$ V. The initial voltage on the capacitor is zero.

a) Calculate $v_o(t)$.
b) Plot $v_o(t)$ versus t.

Solution

a) For $0 \leq t \leq 1$ s,

$$v_o = \frac{-1}{(100 \times 10^3)(0.1 \times 10^{-6})} 50 \times 10^{-3}t + 0$$

$$= -5t \text{ V}, \quad 0 \leq t \leq 1 \text{ s}.$$

For $1 \leq t \leq 2$ s,

$$v_o = (5t - 10) \text{ V}.$$

b) Figure 7.43 shows a plot of $v_o(t)$ versus t.

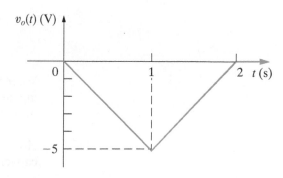

Figure 7.43 ▲ The output voltage for Example 7.14.

Example 7.15   **Analyzing an Integrating Amplifier that has Sequential Switching**

At the instant the switch makes contact with terminal a in the circuit shown in Fig. 7.44, the voltage on the 0.1 μF capacitor is 5 V. The switch remains at terminal a for 9 ms and then moves instantaneously to terminal b. How many milliseconds after making contact with terminal b does the operational amplifier saturate?

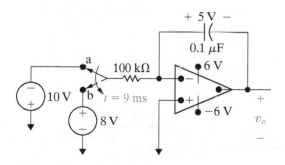

Figure 7.44 ▲ The circuit for Example 7.15.

Solution

The expression for the output voltage during the time the switch is at terminal a is

$$v_o = -5 - \frac{1}{10^{-2}} \int_0^t (-10) \, dy$$

$$= (-5 + 1000t) \text{ V}.$$

Thus, 9 ms after the switch makes contact with terminal a, the output voltage is $-5 + 9$, or 4 V.

The expression for the output voltage after the switch moves to terminal b is

$$v_o = 4 - \frac{1}{10^{-2}} \int_{9 \times 10^{-3}}^t 8 \, dy$$

$$= 4 - 800(t - 9 \times 10^{-3})$$

$$= (11.2 - 800t) \text{ V}.$$

During this time interval, the voltage is decreasing, and the operational amplifier eventually saturates at -6 V. Therefore we set the expression for v_o equal to -6 V to obtain the saturation time t_s:

$$11.2 - 800t_s = -6,$$

or

$$t_s = 21.5 \text{ ms}.$$

Thus the integrating amplifier saturates 21.5 ms after making contact with terminal b.

From the examples, we see that the integrating amplifier can perform the integration function very well, but only within specified limits that avoid saturating the op amp. The op amp saturates due to the accumulation of charge on the feedback capacitor. We can prevent it from saturating by placing a resistor in parallel with the feedback capacitor. We examine such a circuit in Chapter 8.

Note that we can convert the integrating amplifier to a differentiating amplifier by interchanging the input resistance R_s and the feedback capacitor C_f. Then

$$v_o = -R_s C_f \frac{dv_s}{dt}. \qquad (7.70)$$

We leave the derivation of Eq. 7.70 as an exercise for you. The differentiating amplifier is seldom used because in practice it is a source of unwanted or noisy signals.

Finally, we can design both integrating- and differentiating-amplifier circuits by using an inductor instead of a capacitor. However, fabricating capacitors for integrated-circuit devices is much easier, so inductors are rarely used in integrating amplifiers.

✓ASSESSMENT PROBLEMS

Objective 4—Be able to analyze op amp circuits containing resistors and a single capacitor

7.9   There is no energy stored in the capacitor at the time the switch in the circuit makes contact with terminal a. The switch remains at position a for 32 ms and then moves instantaneously to position b. How many milliseconds after making contact with terminal a does the op amp saturate?

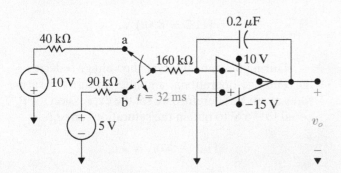

Answer: 262 ms.

NOTE: Also try Chapter Problems 7.94 and 7.95.

7.10   a) When the switch closes in the circuit shown, there is no energy stored in the capacitor. How long does it take to saturate the op amp?

b) Repeat (a) with an initial voltage on the capacitor of 1 V, positive at the upper terminal.

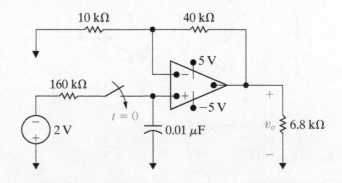

Answer: (a) 1.11 ms;
            (b) 1.76 ms.

Practical Perspective

Artificial Pacemaker

We are now ready to analyze a simple RC circuit, shown in Fig. 7.45, which can generate periodic electrical impulses. This RC circuit can be used in an artificial pacemaker to establish a normal heart rhythm. The box labeled "controller" behaves as an open circuit until the voltage drop across the capacitor reaches a pre-set limit. Once that limit is reached, the capacitor discharges its stored energy in the form of an electrical impulse to the heart and starts to recharge and the process repeats.

Before we develop the analytical expressions that describe the behavior of the circuit, let us develop a feel for how that circuit works. First, when the controller behaves as an open circuit, the dc voltage source will charge the capacitor via the resistor R, toward a value of V_s volts. But once the capacitor voltage reaches V_{max}, the controller behaves like a short circuit, enabling the capacitor to discharge. Once the capacitor discharge is complete, the controller once again acts as an open circuit and the capacitor starts to recharge. This cycle of charging and discharging the capacitor establishes the desired heart rhythm, as shown in Fig. 7.46.

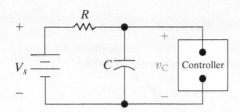

Figure 7.45 ▲ An artificial pacemaker circuit.

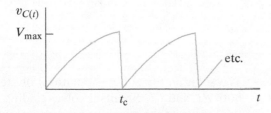

Figure 7.46 ▲ Capacitor voltage versus time for the circuit in Fig. 7.45.

In drawing Fig. 7.46 we have chosen $t = 0$ at the instant the capacitor starts to charge. This figure also assumes that the circuit has reached the repetitive stage of its operation, and that the time to discharge the capacitor is negligible when compared to the recharge time. The design of this artificial pacemaker circuit requires an equation for $v_C(t)$ as a function of V_{max}, R, and C.

To begin the analysis, we assume that the circuit has been in operation for a long time. Let $t = 0$ at the instant when the capacitor has completely discharged and the controller is acting as an open circuit. From the circuit we find

$$v_C(\infty) = V_s,$$

$$v_C(0) = 0,$$

$$\tau = RC.$$

Thus, while the capacitor is charging,

$$v_C(t) = V_s(1 - e^{-t/RC}).$$

Suppose the controller has been programmed to fire an electrical pulse to stimulate the heart when $v_C = 0.75V_s$. Given values of R and C we can determine the resulting heart rate in beats per minute as follows:

$$H = \frac{60}{-RC \ln 0.25} \text{ [beats per minute]}$$

A more realistic design problem requires you to calculate the value of resistance, R, given V_{max} as a percentage of V_s, C, and the desired heart rate in beats per minute. We leave you to develop an equation for resistance in Problem 7.106.

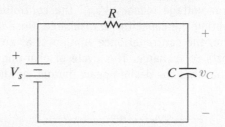

Figure 7.47 ▲ The artificial pacemaker circuit at $t = 0$, when the capacitor is charging.

NOTE: Assess your understanding of the Practical Perspective by solving Chapter Problems 7.104–7.107.

Summary

- A first-order circuit may be reduced to a Thévenin (or Norton) equivalent connected to either a single equivalent inductor or capacitor. (See page 214.)

- The **natural response** is the currents and voltages that exist when stored energy is released to a circuit that contains no independent sources. (See page 212.)

- The **time constant** of an *RL* circuit equals the equivalent inductance divided by the Thévenin resistance as viewed from the terminals of the equivalent inductor. (See page 216.)

- The **time constant** of an *RC* circuit equals the equivalent capacitance times the Thévenin resistance as viewed from the terminals of the equivalent capacitor. (See page 221.)

- The **step response** is the currents and voltages that result from abrupt changes in dc sources connected to a circuit. Stored energy may or may not be present at the time the abrupt changes take place. (See page 224.)

- The solution for either the natural or step response of both *RL* and *RC* circuits involves finding the initial and final value of the current or voltage of interest and the time constant of the circuit. Equations 7.59 and 7.60 summarize this approach. (See page 232.)

- **Sequential switching** in first-order circuits is analyzed by dividing the analysis into time intervals corresponding to specific switch positions. Initial values for a particular interval are determined from the solution corresponding to the immediately preceding interval. (See page 236.)

- An **unbounded response** occurs when the Thévenin resistance is negative, which is possible when the first-order circuit contains dependent sources. (See page 240.)

- An **integrating amplifier** consists of an ideal op amp, a capacitor in the negative feedback branch, and a resistor in series with the signal source. It outputs the integral of the signal source, within specified limits that avoid saturating the op amp. (See page 241.)

Problems

Section 7.1

7.1 The switch in the circuit in Fig. P7.1 has been open
PSPICE   for a long time. At $t = 0$ the switch is closed.
MULTISIM
a) Determine $i_o(0)$ and $i_o(\infty)$.

b) Determine $i_o(t)$ for $t \geq 0$.

c) How many milliseconds after the switch has been
closed will i_o equal 100 mA?

Figure P7.1

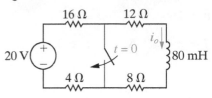

7.2 The switch in the circuit in Fig. P7.2 has been closed
PSPICE   for a long time. At $t = 0$ it is opened.
MULTISIM
a) Write the expression for $i_o(t)$ for $t \geq 0$.

b) Write the expression for $v_o(t)$ for $t \geq 0^+$.

Figure P7.2

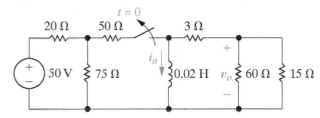

7.3 In the circuit shown in Fig. P7.3, the switch makes
contact with position b just before breaking contact
with position a. As already mentioned, this is
known as a make-before-break switch and is
designed so that the switch does not interrupt the
current in an inductive circuit. The interval of time
between "making" and "breaking" is assumed to be
negligible. The switch has been in the a position for
a long time. At $t = 0$ the switch is thrown from position a to position b.

a) Determine the initial current in the inductor.

b) Determine the time constant of the circuit
for $t > 0$.

c) Find i, v_1, and v_2 for $t \geq 0$.

d) What percentage of the initial energy stored in
the inductor is dissipated in the 90 Ω resistor
1 ms after the switch is thrown from position a to
position b?

Figure P7.3

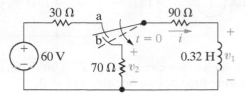

7.4 The switch in the circuit in Fig. P7.4 has been in posi-
PSPICE   tion 1 for a long time. At $t = 0$, the switch moves
MULTISIM instantaneously to position 2. Find $v_o(t)$ for $t \geq 0^+$.

Figure P7.4

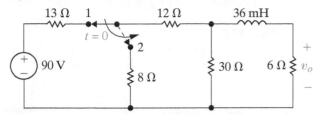

7.5 For the circuit of Fig. P7.4, what percentage of the
initial energy stored in the inductor is eventually
dissipated in the 6 Ω resistor?

7.6 The two switches in the circuit seen in Fig. P7.6 are
synchronized. The switches have been closed for a
long time before opening at $t = 0$.

a) How many microseconds after the switches are
open is the energy dissipated in the 4 kΩ resistor 10% of the initial energy stored in the 6 H
inductor?

b) At the time calculated in (a), what percentage of
the total energy stored in the inductor has been
dissipated?

Figure P7.6

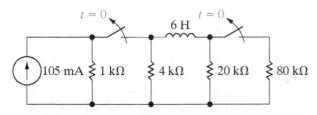

7.7 In the circuit in Fig. P7.7, the switch has been closed
for a long time before opening at $t = 0$.

a) Find the value of L so that $v_o(t)$ equals 0.5 $v_o(0^+)$
when $t = 1$ ms.

b) Find the percentage of the stored energy that
has been dissipated in the 10 Ω resistor when
$t = 1$ ms.

Figure P7.7

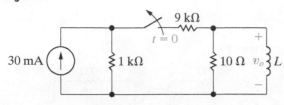

7.8 The switch in the circuit in Fig. P7.8 has been closed
for a long time before opening at $t = 0$.

PSPICE
MULTISIM

a) Find $i_1(0^-)$ and $i_2(0^-)$.

b) Find $i_1(0^+)$ and $i_2(0^+)$.

c) Find $i_1(t)$ for $t \geq 0$.

d) Find $i_2(t)$ for $t \geq 0^+$.

e) Explain why $i_2(0^-) \neq i_2(0^+)$.

Figure P7.8

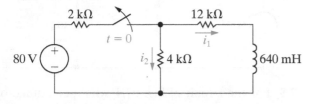

7.9 The switch shown in Fig. P7.9 has been open for a
long time before closing at $t = 0$.

a) Find $i_o(0^-)$, $i_L(0^-)$, and $v_L(0^-)$.

b) Find $i_o(0^+)$, $i_L(0^+)$, and $v_L(0^+)$.

c) Find $i_o(\infty)$, $i_L(\infty)$, and $v_L(\infty)$.

d) Write the expression for $i_L(t)$ for $t \geq 0$.

e) Write the expression for $i_o(t)$ for $t \geq 0^+$.

f) Write the expression for $v_L(t)$ for $t \geq 0^+$.

Figure P7.9

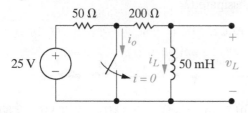

7.10 The switch in the circuit seen in Fig. P7.10 has been
in position 1 for a long time. At $t = 0$, the switch
moves instantaneously to position 2. Find the value
of R so that 10% of the initial energy stored in the
10 mH inductor is dissipated in R in 10 μs.

Figure P7.10

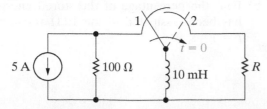

7.11 In the circuit in Fig. P7.10, let I_g represent the dc
current source, σ represent the fraction of initial
energy stored in the inductor that is dissipated in
t_o seconds, and L represent the inductance.

a) Show that

$$R = \frac{L \ln \left[1/(1 - \sigma) \right]}{2t_o}.$$

b) Test the expression derived in (a) by using it to
find the value of R in Problem 7.10.

7.12 In the circuit in Fig. P7.12, the voltage and current
expressions are

$$v = 160e^{-10t} \, \text{V}, \quad t \geq 0^+;$$

$$i = 6.4e^{-10t} \, \text{A}, \quad t \geq 0.$$

Find

a) R.

b) τ (in milliseconds).

c) L.

d) the initial energy stored in the inductor.

e) the time (in milliseconds) it takes to dissipate
60% of the initial stored energy.

Figure P7.12

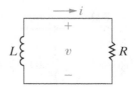

7.13 a) Use component values from Appendix H to create a first-order *RL* circuit (see Fig. 7.4) with a
time constant of 1 ms. Use a single inductor and
a network of resistors, if necessary. Draw your
circuit.

b) Suppose the inductor you chose in part (a) has
an initial current of 10 mA. Write an expression
for the current through the inductor for $t \geq 0$.

c) Using your result from part (b), calculate the
time at which half of the initial energy stored in
the inductor has been dissipated by the resistor.

7.14 The switch in the circuit in Fig. P7.14 has been
closed for a long time before opening at $t = 0$. Find
$v_o(t)$ for $t \geq 0^+$.

PSPICE
MULTISIM

Figure P7.14

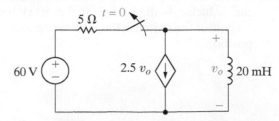

7.15 The switch in Fig. P7.15 has been closed for a long time before opening at $t = 0$. Find

   a) $i_L(t)$, $t \geq 0$.

   b) $v_L(t)$, $t \geq 0^+$.

   c) $i_\Delta(t)$, $t \geq 0^+$.

Figure P7.15

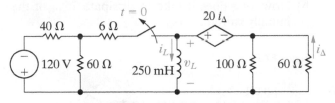

7.16 What percentage of the initial energy stored in the inductor in the circuit in Fig. P7.15 is dissipated by the 60 Ω resistor?

7.17 The two switches shown in the circuit in Fig. P7.17 operate simultaneously. Prior to $t = 0$ each switch has been in its indicated position for a long time. At $t = 0$ the two switches move instantaneously to their new positions. Find

   a) $v_o(t)$, $t \geq 0^+$.

   b) $i_o(t)$, $t \geq 0$.

Figure P7.17

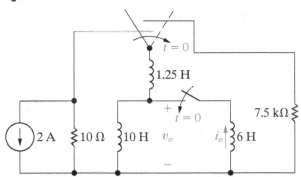

7.18 For the circuit seen in Fig. P7.17, find

   a) the total energy dissipated in the 7.5 kΩ resistor.

   b) the energy trapped in the ideal inductors.

7.19 In the circuit shown in Fig. P7.19, the switch has been in position a for a long time. At $t = 0$, it moves instantaneously from a to b.

   a) Find $i_o(t)$ for $t \geq 0$.

   b) What is the total energy delivered to the 8 Ω resistor?

   c) How many time constants does it take to deliver 95% of the energy found in (b)?

Figure P7.19

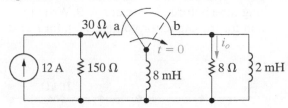

7.20 The 240 V, 2 Ω source in the circuit in Fig. P7.20 is inadvertently short-circuited at its terminals a, b. At the time the fault occurs, the circuit has been in operation for a long time.

   a) What is the initial value of the current i_{ab} in the short-circuit connection between terminals a, b?

   b) What is the final value of the current i_{ab}?

   c) How many microseconds after the short circuit has occurred is the current in the short equal to 114 A?

Figure P7.20

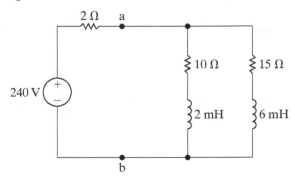

Section 7.2

7.21 The switch in the circuit in Fig. P7.21 has been in the left position for a long time. At $t = 0$ it moves to the right position and stays there.

   a) Find the initial voltage drop across the capacitor.

   b) Find the initial energy stored by the capacitor.

   c) Find the time constant of this circuit for $t > 0$.

   d) Write the expression for the capacitor voltage $v(t)$ for $t \geq 0$..

Figure P7.21

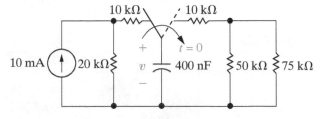

7.22 The switch shown in Fig. P7.22 has been open for a long time before closing at $t = 0$. Write the expression for the capacitor voltage, $v(t)$, for $t \geq 0$.

Figure P7.22

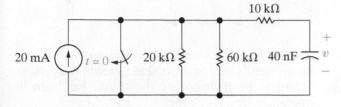

7.23 The switch in the circuit in Fig. P7.23 has been in the left position for a long time. At $t = 0$ it moves to the right position and stays there.

a) Write the expression for the capacitor voltage, $v(t)$, for $t \geq 0$.

b) Write the expression for the current through the $40\ k\Omega$ resistor, $i(t)$, for $t \geq 0^+$.

Figure P7.23

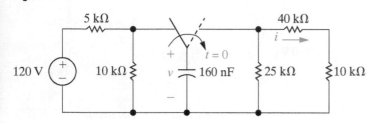

7.24 What percentage of the initial energy stored in the capacitor in Fig. P7.23 is dissipated by the $40\ k\Omega$ resistor?

7.25 The switch in the circuit in Fig. P7.25 has been in position a for a long time and $v_2 = 0$ V. At $t = 0$, the switch is thrown to position b. Calculate

a) i, v_1, and v_2 for $t \geq 0^+$,

b) the energy stored in the $30\ \mu F$ capacitor at $t = 0$, and

c) the energy trapped in the circuit and the total energy dissipated in the $2.5\ k\Omega$ resistor if the switch remains in position b indefinitely.

Figure P7.25

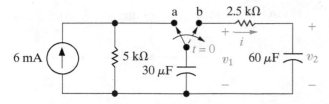

7.26 In the circuit shown in Fig. P7.26, both switches operate together; that is, they either open or close at the same time. The switches are closed a long time before opening at $t = 0$.

a) How many microjoules of energy have been dissipated in the $12\ k\Omega$ resistor 12 ms after the switches open?

b) How long does it take to dissipate 75% of the initially stored energy?

Figure P7.26

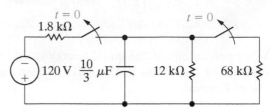

7.27 The switch in the circuit in Fig. P7.27 is closed at $t = 0$ after being open for a long time.

PSPICE
MULTISIM

a) Find $i_1(0^-)$ and $i_2(0^-)$.

b) Find $i_1(0^+)$ and $i_2(0^+)$.

c) Explain why $i_1(0^-) = i_1(0^+)$.

d) Explain why $i_2(0^-) \neq i_2(0^+)$.

e) Find $i_1(t)$ for $t \geq 0$.

f) Find $i_2(t)$ for $t \geq 0^+$.

Figure P7.27

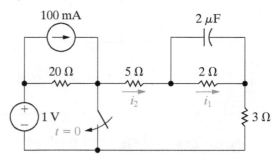

7.28 The switch in the circuit in Fig. P7.28 has been in position 1 for a long time before moving to position 2 at $t = 0$. Find $i_o(t)$ for $t \geq 0^+$.

PSPICE
MULTISIM

Figure P7.28

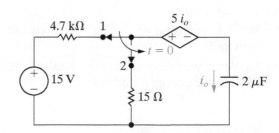

7.29 In the circuit in Fig. P7.29 the voltage and current expressions are

$$v = 72e^{-500t} \text{ V}, \quad t \geq 0;$$

$$i = 9e^{-500t} \text{ mA}, \quad t \geq 0^+.$$

Find

a) R.

b) C.

c) τ (in milliseconds).

d) the initial energy stored in the capacitor.

e) how many microseconds it takes to dissipate 68% of the initial energy stored in the capacitor.

Figure P7.29

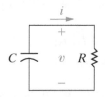

7.30 a) Use component values from Appendix H to create a first-order RC circuit (see Fig. 7.11) with a time constant of 50 ms. Use a single capacitor and a network of resistors, if necessary. Draw your circuit.

b) Suppose the capacitor you chose in part (a) has an initial voltage drop of 50 V. Write an expression for the voltage drop across the capacitor for $t \geq 0$.

c) Using you result from part (b), calculate the time at which the voltage drop across the capacitor has reached 10 V.

7.31 The switch in the circuit seen in Fig. P7.31 has been in position x for a long time. At $t = 0$, the switch moves instantaneously to position y.

a) Find α so that the time constant for $t > 0$ is 40 ms.

b) For the α found in (a), find v_Δ.

Figure P7.31

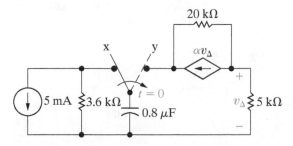

7.32 a) In Problem 7.31, how many microjoules of energy are generated by the dependent current source during the time the capacitor discharges to 0 V?

b) Show that for $t \geq 0$ the total energy stored and generated in the capacitive circuit equals the total energy dissipated.

7.33 After the circuit in Fig. P7.33 has been in operation for a long time, a screwdriver is inadvertently connected across the terminals a, b. Assume the resistance of the screwdriver is negligible.

a) Find the current in the screwdriver at $t = 0^+$ and $t = \infty$.

b) Derive the expression for the current in the screwdriver for $t \geq 0^+$.

Figure P7.33

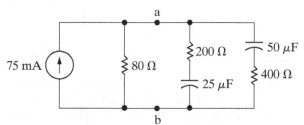

7.34 At the time the switch is closed in the circuit in Fig. P7.34, the voltage across the parallel capacitors is 50 V and the voltage on the 250 nF capacitor is 40 V.

a) What percentage of the initial energy stored in the three capacitors is dissipated in the 24 kΩ resistor?

b) Repeat (a) for the 400 Ω and 16 kΩ resistors.

c) What percentage of the initial energy is trapped in the capacitors?

Figure P7.34

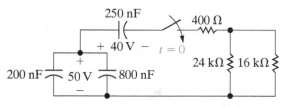

Section 7.3

7.35 After the switch in the circuit of Fig. P7.35 has been open for a long time, it is closed at $t = 0$. Calculate (a) the initial value of i; (b) the final value of i; (c) the time constant for $t \geq 0$; and (d) the numerical expression for $i(t)$ when $t \geq 0$.

Figure P7.35

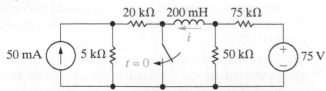

7.36 The switch in the circuit shown in Fig. P7.36 has
PSPICE been in position a for a long time before moving to
MULTISIM position b at $t = 0$.

a) Find the numerical expressions for $i_L(t)$ and
$v_o(t)$ for $t \geq 0$.

b) Find the numerical values of $v_L(0^+)$ and $v_o(0^+)$.

Figure P7.36

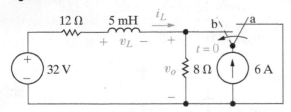

7.37 The switch in the circuit shown in Fig. P7.37 has
PSPICE been in position a for a long time. At $t = 0$, the
MULTISIM switch moves instantaneously to position b.

a) Find the numerical expression for $i_o(t)$ when
$t \geq 0$.

b) Find the numerical expression for $v_o(t)$ for
$t \geq 0^+$.

Figure P7.37

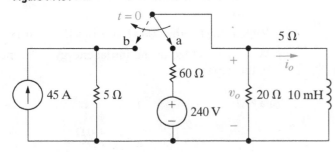

7.38 Repeat Problem 7.37 assuming that the switch in
the circuit in Fig. P7.37 has been in position b for a
long time and then moves to position a at $t = 0$ and
stays there.

7.39 The current and voltage at the terminals of the
inductor in the circuit in Fig. 7.16 are

$$i(t) = (4 + 4e^{-40t}) \text{ A}, \quad t \geq 0;$$

$$v(t) = -80e^{-40t} \text{ V}, \quad t \geq 0^+.$$

a) Specify the numerical values of V_s, R, I_o, and L.

b) How many milliseconds after the switch has
been closed does the energy stored in the inductor reach 9 J?

7.40 a) Use component values from Appendix H to
create a first-order *RL* circuit (see Fig. 7.16)
with a time constant of 8 μs. Use a single inductor and a network of resistors, if necessary.
Draw your circuit.

b) Suppose the inductor you chose in part (a) has
no initial stored energy. At $t = 0$, a switch connects a voltage source with a value of 25 V in
series with the inductor and equivalent resistance. Write an expression for the current
through the inductor for $t \geq 0$.

c) Using your result from part (b), calculate the
time at which the current through the inductor
reaches 75% of its final value.

7.41 The switch in the circuit shown in Fig. P7.41 has
been closed for a long time. The switch opens at
$t = 0$. For $t \geq 0^+$:

a) Find $v_o(t)$ as a function of I_g, R_1, R_2, and L.

b) Explain what happens to $v_o(t)$ as R_2 gets larger
and larger.

c) Find v_{SW} as a function of I_g, R_1, R_2, and L.

d) Explain what happens to v_{SW} as R_2 gets larger
and larger.

Figure P7.41

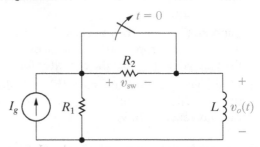

7.42 The switch in the circuit in Fig. P7.42 has been
closed for a long time. A student abruptly opens the
switch and reports to her instructor that when the
switch opened, an electric arc with noticeable persistence was established across the switch, and at
the same time the voltmeter placed across the coil
was damaged. On the basis of your analysis of the
circuit in Problem 7.41, can you explain to the student why this happened?

Figure P7.42

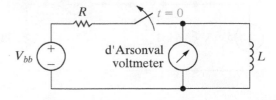

7.43 a) Derive Eq. 7.47 by first converting the Thévenin
equivalent in Fig. 7.16 to a Norton equivalent

and then summing the currents away from the upper node, using the inductor voltage v as the variable of interest.

b) Use the separation of variables technique to find the solution to Eq. 7.47. Verify that your solution agrees with the solution given in Eq. 7.42.

7.44 The switch in the circuit in Fig. P7.44 has been open a long time before closing at $t = 0$. Find $i_o(t)$ for $t \geq 0$.

PSPICE
MULTISIM

Figure P7.44

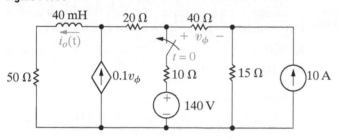

7.45 The switch in the circuit in Fig. P7.45 has been open a long time before closing at $t = 0$. Find $v_o(t)$ for $t \geq 0^+$.

PSPICE
MULTISIM

Figure P7.45

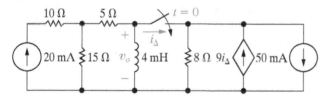

7.46 The switch in the circuit in Fig. P7.46 has been open a long time before closing at $t = 0$. Find $v_o(t)$ for $t \geq 0^+$.

PSPICE
MULTISIM

Figure P7.46

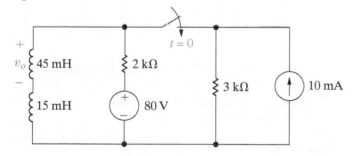

7.47 The switch in the circuit in Fig. P7.47 has been in position 1 for a long time. At $t = 0$ it moves instantaneously to position 2. How many milliseconds after the switch operates does v_o equal 100 V?

PSPICE
MULTISIM

Figure P7.47

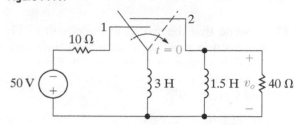

7.48 For the circuit in Fig. P7.47, find (in joules):

a) the total energy dissipated in the 40 Ω resistor;

b) the energy trapped in the inductors, and

c) the initial energy stored in the inductors.

7.49 The make-before-break switch in the circuit of Fig. P7.49 has been in position a for a long time. At $t = 0$, the switch moves instantaneously to position b. Find

PSPICE
MULTISIM

a) $v_o(t)$, $t \geq 0^+$.

b) $i_1(t)$, $t \geq 0$.

c) $i_2(t)$, $t \geq 0$.

Figure P7.49

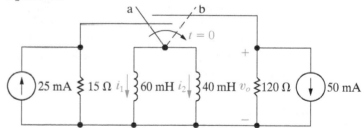

7.50 There is no energy stored in the inductors L_1 and L_2 at the time the switch is opened in the circuit shown in Fig. P7.50.

a) Derive the expressions for the currents $i_1(t)$ and $i_2(t)$ for $t \geq 0$.

b) Use the expressions derived in (a) to find $i_1(\infty)$ and $i_2(\infty)$.

Figure P7.50

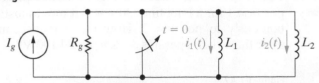

7.51 Assume that the switch in the circuit of Fig. P7.51 has been in position a for a long time and that at $t = 0$ it is moved to position b. Find (a) $v_C(0^+)$; (b) $v_C(\infty)$; (c) τ for $t > 0$; (d) $i(0^+)$; (e) $v_C, t \geq 0$; and (f) $i, t \geq 0^+$.

Figure P7.51

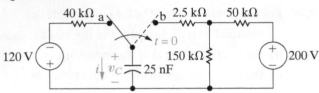

7.52 a) The switch in the circuit in Fig. P7.52 has been in position a for a long time. At $t = 0$, the switch moves instantaneously to position b and stays there. Find the initial and final values of the capacitor voltage, the time constant for $t \geq 0$, and the expression for the capacitor voltage for $t \geq 0$.

   b) Now suppose the switch in the circuit in Fig. P7.52 has been in position b for a long time. At $t = 0$, the switch moves instantaneously to position a and stays there. Find the initial and final values of the capacitor voltage, the time constant for $t \geq 0$, and the expression for the capacitor voltage for $t \geq 0$.

Figure P7.52

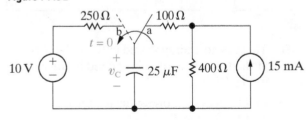

7.53 The switch in the circuit of Fig. P7.53 has been in position a for a long time. At $t = 0$ the switch is moved to position b. Calculate (a) the initial voltage on the capacitor; (b) the final voltage on the capacitor; (c) the time constant (in microseconds) for $t > 0$; and (d) the length of time (in microseconds) required for the capacitor voltage to reach zero after the switch is moved to position b.

Figure P7.53

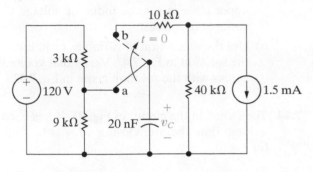

7.54 The switch in the circuit seen in Fig. P7.54 has been in position a for a long time. At $t = 0$, the switch moves instantaneously to position b. For $t \geq 0^+$, find

   a) $v_o(t)$.

   b) $i_o(t)$.

Figure P7.54

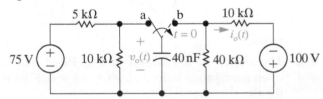

7.55 The switch in the circuit seen in Fig. P7.55 has been in position a for a long time. At $t = 0$, the switch moves instantaneously to position b. Find $v_o(t)$ and $i_o(t)$ for $t \geq 0^+$.

Figure P7.55

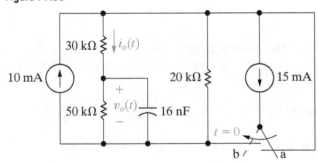

7.56 The circuit in Fig. P7.56 has been in operation for a long time. At $t = 0$, the voltage source reverses polarity and the current source drops from 3 mA to 2 mA. Find $v_o(t)$ for $t \geq 0$.

Figure P7.56

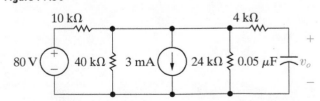

7.57 The switch in the circuit in Fig. P7.57 has been in
PSPICE   position a for a long time. At $t = 0$, the switch
MULTISIM   moves instantaneously to position b. At the instant
the switch makes contact with terminal b, switch 2
opens. Find $v_o(t)$ for $t \geq 0$.

Figure P7.57

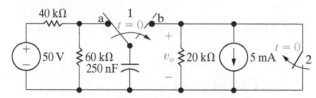

7.58 The current and voltage at the terminals of the
capacitor in the circuit in Fig. 7.21 are

$$i(t) = 3e^{-2500t} \text{ mA}, \qquad t \geq 0^+;$$

$$v(t) = (40 - 24e^{-2500t}) \text{ V}, \qquad t \geq 0.$$

a) Specify the numerical values of I_s, V_o, R, C,
and τ.

b) How many microseconds after the switch has
been closed does the energy stored in the capacitor reach 81% of its final value?

7.59 a) Use component values from Appendix H to create a first-order RC circuit (see Fig. 7.21) with a
time constant of 250 ms. Use a single capacitor
and a network of resistors, if necessary. Draw
your circuit.

b) Suppose the capacitor you chose in part (a) has an
initial voltage drop of 100 V. At $t = 0$, a switch connects a current source with a value of 1 mA in parallel with the capacitor and equivalent resistance.
Write an expression for the voltage drop across
the capacitor for $t \geq 0$.

c) Using your result from part (b), calculate the
time at which the voltage drop across the capici-
tor reaches 50 V.

7.60 The switch in the circuit shown in Fig. P7.60 opens at
PSPICE $t = 0$ after being closed for a long time. How many
MULTISIM   milliseconds after the switch opens is the energy
stored in the capacitor 36% of its final value?

Figure P7.60

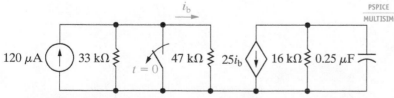

7.61 The switch in the circuit shown in Fig. P7.61 has
PSPICE   been in the OFF position for a long time. At $t = 0$,
MULTISIM   the switch moves instantaneously to the ON posi-
tion. Find $v_o(t)$ for $t \geq 0$.

Figure P7.61

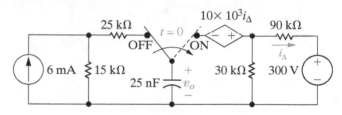

7.62 Assume that the switch in the circuit of Fig. P7.61
PSPICE   has been in the ON position for a long time before
MULTISIM   switching instantaneously to the OFF position at
$t = 0$. Find $v_o(t)$ for $t \geq 0$.

7.63 a) Derive Eq. 7.52 by first converting the Norton
equivalent circuit shown in Fig. 7.21 to a Thévenin
equivalent and then summing the voltages around
the closed loop, using the capacitor current i as the
relevant variable.

b) Use the separation of variables technique to find
the solution to Eq. 7.52. Verify that your solution
agrees with that of Eq. 7.53.

7.64 The switch in the circuit in Fig. P7.64 has been in
position x for a long time. The initial charge on the
60 nF capacitor is zero. At $t = 0$, the switch moves
instantaneously to position y.

a) Find $v_o(t)$ for $t \geq 0^+$.

b) Find $v_1(t)$ for $t \geq 0$.

Figure P7.64

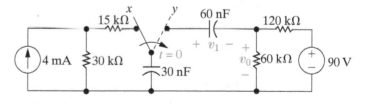

7.65 The switch in the circuit of Fig. P7.65 has been in
PSPICE   position a for a long time. At $t = 0$, it moves instan-
MULTISIM   taneously to position b. For $t \geq 0^+$, find

a) $v_o(t)$.

b) $i_o(t)$.

c) $v_1(t)$.

d) $v_2(t)$.

e) the energy trapped in the capacitors as $t \to \infty$.

Figure P7.65

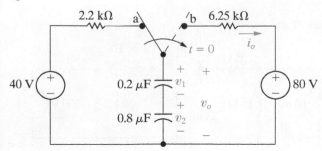

7.66 There is no energy stored in the capacitors C_1 and C_2 at the time the switch is closed in the circuit seen in Fig. P7.66.

a) Derive the expressions for $v_1(t)$ and $v_2(t)$ for $t \geq 0$.

b) Use the expressions derived in (a) to find $v_1(\infty)$ and $v_2(\infty)$.

Figure P7.66

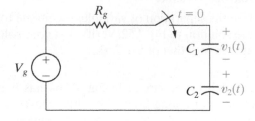

Section 7.4

7.67 Repeat (a) and (b) in Example 7.10 if the mutual inductance is reduced to zero.

7.68 There is no energy stored in the circuit in Fig. P7.68

PSPICE
MULTISIM

at the time the switch is closed.

a) Find $i_o(t)$ for $t \geq 0$.

b) Find $v_o(t)$ for $t \geq 0^+$.

c) Find $i_1(t)$ for $t \geq 0$.

d) Find $i_2(t)$ for $t \geq 0$.

e) Do your answers make sense in terms of known circuit behavior?

Figure P7.68

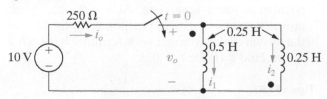

7.69 There is no energy stored in the circuit in Fig. P7.69

PSPICE
MULTISIM

at the time the switch is closed.

a) Find $i(t)$ for $t \geq 0$.

b) Find $v_1(t)$ for $t \geq 0^+$.

c) Find $v_2(t)$ for $t \geq 0$.

d) Do your answers make sense in terms of known circuit behavior?

Figure P7.69

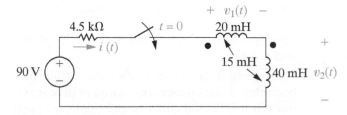

7.70 Repeat Problem 7.69 if the dot on the 40 mH coil is

PSPICE
MULTISIM

at the bottom of the coil.

7.71 There is no energy stored in the circuit of Fig. P7.71 at the time the switch is closed.

a) Find $i_o(t)$ for $t \geq 0$.

b) Find $v_o(t)$ for $t \geq 0^+$.

c) Find $i_1(t)$ for $t \geq 0$.

d) Find $i_2(t)$ for $t \geq 0$.

e) Do your answers make sense in terms of known circuit behavior?

Figure P7.71

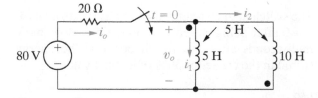

Section 7.5

7.72 The action of the two switches in the circuit seen in Fig. P7.72 is as follows. For $t < 0$, switch 1 is in position a and switch 2 is open. This state has existed for a long time. At $t = 0$, switch 1 moves instantaneously from position a to position b, while switch 2 remains open. Ten milliseconds after switch 1 operates, switch 2 closes, remains closed for 10 ms and then opens. Find $v_o(t)$ 25 ms after switch 1 moves to position b.

PSPICE
MULTISIM

Figure P7.72

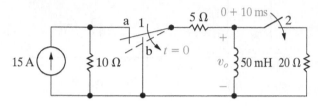

7.73 For the circuit in Fig. P7.72, how many milliseconds after switch 1 moves to position b is the energy stored in the inductor 4% of its initial value?

7.74 In the circuit in Fig. P7.74, switch A has been open and switch B has been closed for a long time. At $t = 0$, switch A closes. Twenty-five milliseconds after switch A closes, switch B opens. Find $i_L(t)$ for $t \geq 0$.

PSPICE
MULTISIM

Figure P7.74

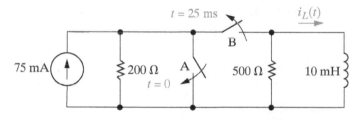

7.75 The switch in the circuit shown in Fig. P7.75 has been in position a for a long time. At $t = 0$, the switch is moved to position b, where it remains for 1 ms. The switch is then moved to position c, where it remains indefinitely. Find

PSPICE
MULTISIM

a) $i(0^+)$.

b) $i(200\ \mu s)$.

c) $i(6\ \text{ms})$.

d) $v(1^-\ \text{ms})$.

e) $v(1^+\ \text{ms})$.

Figure P7.75

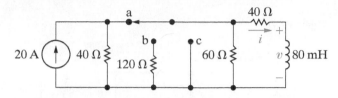

7.76 The capacitor in the circuit seen in Fig. P7.76 has been charged to 300 V. At $t = 0$, switch 1 closes, causing the capacitor to discharge into the resistive network. Switch 2 closes 200 μs after switch 1 closes. Find the magnitude and direction of the current in the second switch 300 μs after switch 1 closes.

PSPICE
MULTISIM

Figure P7.76

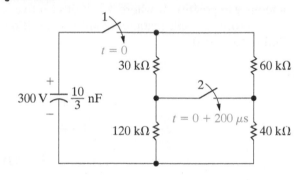

7.77 There is no energy stored in the capacitor in the circuit in Fig. P7.77 when switch 1 closes at $t = 0$. Switch 2 closes 2.5 milliseconds later. Find $v_o(t)$ for $t \geq 0$.

PSPICE
MULTISIM

Figure P7.77

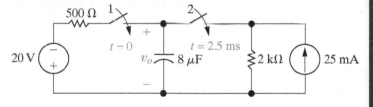

7.78 In the circuit in Fig. P7.78, switch 1 has been in position a and switch 2 has been closed for a long time. At $t = 0$, switch 1 moves instantaneously to position b. Two hundred microseconds later, switch 2 opens, remains open for 600 μs, and then recloses. Find v_o 1 ms after switch 1 makes contact with terminal b.

Figure P7.78

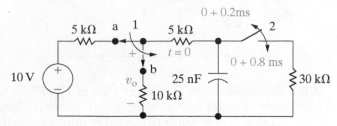

7.79 For the circuit in Fig. P7.78, what percentage of the initial energy stored in the 25 nF capacitor is dissipated in the 30 kΩ resistor?

PSPICE
MULTISIM

7.80 The switch in the circuit in Fig. P7.80 has been in position a for a long time. At $t = 0$, it moves instantaneously to position b, where it remains for five seconds before moving instantaneously to position c. Find v_o for $t \geq 0$.

PSPICE
MULTISIM

Figure P7.80

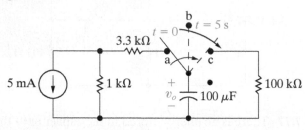

7.81 The current source in the circuit in Fig. P7.81(a) generates the current pulse shown in Fig. P7.81(b). There is no energy stored at $t = 0$.

PSPICE
MULTISIM

a) Derive the numerical expressions for $v_o(t)$ for the time intervals $t < 0$, $0 \leq t \leq 25$ μs, and 25 μs $\leq t < \infty$.

b) Calculate $v_o(25^- \mu s)$ and $v_o(25^+ \mu s)$.

c) Calculate $i_o(25^- \mu s)$ and $i_o(25^+ \mu s)$.

Figure P7.81

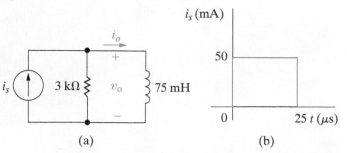

7.82 The voltage waveform shown in Fig. P7.82(a) is applied to the circuit of Fig. P7.82(b). The initial current in the inductor is zero.

PSPICE
MULTISIM

a) Calculate $v_o(t)$.

b) Make a sketch of $v_o(t)$ versus t.

c) Find i_o at $t = 5$ ms.

Figure P7.82

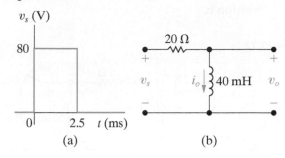

7.83 The voltage signal source in the circuit in Fig. P7.83(a) is generating the signal shown in Fig. P7.83(b). There is no stored energy at $t = 0$.

PSPICE
MULTISIM

a) Derive the expressions for $v_o(t)$ that apply in the intervals $t < 0$; $0 \leq t \leq 25$ μs; 25 μs $\leq t \leq 50$ μs; and 50 μs $\leq t < \infty$.

b) Sketch v_o and v_s on the same coordinate axes.

c) Repeat (a) and (b) with R reduced to 800 Ω.

Figure P7.83

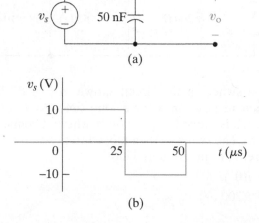

7.84 The voltage waveform shown in Fig. P7.84(a) is applied to the circuit of Fig. P7.84(b). The initial voltage on the capacitor is zero.

PSPICE
MULTISIM

a) Calculate $v_o(t)$.

b) Make a sketch of $v_o(t)$ versus t.

Figure P7.84

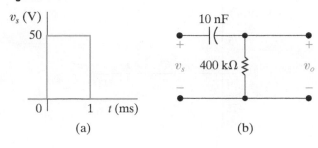

(a)   (b)

Section 7.6

7.85 The inductor current in the circuit in Fig. P7.85 is
25 mA at the instant the switch is opened. The
inductor will malfunction whenever the magnitude
of the inductor current equals or exceeds 5 A. How
long after the switch is opened does the inductor
malfunction?

PSPICE
MULTISIM

Figure P7.85

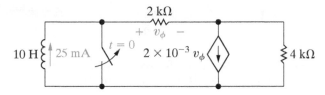

7.86 The gap in the circuit seen in Fig. P7.86 will arc over
whenever the voltage across the gap reaches 30 kV.
The initial current in the inductor is zero. The value
of β is adjusted so the Thévenin resistance with
respect to the terminals of the inductor is $-4\,\text{k}\Omega$.

PSPICE
MULTISIM

a) What is the value of β?

b) How many microseconds after the switch has
been closed will the gap arc over?

Figure P7.86

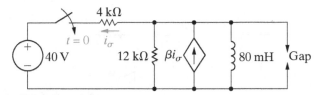

7.87 The capacitor in the circuit shown in Fig. P7.87 is
charged to 20 V at the time the switch is closed. If
the capacitor ruptures when its terminal voltage

PSPICE
MULTISIM

equals or exceeds 20 kV, how long does it take to
rupture the capacitor?

Figure P7.87

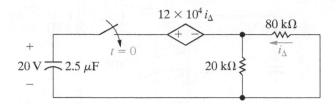

7.88 The switch in the circuit in Fig. P7.88 has been
closed for a long time. The maximum voltage rating
of the 1.6 μF capacitor is 14.4 kV. How long after
the switch is opened does the voltage across the
capacitor reach the maximum voltage rating?

PSPICE
MULTISIM

Figure P7.88

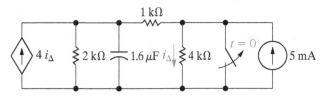

7.89 The circuit shown in Fig. P7.89 is used to close the
switch between a and b for a predetermined length
of time. The electric relay holds its contact arms
down as long as the voltage across the relay coil
exceeds 5 V. When the coil voltage equals 5 V, the
relay contacts return to their initial position by a
mechanical spring action. The switch between a and
b is initially closed by momentarily pressing the
push button. Assume that the capacitor is fully
charged when the push button is first pushed down.
The resistance of the relay coil is 25 kΩ, and the
inductance of the coil is negligible.

a) How long will the switch between a and b
remain closed?

b) Write the numerical expression for i from the
time the relay contacts first open to the time the
capacitor is completely charged.

c) How many milliseconds (after the circuit
between a and b is interrupted) does it take the
capacitor to reach 85% of its final value?

Figure P7.89

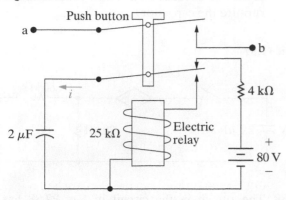

Section 7.7

7.90 The energy stored in the capacitor in the circuit shown in Fig. P7.90 is zero at the instant the switch is closed. The ideal operational amplifier reaches saturation in 15 ms. What is the numerical value of *R* in kilo-ohms?

PSPICE
MULTISIM

Figure P7.90

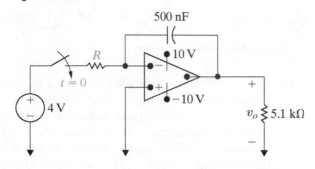

7.91 At the instant the switch is closed in the circuit of Fig. P7.90, the capacitor is charged to 6 V, positive at the right-hand terminal. If the ideal operational amplifier saturates in 40 ms, what is the value of *R*?

PSPICE
MULTISIM

7.92 The voltage pulse shown in Fig. P7.92(a) is applied to the ideal integrating amplifier shown in Fig. P7.92(b). Derive the numerical expressions for $v_o(t)$ when $v_o(0) = 0$ for the time intervals

PSPICE
MULTISIM

a) $t < 0$.

b) $0 \leq t \leq 2$ s.

c) $2\,\text{s} \leq t \leq 4\,\text{s}$.

d) $4\,\text{s} \leq t$

Figure P7.92

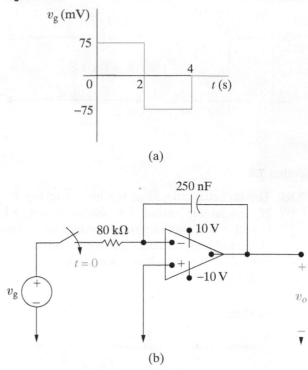

(a)

(b)

7.93 Repeat Problem 7.92 with a 4 MΩ resistor placed across the 250 nF feedback capacitor.

PSPICE
MULTISIM

7.94 There is no energy stored in the capacitors in the circuit shown in Fig. P7.94 at the instant the two switches close. Assume the op amp is ideal.

PSPICE
MULTISIM

a) Find v_o as a function of v_a, v_b, *R*, and *C*.

b) On the basis of the result obtained in (a), describe the operation of the circuit.

c) How long will it take to saturate the amplifier if $v_a = 40$ mV; $v_b = 15$ mV; $R = 50\,\text{k}\Omega$; $C = 10$ nF; and $V_{CC} = 6$ V?

Figure P7.94

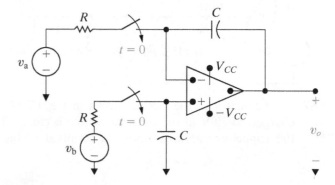

7.95 At the instant the switch of Fig. P7.95 is closed, the voltage on the capacitor is 56 V. Assume an ideal operational amplifier. How many milliseconds after the switch is closed will the output voltage v_o equal zero?

Figure P7.95

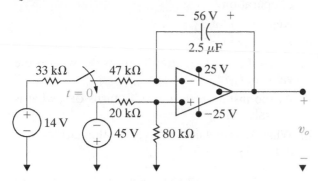

7.96 The voltage source in the circuit in Fig. P7.96(a) is generating the triangular waveform shown in Fig. P7.96(b). Assume the energy stored in the capacitor is zero at $t = 0$ and the op amp is ideal.

a) Derive the numerical expressions for $v_o(t)$ for the following time intervals: $0 \leq t \leq 1 \ \mu s$; $1 \ \mu s \leq t \leq 3 \ \mu s$; and $3 \ \mu s \leq t \leq 4 \ \mu s$.

b) Sketch the output waveform between 0 and 4 μs.

c) If the triangular input voltage continues to repeat itself for $t > 4 \ \mu s$, what would you expect the output voltage to be? Explain.

Figure P7.96

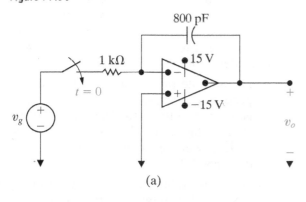

(a)

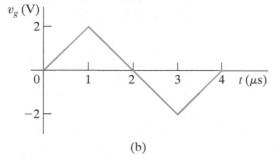

(b)

Sections 7.1–7.7

7.97 The circuit shown in Fig. P7.97 is known as a *monostable multivibrator*. The adjective *monostable* is used to describe the fact that the circuit has one stable state. That is, if left alone, the electronic switch T_2 will be ON, and T_1 will be OFF. (The operation of the ideal transistor switch is described in detail in Problem 7.99.) T_2 can be turned OFF by momentarily closing the switch S. After S returns to its open position, T_2 will return to its ON state.

a) Show that if T_2 is ON, T_1 is OFF and will stay OFF.

b) Explain why T_2 is turned OFF when S is momentarily closed.

c) Show that T_2 will stay OFF for $RC \ln 2$ s.

Figure P7.97

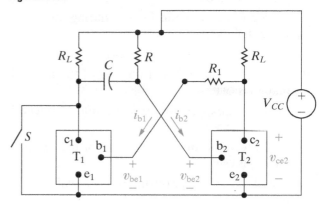

7.98 The parameter values in the circuit in Fig. P7.97 are $V_{CC} = 6$ V; $R_1 = 5.0 \ k\Omega$; $R_L = 20 \ k\Omega$; $C = 250$ pF; and $R = 23{,}083 \ \Omega$.

a) Sketch v_{ce2} versus t, assuming that after S is momentarily closed, it remains open until the circuit has reached its stable state. Assume S is closed at $t = 0$. Make your sketch for the interval $-5 \leq t \leq 10 \ \mu s$.

b) Repeat (a) for i_{b2} versus t.

7.99 The circuit shown in Fig. P7.99 is known as an *astable multivibrator* and finds wide application in pulse circuits. The purpose of this problem is to relate the charging and discharging of the capacitors to the operation of the circuit. The key to analyzing the circuit is to understand the behavior of the ideal transistor switches T_1 and T_2. The circuit is designed so that the switches automatically alternate between ON and OFF. When T_1 is OFF, T_2 is ON and vice versa. Thus in the analysis of this circuit, we assume a switch is either ON or OFF. We also assume that the ideal transistor switch can change its state instantaneously. In other words, it can snap from OFF to ON and vice versa. When a transistor switch is

ON, (1) the base current i_b is greater than zero, (2) the terminal voltage v_{be} is zero, and (3) the terminal voltage v_{ce} is zero. Thus, when a transistor switch is ON, it presents a short circuit between the terminals b,e and c,e. When a transistor switch is OFF, (1) the terminal voltage v_{be} is negative, (2) the base current is zero, and (3) there is an open circuit between the terminals c,e. Thus when a transistor switch is OFF, it presents an open circuit between the terminals b,e and c,e. Assume that T_2 has been ON and has just snapped OFF, while T_1 has been OFF and has just snapped ON. You may assume that at this instance, C_2 is charged to the supply voltage V_{CC}, and the charge on C_1 is zero. Also assume $C_1 = C_2$ and $R_1 = R_2 = 10R_L$.

a) Derive the expression for v_{be2} during the interval that T_2 is OFF.

b) Derive the expression for v_{ce2} during the interval that T_2 is OFF.

c) Find the length of time T_2 is OFF.

d) Find the value of v_{ce2} at the end of the interval that T_2 is OFF.

e) Derive the expression for i_{b1} during the interval that T_2 is OFF.

f) Find the value of i_{b1} at the end of the interval that T_2 is OFF.

g) Sketch v_{ce2} versus t during the interval that T_2 is OFF.

h) Sketch i_{b1} versus t during the interval that T_2 is OFF.

Figure P7.99

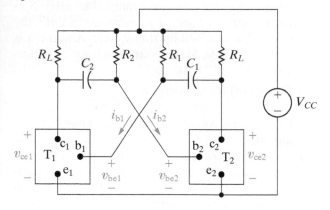

7.100 The component values in the circuit of Fig. P7.99 are $V_{CC} = 9$ V; $R_L = 3$ kΩ; $C_1 = C_2 = 2$ nF; and $R_1 = R_2 = 18$ kΩ.

a) How long is T_2 in the OFF state during one cycle of operation?

b) How long is T_2 in the ON state during one cycle of operation?

c) Repeat (a) for T_1.

d) Repeat (b) for T_1.

e) At the first instant after T_1 turns ON, what is the value of i_{b1}?

f) At the instant just before T_1 turns OFF, what is the value of i_{b1}?

g) What is the value of v_{ce2} at the instant just before T_2 turns ON?

7.101 Repeat Problem 7.100 with $C_1 = 3$ nF and $C_2 = 2.8$ nF. All other component values are unchanged.

7.102 The astable multivibrator circuit in Fig. P7.99 is to satisfy the following criteria: (1) One transistor switch is to be ON for 48 μs and OFF for 36 μs for each cycle; (2) $R_L = 2$ kΩ; (3) $V_{CC} = 5$ V; (4) $R_1 = R_2$; and (5) $6R_L \le R_1 \le 50R_L$. What are the limiting values for the capacitors C_1 and C_2?

7.103 The relay shown in Fig. P7.103 connects the 30 V
PRACTICAL
PERSPECTIVE dc generator to the dc bus as long as the relay current is greater than 0.4 A. If the relay current drops to 0.4 A or less, the spring-loaded relay immediately connects the dc bus to the 30 V standby battery. The resistance of the relay winding is 60 Ω. The inductance of the relay winding is to be determined.

a) Assume the prime motor driving the 30 V dc generator abruptly slows down, causing the generated voltage to drop suddenly to 21 V. What value of L will assure that the standby battery will be connected to the dc bus in 0.5 seconds?

b) Using the value of L determined in (a), state how long it will take the relay to operate if the generated voltage suddenly drops to zero.

Figure P7.103

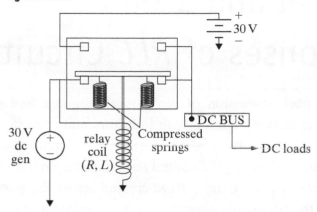

7.104 Derive the expression for heart rate in beats per minute given the values of R and C and assuming that the capacitor discharges when its voltage reaches 75% of the source voltage V_s. The expression, given in the Practical Perspective, is repeated here for convenience:

$$H = \frac{60}{-RC \ln 0.25} \quad \text{[beats per minute]}.$$

7.105 Use an expression similar to the one derived in Problem 7.104 to calculate the heart rate in beats per minute for $R = 150 \text{ k}\Omega$, $C = 6 \text{ }\mu\text{F}$, if the capacitor discharges when its voltage reaches 60% of the source voltage V_s.

7.106 Show that the resistance required to achieve a heart rate H, in beats per minute, is given by the equation

$$R = \frac{-60}{HC \ln\left(1 - \dfrac{V_{max}}{V_s}\right)},$$

where C is the capacitance, V_s is the source voltage, and V_{max} is the capacitor voltage at which discharge occurs.

7.107 Use the expression derived in Problem 7.106 to calculate the resistance required to achieve a heart rate of 70 beats per minute using a capacitance of 2.5 μF and assuming that the capacitor discharges when its voltage reaches 68% of the source voltage.

Natural and Step Responses of *RLC* Circuits

✓CHAPTER OBJECTIVES

1 Be able to determine the natural response and the step response of parallel *RLC* circuits.

2 Be able to determine the natural response and the step response of series *RLC* circuits.

In this chapter, discussion of the natural response and step response of circuits containing both inductors and capacitors is limited to two simple structures: the parallel *RLC* circuit and the series *RLC* circuit. Finding the natural response of a parallel *RLC* circuit consists of finding the voltage created across the parallel branches by the release of energy stored in the inductor or capacitor or both. The task is defined in terms of the circuit shown in Fig. 8.1 on page 266. The initial voltage on the capacitor, V_0, represents the initial energy stored in the capacitor. The initial current through the inductor, I_0, represents the initial energy stored in the inductor. If the individual branch currents are of interest, you can find them after determining the terminal voltage.

We derive the step response of a parallel *RLC* circuit by using Fig. 8.2 on page 266. We are interested in the voltage that appears across the parallel branches as a result of the sudden application of a dc current source. Energy may or may not be stored in the circuit when the current source is applied.

Finding the natural response of a series *RLC* circuit consists of finding the current generated in the series-connected elements by the release of initially stored energy in the inductor, capacitor, or both. The task is defined by the circuit shown in Fig. 8.3 on page 266. As before, the initial inductor current, I_0, and the initial capacitor voltage, V_0, represent the initially stored energy. If any of the individual element voltages are of interest, you can find them after determining the current.

We describe the step response of a series *RLC* circuit in terms of the circuit shown in Fig. 8.4 on page 266. We are interested in the current resulting from the sudden application of the dc voltage source. Energy may or may not be stored in the circuit when the switch is closed.

If you have not studied ordinary differential equations, derivation of the natural and step responses of parallel and series *RLC* circuits may be a bit difficult to follow. However, the results are important enough to warrant presentation at this time. We begin with the natural response of a parallel *RLC* circuit and cover this material over two sections: one to discuss the solution of the differential equation that describes the circuit and one to present the three distinct forms that the solution can take.

Practical Perspective

Clock for Computer Timing

The digital circuits found in most computers require a timing signal that synchronizes the operation of the circuits. Consider a laptop computer whose processor speed is 2 GHz. This means that the central processing unit for this computer can perform about 2×10^9 simple operations every second.

The timing signal, produced by a clock generator chip, is typically a square wave with the required clock frequency. The square wave is obtained from a sinusoidal wave with the required clock frequency. Typically, the sinusoidal wave is generated by precisely-cut quartz crystal with an applied voltage. The crystal produces a very stable frequency suitable for synchronizing digital circuits.

But we can also generate a sinusoidal wave using a circuit with an inductor and a capacitor. By choosing the values of inductance and capacitance, we can create a sinusoid with a specific frequency. We will examine such a design once we have presented the fundamental concepts of second-order circuits.

Scanrail / fotolia

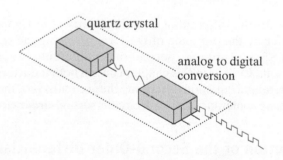

quartz crystal

analog to digital conversion

David J. Green / Alamy

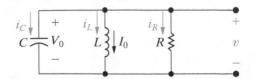

Figure 8.1 ▲ A circuit used to illustrate the natural response of a parallel *RLC* circuit.

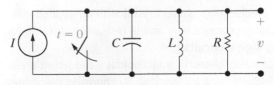

Figure 8.2 ▲ A circuit used to illustrate the step response of a parallel *RLC* circuit.

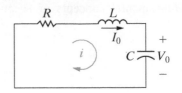

Figure 8.3 ▲ A circuit used to illustrate the natural response of a series *RLC* circuit.

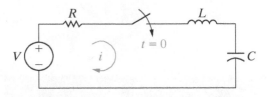

Figure 8.4 ▲ A circuit used to illustrate the step response of a series *RLC* circuit.

After introducing these three forms, we show that the same forms apply to the step response of a parallel *RLC* circuit as well as to the natural and step responses of series *RLC* circuits.

8.1 Introduction to the Natural Response of a Parallel *RLC* Circuit

The first step in finding the natural response of the circuit shown in Fig. 8.1 is to derive the differential equation that the voltage v must satisfy. We choose to find the voltage first, because it is the same for each component. After that, a branch current can be found by using the current-voltage relationship for the branch component. We easily obtain the differential equation for the voltage by summing the currents away from the top node, where each current is expressed as a function of the unknown voltage v:

$$\frac{v}{R} + \frac{1}{L}\int_0^t v\,d\tau + I_0 + C\frac{dv}{dt} = 0. \tag{8.1}$$

We eliminate the integral in Eq. 8.1 by differentiating once with respect to t, and, because I_0 is a constant, we get

$$\frac{1}{R}\frac{dv}{dt} + \frac{v}{L} + C\frac{d^2v}{dt^2} = 0. \tag{8.2}$$

We now divide through Eq. 8.2 by the capacitance C and arrange the derivatives in descending order:

$$\frac{d^2v}{dt^2} + \frac{1}{RC}\frac{dv}{dt} + \frac{v}{LC} = 0. \tag{8.3}$$

Comparing Eq. 8.3 with the differential equations derived in Chapter 7 reveals that they differ by the presence of the term involving the second derivative. Equation 8.3 is an ordinary, second-order differential equation with constant coefficients. Circuits in this chapter contain both inductors and capacitors, so the differential equation describing these circuits is of the second order. Therefore, we sometimes call such circuits **second-order circuits**.

The General Solution of the Second-Order Differential Equation

We can't solve Eq. 8.3 by separating the variables and integrating as we were able to do with the first-order equations in Chapter 7. The classical approach to solving Eq. 8.3 is to assume that the solution is of exponential form, that is, to assume that the voltage is of the form

$$v = Ae^{st}, \tag{8.4}$$

where A and s are unknown constants.

Before showing how this assumption leads to the solution of Eq. 8.3, we need to show that it is rational. The strongest argument we can make in favor of Eq. 8.4 is to note from Eq. 8.3 that the second derivative of the solution, plus a constant times the first derivative, plus a constant times the solution itself, must sum to zero for all values of t. This can occur only if higher order derivatives of the solution have the same form as the solution. The exponential function satisfies this criterion. A second argument in favor of Eq. 8.4 is that the solutions of all the first-order equations we derived in Chapter 7 were exponential. It seems reasonable to assume that the solution of the second-order equation also involves the exponential function.

If Eq. 8.4 is a solution of Eq. 8.3, it must satisfy Eq. 8.3 for all values of t. Substituting Eq. 8.4 into Eq. 8.3 generates the expression

$$As^2 e^{st} + \frac{As}{RC}e^{st} + \frac{Ae^{st}}{LC} = 0,$$

or

$$Ae^{st}\left(s^2 + \frac{s}{RC} + \frac{1}{LC}\right) = 0, \qquad (8.5)$$

which can be satisfied for all values of t only if A is zero or the parenthetical term is zero, because $e^{st} \neq 0$ for any finite values of st. We cannot use $A = 0$ as a general solution because to do so implies that the voltage is zero for all time — a physical impossibility if energy is stored in either the inductor or capacitor. Therefore, in order for Eq. 8.4 to be a solution of Eq. 8.3, the parenthetical term in Eq. 8.5 must be zero, or

$$s^2 + \frac{s}{RC} + \frac{1}{LC} = 0. \qquad (8.6)$$

◀ **Characteristic equation, parallel *RLC* circuit**

Equation 8.6 is called the **characteristic equation** of the differential equation because the roots of this quadratic equation determine the mathematical character of $v(t)$.

The two roots of Eq. 8.6 are

$$s_1 = -\frac{1}{2RC} + \sqrt{\left(\frac{1}{2RC}\right)^2 - \frac{1}{LC}}, \qquad (8.7)$$

$$s_2 = -\frac{1}{2RC} - \sqrt{\left(\frac{1}{2RC}\right)^2 - \frac{1}{LC}}. \qquad (8.8)$$

If either root is substituted into Eq. 8.4, the assumed solution satisfies the given differential equation, that is, Eq. 8.3. Note from Eq. 8.5 that this result holds regardless of the value of A. Therefore, both

$$v = A_1 e^{s_1 t} \text{ and}$$

$$v = A_2 e^{s_2 t}$$

satisfy Eq. 8.3. Denoting these two solutions v_1 and v_2, respectively, we can show that their sum also is a solution. Specifically, if we let

$$v = v_1 + v_2 = A_1 e^{s_1 t} + A_2 e^{s_2 t}, \tag{8.9}$$

then

$$\frac{dv}{dt} = A_1 s_1 e^{s_1 t} + A_2 s_2 e^{s_2 t}, \tag{8.10}$$

$$\frac{d^2 v}{dt^2} = A_1 s_1^2 e^{s_1 t} + A_2 s_2^2 e^{s_2 t}. \tag{8.11}$$

Substituting Eqs. 8.9–8.11 into Eq. 8.3 gives

$$A_1 e^{s_1 t} \left(s_1^2 + \frac{1}{RC} s_1 + \frac{1}{LC} \right) + A_2 e^{s_2 t} \left(s_2^2 + \frac{1}{RC} s_2 + \frac{1}{LC} \right) = 0. \tag{8.12}$$

But each parenthetical term is zero because by definition s_1 and s_2 are roots of the characteristic equation. Hence the natural response of the parallel *RLC* circuit shown in Fig. 8.1 is of the form

$$v = A_1 e^{s_1 t} + A_2 e^{s_2 t}. \tag{8.13}$$

Equation 8.13 is a repeat of the assumption made in Eq. 8.9. We have shown that v_1 is a solution, v_2 is a solution, and $v_1 + v_2$ is a solution. Therefore, the general solution of Eq. 8.3 has the form given in Eq. 8.13. The roots of the characteristic equation (s_1 and s_2) are determined by the circuit parameters $R, L,$ and C. The initial conditions determine the values of the constants A_1 and A_2. Note that the form of Eq. 8.13 must be modified if the two roots s_1 and s_2 are equal. We discuss this modification when we turn to the critically damped voltage response in Section 8.2.

The behavior of $v(t)$ depends on the values of s_1 and s_2. Therefore the first step in finding the natural response is to determine the roots of the characteristic equation. We return to Eqs. 8.7 and 8.8 and rewrite them using a notation widely used in the literature:

$$s_1 = -\alpha + \sqrt{\alpha^2 - \omega_0^2}, \tag{8.14}$$

$$s_2 = -\alpha - \sqrt{\alpha^2 - \omega_0^2}, \tag{8.15}$$

where

Neper frequency, parallel *RLC* circuit ▶

$$\alpha = \frac{1}{2RC}, \tag{8.16}$$

Resonant radian frequency, parallel *RLC* circuit ▶

$$\omega_0 = \frac{1}{\sqrt{LC}}. \tag{8.17}$$

These results are summarized in Table 8.1.

TABLE 8.1   Natural Response Parameters of the Parallel *RLC* Circuit

Parameter	Terminology	Value In Natural Response
s_1, s_2	Characteristic roots	$s_1 = -\alpha + \sqrt{\alpha^2 - \omega_0^2}$ $s_2 = -\alpha - \sqrt{\alpha^2 - \omega_0^2}$
α	Neper frequency	$\alpha = \dfrac{1}{2RC}$
ω_0	Resonant radian frequency	$\omega_0 = \dfrac{1}{\sqrt{LC}}$

The exponent of e must be dimensionless, so both s_1 and s_2 (and hence α and ω_0) must have the dimension of the reciprocal of time, or frequency. To distinguish among the frequencies s_1, s_2, α, and ω_0, we use the following terminology: s_1 and s_2 are referred to as *complex frequencies*, α is called the *neper frequency*, and ω_0 is the *resonant radian frequency*. The full significance of this terminology unfolds as we move through the remaining chapters of this book. All these frequencies have the dimension of angular frequency per time. For complex frequencies, the neper frequency, and the resonant radian frequency, we specify values using the unit *radians per second* (rad/s). The nature of the roots s_1 and s_2 depends on the values of α and ω_0. There are three possible outcomes. First, if $\omega_0^2 < \alpha^2$, both roots will be real and distinct. For reasons to be discussed later, the voltage response is said to be **overdamped** in this case. Second, if $\omega_0^2 > \alpha^2$, both s_1 and s_2 will be complex and, in addition, will be conjugates of each other. In this situation, the voltage response is said to be **underdamped**. The third possible outcome is that $\omega_0^2 = \alpha^2$. In this case, s_1 and s_2 will be real and equal. Here the voltage response is said to be **critically damped**. As we shall see, damping affects the way the voltage response reaches its final (or steady-state) value. We discuss each case separately in Section 8.2.

Example 8.1 illustrates how the numerical values of s_1 and s_2 are determined by the values of R, L, and C.

Example 8.1	**Finding the Roots of the Characteristic Equation of a Parallel *RLC* Circuit**

a) Find the roots of the characteristic equation that governs the transient behavior of the voltage shown in Fig. 8.5 if $R = 200\ \Omega$, $L = 50$ mH, and $C = 0.2\ \mu$F.

b) Will the response be overdamped, underdamped, or critically damped?

c) Repeat (a) and (b) for $R = 312.5\ \Omega$.

d) What value of R causes the response to be critically damped?

Solution

a) For the given values of R, L, and C,

$$\alpha = \frac{1}{2RC} = \frac{10^6}{(400)(0.2)} = 1.25 \times 10^4\ \text{rad/s},$$

$$\omega_0^2 = \frac{1}{LC} = \frac{(10^3)(10^6)}{(50)(0.2)} = 10^8\ \text{rad}^2/\text{s}^2.$$

From Eqs. 8.14 and 8.15,

$$s_1 = -1.25 \times 10^4 + \sqrt{1.5625 \times 10^8 - 10^8}$$

$$= -12{,}500 + 7500 = -5000\ \text{rad/s},$$

$$s_2 = -1.25 \times 10^4 - \sqrt{1.5625 \times 10^8 - 10^8}$$

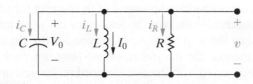

Figure 8.5 ▲ A circuit used to illustrate the natural response of a parallel *RLC* circuit.

b) The voltage response is overdamped because $\omega_0^2 < \alpha^2$.

c) For $R = 312.5\ \Omega$,

$$\alpha = \frac{10^6}{(625)(0.2)} = 8000\ \text{rad/s},$$

$$\alpha^2 = 64 \times 10^6 = 0.64 \times 10^8\ \text{rad}^2/\text{s}^2.$$

As ω_0^2 remains at $10^8\ \text{rad}^2/\text{s}^2$,

$$s_1 = -8000 + j6000\ \text{rad/s},$$

$$s_2 = -8000 - j6000\ \text{rad/s}.$$

(In electrical engineering, the imaginary number $\sqrt{-1}$ is represented by the letter j, because the letter i represents current.)

In this case, the voltage response is underdamped since $\omega_0^2 > \alpha^2$.

d) For critical damping, $\alpha^2 = \omega_0^2$, so

$$\left(\frac{1}{2RC}\right)^2 = \frac{1}{LC} = 10^8,$$

or

$$\frac{1}{2RC} = 10^4,$$

and

$$R = \frac{10^6}{(2 \times 10^4)(0.2)} = 250\ \Omega.$$

✓ **ASSESSMENT PROBLEM**

Objective 1—Be able to determine the natural response and the step response of parallel *RLC* circuits

8.1 The resistance and inductance of the circuit in Fig. 8.5 are 100 Ω and 20 mH, respectively.

a) Find the value of C that makes the voltage response critically damped.

b) If C is adjusted to give a neper frequency of 5 krad/s, find the value of C and the roots of the characteristic equation.

c) If C is adjusted to give a resonant frequency of 20 krad/s, find the value of C and the roots of the characteristic equation.

Answer: (a) 500 nF;

(b) $C = 1\ \mu\text{F}$,
$s_1 = -5000 + j5000\ \text{rad/s}$,
$s_2 = -5000 - j5000\ \text{rad/s}$;

(c) $C = 125\ \text{nF}$,
$s_1 = -5359\ \text{rad/s}$,
$s_2 = -74{,}641\ \text{rad/s}$.

NOTE: Also try Chapter Problem 8.4.

8.2 The Forms of the Natural Response of a Parallel *RLC* Circuit

So far we have seen that the behavior of a second-order *RLC* circuit depends on the values of s_1 and s_2, which in turn depend on the circuit parameters R, L, and C. Therefore, the first step in finding the natural response is to calculate these values and, relatedly, determine whether the response is over-, under-, or critically damped.

Completing the description of the natural response requires finding two unknown coefficients, such as A_1 and A_2 in Eq. 8.13. The method used to do this is based on matching the solution for the natural response to the initial conditions imposed by the circuit, which are the initial value of the current (or voltage) and the initial value of the first derivative of the current (or voltage). Note that these same initial conditions, plus the final value of the variable, will also be needed when finding the step response of a second-order circuit.

In this section, we analyze the natural response form for each of the three types of damping, beginning with the overdamped response. As we will see, the response equations, as well as the equations for evaluating the unknown coefficients, are slightly different for each of the three damping configurations. This is why we want to determine at the outset of the problem whether the response is over-, under-, or critically damped.

The Overdamped Voltage Response

When the roots of the characteristic equation are real and distinct, the voltage response of a parallel *RLC* circuit is said to be overdamped. The solution for the voltage is of the form

$$v = A_1 e^{s_1 t} + A_2 e^{s_2 t}, \qquad (8.18)$$

◀ **Voltage natural response—overdamped parallel *RLC* circuit**

where s_1 and s_2 are the roots of the characteristic equation. The constants A_1 and A_2 are determined by the initial conditions, specifically from the values of $v(0^+)$ and $dv(0^+)/dt$, which in turn are determined from the initial voltage on the capacitor, V_0, and the initial current in the inductor, I_0.

Next, we show how to use the initial voltage on the capacitor and the initial current in the inductor to find A_1 and A_2. First we note from Eq. 8.18 that A_1 and A_2. First we note from Eq. 8.18 that

$$v(0^+) = A_1 + A_2, \qquad (8.19)$$

$$\frac{dv(0^+)}{dt} = s_1 A_1 + s_2 A_2. \qquad (8.20)$$

With s_1 and s_2 known, the task of finding A_1 and A_2 reduces to finding $v(0^+)$ and $dv(0^+)/dt$. The value of $v(0^+)$ is the initial voltage on the capacitor V_0. We get the initial value of dv/dt by first finding the current in the capacitor branch at $t = 0^+$. Then,

$$\frac{dv(0^+)}{dt} = \frac{i_C(0^+)}{C}. \qquad (8.21)$$

We use Kirchhoff's current law to find the initial current in the capacitor branch. We know that the sum of the three branch currents at $t = 0^+$ must be zero. The current in the resistive branch at $t = 0^+$ is the initial voltage V_0 divided by the resistance, and the current in the inductive branch is I_0. Using the reference system depicted in Fig. 8.5, we obtain

$$i_C(0^+) = \frac{-V_0}{R} - I_0. \qquad (8.22)$$

After finding the numerical value of $i_C(0^+)$, we use Eq. 8.21 to find the initial value of dv/dt.

We can summarize the process for finding the overdamped response, $v(t)$, as follows:

1. Find the roots of the characteristic equation, s_1 and s_2, using the values of R, L, and C.

2. Find $v(0^+)$ and $dv(0^+)/dt$ using circuit analysis.

3. Find the values of A_1 and A_2 by solving Eqs. 8.23 and 8.24 simultaneously:

$$v(0^+) = A_1 + A_2, \qquad (8.23)$$

$$\frac{dv(0^+)}{dt} = \frac{i_C(0^+)}{C} = s_1 A_1 + s_2 A_2. \qquad (8.24)$$

4. Substitute the values for s_1, s_2, A_1, and A_2 into Eq. 8.18 to determine the expression for $v(t)$ for $t \geq 0$.

Examples 8.2 and 8.3 illustrate how to find the overdamped response of a parallel *RLC* circuit.

Example 8.2   Finding the Overdamped Natural Response of a Parallel *RLC* Circuit

For the circuit in Fig. 8.6, $v(0^+) = 12$ V, and $i_L(0^+) = 30$ mA.

a) Find the initial current in each branch of the circuit.

b) Find the initial value of dv/dt.

c) Find the expression for $v(t)$.

d) Sketch $v(t)$ in the interval $0 \le t \le 250$ ms.

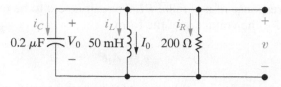

Figure 8.6 ▲ The circuit for Example 8.2.

Solution

a) The inductor prevents an instantaneous change in its current, so the initial value of the inductor current is 30 mA:

$$i_L(0^-) = i_L(0) = i_L(0^+) = 30 \text{ mA}.$$

The capacitor holds the initial voltage across the parallel elements to 12 V. Thus the initial current in the resistive branch, $i_R(0^+)$, is 12/200, or 60 mA. Kirchhoff's current law requires the sum of the currents leaving the top node to equal zero at every instant. Hence

$$i_C(0^+) = -i_L(0^+) - i_R(0^+)$$

$$= -90 \text{ mA}.$$

Note that if we assumed the inductor current and capacitor voltage had reached their dc values at the instant that energy begins to be released, $i_C(0^-) = 0$. In other words, there is an instantaneous change in the capacitor current at $t = 0$.

b) Because $i_C = C(dv/dt)$,

$$\frac{dv(0^+)}{dt} = \frac{-90 \times 10^{-3}}{0.2 \times 10^{-6}} = -450 \text{ kV/s}.$$

c) The roots of the characteristic equation come from the values of R, L, and C. For the values specified and from Eqs. 8.14 and 8.15 along with 8.16 and 8.17,

$$s_1 = -1.25 \times 10^4 + \sqrt{1.5625 \times 10^8 - 10^8}$$

$$= -12{,}500 + 7500 = -5000 \text{ rad/s},$$

$$s_2 = -1.25 \times 10^4 - 2 \overline{1.5625 \times 10^8 - 10^8}$$

$$= -12{,}500 - 7500 = -20{,}000 \text{ rad/s}.$$

Because the roots are real and distinct, we know that the response is overdamped and hence has the form of Eq. 8.18. We find the co-efficients A_1 and A_2 from Eqs. 8.23 and 8.24. We've already determined s_1, s_2, $v(0^+)$, and $dv(0^+)/dt$, so

$$12 = A_1 + A_2,$$

$$-450 \times 10^3 = -5000A_1 - 20{,}000A_2.$$

We solve two equations for A_1 and A_2 to obtain $A_1 = -14$ V and $A_2 = 26$ V. Substituting these values into Eq. 8.18 yields the overdamped voltage response:

$$v(t) = (-14e^{-5000t} + 26e^{-20{,}000t}) \text{ V}, \quad t \ge 0.$$

As a check on these calculations, we note that the solution yields $v(0) = 12$ V and $dv(0^+)/dt = -450{,}000$ V/s.

d) Figure 8.7 shows a plot of $v(t)$ versus t over the interval $0 \le t \le 250$ ms.

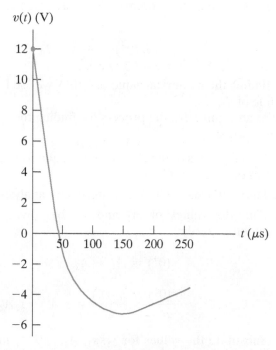

Figure 8.7 ▲ The voltage response for Example 8.2.

Example 8.3   Calculating Branch Currents in the Natural Response of a Parallel *RLC* Circuit

Derive the expressions that describe the three branch currents i_R, i_L, and i_C in Example 8.2 (Fig. 8.6) during the time the stored energy is being released.

Solution

We know the voltage across the three branches from the solution in Example 8.2, namely,

$$v(t) = (-14e^{-5000t} + 26e^{-20,000t})\text{ V}, \quad t \geq 0.$$

The current in the resistive branch is then

$$i_R(t) = \frac{v(t)}{200} = (-70e^{-5000t} + 130e^{-20,000t})\text{ mA}, \quad t \geq 0.$$

There are two ways to find the current in the inductive branch. One way is to use the integral relationship that exists between the current and the voltage at the terminals of an inductor:

$$i_L(t) = \frac{1}{L}\int_0^t v_L(x)\,dx + I_0.$$

A second approach is to find the current in the capacitive branch first and then use the fact that $i_R + i_L + i_C = 0$. Let's use this approach. The current in the capacitive branch is

$$i_C(t) = C\frac{dv}{dt}$$

$$= 0.2 \times 10^{-6}(70,000e^{-5000t} - 520,000e^{-20,000t})$$

$$= (14e^{-5000t} - 104e^{-20,000t})\text{ mA}, \quad t \geq 0^+.$$

Note that $i_C(0^+) = -90\text{ mA}$, which agrees with the result in Example 8.2.

Now we obtain the inductive branch current from the relationship

$$i_L(t) = -i_R(t) - i_C(t)$$

$$= (56e^{-5000t} - 26e^{-20,000t})\text{ mA}, \quad t \geq 0.$$

We leave it to you, in Assessment Problem 8.2, to show that the integral relation alluded to leads to the same result. Note that the expression for i_L agrees with the initial inductor current, as it must.

✓ ASSESSMENT PROBLEMS

Objective 1—Be able to determine the natural response and the step response of parallel *RLC* circuits

8.2   Use the integral relationship between i_L and v to find the expression for i_L in Fig. 8.6.

Answer: $i_L(t) = (56e^{-5000t} - 26e^{-20,000t})$ mA, $t \geq 0$.

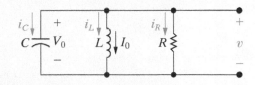

8.3   The element values in the circuit shown are $R = 2\text{ k}\Omega$, $L = 250\text{ mH}$, and $C = 10\text{ nF}$. The initial current I_0 in the inductor is -4 A, and the initial voltage on the capacitor is 0 V. The output signal is the voltage v. Find (a) $i_R(0^+)$; (b) $i_C(0^+)$; (c) $dv(0^+)/dt$; (d) A_1; (e) A_2; and (f) $v(t)$ when $t \geq 0$.

Answer: (a) 0;
   (b) 4 A;
   (c) 4×10^8 V/s;
   (d) 13,333 V;
   (e) $-13,333$ V;
   (f) $13,333(e^{-10,000t} - e^{-40,000t})$ V.

NOTE: Also try Chapter Problems 8.5 and 8.13.

The Underdamped Voltage Response

When $\omega_0^2 > \alpha^2$, the roots of the characteristic equation are complex, and the response is underdamped. For convenience, we express the roots s_1 and s_2 as

$$s_1 = -\alpha + \sqrt{-(\omega_0^2 - \alpha^2)}$$

$$= -\alpha + j\sqrt{\omega_0^2 - \alpha^2}$$

$$= -\alpha + j\omega_d \tag{8.25}$$

$$s_2 = -\alpha - j\omega_d, \tag{8.26}$$

where

Damped radian frequency ▶

$$\omega_d = \sqrt{\omega_0^2 - \alpha^2}. \tag{8.27}$$

The term ω_d is called the **damped radian frequency**. We explain later the reason for this terminology.

The underdamped voltage response of a parallel *RLC* circuit is

Voltage natural response—underdamped parallel *RLC* circuits ▶

$$v(t) = B_1 e^{-\alpha t} \cos \omega_d t + B_2 e^{-\alpha t} \sin \omega_d t, \tag{8.28}$$

which follows from Eq. 8.18. In making the transition from Eq. 8.18 to Eq. 8.28, we use the Euler identity:

$$e^{\pm j\theta} = \cos \theta \pm j \sin \theta. \tag{8.29}$$

Thus,

$$v(t) = A_1 e^{(-\alpha + j\omega_d)t} + A_2 e^{-(\alpha + j\omega_d)t}$$

$$= A_1 e^{-\alpha t} e^{j\omega_d t} + A_2 e^{-\alpha t} e^{-j\omega_d t}$$

$$= e^{-\alpha t}(A_1 \cos \omega_d t + j A_1 \sin \omega_d t + A_2 \cos \omega_d t - j A_2 \sin \omega_d t)$$

$$= e^{-\alpha t}[(A_1 + A_2) \cos \omega_d t + j(A_1 - A_2) \sin \omega_d t].$$

At this point in the transition from Eq. 8.18 to 8.28, replace the arbitrary constants $A_1 + A_2$ and $j(A_1 - A_2)$ with new arbitrary constants denoted B_1 and B_2 to get

$$v = e^{-\alpha t}(B_1 \cos \omega_d t + B_2 \sin \omega_d t)$$

$$= B_1 e^{-\alpha t} \cos \omega_d t + B_2 e^{-\alpha t} \sin \omega_d t.$$

The constants B_1 and B_2 are real, not complex, because the voltage is a real function. Don't be misled by the fact that $B_2 = j(A_1 - A_2)$. In this underdamped case, A_1 and A_2 are complex conjugates, and thus B_1 and B_2 are real. (See Problems 8.12 and 8.13.) The reason for defining the underdamped response in terms of the coefficients B_1 and B_2 is that it yields a simpler expression for the voltage, v. We determine B_1 and B_2 by the initial energy stored in the circuit, in the same way that we found A_1 and A_2 for the overdamped response: by evaluating v at $t = 0^+$ and its derivative at $t = 0^+$. As with s_1 and s_2, α and ω_d are fixed by the circuit parameters R, L, and C.

For the underdamped response, the two simultaneous equations that determine B_1 and B_2 are

$$v(0^+) = V_0 = B_1, \tag{8.30}$$

$$\frac{dv(0^+)}{dt} = \frac{i_c(0^+)}{C} = -\alpha B_1 + \omega_d B_2. \tag{8.31}$$

Let's look at the general nature of the underdamped response. First, the trigonometric functions indicate that this response is oscillatory; that is, the voltage alternates between positive and negative values. The rate at which the voltage oscillates is fixed by ω_d. Second, the amplitude of the oscillation decreases exponentially. The rate at which the amplitude falls off is determined by α. Because α determines how quickly the oscillations subside, it is also referred to as the **damping factor** or **damping coefficient**. That explains why ω_d is called the damped radian frequency. If there is no damping, $\alpha = 0$ and the frequency of oscillation is ω_0. Whenever there is a dissipative element, R, in the circuit, α is not zero and the frequency of oscillation, ω_d, is less than ω_0. Thus when α is not zero, the frequency of oscillation is said to be damped.

The oscillatory behavior is possible because of the two types of energy-storage elements in the circuit: the inductor and the capacitor. (A mechanical analogy of this electric circuit is that of a mass suspended on a spring, where oscillation is possible because energy can be stored in both the spring and the moving mass.) We say more about the characteristics of the underdamped response following Example 8.4, which examines a circuit whose response is underdamped. In summary, note that the overall process for finding the underdamped response is the same as that for the overdamped response, although the response equations and the simultaneous equations used to find the constants are slightly different.

Example 8.4   Finding the Underdamped Natural Response of a Parallel *RLC* Circuit

In the circuit shown in Fig. 8.8, $V_0 = 0$, and $I_0 = -12.25$ mA.

a) Calculate the roots of the characteristic equation.
b) Calculate v and dv/dt at $t = 0^+$.
c) Calculate the voltage response for $t \geq 0$.
d) Plot $v(t)$ versus t for the time interval $0 \leq t \leq 11$ ms.

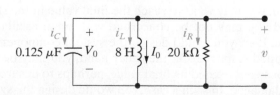

Figure 8.8 ▲ The circuit for Example 8.4.

Solution

a) Because

$$\alpha = \frac{1}{2RC} = \frac{10^6}{2(20)10^3(0.125)} = 200 \text{ rad/s},$$

$$\omega_0 = \frac{1}{\sqrt{LC}} = \sqrt{\frac{10^6}{(8)(0.125)}} = 10^3 \text{ rad/s},$$

we have

$$\omega_0^2 > \alpha^2.$$

Therefore, the response is underdamped. Now,

$$\omega_d = \sqrt{\omega_0^2 - \alpha^2} = \sqrt{10^6 - 4 \times 10^4} = 100\sqrt{96}$$

$$= 979.80 \text{ rad/s},$$

$$s_1 = -\alpha + j\omega_d = -200 + j979.80 \text{ rad/s},$$

$$s_2 = -\alpha - j\omega_d = -200 - j979.80 \text{ rad/s}.$$

For the underdamped case, we do not ordinarily solve for s_1 and s_2 because we do not use them explicitly. However, this example emphasizes why s_1 and s_2 are known as complex frequencies.

b) Because v is the voltage across the terminals of a capacitor, we have

$$v(0) = v(0^+) = V_0 = 0.$$

Because $v(0^+) = 0$, the current in the resistive branch is zero at $t = 0^+$. Hence the current in the capacitor at $t = 0^+$ is the negative of the inductor current:

$$i_C(0^+) = -(-12.25) = 12.25 \text{ mA}.$$

Therefore the initial value of the derivative is

$$\frac{dv(0^+)}{dt} = \frac{(12.25)(10^{-3})}{(0.125)(10^{-6})} = 98,000 \text{ V/s}.$$

c) From Eqs. 8.30 and 8.31, $B_1 = 0$ and

$$B_2 = \frac{98,000}{\omega_d} \approx 100 \text{ V}.$$

Substituting the numerical values of α, ω_d, B_1, and B_2 into the expression for $v(t)$ gives

$$v(t) = 100e^{-200t} \sin 979.80t \text{ V}, \quad t \geq 0.$$

d) Figure 8.9 shows the plot of $v(t)$ versus t for the first 11 ms after the stored energy is released. It clearly indicates the damped oscillatory nature of the underdamped response. The voltage $v(t)$ approaches its final value, alternating between values that are greater than and less than the final value. Furthermore, these swings about the final value decrease exponentially with time.

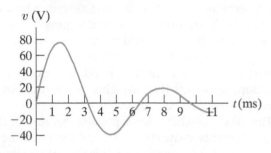

Figure 8.9 ▲ The voltage response for Example 8.4.

Characteristics of the Underdamped Response

The underdamped response has several important characteristics. First, as the dissipative losses in the circuit decrease, the persistence of the oscillations increases, and the frequency of the oscillations approaches ω_0. In other words, as $R \rightarrow \infty$, the dissipation in the circuit in Fig. 8.8 approaches zero because $p = v^2/R$. As $R \rightarrow \infty$, $\alpha \rightarrow 0$, which tells us that $\omega_d \rightarrow \omega_0$. When $\alpha = 0$, the maximum amplitude of the voltage remains constant; thus the oscillation at ω_0 is sustained. In Example 8.4, if R were increased to infinity, the solution for $v(t)$ would become

$$v(t) = 98 \sin 1000t \text{ V}, \quad t \geq 0.$$

Thus, in this case the oscillation is sustained, the maximum amplitude of the voltage is 98 V, and the frequency of oscillation is 1000 rad/s.

We may now describe qualitatively the difference between an underdamped and an overdamped response. In an underdamped system, the response oscillates, or "bounces," about its final value. This oscillation is also referred to as *ringing*. In an overdamped system, the response approaches its final value without ringing or in what is sometimes described as a "sluggish" manner. When specifying the desired response of a second order system, you may want to reach the final value in the shortest time possible, and you may not be concerned with small oscillations about that final value. If so, you would design the system components to achieve an underdamped response. On the other hand, you may be concerned that the response not exceed its final value, perhaps to ensure that components are not damaged. In such a case, you would design the system components to achieve an overdamped response, and you would have to accept a relatively slow rise to the final value.

✓ ASSESSMENT PROBLEM

Objective 1—Be able to determine the natural and the step response of parallel *RLC* circuits

8.4   A 10 mH inductor, a 1 μF capacitor, and a variable resistor are connected in parallel in the circuit shown. The resistor is adjusted so that the roots of the characteristic equation are $-8000 \pm j6000$ rad/s. The initial voltage on the capacitor is 10 V, and the initial current in the inductor is 80 mA. Find

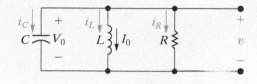

a) R;

b) $dv(0^+)/dt$;

c) B_1 and B_2 in the solution for v; and

d) $i_L(t)$.

Answer: (a) 62.5 Ω;

(b) $-240{,}000$ V/s;

(c) $B_1 = 10$ V, $B_2 = -80/3$ V;

(d) $i_L(t) = 10e^{-8000t}[8 \cos 6000t + (82/3) \sin 6000t]$ mA when $t \geq 0$.

NOTE: Also try Chapter Problems 8.6 and 8.11.

The Critically Damped Voltage Response

The second-order circuit in Fig. 8.8 is critically damped when $\omega_0^2 = \alpha^2$, or $\omega_0 = \alpha$. When a circuit is critically damped, the response is on the verge of oscillating. In addition, the two roots of the characteristic equation are real and equal; that is,

$$s_1 = s_2 = -\alpha = -\frac{1}{2RC}. \tag{8.32}$$

When this occurs, the solution for the voltage no longer takes the form of Eq. 8.18. This equation breaks down because if $s_1 = s_2 = -\alpha$, it predicts that

$$v = (A_1 + A_2)e^{-\alpha t} = A_0 e^{-\alpha t}, \tag{8.33}$$

where A_0 is an arbitrary constant. Equation 8.33 cannot satisfy two independent initial conditions (V_0, I_0) with only one arbitrary constant, A_0. Recall that the circuit parameters R and C fix α.

We can trace this dilemma back to the assumption that the solution takes the form of Eq. 8.18. When the roots of the characteristic equation are equal, the solution for the differential equation takes a different form, namely

$$v(t) = D_1 t e^{-\alpha t} + D_2 e^{-\alpha t}. \tag{8.34}$$

◀ **Voltage natural response—critically damped parallel *RLC* circuit**

Thus in the case of a repeated root, the solution involves a simple exponential term plus the product of a linear and an exponential term. The justification of Eq. 8.34 is left for an introductory course in differential equations. Finding the solution involves obtaining D_1 and D_2 by following the same pattern set in the overdamped and underdamped cases: We use the initial values of the voltage and the derivative of the voltage with respect to time to write two equations containing D_1 and/or D_2.

From Eq. 8.34, the two simultaneous equations needed to determine D_1 and D_2 are

$$v(0^+) = V_0 = D_2, \qquad (8.35)$$

$$\frac{dv(0^+)}{dt} = \frac{i_C(0^+)}{C} = D_1 - \alpha D_2. \qquad (8.36)$$

As we can see, in the case of a critically damped response, both the equation for $v(t)$ and the simultaneous equations for the constants D_1 and D_2 differ from those for over- and underdamped responses, but the general approach is the same. You will rarely encounter critically damped systems in practice, largely because ω_0 must equal a exactly. Both of these quantities depend on circuit parameters, and in a real circuit it is very difficult to choose component values that satisfy an exact equality relationship.

Example 8.5 illustrates the approach for finding the critically damped response of a parallel *RLC* circuit.

Example 8.5   **Finding the Critically Damped Natural Response of a Parallel *RLC* Circuit**

a) For the circuit in Example 8.4 (Fig. 8.8), find the value of R that results in a critically damped voltage response.

b) Calculate $v(t)$ for $t \geq 0$.

c) Plot $v(t)$ versus t for $0 \leq t \leq 7$ ms.

Solution

a) From Example 8.4, we know that $\omega_0^2 = 10^6$. Therefore for critical damping,

$$\alpha = 10^3 = \frac{1}{2RC},$$

or

$$R = \frac{10^6}{(2000)(0.125)} = 4000 \ \Omega.$$

b) From the solution of Example 8.4, we know that $v(0^+) = 0$ and $dv(0^+)/dt = 98,000$ V/s. From Eqs. 8.35 and 8.36, $D_2 = 0$ and $D_1 = 98,000$ V/s.

Substituting these values for a, D_1, and D_2 into Eq. 8.34 gives

$$v(t) = 98,000te^{-1000t} \text{ V}, \quad t \geq 0.$$

c) Figure 8.10 shows a plot of $v(t)$ versus t in the interval $0 \leq t \leq 7$ ms.

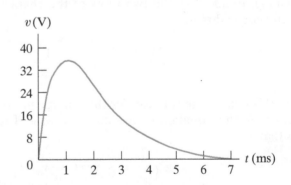

Figure 8.10 ▲ The voltage response for Example 8.5.

✓ASSESSMENT PROBLEM

Objective 1—Be able to determine the natural and the step response of parallel *RLC* circuits

8.5   The resistor in the circuit in Assessment Problem 8.4 is adjusted for critical damping. The inductance and capacitance values are 0.4 H and 10 μF, respectively. The initial energy stored in the circuit is 25 mJ and is distributed equally between the inductor and capacitor. Find (a) R; (b) V_0; (c) I_0; (d) D_1 and D_2 in the solution for v; and (e) i_R, $t \geq 0^+$.

Answer: (a) 100 Ω;

(b) 50 V;

(c) 250 mA;

(d) $-50,000$ V/s, 50 V;

(e) $i_R(t) = (-500te^{-500t} + 0.50e^{-500t})$ A, $t \geq 0^+$.

NOTE: Also try Chapter Problems 8.7 and 8.12.

A Summary of the Results

We conclude our discussion of the parallel *RLC* circuit's natural response with a brief summary of the results. The first step in finding the natural response is to calculate the roots of the characteristic equation. You then know immediately whether the response is overdamped, underdamped, or critically damped.

If the roots are real and distinct ($\omega_0^2 < \alpha^2$), the response is overdamped and the voltage is

$$v(t) = A_1 e^{s_1 t} + A_2 e^{s_2 t},$$

where

$$s_1 = -\alpha + \sqrt{\alpha^2 - \omega_0^2},$$

$$s_2 = -\alpha - \sqrt{\alpha^2 - \omega_0^2},$$

$$\alpha = \frac{1}{2RC},$$

$$\omega_0^2 = \frac{1}{LC}.$$

The values of A_1 and A_2 are determined by solving the following simultaneous equations:

$$v(0^+) = A_1 + A_2,$$

$$\frac{dv(0^+)}{dt} = \frac{i_C(0^+)}{C} = s_1 A_1 + s_2 A_2.$$

If the roots are complex $\omega_0^2 > \alpha^2$ the response is underdamped and the voltage is

$$v(t) = B_1 e^{-\alpha t} \cos \omega_d t + B_2 e^{-\alpha t} \sin \omega_d t,$$

where

$$\omega_d = \sqrt{\omega_0^2 - \alpha^2}.$$

The values of B_1 and B_2 are found by solving the following simultaneous equations:

$$v(0^+) = V_0 = B_1,$$

$$\frac{dv(0^+)}{dt} = \frac{i_C(0^+)}{C} = -\alpha B_1 + \omega_d B_2.$$

If the roots of the characteristic equation are real and equal ($\omega_0^2 = \alpha^2$), the voltage response is

$$v(t) = D_1 t e^{-\alpha t} + D_2 e^{-\alpha t},$$

where α is as in the other solution forms. To determine values for the constants D_1 and D_2, solve the following simultaneous equations:

$$v(0^+) = V_0 = D_2,$$

$$\frac{dv(0^+)}{dt} = \frac{i_C(0^+)}{C} = D_1 - \alpha D_2.$$

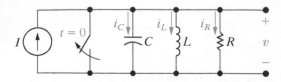

Figure 8.11 ▲ A circuit used to describe the step response of a parallel *RLC* circuit.

8.3 The Step Response of a Parallel *RLC* Circuit

Finding the step response of a parallel *RLC* circuit involves finding the voltage across the parallel branches or the current in the individual branches as a result of the sudden application of a dc current source. There may or may not be energy stored in the circuit when the current source is applied. The task is represented by the circuit shown in Fig. 8.11. To develop a general approach to finding the step response of a second-order circuit, we focus on finding the current in the inductive branch (i_L). This current is of particular interest because it does not approach zero as t increases. Rather, after the switch has been open for a long time, the inductor current equals the dc source current *I*. Because we want to focus on the technique for finding the step response, we assume that the initial energy stored in the circuit is zero. This assumption simplifies the calculations and doesn't alter the basic process involved. In Example 8.10 we will see how the presence of initially stored energy enters into the general procedure.

To find the inductor current i_L, we must solve a second-order differential equation equated to the forcing function *I*, which we derive as follows. From Kirchhoff's current law, we have

$$i_L + i_R + i_C = I,$$

or

$$i_L + \frac{v}{R} + C\frac{dv}{dt} = I. \tag{8.37}$$

Because

$$v = L\frac{di_L}{dt}, \tag{8.38}$$

we get

$$\frac{dv}{dt} = L\frac{d^2i_L}{dt^2}. \tag{8.39}$$

Substituting Eqs. 8.38 and 8.39 into Eq. 8.37 gives

$$i_L + \frac{L}{R}\frac{di_L}{dt} + LC\frac{d^2i_L}{dt^2} = I. \tag{8.40}$$

For convenience, we divide through by *LC* and rearrange terms:

$$\frac{d^2i_L}{dt^2} + \frac{1}{RC}\frac{di_L}{dt} + \frac{i_L}{LC} = \frac{I}{LC}. \tag{8.41}$$

Comparing Eq. 8.41 with Eq. 8.3 reveals that the presence of a nonzero term on the right-hand side of the equation alters the task. Before showing how to solve Eq. 8.41 directly, we obtain the solution indirectly. When we know the solution of Eq. 8.41, explaining the direct approach will be easier.

The Indirect Approach

We can solve for i_L indirectly by first finding the voltage v. We do this with the techniques introduced in Section 8.2, because the differential equation that v must satisfy is identical to Eq. 8.3. To see this, we simply return to Eq. 8.37 and express i_L as a function of v; thus

$$\frac{1}{L}\int_0^t v\,d\tau + \frac{v}{R} + C\frac{dv}{dt} = I. \tag{8.42}$$

Differentiating Eq. 8.42 once with respect to t reduces the right-hand side to zero because I is a constant. Thus

$$\frac{v}{L} + \frac{1}{R}\frac{dv}{dt} + C\frac{d^2v}{dt^2} = 0,$$

or

$$\frac{d^2v}{dt^2} + \frac{1}{RC}\frac{dv}{dt} + \frac{v}{LC} = 0. \tag{8.43}$$

As discussed in Section 8.2, the solution for v depends on the roots of the characteristic equation. Thus the three possible solutions are

$$v = A_1 e^{s_1 t} + A_2 e^{s_2 t}, \tag{8.44}$$

$$v = B_1 e^{-\alpha t}\cos\omega_d t + B_2 e^{-\alpha t}\sin\omega_d t, \tag{8.45}$$

$$v = D_1 t e^{-\alpha t} + D_2 e^{-\alpha t}. \tag{8.46}$$

A word of caution: Because there is a source in the circuit for $t > 0$, you must take into account the value of the source current at $t = 0^+$ when you evaluate the coefficients in Eqs. 8.44–8.46.

To find the three possible solutions for i_L, we substitute Eqs. 8.44–8.46 into Eq. 8.37. You should be able to verify, when this has been done, that the three solutions for i_L will be

$$i_L = I + A_1' e^{s_1 t} + A_2' e^{s_2 t}, \tag{8.47}$$

$$i_L = I + B_1' e^{-\alpha t}\cos\omega_d t + B_2' e^{-\alpha t}\sin\omega_d t, \tag{8.48}$$

$$i_L = I + D_1' t e^{-\alpha t} + D_2' e^{-\alpha t}, \tag{8.49}$$

where A_1', A_2', B_1', B_2', D_1', and D_2', are arbitrary constants.

In each case, the primed constants can be found indirectly in terms of the arbitrary constants associated with the voltage solution. However, this approach is cumbersome.

The Direct Approach

It is much easier to find the primed constants directly in terms of the initial values of the response function. For the circuit being discussed, we would find the primed constants from $i_L(0)$ and $di_L(0)/dt$.

The solution for a second-order differential equation with a constant forcing function equals the forced response plus a response function identical in form to the natural response. Thus we can always write the solution for the step response in the form

$$i = I_f + \left\{\begin{array}{c}\text{function of the same form}\\ \text{as the natural response}\end{array}\right\}, \tag{8.50}$$

or

$$v = V_f + \left\{\begin{array}{c}\text{function of the same form}\\ \text{as the natural response}\end{array}\right\}, \tag{8.51}$$

where I_f and V_f represent the final value of the response function. The final value may be zero, as was, for example, the case with the voltage v in the circuit in Fig. 8.8.

Examples 8.6–8.10 illustrate the technique of finding the step response of a parallel *RLC* circuit using the direct approach.

Example 8.6   Finding the Overdamped Step Response of a Parallel *RLC* Circuit

The initial energy stored in the circuit in Fig. 8.12 is zero. At $t = 0$, a dc current source of 24 mA is applied to the circuit. The value of the resistor is 400 Ω.

a) What is the initial value of i_L?

b) What is the initial value of di_L/dt?

c) What are the roots of the characteristic equation?

d) What is the numerical expression for $i_L(t)$ when $t \geq 0$?

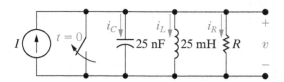

Figure 8.12 ▲ The circuit for Example 8.6.

Solution

a) No energy is stored in the circuit prior to the application of the dc current source, so the initial current in the inductor is zero. The inductor prohibits an instantaneous change in inductor current; therefore $i_L(0) = 0$ immediately after the switch has been opened.

b) The initial voltage on the capacitor is zero before the switch has been opened; therefore it will be zero immediately after. Now, because $v = L di_L/dt$,

$$\frac{di_L}{dt}(0^+) = 0.$$

c) From the circuit elements, we obtain

$$\omega_0^2 = \frac{1}{LC} = \frac{10^{12}}{(25)(25)} = 16 \times 10^8,$$

$$\alpha = \frac{1}{2RC} = \frac{10^9}{(2)(400)(25)} = 5 \times 10^4 \text{ rad/s},$$

or

$$\alpha^2 = 25 \times 10^8.$$

Because $\omega_0^2 < \alpha^2$, the roots of the characteristic equation are real and distinct. Thus

$$s_1 = -5 \times 10^4 + 3 \times 10^4 = -20{,}000 \text{ rad/s},$$

$$s_2 = -5 \times 10^4 - 3 \times 10^4 = -80{,}000 \text{ rad/s}.$$

d) Because the roots of the characteristic equation are real and distinct, the inductor current response will be overdamped. Thus $i_L(t)$ takes the form of Eq. 8.47, namely,

$$i_L = I_f + A_1' e^{s_1 t} + A_2' e^{s_2 t}.$$

▶ **Inductor current in overdamped parallel *RLC* circuit step response**

Hence, from this solution, the two simultaneous equations that determine A_1' and A_2' are

$$i_L(0) = I_f + A_1' + A_2' = 0,$$

$$\frac{di_L}{dt}(0) = s_1 A_1' + s_2 A_2' = 0.$$

Solving for A_1' and A_2' gives

$$A_1' = -32 \text{ mA} \quad \text{and} \quad A_2' = 8 \text{ mA}.$$

The numerical solution for $i_L(t)$ is

$$i_L(t) = (24 - 32e^{-20{,}000t} + 8e^{-80{,}000t}) \text{ mA}, \quad t \geq 0.$$

Example 8.7 Finding the Underdamped Step Response of a Parallel *RLC* Circuit

The resistor in the circuit in Example 8.6 (Fig. 8.12) is increased to 625 Ω. Find $i_L(t)$ for $t \geq 0$.

Solution

Because L and C remain fixed, ω_0^2 has the same value as in Example 8.6; that is, $\omega_0^2 = 16 \times 10^8$. Increasing R to 625 Ω decreases α to 3.2×10^4 rad/s. With $\omega_0^2 > \alpha^2$, the roots of the characteristic equation are complex. Hence

$$s_1 = -3.2 \times 10^4 + j2.4 \times 10^4 \text{ rad/s},$$

$$s_2 = -3.2 \times 10^4 - j2.4 \times 10^4 \text{ rad/s}.$$

The current response is now underdamped and given by Eq. 8.48:

$$i_L(t) = I_f + B_1' e^{-\alpha t} \cos \omega_d t + B_2' e^{-\alpha t} \sin \omega_d t.$$

▶ **Inductor current in underdamped parallel *RLC* circuit step response**

Here, α is 32,000 rad/s, ω_d is 24,000 rad/s, and I_f is 24 mA.

As in Example 8.6, B_1' and B_2' are determined from the initial conditions. Thus the two simultaneous equations are

$$i_L(0) = I_f + B_1' = 0,$$

$$\frac{di_L}{dt}(0) = \omega_d B_2' - \alpha B_1' = 0.$$

Then,

$$B_1' = -24 \text{ mA}$$

and

$$B_2' = -32 \text{ mA}.$$

The numerical solution for $i_L(t)$ is

$$i_L(t) = (24 - 24e^{-32,000t} \cos 24,000t$$
$$- 32e^{-32,000t} \sin 24,000t) \text{ mA}, \quad t \geq 0.$$

Example 8.8 Finding the Critically Damped Step Response of a Parallel *RLC* Circuit

The resistor in the circuit in Example 8.6 (Fig. 8.12) is set at 500 Ω. Find i_L for $t \geq 0$.

Solution

We know that ω_0^2 remains at 16×10^8. With R set at 500 Ω, α becomes 4×10^4 s^{-1}, which corresponds to critical damping. Therefore the solution for $i_L(t)$ takes the form of Eq. 8.49:

$$i_L(t) = I_f + D_1' t e^{-\alpha t} + D_2' e^{-\alpha t}.$$

▶ **Inductor current in critically damped parallel *RLC* circuit step response**

Again, D_1' and D_2' are computed from initial conditions, or

$$i_L(0) = I_f + D_2' = 0,$$

$$\frac{di_L}{dt}(0) = D_1' - \alpha D_2' = 0.$$

Thus

$$D_1' = -960,000 \text{ mA/s} \quad \text{and} \quad D_2' = -24 \text{ mA}.$$

The numerical expression for $i_L(t)$ is

$$i_L(t) = (24 - 960,000t e^{-40,000t} - 24e^{-40,000t}) \text{ mA}, \quad t \geq 0.$$

Example 8.9   Comparing the Three-Step Response Forms

a) Plot on a single graph, over a range from 0 to 220 μs, the overdamped, underdamped, and critically damped responses derived in Examples 8.6–8.8.

b) Use the plots of (a) to find the time required for i_L to reach 90% of its final value.

c) On the basis of the results obtained in (b), which response would you specify in a design that puts a premium on reaching 90% of the final value of the output in the shortest time?

d) Which response would you specify in a design that must ensure that the final value of the current is never exceeded?

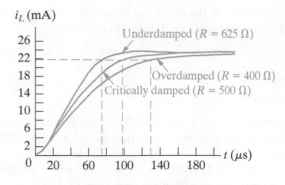

Figure 8.13 ▲ The current plots for Example 8.9.

Solution

a) See Fig. 8.13.

b) The final value of i_L is 24 mA, so we can read the times off the plots corresponding to $i_L = 21.6$ mA. Thus $t_{od} = 130$ μs, $t_{cd} = 97$ μs, and $t_{ud} = 74$ μs.

c) The underdamped response reaches 90% of the final value in the fastest time, so it is the desired response type when speed is the most important design specification.

d) From the plot, you can see that the underdamped response overshoots the final value of current, whereas neither the critically damped nor the overdamped response produces currents in excess of 24 mA. Although specifying either of the latter two responses would meet the design specification, it is best to use the overdamped response. It would be impractical to require a design to achieve the exact component values that ensure a critically damped response.

Example 8.10   Finding Step Response of a Parallel *RLC* Circuit with Initial Stored Energy

Energy is stored in the circuit in Example 8.8 (Fig. 8.12, with $R = 500$ Ω) at the instant the dc current source is applied. The initial current in the inductor is 29 mA, and the initial voltage across the capacitor is 50 V. Find (a) $i_L(0)$; (b) $di_L(0)/dt$; (c) $i_L(t)$ for $t \geq 0$; (d) $v(t)$ for $t \geq 0$.

Solution

a) There cannot be an instantaneous change of current in an inductor, so the initial value of i_L in the first instant after the dc current source has been applied must be 29 mA.

b) The capacitor holds the initial voltage across the inductor to 50 V. Therefore

$$L\frac{di_L}{dt}(0^+) = 50,$$

$$\frac{di_L}{dt}(0^+) = \frac{50}{25} \times 10^3 = 2000 \text{ A/s}.$$

c) From the solution of Example 8.8, we know that the current response is critically damped. Thus

$$i_L(t) = I_f + D_1' t e^{-\alpha t} + D_2' e^{-\alpha t},$$

where

$$\alpha = \frac{1}{2RC} = 40{,}000 \text{ rad/s} \quad \text{and} \quad I_f = 24 \text{ mA}.$$

Notice that the effect of the nonzero initial stored energy is on the calculations for the constants D_1' and D_2', which we obtain from the initial conditions. First we use the initial value of the inductor current:

$$i_L(0) = I_f + D_2' = 29 \text{ mA},$$

from which we get

$$D_2' = 29 - 24 = 5 \text{ mA}.$$

The solution for D_1' is

$$\frac{di_L}{dt}(0^+) = D_1' - \alpha D_2' = 2000,$$

or

$$D_1' = 2000 + \alpha D_2'$$

$$= 2000 + (40,000)(5 \times 10^{-3})$$

$$= 2200 \text{ A/s} = 2.2 \times 10^6 \text{ mA/s}.$$

Thus the numerical expression for $i_L(t)$ is

$$i_L(t) = (24 + 2.2 \times 10^6 t e^{-40,000t}$$

$$+ 5e^{-40,000t}) \text{ mA}, \quad t \geq 0.$$

d) We can get the expression for $v(t)$, $t \geq 0$ by using the relationship between the voltage and current in an inductor:

$$v(t) = L\frac{di_L}{dt}$$

$$= (25 \times 10^{-3})[(2.2 \times 10^6)(-40,000)te^{-40,000t}$$

$$+ 2.2 \times 10^6 e^{-40,000t}$$

$$+ (5)(-40,000)e^{-40,000t}] \times 10^{-3}$$

$$= -2.2 \times 10^6 te^{-40,000t} + 50e^{-40,000t} \text{ V}, \quad t \geq 0.$$

To check this result, let's verify that the initial voltage across the inductor is 50 V:

$$v(0) = -2.2 \times 10^6 (0)(1) + 50(1) = 50 \text{ V}.$$

✓ ASSESSMENT PROBLEM

Objective 1—Be able to determine the natural response and the step response of parallel *RLC* circuits

8.6 In the circuit shown, $R = 500 \ \Omega$, $L = 0.64$ H, $C = 1 \ \mu$F, and $I = -1$ A. The initial voltage drop across the capacitor is 40 V and the initial inductor current is 0.5 A. Find (a) $i_R(0^+)$; (b) $i_C(0^+)$; (c) $di_L(0^+)/dt$; (d) s_1, s_2; (e) $i_L(t)$ for $t \geq 0$; and (f) $v(t)$ for $t \geq 0^+$.

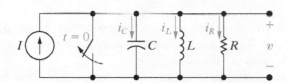

Answer: (a) 80 mA;

(b) −1.58 A;

(c) 62.5 A/s;

(d) $(-1000 + j750)$ rad/s, $(-1000 - j750)$ rad/s;

(e) $[-1 + e^{-1000t}[1.5 \cos 750t + 2.0833 \sin 750t]$ A, for $t \geq 0$;

(f) $e^{-1000t}(40 \cos 750t - 2053.33 \sin 750t)$ V, for $t \geq 0^+$.

NOTE: *Also try Chapter Problems 8.27–8.29.*

8.4 The Natural and Step Response of a Series *RLC* Circuit

The procedures for finding the natural or step responses of a series *RLC* circuit are the same as those used to find the natural or step responses of a parallel *RLC* circuit, because both circuits are described by differential equations that have the same form. We begin by summing the voltages around the closed path in the circuit shown in Fig. 8.14. Thus

$$Ri + L\frac{di}{dt} + \frac{1}{C}\int_0^t i \, d\tau + V_0 = 0. \tag{8.52}$$

We now differentiate Eq. 8.52 once with respect to t to get

$$R\frac{di}{dt} + L\frac{d^2i}{dt^2} + \frac{i}{C} = 0, \tag{8.53}$$

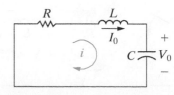

Figure 8.14 ▲ A circuit used to illustrate the natural response of a series *RLC* circuit.

which we can rearrange as

$$\frac{d^2i}{dt^2} + \frac{R}{L}\frac{di}{dt} + \frac{i}{LC} = 0. \qquad (8.54)$$

Comparing Eq. 8.54 with Eq. 8.3 reveals that they have the same form. Therefore, to find the solution of Eq. 8.54, we follow the same process that led us to the solution of Eq. 8.3.

From Eq. 8.54, the characteristic equation for the series *RLC* circuit is

Characteristic equation—series *RLC* circuit ▶

$$s^2 + \frac{R}{L}s + \frac{1}{LC} = 0. \qquad (8.55)$$

The roots of the characteristic equation are

$$s_{1,2} = -\frac{R}{2L} \pm \sqrt{\left(\frac{R}{2L}\right)^2 - \frac{1}{LC}}, \qquad (8.56)$$

or

$$s_{1,2} = -\alpha \pm \sqrt{\alpha^2 - \omega_0^2}. \qquad (8.57)$$

The neper frequency (α) for the series *RLC* circuit is

Neper frequency—series *RLC* circuit ▶

$$\alpha = \frac{R}{2L} \text{ rad/s}, \qquad (8.58)$$

and the expression for the resonant radian frequency is

Resonant radian frequency—series *RLC* circuit ▶

$$\omega_0 = \frac{1}{\sqrt{LC}} \text{ rad/s}. \qquad (8.59)$$

Note that the equation for neper frequency of the series *RLC* circuit differs from that of the parallel *RLC* circuit, but the equations for resonant and damped radian frequencies are the same.

The current response will be overdamped, underdamped, or critically damped according to whether $\omega_0^2 < \alpha^2$, $\omega_0^2 > \alpha^2$, or $\omega_0^2 = \alpha^2$, respectively. Thus the three possible solutions for the current are as follows:

Current natural response forms in series *RLC* circuits F ▶

$$i(t) = A_1 e^{s_1 t} + A_2 e^{s_2 t} \text{ (overdamped)}, \qquad (8.60)$$

$$i(t) = B_1 e^{-\alpha t} \cos \omega_d t + B_2 e^{-\alpha t} \sin \omega_d t \text{ (underdamped)}, \qquad (8.61)$$

$$i(t) = D_1 t e^{-\alpha t} + D_2 e^{-\alpha t} \text{ (critically damped)}. \qquad (8.62)$$

When you have obtained the natural current response, you can find the natural voltage response across any circuit element.

To verify that the procedure for finding the step response of a series *RLC* circuit is the same as that for a parallel *RLC* circuit, we show that the differential equation that describes the capacitor voltage in Fig. 8.15 has the same form as the differential equation that describes the inductor current in Fig. 8.11. For convenience, we assume that zero energy is stored in the circuit at the instant the switch is closed.

Applying Kirchhoff's voltage law to the circuit shown in Fig. 8.15 gives

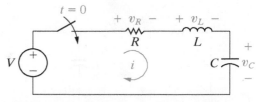

Figure 8.15 ▲ A circuit used to illustrate the step response of a series *RLC* circuit.

$$V = Ri + L\frac{di}{dt} + v_C. \qquad (8.63)$$

The current (i) is related to the capacitor voltage (v_C) by the expression

$$i = C\frac{dv_C}{dt}, \tag{8.64}$$

from which

$$\frac{di}{dt} = C\frac{d^2v_C}{dt^2}. \tag{8.65}$$

Substitute Eqs. 8.64 and 8.65 into Eq. 8.63 and write the resulting expression as

$$\frac{d^2v_C}{dt^2} + \frac{R}{L}\frac{dv_C}{dt} + \frac{v_C}{LC} = \frac{V}{LC}. \tag{8.66}$$

Equation 8.66 has the same form as Eq. 8.41; therefore the procedure for finding v_C parallels that for finding i_L. The three possible solutions for v_C are as follows:

$$v_C = V_f + A_1'e^{s_1t} + A_2'e^{s_2t} \quad \text{(overdamped)}, \tag{8.67}$$

$$v_C = V_f + B_1'e^{-\alpha t}\cos \omega_d t + B_2'e^{-\alpha t}\sin \omega_d t \quad \text{(underdamped)}, \tag{8.68}$$

$$v_C = V_f + D_1'te^{-\alpha t} + D_2'e^{-\alpha t} \quad \text{(critically damped)}, \tag{8.69}$$

◄ **Capacitor voltage step response forms in series *RLC* circuits**

where V_f is the final value of v_C. Hence, from the circuit shown in Fig. 8.15, the final value of v_C is the dc source voltage V.

Example 8.11 and 8.12 illustrate the mechanics of finding the natural and step responses of a series *RLC* circuit.

Example 8.11   **Finding the Underdamped Natural Response of a Series *RLC* Circuit**

The $0.1\ \mu$F capacitor in the circuit shown in Fig. 8.16 is charged to 100 V. At $t = 0$ the capacitor is discharged through a series combination of a 100 mH inductor and a 560 Ω resistor.

a) Find $i(t)$ for $t \geq 0$.
b) Find $v_C(t)$ for $t \geq 0$.

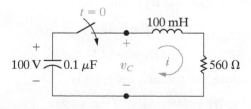

Figure 8.16 ▲ The circuit for Example 8.11.

Solution

a) The first step to finding $i(t)$ is to calculate the roots of the characteristic equation. For the given element values,

$$\omega_0^2 = \frac{1}{LC}$$

$$= \frac{(10^3)(10^6)}{(100)(0.1)} = 10^8,$$

$$\alpha = \frac{R}{2L}$$

$$= \frac{560}{2(100)} \times 10^3$$

$$= 2800 \text{ rad/s}.$$

Next, we compare ω_0^2 to α^2 and note that $\omega_0^2 > \alpha^2$, because

$$\alpha^2 = 7.84 \times 10^6$$

$$= 0.0784 \times 10^8.$$

At this point, we know that the response is underdamped and that the solution for $i(t)$ is of the form

$$i(t) = B_1 e^{-\alpha t} \cos \omega_d t + B_2 e^{-\alpha t} \sin \omega_d t,$$

where $\alpha = 2800$ rad/s and $\omega_d = 9600$ rad/s. The numerical values of B_1 and B_2 come from the initial conditions. The inductor current is zero before the switch has been closed, and hence it is zero immediately after. Therefore

$$i(0) = 0 = B_1.$$

To find B_2, we evaluate $di(0^+)/dt$. From the circuit, we note that, because $i(0) = 0$ immediately after the switch has been closed, there will be no voltage drop across the resistor. Thus the initial voltage on the capacitor appears across the terminals of the inductor, which leads to the expression,

$$L\frac{di(0^+)}{dt} = V_0,$$

or

$$\frac{di(0^+)}{dt} = \frac{V_0}{L} = \frac{100}{100} \times 10^3$$

$$= 1000 \text{ A/s}.$$

Because $B_1 = 0$,

$$\frac{di}{dt} = 400 B_2 e^{-2800t}(24 \cos 9600t - 7 \sin 9600t).$$

Thus

$$\frac{di(0^+)}{dt} = 9600 B_2,$$

$$B_2 = \frac{1000}{9600} \approx 0.1042 \text{ A}.$$

The solution for $i(t)$ is

$$i(t) = 0.1042 e^{-2800t} \sin 9600t \text{ A}, \quad t \geq 0.$$

b) To find $v_C(t)$, we can use either of the following relationships:

$$v_C = -\frac{1}{C}\int_0^t i\, d\tau + 100 \text{ or}$$

$$v_C = iR + L\frac{di}{dt}.$$

Whichever expression is used (the second is recommended), the result is

$$v_C(t) = (100 \cos 9600t + 29.17 \sin 9600t)e^{-2800t} \text{ V}, \quad t \geq 0.$$

Example 8.12   Finding the Underdamped Step Response of a Series *RLC* Circuit

No energy is stored in the 100 mH inductor or the $0.4\ \mu\text{F}$ capacitor when the switch in the circuit shown in Fig. 8.17 is closed. Find $v_C(t)$ for $t \geq 0$.

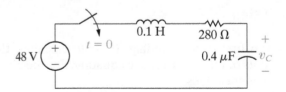

Figure 8.17 ▲ The circuit for Example 8.12.

Solution

The roots of the characteristic equation are

$$s_1 = -\frac{280}{0.2} + \sqrt{\left(\frac{280}{0.2}\right)^2 - \frac{10^6}{(0.1)(0.4)}}$$

$$= (-1400 + j4800) \text{ rad/s},$$

$$s_2 = (-1400 - j4800) \text{ rad/s}.$$

The roots are complex, so the voltage response is underdamped. Thus

$$v_C(t) = 48 + B_1' e^{-1400t} \cos 4800t$$

$$+ B_2' e^{-1400t} \sin 4800t, \quad t \geq 0.$$

No energy is stored in the circuit initially, so both $v_C(0)$ and $dv_C(0^+)/dt$ are zero. Then,

$$v_C(0) = 0 = 48 + B_1',$$

$$\frac{dv_C(0^+)}{dt} = 0 = 4800 B_2' - 1400 B_1'.$$

Solving for B_1' and B_2' yields

$$B_1' = -48 \text{ V},$$

$$B_2' = -14 \text{ V}.$$

Therefore, the solution for $v_C(t)$ is

$$v_C(t) = (48 - 48e^{-1400t} \cos 4800t$$

$$- 14e^{-1400t} \sin 4800t) \text{ V}, \quad t \geq 0.$$

✓ ASSESSMENT PROBLEMS

Objective 2—Be able to determine the natural response and the step response of series *RLC* circuits

8.7   The switch in the circuit shown has been in position a for a long time. At $t = 0$, it moves to position b. Find (a) $i(0^+)$; (b) $v_C(0^+)$; (c) $di(0^+)/dt$; (d) s_1, s_2; and (e) $i(t)$ for $t \geq 0$.

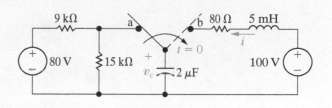

Answer: (a) 0;

(b) 50 V;

(c) 10,000 A/s;

(d) $(-8000 + j6000)$ rad/s, $(-8000 - j6000)$ rad/s;

(e) $(1.67e^{-8000t} \sin 6000t)$ A for $t \geq 0$.

8.8   Find $v_C(t)$ for $t \geq 0$ for the circuit in Assessment Problem 8.7.

Answer: $[100 - e^{-8000t}(50 \cos 6000t + 66.67 \sin 6000t)]$ V for $t \geq 0$.

NOTE: Also try Chapter Problems 8.49–8.51.

8.5   A Circuit with Two Integrating Amplifiers

A circuit containing two integrating amplifiers connected in cascade[1] is also a second-order circuit; that is, the output voltage of the second integrator is related to the input voltage of the first by a second-order differential equation. We begin our analysis of a circuit containing two cascaded amplifiers with the circuit shown in Fig. 8.18.

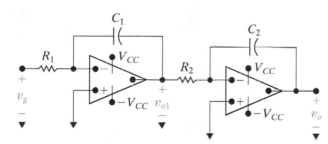

Figure 8.18 ▲ Two integrating amplifiers connected in cascade.

We assume that the op amps are ideal. The task is to derive the differential equation that establishes the relationship between v_o and v_g. We begin the derivation by summing the currents at the inverting input terminal of the first integrator. Because the op amp is ideal,

$$\frac{0 - v_g}{R_1} + C_1 \frac{d}{dt}(0 - v_{o1}) = 0. \tag{8.70}$$

From Eq. 8.70,

$$\frac{dv_{o1}}{dt} = -\frac{1}{R_1 C_1} v_g. \tag{8.71}$$

---

[1] In a cascade connection, the output signal of the first amplifier (v_{o1} in Fig. 8.18) is the input signal for the second amplifier.

Now we sum the currents away from the inverting input terminal of the second integrating amplifier:

$$\frac{0 - v_{o1}}{R_2} + C_2\frac{d}{dt}(0 - v_o) = 0, \tag{8.72}$$

or

$$\frac{dv_o}{dt} = -\frac{1}{R_2C_2}v_{o1}. \tag{8.73}$$

Differentiating Eq. 8.73 gives

$$\frac{d^2v_o}{dt^2} = -\frac{1}{R_2C_2}\frac{dv_{o1}}{dt}. \tag{8.74}$$

We find the differential equation that governs the relationship between v_o and v_g by substituting Eq. 8.71 into Eq. 8.74:

$$\frac{d^2v_o}{dt^2} = \frac{1}{R_1C_1}\frac{1}{R_2C_2}v_g. \tag{8.75}$$

Example 8.13 illustrates the step response of a circuit containing two cascaded integrating amplifiers.

Example 8.13 Analyzing Two Cascaded Integrating Amplifiers

No energy is stored in the circuit shown in Fig. 8.19 when the input voltage v_g jumps instantaneously from 0 to 25 mV.

a) Derive the expression for $v_o(t)$ for $0 \le t \le t_{sat}$.
b) How long is it before the circuit saturates?

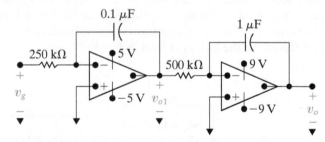

Figure 8.19 ▲ The circuit for Example 8.13.

Solution

a) Figure 8.19 indicates that the amplifier scaling factors are

$$\frac{1}{R_1C_1} = \frac{1000}{(250)(0.1)} = 40,$$

$$\frac{1}{R_2C_2} = \frac{1000}{(500)(1)} = 2.$$

Now, because $v_g = 25$ mV for $t > 0$, Eq. 8.75 becomes

$$\frac{d^2v_o}{dt^2} = (40)(2)(25 \times 10^{-3}) = 2.$$

To solve for v_o, we let

$$g(t) = \frac{dv_o}{dt},$$

then,

$$\frac{dg(t)}{dt} = 2, \quad \text{and} \quad dg(t) = 2dt.$$

Hence

$$\int_{g(0)}^{g(t)} dy = 2\int_0^t dx,$$

from which

$$g(t) - g(0) = 2t.$$

However,

$$g(0) = \frac{dv_o(0)}{dt} = 0,$$

because the energy stored in the circuit initially is zero, and the op amps are ideal. (See Problem 8.57.) Then,

$$\frac{dv_o}{dt} = 2t, \quad \text{and} \quad v_o = t^2 + v_o(0).$$

But $v_o(0) = 0$, so the experssion for v_o becomes

$$v_o = t^2, \quad 0 \le t \le t_{sat}.$$

b) The second integrating amplifier saturates when v_o reaches 9 V or $t = 3$ s. But it is possible that the first integrating amplifier saturates before $t = 3$ s. To explore this possibility, use Eq. 8.71 to find dv_{o1}/dt:

$$\frac{dv_{o1}}{dt} = -40(25) \times 10^{-3} = -1.$$

Solving for v_{o1} yields

$$v_{o1} = -t.$$

Thus, at $t = 3$ s, $v_{o1} = -3$ V, and, because the power supply voltage on the first integrating amplifier is ± 5 V, the circuit reaches saturation when the second amplifier saturates. When one of the op amps saturates, we no longer can use the linear model to predict the behavior of the circuit.

NOTE: *Assess your understanding of this material by trying Chapter Problem 8.63.*

Two Integrating Amplifiers with Feedback Resistors

Figure 8.20 depicts a variation of the circuit shown in Fig. 8.18. Recall from Section 7.7 that the reason the op amp in the integrating amplifier saturates is the feedback capacitor's accumulation of charge. Here, a resistor is placed in parallel with each feedback capacitor (C_1 and C_2) to overcome this problem. We rederive the equation for the output voltage, v_o, and determine the impact of these feedback resistors on the integrating amplifiers from Example 8.13.

We begin the derivation of the second-order differential equation that relates v_{o1} to v_g by summing the currents at the inverting input node of the first integrator:

$$\frac{0 - v_g}{R_a} + \frac{0 - v_{o1}}{R_1} + C_1\frac{d}{dt}(0 - v_{o1}) = 0. \tag{8.76}$$

We simplify Eq. 8.76 to read

$$\frac{dv_{o1}}{dt} + \frac{1}{R_1 C_1}v_{o1} = \frac{-v_g}{R_a C_1}. \tag{8.77}$$

For convenience, we let $\tau_1 = R_1 C_1$ and write Eq. 8.77 as

$$\frac{dv_{o1}}{dt} + \frac{v_{o1}}{\tau_1} = \frac{-v_g}{R_a C_1}. \tag{8.78}$$

The next step is to sum the currents at the inverting input terminal of the second integrator:

$$\frac{0 - v_{o1}}{R_b} + \frac{0 - v_o}{R_2} + C_2\frac{d}{dt}(0 - v_o) = 0. \tag{8.79}$$

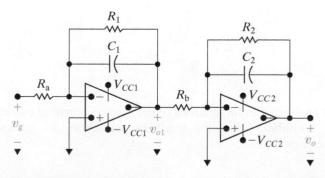

Figure 8.20 ▲ Cascaded integrating amplifiers with feedback resistors.

We rewrite Eq. 8.79 as

$$\frac{dv_o}{dt} + \frac{v_o}{\tau_2} = \frac{-v_{o1}}{R_b C_2}, \tag{8.80}$$

where $\tau_2 = R_2 C_2$. Differentiating Eq. 8.80 yields

$$\frac{d^2 v_o}{dt^2} + \frac{1}{\tau_2}\frac{dv_o}{dt} = -\frac{1}{R_b C_2}\frac{dv_{o1}}{dt}. \tag{8.81}$$

From Eq. 8.78,

$$\frac{dv_{o1}}{dt} = \frac{-v_{o1}}{\tau_1} - \frac{v_g}{R_a C_1}, \tag{8.82}$$

and from Eq. 8.80,

$$v_{o1} = -R_b C_2 \frac{dv_o}{dt} - \frac{R_b C_2}{\tau_2} v_o. \tag{8.83}$$

We use Eqs. 8.82 and 8.83 to eliminate dv_{o1}/dt from Eq. 8.81 and obtain the desired relationship:

$$\frac{d^2 v_o}{dt^2} + \left(\frac{1}{\tau_1} + \frac{1}{\tau_2}\right)\frac{dv_o}{dt} + \left(\frac{1}{\tau_1 \tau_2}\right)v_o = \frac{v_g}{R_a C_1 R_b C_2}. \tag{8.84}$$

From Eq. 8.84, the characteristic equation is

$$s^2 + \left(\frac{1}{\tau_1} + \frac{1}{\tau_2}\right)s + \frac{1}{\tau_1 \tau_2} = 0. \tag{8.85}$$

The roots of the characteristic equation are real, namely,

$$s_1 = \frac{-1}{\tau_1}, \tag{8.86}$$

$$s_2 = \frac{-1}{\tau_2}. \tag{8.87}$$

Example 8.14 illustrates the analysis of the step response of two cascaded integrating amplifiers when the feedback capacitors are shunted with feedback resistors.

Example 8.14   **Analyzing Two Cascaded Integrating Amplifiers with Feedback Resistors**

The parameters for the circuit shown in Fig. 8.20 are $R_a = 100\,\text{k}\Omega$, $R_1 = 500\,\text{k}\Omega$, $C_1 = 0.1\,\mu\text{F}$, $R_b = 25\,\text{k}\Omega$, $R_2 = 100\,\text{k}\Omega$, and $C_2 = 1\,\mu\text{F}$. The power supply voltage for each op amp is ± 6 V. The signal voltage (v_g) for the cascaded integrating amplifiers jumps from 0 to 250 mV at $t = 0$. No energy is stored in the feedback capacitors at the instant the signal is applied.

a) Find the numerical expression of the differential equation for v_o.

b) Find $v_o(t)$ for $t \geq 0$.

c) Find the numerical expression of the differential equation for v_{o1}.

d) Find $v_{o1}(t)$ for $t \geq 0$.

Solution

a) From the numerical values of the circuit parameters, we have $\tau_1 = R_1 C_1 = 0.05$ s; $\tau_2 = R_2 C_2 = 0.10$ s, and $v_g / R_a C_1 R_b C_2 = 1000\ \text{V/s}^2$. Substituting these values into Eq. 8.84 gives

$$\frac{d^2 v_o}{dt^2} + 30\frac{dv_o}{dt} + 200v_o = 1000.$$

b) The roots of the characteristic equation are $s_1 = -20$ rad/s and $s_2 = -10$ rad/s. The final value of v_o is the input voltage times the gain of each stage, because the capacitors behave as open circuits as $t \to \infty$. Thus,

$$v_o(\infty) = (250 \times 10^{-3})\frac{(-500)}{100}\frac{(-100)}{25} = 5\ \text{V}.$$

The solution for v_o thus takes the form:

$$v_o = 5 + A_1' e^{-10t} + A_2' e^{-20t}.$$

With $v_o(0) = 0$ and $dv_o(0)/dt = 0$, the numerical values of A_1' and A_2' are $A_1' = -10$ V and $A_2' = 5$ V. Therefore, the solution for v_o is

$$v_o(t) = (5 - 10e^{-10t} + 5e^{-20t})\ \text{V}, \quad t \geq 0.$$

The solution assumes that neither op amp saturates. We have already noted that the final value of v_o is 5 V, which is less than 6 V; hence the second op amp does not saturate. The final value of v_{o1} is $(250 \times 10^{-3})(-500/100)$, or -1.25 V. Therefore, the first op amp does not saturate, and our assumption and solution are correct.

c) Substituting the numerical values of the parameters into Eq. 8.78 generates the desired differential equation:

$$\frac{dv_{o1}}{dt} + 20v_{o1} = -25.$$

d) We have already noted the initial and final values of v_{o1}, along with the time constant τ_1. Thus we write the solution in accordance with the technique developed in Section 7.4:

$$v_{o1} = -1.25 + [0 - (-1.25)]e^{-20t}$$

$$= -1.25 + 1.25e^{-20t}\ \text{V}, \quad t \geq 0.$$

NOTE: Assess your understanding of this material by trying Chapter Problem 8.64.

Practical Perspective

Clock for Computer Timing
Consider the circuit in Fig. 8.21, where the output is the voltage drop across the capacitor. For $t \geq 0$ this circuit looks like a series *RLC* natural-response circuit of Fig. 8.3 without its resistor. When we analyze this *LC* circuit, we will discover that its output is an undamped sinusoid, which could be used by a computer's clock generator instead of the typical quartz crystal oscillator. We will be able to specify the frequency of the clock by selecting appropriate values for the inductor and capacitor.

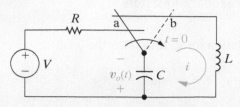

Figure 8.21 ▲ An *LC* natural response circuit.

Begin by writing the *KVL* equation for the circuit in Fig. 8.21, using the current i, for $t \geq 0$:

$$L\frac{di(t)}{dt} + \frac{1}{C}\int_0^t i(x)dx = 0.$$

To get rid of the integral term, integral both sides with respect to t to get

$$L\frac{d^2i(t)}{dt^2} + \frac{1}{C}i(t) = 0.$$

The describing differential equation is thus

$$\frac{d^2i(t)}{dt^2} + \frac{1}{LC}i(t) = 0.$$

What mathematical function can be added to its second derivative to get zero? A sinusoid in the form $i(t) = A\cos\omega_0 t$ will work:

$$\frac{d^2}{dt^2}A\cos\omega_0 t + \frac{1}{LC}A\cos\omega_0 t = -\omega_0^2 A\cos\omega_0 t + \frac{1}{LC}A\cos\omega_0 t = 0.$$

This equation is satisfied when

$$\omega_0^2 = \frac{1}{LC} \quad \text{or when} \quad \omega_0 = \sqrt{\frac{1}{LC}}.$$

The frequency ω_0 is the familiar resonant radian frequency of both the series and parallel *RLC* circuits, whose units are radians/second. Note that the *LC* circuit does not have a neper frequency, α.

We choose the value of A to satisfy the initial condition for the current in the inductor:

$$i(0) = A\cos\omega_0(0) = \frac{V}{R} \quad \text{so} \quad A = \frac{V}{R}.$$

Therefore, the current for the circuit in Fig. 8.21 is

$$i(t) = \frac{V}{R}\cos\omega_0(t), \quad \text{where} \quad \omega_0 = \sqrt{\frac{1}{LC}}.$$

We can now use the expression for the current in the circuit to find the voltage output by the capacitor:

$$v_C(t) = \frac{1}{C}\int_0^t i(x)dx = \frac{1}{C}\int_0^t \frac{V}{R}\cos\omega_0 x\,dx = \frac{V}{\omega_0 RC}\sin\omega_0 t.$$

By choosing values for L and C we can use the circuit in Fig. 8.21 to generate an undamped sinusoid for $t \geq 0$ for a computer's clock generator.

So why is a quartz crystal used to generate the sinusoid for the clock generator instead of the *LC* circuit of Fig. 8.21? Remember that our analysis of the *LC* circuit assumed that the inductor and capacitor are ideal. But ideal inductors and capacitors do not exist – real inductors and capacitors have a small amount of resistance. We leave it to you to examine the effect of this small amount of resistance on the performance of an *LC* oscillator in the Chapter Problems.

NOTE: Assess your understanding of the Practical Perspective by solving Chapter Problems 8.66–8.68.

Summary

- The **characteristic equation** for both the parallel and series RLC circuits has the form

$$s^2 + 2\alpha s + \omega_0^2 = 0,$$

where $\alpha = 1/2RC$ for the parallel circuit, $\alpha = R/2L$ for the series circuit, and $\omega_0^2 = 1/LC$ for both the parallel and series circuits. (See pages 267 and 286.)

- The roots of the characteristic equation are

$$s_{1,2} = -\alpha \pm \sqrt{\alpha^2 - \omega_0^2}.$$

(See page 268.)

- The form of the natural and step responses of series and parallel RLC circuits depends on the values of α^2 and ω_0^2; such responses can be **overdamped**, **underdamped**, or **critically damped**. These terms describe the impact of the dissipative element (R) on the response. The **neper frequency**, α, reflects the effect of R. (See pages 268 and 269.)

- The response of a second-order circuit is overdamped, underdamped, or critically damped as shown in Table 8.2.

- In determining the **natural response** of a second-order circuit, we first determine whether it is over-, under-, or critically damped, and then we solve the appropriate equations as shown in Table 8.3.

- In determining the **step response** of a second-order circuit, we apply the appropriate equations depending on the damping, as shown in Table 8.4.

- For each of the three forms of response, the unknown coefficients (i.e., the As, Bs, and Ds) are obtained by evaluating the circuit to find the initial value of the response, $x(0)$, and the initial value of the first derivative of the response, $dx(0)/dt$.

- When two integrating amplifiers with ideal op amps are connected in cascade, the output voltage of the second integrator is related to the input voltage of the first by an ordinary, second-order differential equation. Therefore, the techniques developed in this chapter may be used to analyze the behavior of a cascaded integrator. (See pages 289 and 290.)

- We can overcome the limitation of a simple integrating amplifier—the saturation of the op amp due to charge accumulating in the feedback capacitor—by placing a resistor in parallel with the capacitor in the feedback path. (See page 291.)

TABLE 8.2   The Response of a Second-Order Circuit is Overdamped, Underdamped, or Critically Damped

The Circuit is	When	Qualitative Nature of the Response
Overdamped	$\alpha^2 > \omega_0^2$	The voltage or current approaches its final value without oscillation
Underdamped	$\alpha^2 < \omega_0^2$	The voltage or current oscillates about its final value
Critically damped	$\alpha^2 = \omega_0^2$	The voltage or current is on the verge of oscillating about its final value

TABLE 8.3   In Determining the Natural Response of a Second-Order Circuit, We First Determine Whether it is Over-, Under-, or Critically Damped, and Then We Solve the Appropriate Equations

Damping	Natural Response Equations	Coefficient Equations
Overdamped	$x(t) = A_1 e^{s_1 t} + A_2 e^{s_2 t}$	$x(0) = A_1 + A_2$; $dx/dt(0) = A_1 s_1 + A_2 s_2$
Underdamped	$x(t) = (B_1 \cos \omega_d t + B_2 \sin \omega_d t)e^{-\alpha t}$	$x(0) = B_1$; $dx/dt(0) = -\alpha B_1 + \omega_d B_2$, where $\omega_d = \sqrt{\omega_0^2 - \alpha^2}$
Critically damped	$x(t) = (D_1 t + D_2)e^{-\alpha t}$	$x(0) = D_2$, $dx/dt(0) = D_1 - \alpha D_2$

TABLE 8.4 In Determining the Step Response of a Second-Order Circuit, We Apply the Appropriate Equations Depending on the Damping

Damping	Step Response Equations[a]	Coefficient Equations
Overdamped	$x(t) = X_f + A'_1 e^{s_1 t} + A'_2 e^{s_2 t}$	$x(0) = X_f + A'_1 + A'_2;$ $dx/dt(0) = A'_1 s_1 + A'_2 s_2$
Underdamped	$x(t) = X_f + (B'_1 \cos \omega_d t + B'_2 \sin \omega_d t) e^{-\alpha t}$	$x(0) = X_f + B'_1;$ $dx/dt(0) = -\alpha B'_1 + \omega_d B'_2$
Critically damped	$x(t) = X_f + D'_1 t e^{-\alpha t} + D'_2 e^{-\alpha t}$	$x(0) = X_f + D'_2;$ $dx/dt(0) = D'_1 - \alpha D'_2$

[a] where X_f is the final value of $x(t)$.

Problems

Sections 8.1–8.2

8.1 The circuit elements in the circuit in Fig. 8.1 are
PSPICE $R = 125 \ \Omega$, $L = 200$ mH, and $C = 5 \ \mu$F. The
MULTISIM initial inductor current is -0.3 A and the initial capacitor voltage is 25 V.

    a) Calculate the initial current in each branch of the circuit.

    b) Find $v(t)$ for $t \geq 0$.

    c) Find $i_L(t)$ for $t \geq 0$.

8.2 The resistance in Problem 8.1 is decreased to
PSPICE $100 \ \Omega$. Find the expression for $v(t)$ for $t \geq 0$.
MULTISIM

8.3 The resistance in Problem 8.1 is decreased to $80 \ \Omega$.
PSPICE Find the expression for $v(t)$ for $t \geq 0$.
MULTISIM

8.4 The resistance, inductance, and capacitance in a parallel *RLC* circuit are $2000 \ \Omega$, 250 mH, and 10 nF, respectively.

    a) Calculate the roots of the characteristic equation that describe the voltage response of the circuit.

    b) Will the response be over-, under-, or critically damped?

    c) What value of R will yield a damped frequency of 12 krad/s?

    d) What are the roots of the characteristic equation for the value of R found in (c)?

    e) What value of R will result in a critically damped response?

8.5 Suppose the inductor in the circuit shown in Fig. 8.1 has a value of 10 mH. The voltage response for $t \geq 0$ is

$$v(t) = 40e^{-1000t} - 90e^{-4000t} \text{ V}.$$

    a) Determine the numerical values of ω_0, α, C, and R.

    b) Calculate $i_R(t)$, $i_L(t)$, and $i_C(t)$ for $t \geq 0^+$.

8.6 The natural voltage response of the circuit in Fig. 8.1 is

$$v(t) = 120e^{-400t} \cos 300t + 80e^{-400t} \sin 300t \text{ V},$$

when the capacitor is $250 \ \mu$F. Find (a) L; (b) R; (c) V_0; (d) I_0; and (e) $i_L(t)$.

8.7 The voltage response for the circuit in Fig. 8.1 is known to be

$$v(t) = D_1 t e^{-80t} + D_2 e^{-80t}, \quad t \geq 0.$$

The initial current in the inductor (I_0) is -25 mA, and the initial voltage on the capacitor (V_0) is 5 V. The resistor has a value of $50 \ \Omega$.

    a) Find the values of C, L, D_1, and D_2.

    b) Find $i_C(t)$ for $t \geq 0^+$.

8.8 In the circuit shown in Fig. 8.1, a 20 mH inductor is
PSPICE shunted by a 500 nF capacitor, the resistor R is
MULTISIM adjusted for critical damping, and $I_0 = 120$ mA.

a) Calculate the numerical value of R.

b) Calculate $v(t)$ for $t \geq 0$.

c) Find $v(t)$ when $i_C(t) = 0$.

d) What percentage of the initially stored energy remains stored in the circuit at the instant $i_C(t)$ is 0?

8.9 The natural response for the circuit shown in Fig. 8.1 is known to be

$$v(t) = -11e^{-100t} + 20e^{-400t} \text{ V}, \quad t \geq 0.$$

If $C = 2 \,\mu\text{F}$ and $L = 12.5$ H, find $i_L(0^+)$ in milliamperes.

8.10 The resistor in the circuit in Example 8.4 is changed to 3200 Ω.

PSPICE

MULTISIM

a) Find the numerical expression for $v(t)$ when $t \geq 0$.

b) Plot $v(t)$ versus t for the time interval $0 \leq t \leq 7$ ms. Compare this response with the one in Example 8.4 ($R = 20$ kΩ) and Example 8.5 ($R = 4$ kΩ). In particular, compare peak values of $v(t)$ and the times when these peak values occur.

8.11 The two switches in the circuit seen in Fig. P8.11 operate synchronously. When switch 1 is in position a, switch 2 is in position d. When switch 1 moves to position b, switch 2 moves to position c. Switch 1 has been in position a for a long time. At $t = 0$, the switches move to their alternate positions. Find $v_o(t)$ for $t \geq 0$.

PSPICE

MULTISIM

Figure P8.11

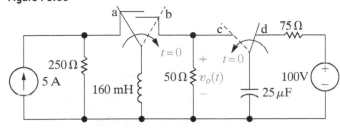

8.12 The resistor in the circuit of Fig. P8.11 is decreased from 50 Ω to 40 Ω. Find $v_o(t)$ for $t \geq 0$.

PSPICE

MULTISIM

8.13 The resistor in the circuit of Fig. P8.11 is decreased from 50 Ω to 32 Ω. Find $v_o(t)$ for $t \geq 0$.

PSPICE

MULTISIM

8.14 The switch in the circuit of Fig. P8.14 has been in position a for a long time. At $t = 0$ the switch moves instantaneously to position b. Find $v_o(t)$ for $t \geq 0$.

PSPICE

MULTISIM

Figure P8.14

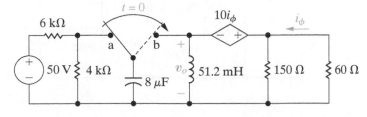

8.15 The inductor in the circuit of Fig. P8.14 is increased to 80 mH. Find $v_o(t)$ for $t \geq 0$.

8.16 The inductor in the circuit of Fig. P8.14 is increased to 125 mH. Find $v_o(t)$ for $t \geq 0$.

8.17 a) Design a parallel RLC circuit (see Fig. 8.1) using component values from Appendix H, with a resonant radian frequency of 5000 rad/s. Choose a resistor or create a resistor network so that the response is critically damped. Draw your circuit.

b) Calculate the roots of the characteristic equation for the resistance in part (a).

8.18 a) Change the resistance for the circuit you designed in Problem 8.5(a) so that the response is underdamped. Continue to use components from Appendix H. Calculate the roots of the characteristic equation for this new resistance.

b) Change the resistance for the circuit you designed in Problem 8.5(a) so that the response is overdamped. Continue to use components from Appendix H. Calculate the roots of the characteristic equation for this new resistance.

8.19 In the circuit in Fig. 8.1, $R = 5$ kΩ, $L = 8$ H, $C = 125$ nF, $V_0 = 30$ V, and $I_0 = 6$ mA.

PSPICE

MULTISIM

a) Find $v(t)$ for $t \geq 0$.

b) Find the first three values of t for which dv/dt is zero. Let these values of t be denoted t_1, t_2, and t_3.

c) Show that $t_3 - t_1 = T_d$.

d) Show that $t_2 - t_1 = T_d/2$.

e) Calculate $v(t_1)$, $v(t_2)$, and $v(t_3)$.

f) Sketch $v(t)$ versus t for $0 \leq t \leq t_2$.

8.20 a) Find $v(t)$ for $t \geq 0$ in the circuit in Problem 8.19 if the 5 kΩ resistor is removed from the circuit.

PSPICE

MULTISIM

b) Calculate the frequency of $v(t)$ in hertz.

c) Calculate the maximum amplitude of $v(t)$ in volts.

8.21 Assume the underdamped voltage response of the circuit in Fig. 8.1 is written as

$$v(t) = (A_1 + A_2)e^{-\alpha t} \cos \omega_d t + j(A_1 - A_2)e^{-\alpha t} \sin \omega_d t$$

The initial value of the inductor current is I_0, and the initial value of the capacitor voltage is V_0. Show that A_2 is the conjugate of A_1. (Hint: Use the same process as outlined in the text to find A_1 and A_2.)

8.22 Show that the results obtained from Problem 8.21 — that is, the expressions for A_1 and A_2—are consistent with Eqs. 8.30 and 8.31 in the text.

8.23 The initial value of the voltage v in the circuit in Fig. 8.1 is zero, and the initial value of the capacitor current, $i_c(0^+)$, is 45 mA. The expression for the capacitor current is known to be

$$i_c(t) = A_1 e^{-200t} + A_2 e^{-800t}, \quad t \geq 0^+,$$

when R is 250 Ω. Find

a) the values of $\alpha, \omega_0, L, C, A_1,$ and A_2

$$\left(\text{Hint:} \frac{di_C(0^+)}{dt} = -\frac{di_L(0^+)}{dt} - \frac{di_R(0^+)}{dt} = \frac{-v(0)}{L} - \frac{1}{R} \frac{i_C(0^+)}{C} \right)$$

b) the expression for $v(t), t \geq 0$,

c) the expression for $i_R(t) \geq 0$,

d) the expression for $i_L(t) \geq 0$.

Section 8.3

8.24 For the circuit in Example 8.6, find, for $t \geq 0$, (a) $v(t)$; (b) $i_R(t)$; and (c) $i_C(t)$.

8.25 For the circuit in Example 8.7, find, for $t \geq 0$, (a) $v(t)$ and (b) $i_C(t)$.

8.26 For the circuit in Example 8.8, find $v(t)$ for $t \geq 0$.

8.27 Assume that at the instant the 2A dc current source is applied to the circuit in Fig. P8.27, the initial current in the 25 mH inductor is 1 A, and the initial voltage on the capacitor is 50 V (positive at the upper terminal). Find the expression for $i_L(t)$ for $t \geq 0$ if R equals 12.5 Ω.

Figure P8.27

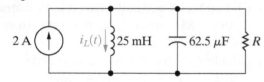

8.28 The resistance in the circuit in Fig. P8.27 is changed to 8 Ω. Find $i_L(t)$ for $t \geq 0$.

8.29 The resistance in the circuit in Fig. P8.27 is changed to 10 Ω. Find $i_L(t)$ for $t \geq 0$.

8.30 The switch in the circuit in Fig. P8.30 has been open a long time before closing at $t = 0$. At the time the switch closes, the capacitor has no stored energy. Find v_o for $t \geq 0$.

Figure P8.30

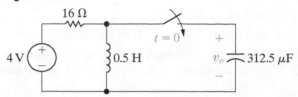

8.31 The switch in the circuit in Fig. P8.31 has been open for a long time before closing at $t = 0$. Find $i_o(t)$ for $t \geq 0$.

Figure P8.31

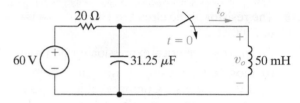

8.32 a) For the circuit in Fig. P8.31, find v_o for $t \geq 0$.

b) Show that your solution for v_o is consistent with the solution for i_o in Problem 8.31.

8.33 There is no energy stored in the circuit in Fig. P8.33 when the switch is closed at $t = 0$. Find $i_o(t)$ for $t \geq 0$.

Figure P8.33

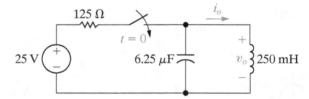

8.34 a) For the circuit in Fig. P8.33, find v_o for $t \geq 0$.

b) Show that your solution for v_o is consistent with the solution for i_o in Problem 8.33.

8.35 The switch in the circuit in Fig. P8.35 has been in the left position for a long time before moving to the right position at $t = 0$. Find

a) $i_L(t)$ for $t \geq 0$,

b) $v_C(t)$ for $t \geq 0$.

Figure P8.35

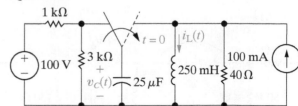

8.36 Use the circuit in Fig. P8.35

PSPICE

MULTISIM

a) Find the total energy delivered to the inductor.

b) Find the total energy delivered to the 40 Ω resistor.

c) Find the total energy delivered to the capacitor.

d) Find the total energy delivered by the current source.

e) Check the results of parts (a) through (d) against the conservation of energy principle.

8.37 The switch in the circuit in Fig. P8.37 has been

PSPICE open a long time before closing at $t = 0$. Find $i_L(t)$

MULTISIM for $t \geq 0$.

Figure P8.37

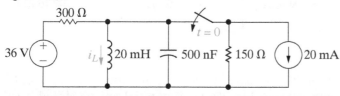

8.38 Switches 1 and 2 in the circuit in Fig. P8.38 are syn-

PSPICE chronized. When switch 1 is opened, switch 2 closes

MULTISIM and vice versa. Switch 1 has been open a long time before closing at $t = 0$. Find $i_L(t)$ for $t \geq 0$.

Figure P8.38

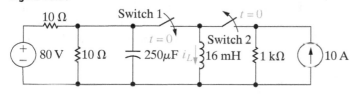

Section 8.4

8.39 The current in the circuit in Fig. 8.3 is known to be

$$i = B_1 e^{-2000t} \cos 1500t + B_2 e^{-2000t} \sin 1500t, \quad t \geq 0.$$

The capacitor has a value of 80 nF; the initial value of the current is 7.5 mA; and the initial voltage on the capacitor is –30 V. Find the values of R, L, B_1, and B_2.

8.40 Find the voltage across the 80 nF capacitor for the circuit described in Problem 8.39. Assume the reference polarity for the capacitor voltage is positive at the upper terminal.

8.41 The initial energy stored in the 31.25 nF capacitor in the circuit in Fig. P8.41 is 9 μJ. The initial energy stored in the inductor is zero. The roots of the characteristic equation that describes the natural

behavior of the current i are $-4000 \, \text{s}^{-1}$ and $-16,000 \, \text{s}^{-1}$

a) Find the numerical values of R and L.

b) Find the numerical values of $i(0)$ and $di(0)/dt$ immediately after the switch has been closed.

c) Find $i(t)$ for $t \geq 0$.

d) How many microseconds after the switch closes does the current reach its maximum value?

e) What is the maximum value of i in milliamperes?

f) Find $v_L(t)$ for $t \geq 0$.

Figure P8.41

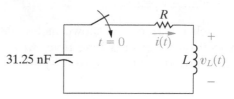

8.42 In the circuit in Fig. P8.42, the resistor is adjusted

PSPICE for critical damping. The initial capacitor voltage is

MULTISIM 15 V, and the initial inductor current is 6 mA.

a) Find the numerical value of R.

b) Find the numerical values of i and di/dt immediately after the switch is closed.

c) Find $v_C(t)$ for $t \geq 0$.

Figure P8.42

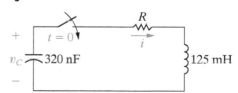

8.43 a) Design a series RLC circuit (see Fig. 8.3) using component values from Appendix H, with a resonant radian frequency of 20 krad/s. Choose a resistor or create a resistor network so that the response is critically damped. Draw your circuit.

b) Calculate the roots of the characteristic equation for the resistance in part (a).

8.44 a) Change the resistance for the circuit you designed in Problem 8.43(a) so that the response is underdamped. Continue to use components from Appendix H. Calculate the roots of the characteristic equation for this new resistance.

b) Change the resistance for the circuit you designed in Problem 8.43(a) so that the response is overdamped. Continue to use components from Appendix H. Calculate the roots of the characteristic equation for this new resistance.

8.45 The circuit shown in Fig. P8.45 has been in operation for a long time. At $t = 0$, the two switches move to the new positions shown in the figure. Find

a) $i_o(t)$ for $t \geq 0$,

b) $v_o(t)$ for $t \geq 0$.

Figure P8.45

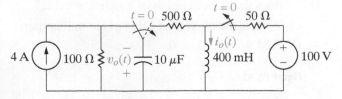

8.46 The switch in the circuit shown in Fig. P8.46 has been in position a for a long time. At $t = 0$, the switch is moved instantaneously to position b. Find $i(t)$ for $t \geq 0$.

Figure P8.46

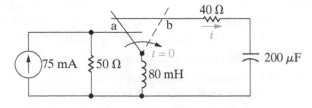

8.47 The switch in the circuit shown in Fig. P8.47 has been closed for a long time. The switch opens at $t = 0$. Find $v_o(t)$ for $t \geq 0^+$.

Figure P8.47

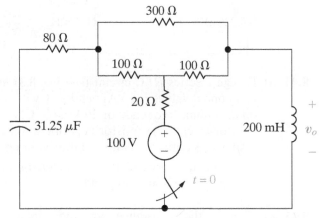

8.48 The switch in the circuit in Fig. P8.48 has been in position a for a long time. At $t = 0$, the switch moves instantaneously to position b.

a) What is the initial value of v_a?

b) What is the initial value of dv_a/dt?

c) What is the numerical expression for $v_a(t)$ for $t \geq 0$?

Figure P8.48

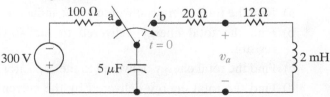

8.49 The initial energy stored in the circuit in Fig. P8.49 is zero. Find $v_o(t)$ for $t \geq 0$.

Figure P8.49

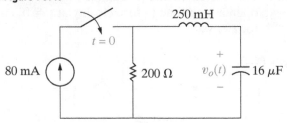

8.50 The resistor in the circuit shown in Fig. P8.49 is changed to 250 Ω. The initial energy stored is still zero. Find $v_o(t)$ for $t \geq 0$.

8.51 The resistor in the circuit shown in Fig. P8.49 is changed to 312.5 Ω. The initial energy stored is still zero. Find $v_o(t)$ for $t \geq 0$.

8.52 The switch in the circuit of Fig. P8.52 has been in position a for a long time. At $t = 0$ the switch moves instantaneously to position b. Find $v_o(t)$ for $t \geq 0$.

Figure P8.52

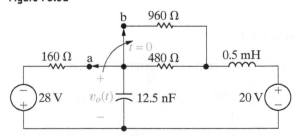

8.53 The circuit shown in Fig. P8.53 has been in operation for a long time. At $t = 0$, the source voltage suddenly drops to 150 V. Find $v_o(t)$ for $t \geq 0$.

Figure P8.53

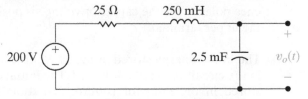

8.54 The two switches in the circuit seen in Fig. P8.55 operate synchronously. When switch 1 is in position a, switch 2 is closed. When switch 1 is in position b, switch 2 is open. Switch 1 has been in position a for a long time. At $t = 0$, it moves instantaneously to position b. Find $v_c(t)$ for $t \geq 0$.

Figure P8.54

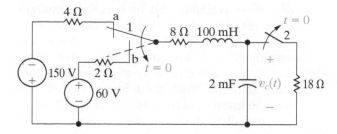

8.55 The switch in the circuit shown in Fig. P8.55 has been closed for a long time before it is opened at $t = 0$. Assume that the circuit parameters are such that the response is underdamped.

a) Derive the expression for $v_o(t)$ as a function of V_g, α, ω_d, C, and R for $t \geq 0$.

b) Derive the expression for the value of t when the magnitude of v_o is maximum.

Figure P8.55

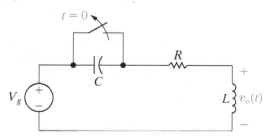

8.56 The circuit parameters in the circuit of Fig. P8.55 are $R = 480\ \Omega$, $L = 8\ \text{mH}$, $C = 50\ \text{nF}$, and $v_g = -24\ \text{V}$.

a) Express $v_o(t)$ numerically for $t \geq 0$.

b) How many microseconds after the switch opens is the inductor voltage maximum?

c) What is the maximum value of the inductor voltage?

d) Repeat (a)–(c) with R reduced to $96\ \Omega$.

8.57 Assume that the capacitor voltage in the circuit of Fig. 8.15 is underdamped. Also assume that no energy is stored in the circuit elements when the switch is closed.

a) Show that $dv_C/dt = (\omega_0^2/\omega_d)Ve^{-\alpha t}\sin \omega_d t$.

b) Show that $dv_C/dt = 0$ when $t = n\pi/\omega_d$, where $n = 0, 1, 2, \ldots$.

c) Let $t_n = n\pi/\omega_d$, and show that $v_C(t_n) = V - V(-1)^n e^{-\alpha n\pi/\omega_d}$.

d) Show that

$$\alpha = \frac{1}{T_d}\ln\frac{v_C(t_1) - V}{v_C(t_3) - V},$$

where $T_d = t_3 - t_1$.

8.58 The voltage across a 100 nF capacitor in the circuit of Fig. 8.15 is described as follows: After the switch has been closed for several seconds, the voltage is constant at 100 V. The first time the voltage exceeds 100 V, it reaches a peak of 163.84 V. This occurs $\pi/7$ ms after the switch has been closed. The second time the voltage exceeds 100 V, it reaches a peak of 126.02 V. This second peak occurs $3\pi/7$ after the switch has been closed. At the time when the switch is closed, there is no energy stored in either the capacitor or the inductor. Find the numerical values of R and L. (Hint: Work Problem 8.57 first.)

Section 8.5

8.59 Show that, if no energy is stored in the circuit shown in Fig. 8.19 at the instant v_g jumps in value, then dv_o/dt equals zero at $t = 0$.

8.60 a) Find the equation for $v_o(t)$ for $0 \leq t \leq t_{\text{sat}}$ in the circuit shown in Fig. 8.19 if $v_{o1}(0) = 5\ \text{V}$ and $v_o(0) = 8\ \text{V}$.

b) How long does the circuit take to reach saturation?

8.61 a) Rework Example 8.14 with feedback resistors R_1 and R_2 removed.

b) Rework Example 8.14 with $v_{o1}(0) = -2\ \text{V}$ and $v_o(0) = 4\ \text{V}$.

8.62 a) Derive the differential equation that relates the output voltage to the input voltage for the circuit shown in Fig. P8.62.

b) Compare the result with Eq. 8.75 when $R_1C_1 = R_2C_2 = RC$ in Fig. 8.18.

c) What is the advantage of the circuit shown in Fig. P8.62?

Figure P8.62

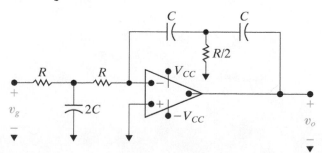

8.63 The voltage signal of Fig. P8.63(a) is applied to the cascaded integrating amplifiers shown in Fig. P8.63(b). There is no energy stored in the capacitors at the instant the signal is applied.

PSPICE
MULTISIM

a) Derive the numerical expressions for $v_o(t)$ and $v_{o1}(t)$ for the time intervals $0 \leq t \leq 0.5$ s and 0.5 s $\leq t \leq t_{sat}$.

b) Compute the value of t_{sat}.

Figure P8.63

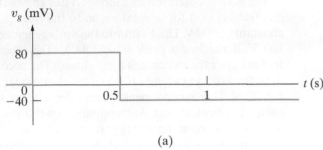

(a)

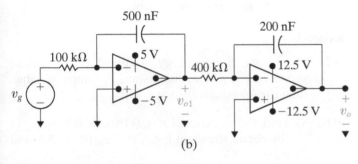

(b)

8.64 The circuit in Fig. P8.63(b) is modified by adding a 1 MΩ resistor in parallel with the 500 nF capacitor and a 5 MΩ resistor in parallel with the 200 nF capacitor. As in Problem 8.63, there is no energy stored in the capacitors at the time the signal is applied. Derive the numerical expressions for $v_o(t)$ and $v_{o1}(t)$ for the time intervals $0 \leq t \leq 0.5$ s and $t \geq 0.5$ s.

PSPICE
MULTISIM

8.65 We now wish to illustrate how several op amp circuits can be interconnected to solve a differential equation.

a) Derive the differential equation for the spring-mass system shown in Fig. P8.65(a). Assume that the force exerted by the spring is directly

proportional to the spring displacement, that the mass is constant, and that the frictional force is directly proportional to the velocity of the moving mass.

b) Rewrite the differential equation derived in (a) so that the highest order derivative is expressed as a function of all the other terms in the equation. Now assume that a voltage equal to d^2x/dt^2 is available and by successive integrations generates dx/dt and x. We can synthesize the coefficients in the equations by scaling amplifiers, and we can combine the terms required to generate d^2x/dt^2 by using a summing amplifier. With these ideas in mind, analyze the interconnection shown in Fig. P8.65(b). In particular, describe the purpose of each shaded area in the circuit and describe the signal at the points labeled B, C, D, E, and F, assuming the signal at A represents d^2x/dt^2. Also discuss the parameters R; R_1, C_1; R_2, C_2; R_3, R_4; R_5, R_6; and R_7, R_8 in terms of the coefficients in the differential equation.

Sections 8.1–8.5

8.66 a) Suppose the circuit in Fig. 8.21 has a 5 nH inductor and a 2 pF capacitor. Calculate the frequency, in GHz, of the sinusoidal output for $t \geq 0$.

b) The dc voltage source and series-connected resistor in Fig. 8.21 are used to establish the initial energy in the inductor. If $V = 10 V$ and $R = 25 \, \Omega$, calculate the initial energy stored in the inductor.

c) What is the total energy stored in the LC circuit for any time $t \geq 0$?

8.67 Consider the LC oscillator circuit in Fig. 8.21. Assume that $V = 4 V$, $R = 10 \, \Omega$, and $L = 1$ nH.

a) Calculate the value of capacitance, C, that will produce a sinusoidal output with a frequency of 2 GHz for $t \geq 0$.

b) Write the expression for the output voltage, $v_o(t)$, for $t \geq 0$.

Figure P8.65

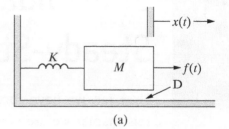

(a)

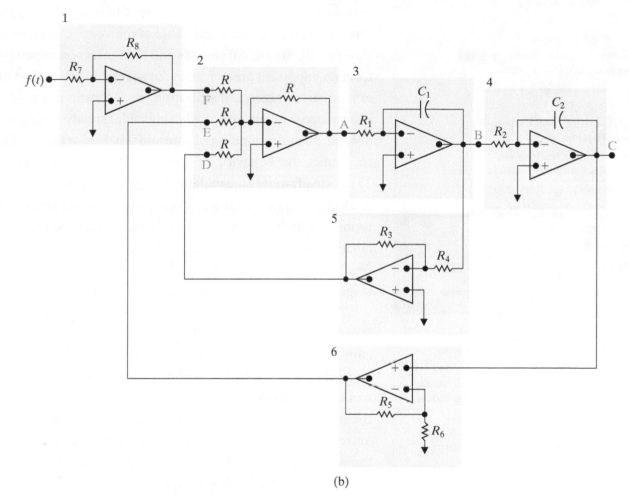

(b)

8.68 Suppose the inductor and capacitor in the LC oscillator circuit in Fig. 8.21 are not ideal, but instead have some small resistance that can be lumped together. Assume that $V = 10$ V, $R = 25$ Ω, $L = 5$ nH, and $C = 2$ pF, just as in Problem 8.66. Suppose the resistance associated with the inductor and capacitor is 10 mΩ.

a) Calculate the values of the neper frequency, α, and the resonant radian frequency, ω_0.

b) Is the response of this circuit over-, under-, or critically damped?

c) What is the actual frequency of oscillation, in GHz?

d) Approximately how long will the circuit oscillate?

Sinusoidal Steady-State Analysis

✓ CHAPTER OBJECTIVES

1 Understand phasor concepts and be able to perform a phasor transform and an inverse phasor transform.

2 Be able to transform a circuit with a sinusoidal source into the frequency domain using phasor concepts.

3 Know how to use the following circuit analysis techniques to solve a circuit in the frequency domain:

- Kirchhoff's laws;
- Series, parallel, and delta-to-wye simplifications;
- Voltage and current division;
- Thévenin and Norton equivalents;
- Node-voltage method; and
- Mesh-current method.

4 Be able to analyze circuits containing linear transformers using phasor methods.

5 Understand the ideal transformer constraints and be able to analyze circuits containing ideal transformers using phasor methods.

Thus far, we have focused on circuits with constant sources; in this chapter we are now ready to consider circuits energized by time-varying voltage or current sources. In particular, we are interested in sources in which the value of the voltage or current varies sinusoidally. Sinusoidal sources and their effect on circuit behavior form an important area of study for several reasons. First, the generation, transmission, distribution, and consumption of electric energy occur under essentially sinusoidal steady-state conditions. Second, an understanding of sinusoidal behavior makes it possible to predict the behavior of circuits with nonsinusoidal sources. Third, steady-state sinusoidal behavior often simplifies the design of electrical systems. Thus a designer can spell out specifications in terms of a desired steady-state sinusoidal response and design the circuit or system to meet those characteristics. If the device satisfies the specifications, the designer knows that the circuit will respond satisfactorily to nonsinusoidal inputs.

The subsequent chapters of this book are largely based on a thorough understanding of the techniques needed to analyze circuits driven by sinusoidal sources. Fortunately, the circuit analysis and simplification techniques first introduced in Chapters 1–4 work for circuits with sinusoidal as well as dc sources, so some of the material in this chapter will be very familiar to you. The challenges in first approaching sinusoidal analysis include developing the appropriate modeling equations and working in the mathematical realm of complex numbers.

Practical Perspective

A Household Distribution Circuit

Power systems that generate, transmit, and distribute electrical power are designed to operate in the sinusoidal steady state. The standard household distribution circuit used in the United States is the three-wire, 240/120 V circuit shown in the accompanying figure.

The transformer is used to reduce the utility distribution voltage from 13.2 kV to 240 V. The center tap on the secondary winding provides the 120 V service. The operating frequency of power systems in the United States is 60 Hz. Both 50 and 60 Hz systems are found outside the United States.

The voltage ratings alluded to above are rms values. The reason for defining an rms value of a time-varying signal is explained in Chapter 10.

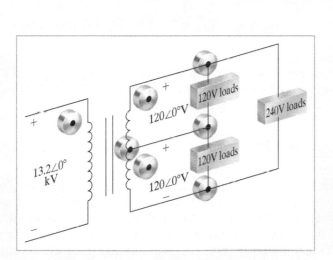

Steve Cole / Photodisc / Getty Images, Inc.

9.1 The Sinusoidal Source

A **sinusoidal voltage source** (independent or dependent) produces a voltage that varies sinusoidally with time. A **sinusoidal current source** (independent or dependent) produces a current that varies sinusoidally with time. In reviewing the sinusoidal function, we use a voltage source, but our observations also apply to current sources.

We can express a sinusoidally varying function with either the sine function or the cosine function. Although either works equally well, we cannot use both functional forms simultaneously. We will use the cosine function throughout our discussion. Hence, we write a sinusoidally varying voltage as

$$v = V_m \cos(\omega t + \phi). \tag{9.1}$$

To aid discussion of the parameters in Eq. 9.1, we show the voltage versus time plot in Fig. 9.1.

Note that the sinusoidal function repeats at regular intervals. Such a function is called periodic. One parameter of interest is the length of time required for the sinusoidal function to pass through all its possible values. This time is referred to as the **period** of the function and is denoted T. It is measured in seconds. The reciprocal of T gives the number of cycles per second, or the frequency, of the sine function and is denoted f, or

$$f = \frac{1}{T}. \tag{9.2}$$

A cycle per second is referred to as a hertz, abbreviated Hz. (The term *cycles per second* rarely is used in contemporary technical literature.) The coefficient of t in Eq. 9.1 contains the numerical value of T or f. Omega (ω) represents the angular frequency of the sinusoidal function, or

$$\omega = 2\pi f = 2\pi/T \text{ (radians/second)}. \tag{9.3}$$

Equation 9.3 is based on the fact that the cosine (or sine) function passes through a complete set of values each time its argument, ωt, passes through 2π rad ($360°$). From Eq. 9.3, note that, whenever t is an integral multiple of T, the argument ωt increases by an integral multiple of 2π rad.

The coefficient V_m gives the maximum amplitude of the sinusoidal voltage. Because ± 1 bounds the cosine function, $\pm V_m$ bounds the amplitude. Figure 9.1 shows these characteristics.

The angle ϕ in Eq. 9.1 is known as the **phase angle** of the sinusoidal voltage. It determines the value of the sinusoidal function at $t = 0$; therefore, it fixes the point on the periodic wave at which we start measuring time. Changing the phase angle ϕ shifts the sinusoidal function along the time axis but has no effect on either the amplitude (V_m) or the angular frequency (ω). Note, for example, that reducing ϕ to zero shifts the sinusoidal function shown in Fig. 9.1 ϕ/ω time units to the right, as shown in Fig. 9.2. Note also that if ϕ is positive, the sinusoidal function shifts to the left, whereas if ϕ is negative, the function shifts to the right. (See Problem 9.5.)

A comment with regard to the phase angle is in order: ωt and ϕ must carry the same units, because they are added together in the argument of the sinusoidal function. With ωt expressed in radians, you would expect ϕ to be also. However, ϕ normally is given in degrees, and ωt is converted from radians to degrees before the two quantities are added. We continue

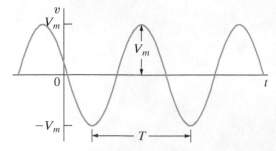

Figure 9.1 ▲ A sinusoidal voltage.

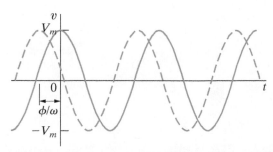

Figure 9.2 ▲ The sinusoidal voltage from Fig. 9.1 shifted to the right when $\phi = 0$.

this bias toward degrees by expressing the phase angle in degrees. Recall from your studies of trigonometry that the conversion from radians to degrees is given by

$$\text{(number of degrees)} = \frac{180°}{\pi}\text{(number of radians).} \qquad (9.4)$$

Another important characteristic of the sinusoidal voltage (or current) is its **rms value**. The rms value of a periodic function is defined as the square root of the mean value of the squared function. Hence, if $v = V_m \cos(\omega t + \phi)$, the rms value of v is

$$V_{\text{rms}} = \sqrt{\frac{1}{T} \int_{t_0}^{t_0+T} V_m^2 \cos^2(\omega t + \phi)\, dt.} \qquad (9.5)$$

Note from Eq. 9.5 that we obtain the mean value of the squared voltage by integrating v^2 over one period (that is, from t_0 to $t_0 + T$) and then dividing by the range of integration, T. Note further that the starting point for the integration t_0 is arbitrary.

The quantity under the radical sign in Eq. 9.5 reduces to $V_m^2/2$. (See Problem 9.6.) Hence the rms value of v is

$$V_{\text{rms}} = \frac{V_m}{\sqrt{2}}. \qquad (9.6) \qquad \blacktriangleleft \text{ rms value of a sinusoidal voltage source}$$

The rms value of the sinusoidal voltage depends only on the maximum amplitude of v, namely, V_m. The rms value is not a function of either the frequency or the phase angle. We stress the importance of the rms value as it relates to power calculations in Chapter 10 (see Section 10.3).

Thus, we can completely describe a specific sinusoidal signal if we know its frequency, phase angle, and amplitude (either the maximum or the rms value). Examples 9.1, 9.2, and 9.3 illustrate these basic properties of the sinusoidal function. In Example 9.4, we calculate the rms value of a periodic function, and in so doing we clarify the meaning of *root mean square*.

Example 9.1   **Finding the Characteristics of a Sinusoidal Current**

A sinusoidal current has a maximum amplitude of 20 A. The current passes through one complete cycle in 1 ms. The magnitude of the current at zero time is 10 A.

a) What is the frequency of the current in hertz?

b) What is the frequency in radians per second?

c) Write the expression for $i(t)$ using the cosine function. Express ϕ in degrees.

d) What is the rms value of the current?

Solution

a) From the statement of the problem, $T = 1$ ms; hence $f = 1/T = 1000$ Hz.

b) $\omega = 2\pi f = 2000\pi$ rad/s.

c) We have $i(t) = I_m \cos(\omega t + \phi) = 20 \cos(2000\pi t + \phi)$, but $i(0) = 10$ A. Therefore $10 = 20 \cos \phi$ and $\phi = 60°$. Thus the expression for $i(t)$ becomes

$$i(t) = 20 \cos(2000\pi t + 60°).$$

d) From the derivation of Eq. 9.6, the rms value of a sinusoidal current is $I_m/\sqrt{2}$. Therefore the rms value is $20/\sqrt{2}$, or 14.14 A.

Example 9.2   Finding the Characteristics of a Sinusoidal Voltage

A sinusoidal voltage is given by the expression $v = 300 \cos(120\pi t + 30°)$.

a) What is the period of the voltage in milliseconds?

b) What is the frequency in hertz?

c) What is the magnitude of v at $t = 2.778$ ms?

d) What is the rms value of v?

Solution

a) From the expression for v, $\omega = 120\pi$ rad/s. Because $\omega = 2\pi/T$, $T = 2\pi/\omega = \frac{1}{60}$ s, or 16.667 ms.

b) The frequency is $1/T$, or 60 Hz.

c) From (a), $\omega = 2\pi/16.667$; thus, at $t = 2.778$ ms, ωt is nearly 1.047 rad, or $60°$. Therefore, $v(2.778 \text{ ms}) = 300 \cos(60° + 30°) = 0$ V.

d) $V_{rms} = 300/\sqrt{2} = 212.13$ V.

Example 9.3   Translating a Sine Expression to a Cosine Expression

We can translate the sine function to the cosine function by subtracting $90°$ ($\pi/2$ rad) from the argument of the sine function.

a) Verify this translation by showing that

$$\sin(\omega t + \theta) = \cos(\omega t + \theta - 90°).$$

b) Use the result in (a) to express $\sin(\omega t + 30°)$ as a cosine function.

Solution

a) Verification involves direct application of the trigonometric identity

$$\cos(\alpha - \beta) = \cos \alpha \cos \beta + \sin \alpha \sin \beta.$$

We let $\alpha = \omega t + \theta$ and $\beta = 90°$. As $\cos 90° = 0$ and $\sin 90° = 1$, we have

$$\cos(\alpha - \beta) = \sin \alpha = \sin(\omega t + \theta) = \cos(\omega t + \theta - 90°).$$

b)   From (a) we have

$$\sin(\omega t + 30°) = \cos(\omega t + 30° - 90°) = \cos(\omega t - 60°).$$

Example 9.4   Calculating the rms Value of a Triangular Waveform

Calculate the rms value of the periodic triangular current shown in Fig. 9.3. Express your answer in terms of the peak current I_p.

Solution

From Eq. 9.5, the rms value of i is

$$I_{rms} = \sqrt{\frac{1}{T} \int_{t_0}^{t_0+T} i^2 dt}.$$

Interpreting the integral under the radical sign as the area under the squared function for an interval of one period is helpful in finding the rms value. The squared function with the area between 0 and T shaded is shown in Fig. 9.4, which also indicates that for this particular function, the area under the

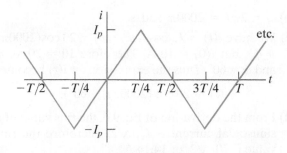

Figure 9.3 ▲ Periodic triangular current.

squared current for an interval of one period is equal to four times the area under the squared current for the interval 0 to $T/4$ seconds; that is,

$$\int_{t_0}^{t_0+T} i^2 dt = 4 \int_0^{T/4} i^2 dt.$$

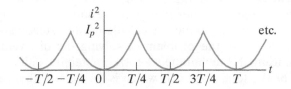

Figure 9.4 ▲ i^2 versus t.

The analytical expression for i in the interval 0 to $T/4$ is

$$i = \frac{4I_p}{T}t, \quad 0 < t < T/4.$$

The area under the squared function for one period is

$$\int_{t_0}^{t_0+T} i^2 dt = 4 \int_0^{T/4} \frac{16I_p^2}{T^2}t^2 dt = \frac{I_p^2 T}{3}.$$

The mean, or average, value of the function is simply the area for one period divided by the period. Thus

$$i_{mean} = \frac{1}{T}\frac{I_p^2 T}{3} = \frac{1}{3}I_p^2.$$

The rms value of the current is the square root of this mean value. Hence

$$I_{rms} = \frac{I_p}{\sqrt{3}}.$$

NOTE: Assess your understanding of this material by trying Chapter Problems 9.1, 9.3 and 9.7.

9.2 The Sinusoidal Response

Before focusing on the steady-state response to sinusoidal sources, let's consider the problem in broader terms, that is, in terms of the total response. Such an overview will help you keep the steady-state solution in perspective. The circuit shown in Fig. 9.5 describes the general nature of the problem. There, v_s is a sinusoidal voltage, or

$$v_s = V_m \cos(\omega t + \phi). \tag{9.7}$$

For convenience, we assume the initial current in the circuit to be zero and measure time from the moment the switch is closed. The task is to derive the expression for $i(t)$ when $t \geq 0$. It is similar to finding the step response of an RL circuit, as in Chapter 7. The only difference is that the voltage source is now a time-varying sinusoidal voltage rather than a constant, or dc, voltage. Direct application of Kirchhoff's voltage law to the circuit shown in Fig. 9.5 leads to the ordinary differential equation

$$L\frac{di}{dt} + Ri = V_m \cos(\omega t + \phi), \tag{9.8}$$

the formal solution of which is discussed in an introductory course in differential equations. We ask those of you who have not yet studied differential equations to accept that the solution for i is

$$i = \frac{-V_m}{\sqrt{R^2 + \omega^2 L^2}}\cos(\phi - \theta)e^{-(R/L)t} + \frac{V_m}{\sqrt{R^2 + \omega^2 L^2}}\cos(\omega t + \phi - \theta), \tag{9.9}$$

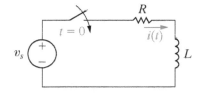

Figure 9.5 ▲ An *RL* circuit excited by a sinusoidal voltage source.

where θ is defined as the angle whose tangent is $\omega L/R$. Thus we can easily determine θ for a circuit driven by a sinusoidal source of known frequency.

We can check the validity of Eq. 9.9 by determining that it satisfies Eq. 9.8 for all values of $t \geq 0$; this exercise is left for your exploration in Problem 9.10.

The first term on the right-hand side of Eq. 9.9 is referred to as the **transient component** of the current because it becomes infinitesimal as time elapses. The second term on the right-hand side is known as the **steady-state component** of the solution. It exists as long as the switch remains closed and the source continues to supply the sinusoidal voltage. In this chapter, we develop a technique for calculating the steady-state response directly, thus avoiding the problem of solving the differential equation. However, in using this technique we forfeit obtaining either the transient component or the total response, which is the sum of the transient and steady-state components.

We now focus on the steady-state portion of Eq. 9.9. It is important to remember the following characteristics of the steady-state solution:

1. The steady-state solution is a sinusoidal function.

2. The frequency of the response signal is identical to the frequency of the source signal. This condition is always true in a linear circuit when the circuit parameters, R, L, and C, are constant. (If frequencies in the response signals are not present in the source signals, there is a nonlinear element in the circuit.)

3. The maximum amplitude of the steady-state response, in general, differs from the maximum amplitude of the source. For the circuit being discussed, the maximum amplitude of the response signal is $V_m/\sqrt{R^2 + \omega^2 L^2}$, and the maximum amplitude of the signal source is V_m.

4. The phase angle of the response signal, in general, differs from the phase angle of the source. For the circuit being discussed, the phase angle of the current is $\phi - \theta$ and that of the voltage source is ϕ.

These characteristics are worth remembering because they help you understand the motivation for the phasor method, which we introduce in Section 9.3. In particular, note that once the decision has been made to find only the steady-state response, the task is reduced to finding the maximum amplitude and phase angle of the response signal. The waveform and frequency of the response are already known.

NOTE: Assess your understanding of this material by trying Chapter Problem 9.9.

9.3 The Phasor

The **phasor** is a complex number that carries the amplitude and phase angle information of a sinusoidal function.[1] The phasor concept is rooted in Euler's identity, which relates the exponential function to the trigonometric function:

$$e^{\pm j\theta} = \cos \theta \pm j \sin \theta. \tag{9.10}$$

Equation 9.10 is important here because it gives us another way of expressing the cosine and sine functions. We can think of the cosine function as the

---

[1] If you feel a bit uneasy about complex numbers, peruse Appendix B.

real part of the exponential function and the sine function as the imaginary part of the exponential function; that is,

$$\cos \theta = \Re\{e^{j\theta}\}, \qquad (9.11)$$

and

$$\sin \theta = \Im\{e^{j\theta}\}, \qquad (9.12)$$

where $\Re$ means "the real part of" and $\Im$ means "the imaginary part of."

Because we have already chosen to use the cosine function in analyzing the sinusoidal steady state (see Section 9.1), we can apply Eq. 9.11 directly. In particular, we write the sinusoidal voltage function given by Eq. 9.1 in the form suggested by Eq. 9.11:

$$v = V_m \cos (\omega t + \phi)$$

$$= V_m \Re\{e^{j(\omega t + \phi)}\}$$

$$= V_m \Re\{e^{j\omega t} e^{j\phi}\}. \qquad (9.13)$$

We can move the coefficient V_m inside the argument of the real part of the function without altering the result. We can also reverse the order of the two exponential functions inside the argument and write Eq. 9.13 as

$$v = \Re\{V_m e^{j\phi} e^{j\omega t}\}. \qquad (9.14)$$

In Eq. 9.14, note that the quantity $V_m e^{j\phi}$ is a complex number that carries the amplitude and phase angle of the given sinusoidal function. This complex number is by definition the **phasor representation**, or **phasor transform**, of the given sinusoidal function. Thus

$$\mathbf{V} = V_m e^{j\phi} = \mathcal{P}\{V_m \cos (\omega t + \phi)\}, \qquad (9.15)$$

◀ Phasor transform

where the notation $\mathcal{P}\{V_m \cos (\omega t + \phi)\}$ is read "the phasor transform of $V_m \cos (\omega t + \phi)$." Thus the phasor transform transfers the sinusoidal function from the time domain to the complex-number domain, which is also called the **frequency domain**, since the response depends, in general, on ω. As in Eq. 9.15, throughout this book we represent a phasor quantity by using a boldface letter.

Equation 9.15 is the polar form of a phasor, but we also can express a phasor in rectangular form. Thus we rewrite Eq. 9.15 as

$$\mathbf{V} = V_m \cos \phi + jV_m \sin \phi. \qquad (9.16)$$

Both polar and rectangular forms are useful in circuit applications of the phasor concept.

One additional comment regarding Eq. 9.15 is in order. The frequent occurrence of the exponential function $e^{j\phi}$ has led to an abbreviation that lends itself to text material. This abbreviation is the angle notation

$$1\underline{/\phi^\circ} \equiv 1e^{j\phi}.$$

We use this notation extensively in the material that follows.

Inverse Phasor Transform

So far we have emphasized moving from the sinusoidal function to its phasor transform. However, we may also reverse the process. That is, for a phasor we may write the expression for the sinusoidal function. Thus for $\mathbf{V} = 100\underline{/-26°}$, the expression for v is $100\cos(\omega t - 26°)$ because we have decided to use the cosine function for all sinusoids. Observe that we cannot deduce the value of ω from the phasor. The phasor carries only amplitude and phase information. The step of going from the phasor transform to the time-domain expression is referred to as *finding the inverse phasor transform* and is formalized by the equation

$$\mathcal{P}^{-1}\{V_m e^{j\phi}\} = \Re\{V_m e^{j\phi} e^{j\omega t}\}, \tag{9.17}$$

where the notation $\mathcal{P}^{-1}\{V_m e^{j\phi}\}$ is read as "the inverse phasor transform of $V_m e^{j\phi}$." Equation 9.17 indicates that to find the inverse phasor transform, we multiply the phasor by $e^{j\omega t}$ and then extract the real part of the product.

The phasor transform is useful in circuit analysis because it reduces the task of finding the maximum amplitude and phase angle of the steady-state sinusoidal response to the algebra of complex numbers. The following observations verify this conclusion:

1. The transient component vanishes as time elapses, so the steady-state component of the solution must also satisfy the differential equation. (See Problem 9.10[b].)

2. In a linear circuit driven by sinusoidal sources, the steady-state response also is sinusoidal, and the frequency of the sinusoidal response is the same as the frequency of the sinusoidal source.

3. Using the notation introduced in Eq. 9.11, we can postulate that the steady-state solution is of the form $\Re\{Ae^{j\beta}e^{j\omega t}\}$, where A is the maximum amplitude of the response and β is the phase angle of the response.

4. When we substitute the postulated steady-state solution into the differential equation, the exponential term $e^{j\omega t}$ cancels out, leaving the solution for A and β in the domain of complex numbers.

We illustrate these observations with the circuit shown in Fig. 9.5 (see p. 309). We know that the steady-state solution for the current i is of the form

$$i_{ss}(t) = \Re\{I_m e^{j\beta} e^{j\omega t}\}, \tag{9.18}$$

where the subscript "ss" emphasizes that we are dealing with the steady-state solution. When we substitute Eq. 9.18 into Eq. 9.8, we generate the expression

$$\Re\{j\omega L I_m e^{j\beta} e^{j\omega t}\} + \Re\{R I_m e^{j\beta} e^{j\omega t}\} = \Re\{V_m e^{j\phi} e^{j\omega t}\}. \tag{9.19}$$

In deriving Eq. 9.19 we recognized that both differentiation and multiplication by a constant can be taken inside the real part of an operation. We also rewrote the right-hand side of Eq. 9.8, using the notation of Eq. 9.11. From the algebra of complex numbers, we know that the sum of the real parts is the same as the real part of the sum. Therefore we may reduce the left-hand side of Eq. 9.19 to a single term:

$$\Re\{(j\omega L + R)I_m e^{j\beta}e^{j\omega t}\} = \Re\{V_m e^{j\phi}e^{j\omega t}\}. \tag{9.20}$$

Recall that our decision to use the cosine function in analyzing the response of a circuit in the sinusoidal steady state results in the use of the $\Re$ operator in deriving Eq. 9.20. If instead we had chosen to use the sine function in our sinusoidal steady-state analysis, we would have applied Eq. 9.12 directly, in place of Eq. 9.11, and the result would be Eq. 9.21:

$$\Im\{(j\omega L + R)I_m e^{j\beta}e^{j\omega t}\} = \Im\{V_m e^{j\phi}e^{j\omega t}\}. \tag{9.21}$$

Note that the complex quantities on either side of Eq. 9.21 are identical to those on either side of Eq. 9.20. When both the real and imaginary parts of two complex quantities are equal, then the complex quantities are themselves equal. Therefore, from Eqs. 9.20 and 9.21,

$$(j\omega L + R)I_m e^{j\beta} = V_m e^{j\phi},$$

or

$$I_m e^{j\beta} = \frac{V_m e^{j\phi}}{R + j\omega L}. \tag{9.22}$$

Note that $e^{j\omega t}$ has been eliminated from the determination of the amplitude (I_m) and phase angle (β) of the response. Thus, for this circuit, the task of finding I_m and β involves the algebraic manipulation of the complex quantities $V_m e^{j\phi}$ and $R + j\omega L$. Note that we encountered both polar and rectangular forms.

An important warning is in order: The phasor transform, along with the inverse phasor transform, allows you to go back and forth between the time domain and the frequency domain. Therefore, when you obtain a solution, you are either in the time domain or the frequency domain. You cannot be in both domains simultaneously. Any solution that contains a mixture of time domain and phasor domain nomenclature is nonsensical.

The phasor transform is also useful in circuit analysis because it applies directly to the sum of sinusoidal functions. Circuit analysis involves summing currents and voltages, so the importance of this observation is obvious. We can formalize this property as follows: If

$$v = v_1 + v_2 + \cdots + v_n \tag{9.23}$$

where all the voltages on the right-hand side are sinusoidal voltages of the same frequency, then

$$\mathbf{V} = \mathbf{V}_1 + \mathbf{V}_2 + \cdots + \mathbf{V}_n. \tag{9.24}$$

Thus the phasor representation is the sum of the phasors of the individual terms. We discuss the development of Eq. 9.24 in Section 9.5.

Before applying the phasor transform to circuit analysis, we illustrate its usefulness in solving a problem with which you are already familiar: adding sinusoidal functions via trigonometric identities. Example 9.5 shows how the phasor transform greatly simplifies this type of problem.

Example 9.5   **Adding Cosines Using Phasors**

If $y_1 = 20 \cos (\omega t - 30°)$ and $y_2 = 40 \cos (\omega t + 60°)$, express $y = y_1 + y_2$ as a single sinusoidal function.

a) Solve by using trigonometric identities.

b) Solve by using the phasor concept.

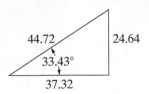

Figure 9.6 ▲ A right triangle used in the solution for y.

Solution

a) First we expand both y_1 and y_2, using the cosine of the sum of two angles, to get

$$y_1 = 20 \cos \omega t \cos 30° + 20 \sin \omega t \sin 30°;$$

$$y_2 = 40 \cos \omega t \cos 60° - 40 \sin \omega t \sin 60°.$$

Adding y_1 and y_2, we obtain

$$y = (20 \cos 30 + 40 \cos 60) \cos \omega t$$

$$+ (20 \sin 30 - 40 \sin 60) \sin \omega t$$

$$= 37.32 \cos \omega t - 24.64 \sin \omega t.$$

To combine these two terms we treat the co-efficients of the cosine and sine as sides of a right triangle (Fig. 9.6) and then multiply and divide the right-hand side by the hypotenuse. Our expression for y becomes

$$y = 44.72 \left(\frac{37.32}{44.72} \cos \omega t - \frac{24.64}{44.72} \sin \omega t \right)$$

$$= 44.72 (\cos 33.43° \cos \omega t - \sin 33.43° \sin \omega t).$$

Again, we invoke the identity involving the cosine of the sum of two angles and write

$$y = 44.72 \cos (\omega t + 33.43°).$$

b) We can solve the problem by using phasors as follows: Because

$$y = y_1 + y_2,$$

then, from Eq. 9.24,

$$\mathbf{Y} = \mathbf{Y}_1 + \mathbf{Y}_2$$

$$= 20\underline{/-30°} + 40\underline{/60°}$$

$$= (17.32 - j10) + (20 + j34.64)$$

$$= 37.32 + j24.64$$

$$= 44.72\underline{/33.43°}.$$

Once we know the phasor $\mathbf{Y}$, we can write the corresponding trigonometric function for y by taking the inverse phasor transform:

$$y = \mathscr{P}^{-1}\{44.72 e^{j33.43}\} = \Re\{44.72 e^{j33.43} e^{j\omega t}\}$$

$$= 44.72 \cos (\omega t + 33.43°).$$

The superiority of the phasor approach for adding sinusoidal functions should be apparent. Note that it requires the ability to move back and forth between the polar and rectangular forms of complex numbers.

✓ASSESSMENT PROBLEMS

Objective 1—Understand phasor concepts and be able to perform a phasor transform and an inverse phasor transform

9.1   Find the phasor transform of each trigonometric function:

a) $v = 170 \cos (377t - 40°)$ V.

b) $i = 10 \sin (1000t + 20°)$ A.

c) $i = [5 \cos (\omega t + 36.87°) + 10 \cos(\omega t - 53.13°)]$ A.

d) $v = [300 \cos (20{,}000\pi t + 45°) - 100 \sin(20{,}000\pi t + 30°)]$ mV.

Answer: (a) $170\underline{/-40°}$ V;

(b) $10\underline{/-70°}$ A;

(c) $11.18\underline{/-26.57°}$ A;

(d) $339.90\underline{/61.51°}$ mV.

9.2   Find the time-domain expression corresponding to each phasor:

a) $\mathbf{V} = 18.6\underline{/-54°}$ V.

b) $\mathbf{I} = (20\underline{/45°} - 50\underline{/-30°})$ mA.

c) $\mathbf{V} = (20 + j80 - 30\underline{/15°})$ V.

Answer: (a) $18.6 \cos (\omega t - 54°)$ V;

(b) $48.81 \cos (\omega t + 126.68°)$ mA;

(c) $72.79 \cos (\omega t + 97.08°)$ V.

NOTE: Also try Chapter Problem 9.11.

9.4 The Passive Circuit Elements in the Frequency Domain

The systematic application of the phasor transform in circuit analysis requires two steps. First, we must establish the relationship between the phasor current and the phasor voltage at the terminals of the passive circuit elements. Second, we must develop the phasor-domain version of Kirchhoff's laws, which we discuss in Section 9.5. In this section, we establish the relationship between the phasor current and voltage at the terminals of the resistor, inductor, and capacitor. We begin with the resistor and use the passive sign convention in all the derivations.

The V-I Relationship for a Resistor

From Ohm's law, if the current in a resistor varies sinusoidally with time— that is, if $i = I_m \cos (\omega t + \theta_i)$—the voltage at the terminals of the resistor, as shown in Fig. 9.7, is

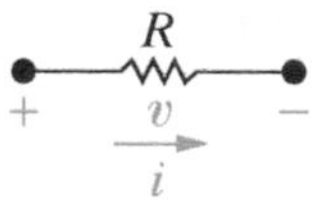

$$v = R[I_m \cos (\omega t + \theta_i)]$$

$$= RI_m[\cos (\omega t + \theta_i)], \qquad (9.25)$$

where I_m is the maximum amplitude of the current in amperes and θ_i is the phase angle of the current.

The phasor transform of this voltage is

$$\mathbf{V} = RI_m e^{j\theta_i} = RI_m\underline{/\theta_i}. \qquad (9.26)$$

But $I_m\underline{/\theta_i}$ is the phasor representation of the sinusoidal current, so we can write Eq. 9.26 as

$$\mathbf{V} = R\mathbf{I}, \qquad (9.27)$$

Figure 9.7 ▲ A resistive element carrying a sinusoidal current.

◀ **Relationship between phasor voltage and phasor current for a resistor**

Figure 9.8 ▲ The frequency-domain equivalent circuit of a resistor.

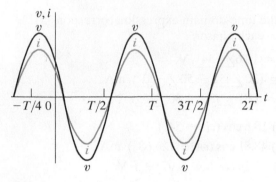

Figure 9.9 ▲ A plot showing that the voltage and current at the terminals of a resistor are in phase.

which states that the phasor voltage at the terminals of a resistor is simply the resistance times the phasor current. Figure 9.8 shows the circuit diagram for a resistor in the frequency domain.

Equations 9.25 and 9.27 both contain another important piece of information—namely, that at the terminals of a resistor, there is no phase shift between the current and voltage. Figure 9.9 depicts this phase relationship, where the phase angle of both the voltage and the current waveforms is 60°. The signals are said to be **in phase** because they both reach corresponding values on their respective curves at the same time (for example, they are at their positive maxima at the same instant).

The V-I Relationship for an Inductor

We derive the relationship between the phasor current and phasor voltage at the terminals of an inductor by assuming a sinusoidal current and using $L\,di/dt$ to establish the corresponding voltage. Thus, for $i = I_m \cos(\omega t + \theta_i)$, the expression for the voltage is

$$v = L\frac{di}{dt} = -\omega L I_m \sin(\omega t + \theta_i).\qquad(9.28)$$

We now rewrite Eq. 9.28 using the cosine function:

$$v = -\omega L I_m \cos(\omega t + \theta_i - 90°).\qquad(9.29)$$

The phasor representation of the voltage given by Eq. 9.29 is

Relationship between phasor voltage and ▶ phasor current for an inductor

$$\begin{aligned}\mathbf{V} &= -\omega L I_m e^{j(\theta_i - 90°)}\\[2mm]
&= -\omega L I_m e^{j\theta_i} e^{-j90°}\\[2mm]
&= j\omega L I_m e^{j\theta_i}\\[2mm]
&= j\omega L\mathbf{I}.\end{aligned}\qquad(9.30)$$

Note that in deriving Eq. 9.30 we used the identity

$$e^{-j90°} = \cos 90° - j\sin 90° = -j.$$

Figure 9.10 ▲ The frequency-domain equivalent circuit for an inductor.

Equation 9.30 states that the phasor voltage at the terminals of an inductor equals $j\omega L$ times the phasor current. Figure 9.10 shows the frequency-domain equivalent circuit for the inductor. It is important to note that the relationship between phasor voltage and phasor current for an inductor applies as well for the mutual inductance in one coil due to current flowing in another mutually coupled coil. That is, the phasor voltage at the terminals of one coil in a mutually coupled pair of coils equals $j\omega M$ times the phasor current in the other coil.

We can rewrite Eq. 9.30 as

$$\mathbf{V} = (\omega L \, \underline{/90^\circ}) I_m \underline{/\theta_i}$$

$$= \omega L I_m \, \underline{/(\theta_i + 90)^\circ}, \tag{9.31}$$

which indicates that the voltage and current are out of phase by exactly 90°. In particular, the voltage leads the current by 90°, or, equivalently, the current lags behind the voltage by 90°. Figure 9.11 illustrates this concept of *voltage leading current* or *current lagging voltage*. For example, the voltage reaches its negative peak exactly 90° before the current reaches its negative peak. The same observation can be made with respect to the zero-going-positive crossing or the positive peak.

We can also express the phase shift in seconds. A phase shift of 90° corresponds to one-fourth of a period; hence the voltage leads the current by $T/4$, or $\frac{1}{4f}$ second.

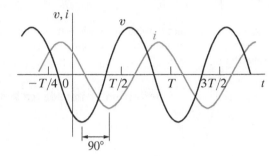

Figure 9.11 ▲ A plot showing the phase relationship between the current and voltage at the terminals of an inductor ($\theta_i = 60^\circ$).

The V-I Relationship for a Capacitor

We obtain the relationship between the phasor current and phasor voltage at the terminals of a capacitor from the derivation of Eq. 9.30. In other words, if we note that for a capacitor that

$$i = C\frac{dv}{dt},$$

and assume that

$$v = V_m \cos(\omega t + \theta_v),$$

then

$$\mathbf{I} = j\omega C \mathbf{V}. \tag{9.32}$$

Now if we solve Eq. 9.32 for the voltage as a function of the current, we get

$$\mathbf{V} = \frac{1}{j\omega C} \mathbf{I}. \tag{9.33}$$

◀ **Relationship between phasor voltage and phasor current for a capacitor**

Equation 9.33 demonstrates that the equivalent circuit for the capacitor in the phasor domain is as shown in Fig. 9.12.

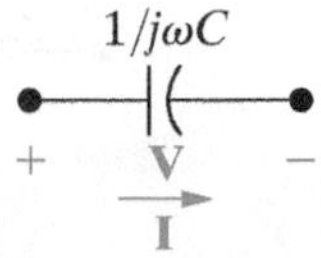

The voltage across the terminals of a capacitor lags behind the current by exactly 90°. We can easily show this relationship by rewriting Eq. 9.33 as

$$\mathbf{V} = \frac{1}{\omega C} \, \underline{/-90^\circ} \, I_m \, \underline{/\theta_i^\circ}$$

$$= \frac{I_m}{\omega C} \, \underline{/(\theta_i - 90)^\circ}. \tag{9.34}$$

Figure 9.12 ▲ The frequency domain equivalent circuit of a capacitor.

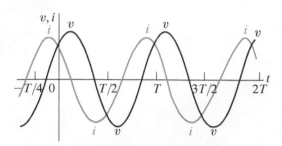

Figure 9.13 ▲ A plot showing the phase relationship between the current and voltage at the terminals of a capacitor ($\theta_i = 60°$).

The alternative way to express the phase relationship contained in Eq. 9.34 is to say that the current leads the voltage by 90°. Figure 9.13 shows the phase relationship between the current and voltage at the terminals of a capacitor.

Impedance and Reactance

We conclude this discussion of passive circuit elements in the frequency domain with an important observation. When we compare Eqs. 9.27, 9.30, and 9.33, we note that they are all of the form

Definition of impedance ▶

$$\mathbf{V} = Z\mathbf{I}, \qquad (9.35)$$

where Z represents the **impedance** of the circuit element. Solving for Z in Eq. 9.35, you can see that impedance is the ratio of a circuit element's voltage phasor to its current phasor. Thus the impedance of a resistor is R, the impedance of an inductor is $j\omega L$, the impedance of mutual inductance is $j\omega M$, and the impedance of a capacitor is $1/j\omega C$. In all cases, impedance is measured in ohms. Note that, although impedance is a complex number, it is not a phasor. Remember, a phasor is a complex number that shows up as the coefficient of $e^{j\omega t}$. Thus, although all phasors are complex numbers, not all complex numbers are phasors.

Impedance in the frequency domain is the quantity analogous to resistance, inductance, and capacitance in the time domain. The imaginary part of the impedance is called **reactance**. The values of impedance and reactance for each of the component values are summarized in Table 9.1.

And finally, a reminder. If the reference direction for the current in a passive circuit element is in the direction of the voltage rise across the element, you must insert a minus sign into the equation that relates the voltage to the current.

TABLE 9.1 Impedance and Reactance Values

Circuit Element	Impedance	Reactance
Resistor	R	—
Inductor	$j\omega L$	ωL
Capacitor	$j(-1/\omega C)$	$-1/\omega C$

✓ ASSESSMENT PROBLEMS

Objective 2—Be able to transform a circuit with a sinusoidal source into the frequency domain using phasor concepts

9.3 The current in the 20 mH inductor is $10\cos(10{,}000t + 30°)$ mA. Calculate (a) the inductive reactance; (b) the impedance of the inductor; (c) the phasor voltage $\mathbf{V}$; and (d) the steady-state expression for $v(t)$.

20 mH

Answer: (a) 200 Ω;
(b) $j200$ Ω;
(c) $2\,\underline{/120°}$ V;
(d) $2\cos(10{,}000t + 120°)$ V.

9.4 The voltage across the terminals of the 5 μF capacitor is $30\cos(4000t + 25°)$ V. Calculate (a) the capacitive reactance; (b) the impedance of the capacitor; (c) the phasor current $\mathbf{I}$; and (d) the steady-state expression for $i(t)$.

5 μF

Answer: (a) -50 Ω;
(b) $-j50$ Ω;
(c) $0.6\,\underline{/115°}$ A;
(d) $0.6\cos(4000t + 115°)$ A.

NOTE: Also try Chapter Problems 9.12 and 9.13.

9.5 Kirchhoff's Laws in the Frequency Domain

We pointed out in Section 9.3, with reference to Eqs. 9.23 and 9.24, that the phasor transform is useful in circuit analysis because it applies to the sum of sinusoidal functions. We illustrated this usefulness in Example 9.5. We now formalize this observation by developing Kirchhoff's laws in the frequency domain.

Kirchhoff's Voltage Law in the Frequency Domain

We begin by assuming that $v_1 - v_n$ represent voltages around a closed path in a circuit. We also assume that the circuit is operating in a sinusoidal steady state. Thus Kirchhoff's voltage law requires that

$$v_1 + v_2 + \cdots + v_n = 0, \tag{9.36}$$

which in the sinusoidal steady state becomes complex

$$V_{m_1} \cos(\omega t + \theta_1) + V_{m_2} \cos(\omega t + \theta_2) + \cdots + V_{m_n} \cos(\omega t + \theta_n) = 0. \tag{9.37}$$

We now use Euler's identity to write Eq. 9.37 as

$$\Re\{V_{m_1} e^{j\theta_1} e^{j\omega t}\} + \Re\{V_{m_2} e^{j\theta_2} e^{j\omega t}\} + \cdots + \Re\{V_{m_n} e^{j\theta_n} e^{j\omega t}\} \tag{9.38}$$

which we rewrite as

$$\Re\{V_{m_1} e^{j\theta_1} e^{j\omega t} + V_{m_2} e^{j\theta_2} e^{j\omega t} + \cdots + V_{m_n} e^{j\theta_n} e^{j\omega t}\} = 0. \tag{9.39}$$

Factoring the term $e^{j\omega t}$ from each term yields

$$\Re\{(V_{m_1} e^{j\theta_1} + V_{m_2} e^{j\theta_2} + \cdots + V_{m_n} e^{j\theta_n}) e^{j\omega t}\} = 0,$$

or

$$\Re\{(\mathbf{V}_1 + \mathbf{V}_2 + \cdots + \mathbf{V}_n) e^{j\omega t}\} = 0. \tag{9.40}$$

But $e^{j\omega t} \neq 0$, so

$$\mathbf{V}_1 + \mathbf{V}_2 + \cdots + \mathbf{V}_n = 0, \tag{9.41}$$

◀ **KVL in the frequency domain**

which is the statement of Kirchhoff's voltage law as it applies to phasor voltages. In other words, Eq. 9.36 applies to a set of sinusoidal voltages in the time domain, and Eq. 9.41 is the equivalent statement in the frequency domain.

Kirchhoff's Current Law in the Frequency Domain

A similar derivation applies to a set of sinusoidal currents. Thus if

$$i_1 + i_2 + \cdots + i_n = 0, \tag{9.42}$$

then

KCL in the frequency domain ▶

$$I_1 + I_2 + \cdots + I_n = 0, \tag{9.43}$$

where $I_1, I_2, \cdots, I_n$ are the phasor representations of the individual currents $i_1, i_2, \cdots, i_n$.

Equations 9.35, 9.41, and 9.43 form the basis for circuit analysis in the frequency domain. Note that Eq. 9.35 has the same algebraic form as Ohm's law, and that Eqs. 9.41 and 9.43 state Kirchhoff's laws for phasor quantities. Therefore you may use all the techniques developed for analyzing resistive circuits to find phasor currents and voltages. You need learn no new analytic techniques; the basic circuit analysis and simplification tools covered in Chapters 2–4 can all be used to analyze circuits in the frequency domain. Phasor circuit analysis consists of two fundamental tasks: (1) You must be able to construct the frequency-domain model of a circuit; and (2) you must be able to manipulate complex numbers and/or quantities algebraically. We illustrate these aspects of phasor analysis in the discussion that follows, beginning with series, parallel, and delta-to-wye simplifications.

✓ ASSESSMENT PROBLEM

Objective 3—Know how to use circuit analysis techniques to solve a circuit in the frequency domain

9.5 Four branches terminate at a common node. The reference direction of each branch current ($i_1, i_2, i_3,$ and i_4) is toward the node. If

$i_1 = 100 \cos(\omega t + 25°)$ A,
$i_2 = 100 \cos(\omega t + 145°)$ A, and
$i_3 = 100 \cos(\omega t - 95°)$ A, find i_4.

NOTE: Also try Chapter Problem 9.15.

Answer: $i_4 = 0$.

9.6 Series, Parallel, and Delta-to-Wye Simplifications

The rules for combining impedances in series or parallel and for making delta-to-wye transformations are the same as those for resistors. The only difference is that combining impedances involves the algebraic manipulation of complex numbers.

Combining Impedances in Series and Parallel

Impedances in series can be combined into a single impedance by simply adding the individual impedances. The circuit shown in Fig. 9.14 defines the problem in general terms. The impedances $Z_1, Z_2, \cdots, Z_n$ are connected in series between terminals a,b. When impedances are in series, they carry the same phasor current **I**. From Eq. 9.35, the voltage drop across each impedance is $Z_1\mathbf{I}, Z_2\mathbf{I}, \cdots, Z_n\mathbf{I}$, and from Kirchhoff's voltage law,

$$\mathbf{V}_{ab} = Z_1\mathbf{I} + Z_2\mathbf{I} + \cdots + Z_n\mathbf{I}$$
$$= (Z_1 + Z_2 + \cdots + Z_n)\mathbf{I}. \tag{9.44}$$

The equivalent impedance between terminals a,b is

$$Z_{ab} = \frac{\mathbf{V}_{ab}}{\mathbf{I}} = Z_1 + Z_2 + \cdots + Z_n. \tag{9.45}$$

Example 9.6 illustrates a numerical application of Eq. 9.45.

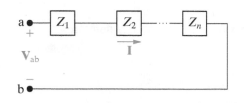

Figure 9.14 ▲ Impedances in series.

Example 9.6   **Combining Impedances in Series**

A 90 Ω resistor, a 32 mH inductor, and a 5 μF capacitor are connected in series across the terminals of a sinusoidal voltage source, as shown in Fig. 9.15. The steady-state expression for the source voltage v_s is 750 cos (5000t + 30°) V.

a) Construct the frequency-domain equivalent circuit.

b) Calculate the steady-state current i by the phasor method.

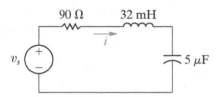

Figure 9.15 ▲ The circuit for Example 9.6.

Solution

a) From the expression for v_s, we have $\omega = 5000$ rad/s. Therefore the impedance of the 32 mH inductor is

$$Z_L = j\omega L = j(5000)(32 \times 10^{-3}) = j160 \ \Omega,$$

and the impedance of the capacitor is

$$Z_C = j\frac{-1}{\omega C} = -j\frac{10^6}{(5000)(5)} = -j40 \ \Omega.$$

The phasor transform of v_s is

$$\mathbf{V}_s = 750 \underline{/30°} \text{ V}.$$

Figure 9.16 illustrates the frequency-domain equivalent circuit of the circuit shown in Fig. 9.15.

b) We compute the phasor current simply by dividing the voltage of the voltage source by the equivalent impedance between the terminals a,b. From Eq. 9.45,

$$Z_{ab} = 90 + j160 - j40$$
$$= 90 + j120 = 150\underline{/53.13°} \ \Omega.$$

Thus

$$\mathbf{I} = \frac{750\underline{/30°}}{150\underline{/53.13°}} = 5\underline{/-23.13°} \text{ A}.$$

We may now write the steady-state expression for i directly:

$$i = 5 \cos (5000t - 23.13°) \text{ A}.$$

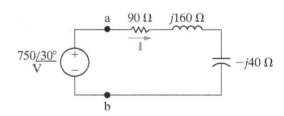

Figure 9.16 ▲ The frequency-domain equivalent circuit of the circuit shown in Fig. 9.15.

✓ **ASSESSMENT PROBLEM**

Objective 3—Know how to use circuit analysis techniques to solve a circuit in the frequency domain

9.6   Using the values of resistance and inductance in the circuit of Fig. 9.15, let $\mathbf{V}_s = 125\underline{/-60°}$ V and $\omega = 5000$ rad/s. Find

a) the value of capacitance that yields a steady-state output current i with a phase angle of −105°.

b) the magnitude of the steady-state output current i.

Answer: (a) 2.86 μF;

(b) 0.982 A.

NOTE: Also try Chapter Problem 9.17.

Impedances connected in parallel may be reduced to a single equivalent impedance by the reciprocal relationship

$$\frac{1}{Z_{ab}} = \frac{1}{Z_1} + \frac{1}{Z_2} + \cdots + \frac{1}{Z_n}. \tag{9.46}$$

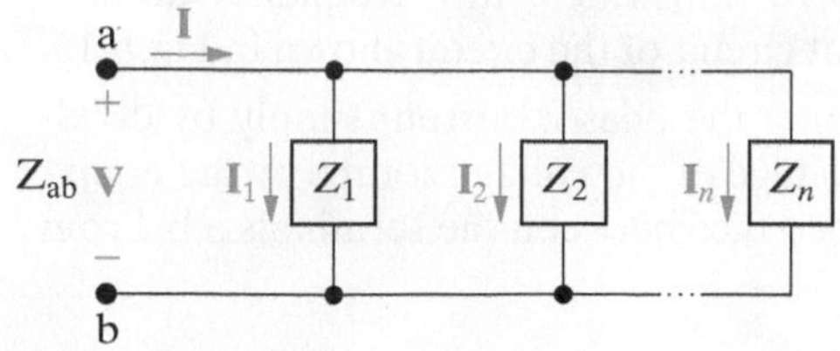

Figure 9.17 ▲ Impedances in parallel.

Figure 9.17 depicts the parallel connection of impedances. Note that when impedances are in parallel, they have the same voltage across their terminals. We derive Eq. 9.46 directly from Fig. 9.17 by simply combining Kirchhoff's current law with the phasor-domain version of Ohm's law, that is, Eq. 9.35. From Fig. 9.17,

$$\mathbf{I} = \mathbf{I}_1 + \mathbf{I}_2 + \cdots + \mathbf{I}_n,$$

or

$$\frac{\mathbf{V}}{Z_{ab}} = \frac{\mathbf{V}}{Z_1} + \frac{\mathbf{V}}{Z_2} + \cdots + \frac{\mathbf{V}}{Z_n}. \tag{9.47}$$

Canceling the common voltage term out of Eq. 9.47 reveals Eq. 9.46.

From Eq. 9.46, for the special case of just two impedances in parallel,

$$Z_{ab} = \frac{Z_1 Z_2}{Z_1 + Z_2}. \tag{9.48}$$

We can also express Eq. 9.46 in terms of **admittance**, defined as the reciprocal of impedance and denoted Y. Thus

$$Y = \frac{1}{Z} = G + jB \text{ (siemens)}. \tag{9.49}$$

Admittance is, of course, a complex number, whose real part, G, is called **conductance** and whose imaginary part, B, is called **susceptance**. Like admittance, conductance and susceptance are measured in siemens (S). Using Eq. 9.49 in Eq. 9.46, we get

$$Y_{ab} = Y_1 + Y_2 + \cdots + Y_n. \tag{9.50}$$

The admittance of each of the ideal passive circuit elements also is worth noting and is summarized in Table 9.2.

Example 9.7 illustrates the application of Eqs. 9.49 and 9.50 to a specific circuit.

TABLE 9.2   **Admittance and Susceptance Values**

Circuit Element	Admittance (Y)	Susceptance
Resistor	G (conductance)	—
Inductor	$j(-1/\omega L)$	$-1/\omega L$
Capacitor	$j\omega C$	ωC

| Example 9.7 | **Combining Impedances in Series and in Parallel** |

The sinusoidal current source in the circuit shown in Fig. 9.18 produces the current $i_s = 8\cos 200{,}000t$ A.

a) Construct the frequency-domain equivalent circuit.

b) Find the steady-state expressions for v, i_1, i_2, and i_3.

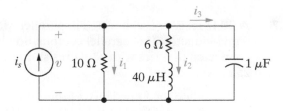

Figure 9.18 ▲ The circuit for Example 9.7.

Solution

a) The phasor transform of the current source is $8\underline{/0°}$; the resistors transform directly to the frequency domain as 10 and 6 Ω; the 40 μH inductor has an impedance of $j8$ Ω at the given frequency of 200,000 rad/s; and at this frequency the 1 μF capacitor has an impedance of $-j5$ Ω. Figure 9.19 shows the frequency-domain equivalent circuit and symbols representing the phasor transforms of the unknowns.

b) The circuit shown in Fig. 9.19 indicates that we can easily obtain the voltage across the current source once we know the equivalent impedance of the three parallel branches. Moreover, once we know **V**, we can calculate the three phasor currents $\mathbf{I}_1$, $\mathbf{I}_2$, and $\mathbf{I}_3$ by using Eq. 9.35. To find the equivalent impedance of the three branches, we first find the equivalent admittance simply by adding the admittances of each branch. The admittance of the first branch is

$$Y_1 = \frac{1}{10} = 0.1 \text{ S},$$

the admittance of the second branch is

$$Y_2 = \frac{1}{6 + j8} = \frac{6 - j8}{100} = 0.06 - j0.08 \text{ S},$$

and the admittance of the third branch is

$$Y_3 = \frac{1}{-j5} = j0.2 \text{ S}.$$

The admittance of the three branches is

$$Y = Y_1 + Y_2 + Y_3$$
$$= 0.16 + j0.12$$
$$= 0.2\underline{/36.87°} \text{ S}.$$

The impedance at the current source is

$$Z = \frac{1}{Y} = 5\underline{/-36.87°} \ \Omega.$$

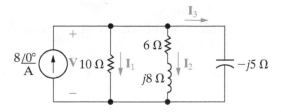

Figure 9.19 ▲ The frequency-domain equivalent circuit.

The Voltage **V** is

$$\mathbf{V} = \mathbf{ZI} = 40\underline{/-36.87°} \text{ V}.$$

Hence

$$\mathbf{I}_1 = \frac{40\underline{/-36.87°}}{10} = 4\underline{/-36.87°} = 3.2 - j2.4 \text{ A},$$

$$\mathbf{I}_2 = \frac{40\underline{/-36.87°}}{6 + j8} = 4\underline{/-90°} = -j4 \text{ A},$$

and

$$\mathbf{I}_3 = \frac{40\underline{/-36.87°}}{5\underline{/-90°}} = 8\underline{/53.13°} = 4.8 + j6.4 \text{ A}.$$

We check the computations at this point by verifying that

$$\mathbf{I}_1 + \mathbf{I}_2 + \mathbf{I}_3 = \mathbf{I}.$$

Specifically,

$$3.2 - j2.4 - j4 + 4.8 + j6.4 = 8 + j0.$$

The corresponding steady-state time-domain expressions are

$$v = 40\cos(200{,}000t - 36.87°) \text{ V},$$
$$i_1 = 4\cos(200{,}000t - 36.87°) \text{ A},$$
$$i_2 = 4\cos(200{,}000t - 90°) \text{ A},$$
$$i_3 = 8\cos(200{,}000t + 53.13°) \text{ A}.$$

✓ ASSESSMENT PROBLEMS

Objective 3—Know how to use circuit analysis techniques to solve a circuit in the frequency domain

9.7 A 20 Ω resistor is connected in parallel with a 5 mH inductor. This parallel combination is connected in series with a 5 Ω resistor and a 25 μF capacitor.

    a) Calculate the impedance of this interconnection if the frequency is 2 krad/s.

    b) Repeat (a) for a frequency of 8 krad/s.

    c) At what finite frequency does the impedance of the interconnection become purely resistive?

    d) What is the impedance at the frequency found in (c)?

Answer: (a) $9 - j12 \; \Omega$;
            (b) $21 + j3 \; \Omega$;
            (c) 4 krad/s;
            (d) $15 \; \Omega$.

9.8 The interconnection described in Assessment Problem 9.7 is connected across the terminals of a voltage source that is generating $v = 150 \cos 4000t$ V. What is the maximum amplitude of the current in the 5 mH inductor?

Answer: 7.07 A.

NOTE: *Also try Chapter Problems 9.29, 9.34, and 9.35.*

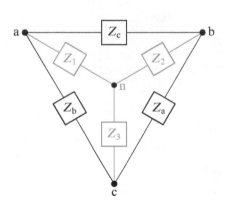

Figure 9.20 ▲ The delta-to-wye transformation.

Delta-to-Wye Transformations

The Δ-to-Y transformation that we discussed in Section 3.7 with regard to resistive circuits also applies to impedances. Figure 9.20 defines the Δ-connected impedances along with the Y-equivalent circuit. The Y impedances as functions of the Δ impedances are

$$Z_1 = \frac{Z_b Z_c}{Z_a + Z_b + Z_c}, \tag{9.51}$$

$$Z_2 = \frac{Z_c Z_a}{Z_a + Z_b + Z_c}, \tag{9.52}$$

$$Z_3 = \frac{Z_a Z_b}{Z_a + Z_b + Z_c}. \tag{9.53}$$

The Δ-to-Y transformation also may be reversed; that is, we can start with the Y structure and replace it with an equivalent Δ structure. The Δ impedances as functions of the Y impedances are

$$Z_a = \frac{Z_1 Z_2 + Z_2 Z_3 + Z_3 Z_1}{Z_1}, \tag{9.54}$$

$$Z_b = \frac{Z_1 Z_2 + Z_2 Z_3 + Z_3 Z_1}{Z_2}, \tag{9.55}$$

$$Z_c = \frac{Z_1 Z_2 + Z_2 Z_3 + Z_3 Z_1}{Z_3}. \tag{9.56}$$

The process used to derive Eqs. 9.51–9.53 or Eqs. 9.54–9.56 is the same as that used to derive the corresponding equations for pure resistive circuits. In fact, comparing Eqs. 3.44–3.46 with Eqs. 9.51–9.53, and Eqs. 3.47–3.49 with Eqs. 9.54–9.56, reveals that the symbol Z has replaced the symbol R. You may want to review Problem 3.62 concerning the derivation of the Δ-to-Y transformation.

Example 9.8 illustrates the usefulness of the Δ-to-Y transformation in phasor circuit analysis.

Example 9.8   Using a Delta-to-Wye Transform in the Frequency Domain

Use a Δ-to-Y impedance transformation to find $\mathbf{I}_0$, $\mathbf{I}_1$, $\mathbf{I}_2$, $\mathbf{I}_3$, $\mathbf{I}_4$, $\mathbf{I}_5$, $\mathbf{V}_1$, and $\mathbf{V}_2$ in the circuit in Fig. 9.21.

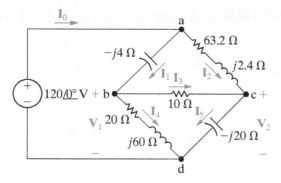

Figure 9.21 ▲ The circuit for Example 9.8.

Solution

First note that the circuit is not amenable to series or parallel simplification as it now stands. A Δ-to-Y impedance transformation allows us to solve for all the branch currents without resorting to either the node-voltage or the mesh-current method. If we replace either the upper delta (abc) or the lower delta (bcd) with its Y equivalent, we can further simplify the resulting circuit by series-parallel combinations. In deciding which delta to replace, the sum of the impedances around each delta is worth checking because this quantity forms the denominator for the equivalent Y impedances. The sum around the lower delta is $30 + j40$, so we choose to eliminate it from the circuit. The Y impedance connecting to terminal b is

$$Z_1 = \frac{(20 + j60)(10)}{30 + j40} = 12 + j4\,\Omega,$$

the Y impedance connecting to terminal c is

$$Z_2 = \frac{10(-j20)}{30 + j40} = -3.2 - j2.4\ \Omega,$$

and the Y impedance connecting to terminal d is

$$Z_3 = \frac{(20 + j60)(-j20)}{30 + j40} = 8 - j24\ \Omega.$$

Inserting the Y-equivalent impedances into the circuit, we get the circuit shown in Fig 9.22, which we can now simplify by series-parallel reductions. The impedence of the abn branch is

$$Z_{abn} = 12 + j4 - j4 = 12\ \Omega,$$

and the impedance of the acn branch is

$$Z_{acn} = 63.2 + j2.4 - j2.4 - 3.2 = 60\ \Omega.$$

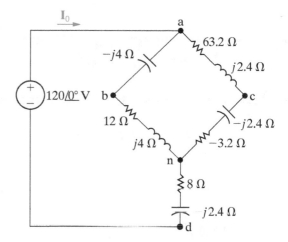

Figure 9.22 ▲ The circuit shown in Fig. 9.21, with the lower delta replaced by its equivalent wye.

Note that the abn branch is in parallel with the acn branch. Therefore we may replace these two branches with a single branch having an impedance of

$$Z_{an} = \frac{(60)(12)}{72} = 10\ \Omega.$$

Combining this $10\ \Omega$ resistor with the impedance between n and d reduces the circuit shown in Fig. 9.22 to the one shown in Fig. 9.23. From the latter circuit,

$$\mathbf{I}_0 = \frac{120\ \angle 0^\circ}{18 - j24} = 4\ \angle 53.13^\circ = 2.4 + j3.2\ A.$$

Once we know $\mathbf{I}_0$, we can work back through the equivalent circuits to find the branch currents in the original circuit. We begin by noting that $\mathbf{I}_0$ is the current in the branch nd of Fig. 9.22. Therefore

$$\mathbf{V}_{nd} = (8 - j24)\mathbf{I}_0 = 96 - j32\ V.$$

We may now calculate the voltage $\mathbf{V}_{an}$ because

$$\mathbf{V} = \mathbf{V}_{an} + \mathbf{V}_{nd}$$

and both $\mathbf{V}$ and $\mathbf{V}_{nd}$ are known. Thus

$$\mathbf{V}_{an} = 120 - 96 + j32 = 24 + j32 \text{ V}.$$

We now compute the branch currents $\mathbf{I}_{abn}$ and $\mathbf{I}_{acn}$:

$$\mathbf{I}_{abn} = \frac{24 + j32}{12} = 2 + j\frac{8}{3} \text{ A},$$

$$\mathbf{I}_{acn} = \frac{24 + j32}{60} = \frac{4}{10} + j\frac{8}{15} \text{ A}.$$

In terms of the branch currents defined in Fig. 9.21,

$$\mathbf{I}_1 = \mathbf{I}_{abn} = 2 + j\frac{8}{3} \text{ A},$$

$$\mathbf{I}_2 = \mathbf{I}_{acn} = \frac{4}{10} + j\frac{8}{15} \text{ A}.$$

We check the calculations of $\mathbf{I}_1$ and $\mathbf{I}_2$ by noting that

$$\mathbf{I}_1 + \mathbf{I}_2 = 2.4 + j3.2 = \mathbf{I}_0.$$

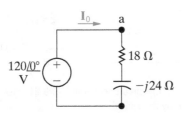

Figure 9.23 ▲ A simplified version of the circuit shown in Fig. 9.22.

To find the branch currents $\mathbf{I}_3$, $\mathbf{I}_4$, and $\mathbf{I}_5$, we must first calculate the voltages $\mathbf{V}_1$ and $\mathbf{V}_2$. Refering to Fig. 9.21, we note that

$$\mathbf{V}_1 = 120\,\underline{/0°} - (-j4)\mathbf{I}_1 = \frac{328}{3} + j8 \text{ V},$$

$$\mathbf{V}_2 = 120\,\underline{/0°} - (63.2 + j2.4)\mathbf{I}_2 = 96 - j\frac{104}{3} \text{ V}.$$

We now calculate the branch currents $\mathbf{I}_3$, $\mathbf{I}_4$, and $\mathbf{I}_5$:

$$\mathbf{I}_3 = \frac{\mathbf{V}_1 - \mathbf{V}_2}{10} = \frac{4}{3} + j\frac{12.8}{3} \text{ A},$$

$$\mathbf{I}_4 = \frac{\mathbf{V}_1}{20 + j60} = \frac{2}{3} - j1.6 \text{ A},$$

$$\mathbf{I}_5 = \frac{\mathbf{V}_2}{-j20} = \frac{26}{15} + j4.8 \text{ A}.$$

We check the calculations by noting that

$$\mathbf{I}_4 + \mathbf{I}_5 = \frac{2}{3} + \frac{26}{15} - j1.6 + j4.8 = 2.4 + j3.2 = \mathbf{I}_0,$$

$$\mathbf{I}_3 + \mathbf{I}_4 = \frac{4}{3} + \frac{2}{3} + j\frac{12.8}{3} - j1.6 = 2 + j\frac{8}{3} = \mathbf{I}_1,$$

$$\mathbf{I}_3 + \mathbf{I}_2 = \frac{4}{3} + \frac{4}{10} + j\frac{12.8}{3} + j\frac{8}{15} = \frac{26}{15} + j4.8 = \mathbf{I}_5.$$

✓ ASSESSMENT PROBLEM

Objective 3—Know how to use circuit analysis techniques to solve a circuit in the frequency domain

9.9   Use a Δ-to-Y transformation to find the current **I** in the circuit shown.

Answer: $\mathbf{I} = 4\,\underline{/28.07°}$ A.

NOTE: Also try Chapter Problem 9.42.

9.7 Source Transformations and Thévenin-Norton Equivalent Circuits

The source transformations introduced in Section 4.9 and the Thévenin-Norton equivalent circuits discussed in Section 4.10 are analytical techniques that also can be applied to frequency-domain circuits. We prove the validity of these techniques by following the same process used in Sections 4.9 and 4.10, except that we substitute impedance (Z) for resistance (R). Figure 9.24 shows a source-transformation equivalent circuit with the nomenclature of the frequency domain.

Figure 9.25 illustrates the frequency-domain version of a Thévenin equivalent circuit. Figure 9.26 shows the frequency-domain equivalent of a Norton equivalent circuit. The techniques for finding the Thévenin equivalent voltage and impedance are identical to those used for resistive circuits, except that the frequency-domain equivalent circuit involves the manipulation of complex quantities. The same holds for finding the Norton equivalent current and impedance.

Example 9.9 demonstrates the application of the source-transformation equivalent circuit to frequency-domain analysis. Example 9.10 illustrates the details of finding a Thévenin equivalent circuit in the frequency domain.

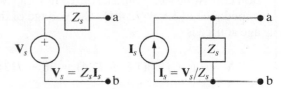

Figure 9.24 ▲ A source transformation in the frequency domain.

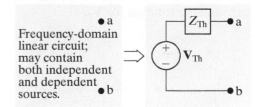

Figure 9.25 ▲ The frequency-domain version of a Thévenin equivalent circuit.

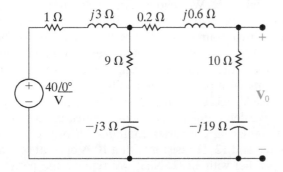

Figure 9.26 ▲ The frequency-domain version of a Norton equivalent circuit.

Example 9.9   **Performing Source Transformations in the Frequency Domain**

Use the concept of source transformation to find the phasor voltage V_0 in the circuit shown in Fig. 9.27.

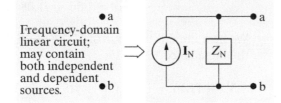

Figure 9.27 ▲ The circuit for Example 9.9.

Solution

We can replace the series combination of the voltage source $(40 \underline{/0°})$ and the impedance of $1 + j3\ \Omega$ with the parallel combination of a current source and the $1 + j3\ \Omega$ impedance. The source current is

$$\mathbf{I} = \frac{40}{1 + j3} = \frac{40}{10}(1 - j3) = 4 - j12 \text{ A.}$$

Thus we can modify the circuit shown in Fig. 9.27 to the one shown in Fig. 9.28. Note that the polarity reference of the 40 V source determines the reference direction for $\mathbf{I}$.

Next, we combine the two parallel branches into a single impedance,

$$Z = \frac{(1 + j3)(9 - j3)}{10} = 1.8 + j2.4\ \Omega,$$

which is in parallel with the current source of $4 - j12$ A. Another source transformation converts this parallel combination to a series combination consisting of a voltage source in series with the impedance of $1.8 + j2.4 \, \Omega$. The voltage of the voltage source is

$$\mathbf{V} = (4 - j12)(1.8 + j2.4) = 36 - j12 \text{ V}.$$

Using this source transformation, we redraw the circuit as Fig. 9.29. Note the polarity of the voltage source. We added the current $\mathbf{I}_0$ to the circuit to expedite the solution for $\mathbf{V}_0$.

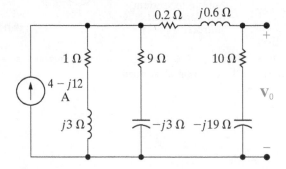

Figure 9.28 ▲ The first step in reducing the circuit shown in Fig. 9.27.

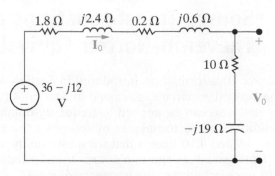

Figure 9.29 ▲ The second step in reducing the circuit shown in Fig. 9.27.

Also note that we have reduced the circuit to a simple series circuit. We calculate the current $\mathbf{I}_0$ by dividing the voltage of the source by the total series impedance:

$$\mathbf{I}_0 = \frac{36 - j12}{12 - j16} = \frac{12(3 - j1)}{4(3 - j4)}$$

$$= \frac{39 + j27}{25} = 1.56 + j1.08 \text{ A}.$$

We now obtain the value of $\mathbf{V}_0$ by multiplying $\mathbf{I}_0$ by the impedance $10 - j19$:

$$\mathbf{V}_0 = (1.56 + j1.08)(10 - j19) = 36.12 - j18.84 \text{ V}.$$

Example 9.10   Finding a Thévenin Equivalent in the Frequency Domain

Find the Thévenin equivalent circuit with respect to terminals a,b for the circuit shown in Fig. 9.30.

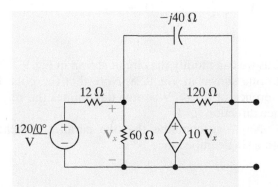

Figure 9.30 ▲ The circuit for Example 9.10.

Solution

We first determine the Thévenin equivalent voltage. This voltage is the open-circuit voltage appearing at terminals a,b. We choose the reference for the Thévenin voltage as positive at terminal a. We can make two source transformations relative to the 120 V, 12 Ω, and 60 Ω circuit elements to simplify this portion of the circuit. At the same time, these transformations must preserve the identity of the controlling voltage $\mathbf{V}_x$ because of the dependent voltage source.

We determine the two source transformations by first replacing the series combination of the 120 V source and 12 Ω resistor with a 10 A current source in parallel with 12 Ω. Next, we replace the parallel combination of the 12 and 60 Ω resistors with a single 10 Ω resistor. Finally, we replace the 10 A source in parallel with 10 Ω with a 100 V source in series with 10 Ω. Figure 9.31 shows the resulting circuit.

We added the current $\mathbf{I}$ to Fig. 9.31 to aid further discussion. Note that once we know the current

I, we can compute the Thévenin voltage. We find **I** by summing the voltages around the closed path in the circuit shown in Fig. 9.31. Hence

$$100 = 10\mathbf{I} - j40\mathbf{I} + 120\mathbf{I} + 10\mathbf{V}_x = (130 - j40)\mathbf{I} + 10\mathbf{V}_x.$$

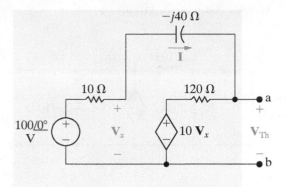

Figure 9.31 ▲ A simplified version of the circuit shown in Fig. 9.30.

We relate the controlling voltage $\mathbf{V}_x$ to the current **I** by noting from Fig. 9.31 that

$$\mathbf{V}_x = 100 - 10\mathbf{I}.$$

Then,

$$\mathbf{I} = \frac{-900}{30 - j40} = 18\ \underline{/-126.87°}\ \text{A}.$$

we now calculate $\mathbf{V}_x$:

$$\mathbf{V}_x = 100 - 180\ \underline{/-126.87°} - 208 + j144\ \text{V}.$$

Finally, we note from Fig. 9.31 that

$$\mathbf{V}_{\text{Th}} = 10\mathbf{V}_x + 120\mathbf{I}$$

$$= 2080 + j1440 + 120(18)\ \underline{/-126.87°}$$

$$= 784 - j288 = 835.22\ \underline{/-20.17°}\ \text{V}.$$

To obtain the Thévenin impedance, we may use any of the techniques previously used to find the Thévenin resistance. We illustrate the test-source method in this example. Recall that in using this method, we deactivate all independent sources from the circuit and then apply either a test voltage source or a test current source to the terminals of interest. The ratio of the voltage to the current at the source is the Thévenin imped-ance. Figure 9.32 shows the result of applying this technique to the circuit shown in Fig. 9.30. Note that we chose a test voltage source $\mathbf{V}_T$. Also note that we deactivated the independent voltage source with an appropriate short-circuit and pre-served the identity of $\mathbf{V}_x$.

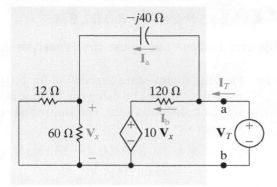

Figure 9.32 ▲ A circuit for calculating the Thévenin equivalent impedance.

The branch currents $\mathbf{I}_a$ and $\mathbf{I}_b$ have been added to the circuit to simplify the calculation of $\mathbf{I}_T$. By straightforward applications of Kirchhoff's circuit laws, you should be able to verify the following relationships:

$$\mathbf{I}_a = \frac{\mathbf{V}_T}{10 - j40}, \quad \mathbf{V}_x = 10\mathbf{I}_a,$$

$$\mathbf{I}_b = \frac{\mathbf{V}_T - 10\mathbf{V}_x}{120}$$

$$= \frac{-\mathbf{V}_T(9 + j4)}{120(1 - j4)},$$

$$\mathbf{I}_T = \mathbf{I}_a + \mathbf{I}_b$$

$$= \frac{\mathbf{V}_T}{10 - j40}\left(1 - \frac{9 + j4}{12}\right)$$

$$= \frac{\mathbf{V}_T(3 - j4)}{12(10 - j40)},$$

$$Z_{\text{Th}} = \frac{\mathbf{V}_T}{\mathbf{I}_T} = 91.2 - j38.4\ \Omega.$$

Figure 9.33 depicts the Thévenin equivalent circuit.

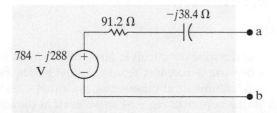

Figure 9.33 ▲ The Thévenin equivalent for the circuit shown in Fig. 9.30.

✓**ASSESSMENT PROBLEMS**

Objective 3—Know how to use circuit analysis techniques to solve a circuit in the frequency domain

9.10 Find the steady-state expression for $v_o(t)$ in the circuit shown by using the technique of source transformations. The sinusoidal voltage sources are

$$v_1 = 240 \cos (4000t + 53.13°) \text{ V},$$
$$v_2 = 96 \sin 4000t \text{ V}.$$

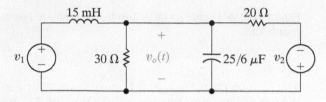

Answer: $48 \cos (4000t + 36.87°) \text{ V}$

NOTE: *Also try Chapter Problems 9.44, 9.45, and 9.48.*

9.11 Find the Thévenin equivalent with respect to terminals a,b in the circuit shown.

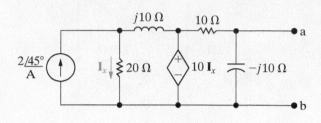

Answer: $\mathbf{V}_{Th} = \mathbf{V}_{ab} = 10 \underline{/45°} \text{ V};$
$Z_{Th} = 5 - j5 \ \Omega.$

9.8 The Node-Voltage Method

In Sections 4.2–4.4, we introduced the basic concepts of the node-voltage method of circuit analysis. The same concepts apply when we use the node-voltage method to analyze frequency-domain circuits. Example 9.11 illustrates the solution of such a circuit by the node-voltage technique. Assessment Problem 9.12 and many of the Chapter Problems give you an opportunity to use the node-voltage method to solve for steady-state sinusoidal responses.

Example 9.11 Using the Node-Voltage Method in the Frequency Domain

Use the node-voltage method to find the branch currents $\mathbf{I}_a$, $\mathbf{I}_b$, and $\mathbf{I}_c$ in the circuit shown in Fig. 9.34.

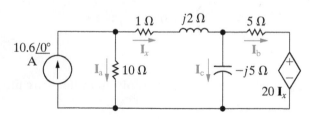

Figure 9.34 ▲ The circuit for Example 9.11.

Solution

We can describe the circuit in terms of two node voltages because it contains three essential nodes. Four branches terminate at the essential node that stretches across the bottom of Fig. 9.34, so we use it as the reference node. The remaining two essential nodes are labeled 1 and 2, and the appropriate node voltages are designated $\mathbf{V}_1$ and $\mathbf{V}_2$. Figure 9.35 reflects the choice of reference node and the terminal labels.

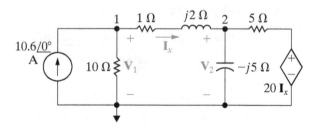

Figure 9.35 ▲ The circuit shown in Fig. 9.34, with the node voltages defined.

Summing the currents away from node 1 yields

$$-10.6 + \frac{\mathbf{V}_1}{10} + \frac{\mathbf{V}_1 - \mathbf{V}_2}{1 + j2} = 0.$$

Multiplying by $1 + j2$ and collecting the coefficients of $\mathbf{V}_1$ and $\mathbf{V}_2$ generates the expression

$$\mathbf{V}_1(1.1 + j0.2) - \mathbf{V}_2 = 10.6 + j21.2.$$

Summing the currents away from node 2 gives

$$\frac{\mathbf{V}_2 - \mathbf{V}_1}{1 + j2} + \frac{\mathbf{V}_2}{-j5} + \frac{\mathbf{V}_2 - 20\mathbf{I}_x}{5} = 0.$$

The controlling current $\mathbf{I}_x$ is

$$\mathbf{I}_x = \frac{\mathbf{V}_1 - \mathbf{V}_2}{1 + j2}.$$

Substituting this expression for $\mathbf{I}_x$ into the node 2 equation, multiplying by $1 + j2$, and collecting coefficients of $\mathbf{V}_1$ and $\mathbf{V}_2$ produces the equation

$$-5\mathbf{V}_1 + (4.8 + j0.6)\mathbf{V}_2 = 0.$$

The solutions for $\mathbf{V}_1$ and $\mathbf{V}_2$ are

$$\mathbf{V}_1 = 68.40 - j16.80 \text{ V},$$
$$\mathbf{V}_2 = 68 - j26 \text{ V}.$$

Hence the branch currents are

$$\mathbf{I}_a = \frac{\mathbf{V}_1}{10} = 6.84 - j1.68 \text{ A},$$

$$\mathbf{I}_x = \frac{\mathbf{V}_1 - \mathbf{V}_2}{1 + j2} = 3.76 + j1.68 \text{ A},$$

$$\mathbf{I}_b = \frac{\mathbf{V}_2 - 20\mathbf{I}_x}{5} = -1.44 - j11.92 \text{ A},$$

$$\mathbf{I}_c = \frac{\mathbf{V}_2}{-j5} = 5.2 + j13.6 \text{ A}.$$

To check our work, we note that

$$\mathbf{I}_a + \mathbf{I}_x = 6.84 - j1.68 + 3.76 + j1.68$$
$$= 10.6 \text{ A},$$
$$\mathbf{I}_x = \mathbf{I}_b + \mathbf{I}_c = -1.44 - j11.92 + 5.2 + j13.6$$
$$= 3.76 + j1.68 \text{ A}.$$

✓ ASSESSMENT PROBLEM

Objective 3—Know how to use circuit analysis techniques to solve a circuit in the frequency domain

9.12   Use the node-voltage method to find the steady-state expression for $v(t)$ in the circuit shown. The sinusoidal sources are $i_s = 10 \cos \omega t$ A and $v_s = 100 \sin \omega t$ V, where $\omega = 50$ krad/s.

Answer: $v(t) = 31.62 \cos(50{,}000t - 71.57°)$ V.

NOTE: Also try Chapter Problems 9.54 and 9.58.

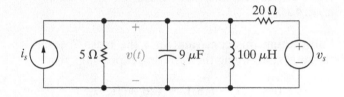

9.9   The Mesh-Current Method

We can also use the mesh-current method to analyze frequency-domain circuits. The procedures used in frequency-domain applications are the same as those used in analyzing resistive circuits. In Sections 4.5–4.7, we introduced the basic techniques of the mesh-current method; we demonstrate the extension of this method to frequency-domain circuits in Example 9.12.

Example 9.12   **Using the Mesh-Current Method in the Frequency Domain**

Use the mesh-current method to find the voltages $\mathbf{V}_1, \mathbf{V}_2,$ and $\mathbf{V}_3$ in the circuit shown in Fig. 9.36 on the next page.

Solution

The circuit has two meshes and a dependent voltage source, so we must write two mesh-current equations and a constraint equation. The reference direction for the mesh currents $\mathbf{I}_1$ and $\mathbf{I}_2$ is clockwise, as shown in Fig. 9.37. Once we know $\mathbf{I}_1$ and $\mathbf{I}_2$, we can easily find the unknown voltages. Summing the voltages around mesh 1 gives

$$150 = (1 + j2)\mathbf{I}_1 + (12 - j16)(\mathbf{I}_1 - \mathbf{I}_2),$$

or

$$150 = (13 - j14)\mathbf{I}_1 - (12 - j16)\mathbf{I}_2.$$

Summing the voltages around mesh 2 generates the equation

$$0 = (12 - j16)(\mathbf{I}_2 - \mathbf{I}_1) + (1 + j3)\mathbf{I}_2 + 39\mathbf{I}_x.$$

Figure 9.37 reveals that the controlling current $\mathbf{I}_x$ is the difference between $\mathbf{I}_1$ and $\mathbf{I}_2$; that is, the constraint is

$$\mathbf{I}_x = \mathbf{I}_1 - \mathbf{I}_2.$$

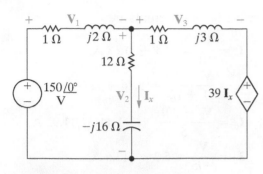

Figure 9.36 ▲ The circuit for Example 9.12.

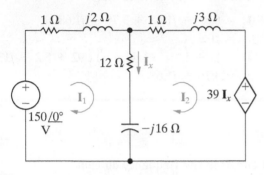

Figure 9.37 ▲ Mesh currents used to solve the circuit shown in Fig. 9.36.

Substituting this constraint into the mesh 2 equation and simplifying the resulting expression gives

$$0 = (27 + j16)\mathbf{I}_1 - (26 + j13)\mathbf{I}_2.$$

Solving for $\mathbf{I}_1$ and $\mathbf{I}_2$ yields

$$\mathbf{I}_1 = -26 - j52 \text{ A},$$

$$\mathbf{I}_2 = -24 - j58 \text{ A},$$

$$\mathbf{I}_x = -2 + j6 \text{ A}.$$

The three voltages are

$$\mathbf{V}_1 = (1 + j2)\mathbf{I}_1 = 78 - j104 \text{ V},$$

$$\mathbf{V}_2 = (12 - j16)\mathbf{I}_x = 72 + j104 \text{ V},$$

$$\mathbf{V}_3 = (1 + j3)\mathbf{I}_2 = 150 - j130 \text{ V}.$$

Also

$$39\mathbf{I}_x = -78 + j234 \text{ V}.$$

We check these calculations by summing the voltages around closed paths:

$$-150 + \mathbf{V}_1 + \mathbf{V}_2 = -150 + 78 - j104 + 72$$
$$+ j104 = 0,$$

$$-\mathbf{V}_2 + \mathbf{V}_3 + 39\mathbf{I}_x = -72 - j104 + 150 - j130$$
$$- 78 + j234 = 0,$$

$$-150 + \mathbf{V}_1 + \mathbf{V}_3 + 39\mathbf{I}_x = -150 + 78 - j104 + 150$$
$$- j130 - 78 + j234 = 0.$$

✓ **ASSESSMENT PROBLEM**

Objective 3—Know how to use circuit analysis techniques to solve a circuit in the frequency domain

9.13 Use the mesh-current method to find the phasor current **I** in the circuit shown.

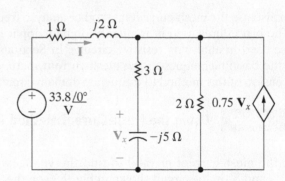

Answer: $\mathbf{I} = 29 + j2 = 29.07 \,\underline{/3.95°}$ A.

NOTE: Also try Chapter Problems 9.60 and 9.64.

9.10 The Transformer

A transformer is a device that is based on magnetic coupling. Transformers are used in both communication and power circuits. In communication circuits, the transformer is used to match impedances and eliminate dc signals from portions of the system. In power circuits, transformers are used to establish ac voltage levels that facilitate the transmission, distribution, and consumption of electrical power. A knowledge of the sinusoidal steady-state behavior of the transformer is required in the analysis of both communication and power systems. In this section, we will discuss the sinusoidal steady-state behavior of the **linear transformer**, which is found primarily in communication circuits. In Section 9.11, we will deal with the **ideal transformer**, which is used to model the ferromagnetic transformer found in power systems.

Before starting we make a useful observation. When analyzing circuits containing mutual inductance use the meshor loop-current method for writing circuit equations. The node-voltage method is cumbersome to use when mutual inductance in involved. This is because the currents in the various coils cannot be written by inspection as functions of the node voltages.

The Analysis of a Linear Transformer Circuit

A simple **transformer** is formed when two coils are wound on a single core to ensure magnetic coupling. Figure 9.38 shows the frequency-domain circuit model of a system that uses a transformer to connect a load to a source. In discussing this circuit, we refer to the transformer winding connected to the source as the **primary winding** and the winding connected to the load as the **secondary winding**. Based on this terminology, the transformer circuit parameters are

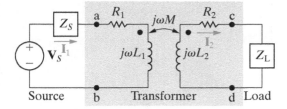

Figure 9.38 ▲ The frequency domain circuit model for a transformer used to connect a load to a source.

R_1 = the resistance of the primary winding,

R_2 = the resistance of the secondary winding,

L_1 = the self-inductance of the primary winding,

L_2 = the self-inductance of the secondary winding,

M = the mutual inductance.

The internal voltage of the sinusoidal source is $\mathbf{V}_s$, and the internal impedance of the source is Z_s. The impedance Z_L represents the load connected to the secondary winding of the transformer. The phasor currents $\mathbf{I}_1$ and $\mathbf{I}_2$ represent the primary and secondary currents of the transformer, respectively.

Analysis of the circuit in Fig. 9.38 consists of finding $\mathbf{I}_1$ and $\mathbf{I}_2$ as functions of the circuit parameters $\mathbf{V}_s$, Z_s, R_1, L_1, L_2, R_2, M, Z_L, and ω. We are also interested in finding the impedance seen looking into the transformer from the terminals a,b. To find $\mathbf{I}_1$ and $\mathbf{I}_2$, we first write the two mesh-current equations that describe the circuit:

$$\mathbf{V}_s = (Z_s + R_1 + j\omega L_1)\mathbf{I}_1 - j\omega M \mathbf{I}_2, \tag{9.57}$$

$$0 = -j\omega M \mathbf{I}_1 + (R_2 + j\omega L_2 + Z_L)\mathbf{I}_2. \tag{9.58}$$

To facilitate the algebraic manipulation of Eqs. 9.57 and 9.58, we let

$$Z_{11} = Z_s + R_1 + j\omega L_1, \tag{9.59}$$

$$Z_{22} = R_2 + j\omega L_2 + Z_L, \tag{9.60}$$

where Z_{11} is the total self-impedance of the mesh containing the primary winding of the transformer, and Z_{22} is the total self-impedance of the mesh containing the secondary winding. Based on the notation introduced in Eqs. 9.59 and 9.60, the solutions for $\mathbf{I}_1$ and $\mathbf{I}_2$ from Eqs. 9.57 and 9.58 are

$$\mathbf{I}_1 = \frac{Z_{22}}{Z_{11}Z_{22} + \omega^2 M^2}\mathbf{V}_s, \tag{9.61}$$

$$\mathbf{I}_2 = \frac{j\omega M}{Z_{11}Z_{22} + \omega^2 M^2}\mathbf{V}_s = \frac{j\omega M}{Z_{22}}\mathbf{I}_1. \tag{9.62}$$

To the internal source voltage $\mathbf{V}_s$, the impedance appears as $\mathbf{V}_s/\mathbf{I}_1$, or

$$\frac{\mathbf{V}_s}{\mathbf{I}_1} = Z_{\text{int}} = \frac{Z_{11}Z_{22} + \omega^2 M^2}{Z_{22}} = Z_{11} + \frac{\omega^2 M^2}{Z_{22}}. \tag{9.63}$$

The impedance at the terminals of the source is $Z_{\text{int}} - Z_s$, so

$$Z_{ab} = Z_{11} + \frac{\omega^2 M^2}{Z_{22}} - Z_s = R_1 + j\omega L_1 + \frac{\omega^2 M^2}{(R_2 + j\omega L_2 + Z_L)}. \tag{9.64}$$

Note that the impedance Z_{ab} is independent of the magnetic polarity of the transformer. The reason is that the mutual inductance appears in Eq. 9.64 as a squared quantity. This impedance is of particular interest because it shows how the transformer affects the impedance of the load as seen from the source. Without the transformer, the load would be connected directly to the source, and the source would see a load impedance of Z_L; with the transformer, the load is connected to the source through the transformer, and the source sees a load impedance that is a modified version of Z_L, as seen in the third term of Eq. 9.64.

Reflected Impedance

The third term in Eq. 9.64 is called the **reflected impedance** (Z_r), because it is the equivalent impedance of the secondary coil and load impedance transmitted, or reflected, to the primary side of the transformer. Note that the reflected impedance is due solely to the existence of mutual inductance; that is, if the two coils are decoupled, M becomes zero, Z_r becomes zero, and Z_{ab} reduces to the self-impedance of the primary coil.

To consider reflected impedance in more detail, we first express the load impedance in rectangular form:

$$Z_L = R_L + jX_L, \tag{9.65}$$

where the load reactance X_L carries its own algebraic sign. In other words, X_L is a positive number if the load is inductive and a negative number if the load is capacitive. We now use Eq. 9.65 to write the reflected impedance in rectangular form:

$$
\begin{aligned}
Z_r &= \frac{\omega^2 M^2}{R_2 + R_L + j(\omega L_2 + X_L)} \\
&= \frac{\omega^2 M^2[(R_2 + R_L) - j(\omega L_2 + X_L)]}{(R_2 + R_L)^2 + (\omega L_2 + X_L)^2} \\
&= \frac{\omega^2 M^2}{|Z_{22}|^2}[(R_2 + R_L) - j(\omega L_2 + X_L)].
\end{aligned} \tag{9.66}
$$

The derivation of Eq. 9.66 takes advantage of the fact that, when Z_L is written in rectangular form, the self-impedance of the mesh containing the secondary winding is

$$Z_{22} = R_2 + R_L + j(\omega L_2 + X_L). \tag{9.67}$$

Now observe from Eq. 9.66 that the self-impedance of the secondary circuit is reflected into the primary circuit by a scaling factor of $(\omega M/|Z_{22}|)^2$, and that the sign of the reactive component $(\omega L_2 + X_L)$ is reversed. Thus the linear transformer reflects the conjugate of the self-impedance of the secondary circuit (Z_{22}^*) into the primary winding by a scalar multiplier. Example 9.13 illustrates mesh current analysis for a circuit containing a linear transformer.

Example 9.13   Analyzing a Linear Transformer in the Frequency Domain

The parameters of a certain linear transformer are $R_1 = 200\ \Omega$, $R_2 = 100\ \Omega$, $L_1 = 9\ \text{H}$, $L_2 = 4\ \text{H}$, and $k = 0.5$. The transformer couples an impedance consisting of an 800 Ω resistor in series with a 1 μF capacitor to a sinusoidal voltage source. The 300 V (rms) source has an internal impedance of $500 + j100\ \Omega$ and a frequency of 400 rad/s.

a) Construct a frequency-domain equivalent circuit of the system.

b) Calculate the self-impedance of the primary circuit.

c) Calculate the self-impedance of the secondary circuit.

d) Calculate the impedance reflected into the primary winding.

e) Calculate the scaling factor for the reflected impedance.

f) Calculate the impedance seen looking into the primary terminals of the transformer.

g) Calculate the Thévenin equivalent with respect to the terminals c,d.

Solution

a) Figure 9.39 shows the frequency-domain equivalent circuit. Note that the internal voltage of the source serves as the reference phasor, and that $\mathbf{V}_1$ and $\mathbf{V}_2$ represent the terminal voltages of the transformer. In constructing the circuit in Fig. 9.39, we made the following calculations:

$$j\omega L_1 = j(400)(9) = j3600\ \Omega,$$

$$j\omega L_2 = j(400)(4) = j1600\ \Omega,$$

$$M = 0.5\sqrt{(9)(4)} = 3\ \text{H},$$

$$j\omega M = j(400)(3) = j1200\ \Omega,$$

$$\frac{1}{j\omega C} = \frac{10^6}{j400} = -j2500\ \Omega.$$

b) The self-impedance of the primary circuit is

$$Z_{11} = 500 + j100 + 200 + j3600 = 700 + j3700\ \Omega.$$

c) The self-impedance of the secondary circuit is

$$Z_{22} = 100 + j1600 + 800 - j2500 = 900 - j900\ \Omega.$$

d) The impedance reflected into the primary winding is

$$Z_r = \left(\frac{1200}{|900 - j900|}\right)^2 (900 + j900)$$

$$= \frac{8}{9}(900 + j900) = 800 + j800\ \Omega.$$

e) The scaling factor by which Z_{22}^* is reflected is 8/9.

f) The impedance seen looking into the primary terminals of the transformer is the impedance of the primary winding plus the reflected impedance; thus

$$Z_{ab} = 200 + j3600 + 800 + j800 = 1000 + j4400\ \Omega.$$

g) The Thévenin voltage will equal the open circuit value of $\mathbf{V}_{cd}$. The open circuit value of $\mathbf{V}_{cd}$ will equal $j1200$ times the open circuit value of $\mathbf{I}_1$. The open circuit value of $\mathbf{I}_1$ is

$$\mathbf{I}_1 = \frac{300\ \underline{/0^\circ}}{700 + j3700}$$

$$= 79.67\ \underline{/-79.29^\circ}\ \text{mA}.$$

Therefore

$$\mathbf{V}_{\text{Th}} = j1200(79.67\ \underline{/-79.29^\circ}) \times 10^{-3}$$

$$= 95.60\ \underline{/10.71^\circ}\ \text{V}.$$

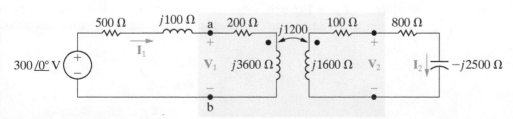

Figure 9.39 ▲ The frequency-domain equivalent circuit for Example 9.13.

The Thévenin impedance will be equal to the impedance of the secondary winding plus the impedance reflected from the primary when the voltage source is replaced by a short-circuit. Thus

$$Z_{\text{Th}} = 100 + j1600 + \left(\frac{1200}{|700 + j3700|}\right)^2 (700 - j3700)$$

$$= 171.09 + j1224.26 \ \Omega.$$

The Thévenin equivalent is shown in Fig. 9.40.

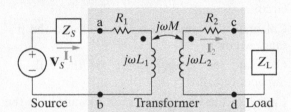

Figure 9.40 ▲ The Thévenin equivalent circuit for Example 9.13.

✓ ASSESSMENT PROBLEM

Objective 4—Be able to analyze circuits containing linear transformers using phasor methods

9.14 A linear transformer couples a load consisting of a 360 Ω resistor in series with a 0.25 H inductor to a sinusoidal voltage source, as shown. The voltage source has an internal impedance of $184 + j0 \ \Omega$ and a maximum voltage of 245.20 V, and it is operating at 800 rad/s. The transformer parameters are $R_1 = 100 \ \Omega$, $L_1 = 0.5$ H, $R_2 = 40 \ \Omega$, $L_2 = 0.125$ H, and $k = 0.4$. Calculate (a) the reflected impedance; (b) the primary current; and (c) the secondary current.

Answer: (a) $10.24 - j7.68 \ \Omega$;

(b) $0.5 \cos(800t - 53.13°)$ A;

(c) $0.08 \cos 800t$ A.

NOTE: Also try Chapter Problems 9.76 and 9.77.

9.11 The Ideal Transformer

An **ideal transformer** consists of two magnetically coupled coils having N_1 and N_2 turns, respectively, and exhibiting these three properties:

1. The coefficient of coupling is unity ($k = 1$).
2. The self-inductance of each coil is infinite ($L_1 = L_2 = \infty$).
3. The coil losses, due to parasitic resistance, are negligible.

Understanding the behavior of ideal transformers begins with Eq. 9.64 which describes the impedance at the terminals of a source connected to a linear transformer. We repeat this equation below and examine it further.

Exploring Limiting Values

A useful relationship between the input impedance and load impedance, as given by Z_{ab} in Eq. 9.68, emerges as L_1 and L_2 each become infinitely large and, at the same time, the coefficient of coupling approaches unity:

$$Z_{ab} = Z_{11} + \frac{\omega^2 M^2}{Z_{22}} - Z_s$$

$$= R_1 + j\omega L_1 + \frac{\omega^2 M^2}{(R_2 + j\omega L_2 + Z_{\text{L}})}. \tag{9.68}$$

Transformers wound on ferromagnetic cores can approach this condition. Even though such transformers are nonlinear, we can obtain some useful information by constructing an ideal model that ignores the nonlinearities.

To show how Z_{ab} changes when $k = 1$ and L_1 and L_2 approach infinity, we first introduce the notation

$$Z_{22} = R_2 + R_L + j(\omega L_2 + X_L) = R_{22} + jX_{22}$$

and then rearrange Eq. 9.68:

$$Z_{ab} = R_1 + \frac{\omega^2 M^2 R_{22}}{R_{22}^2 + X_{22}^2} + j\left(\omega L_1 - \frac{\omega^2 M^2 X_{22}}{R_{22}^2 + X_{22}^2}\right)$$
$$= R_{ab} + jX_{ab}. \tag{9.69}$$

At this point, we must be careful with the coefficient of j in Eq. 9.69 because, as L_1 and L_2 approach infinity, this coefficient is the difference between two large quantities. Thus, before letting L_1 and L_2 increase, we write the coefficient as

$$X_{ab} = \omega L_1 - \frac{(\omega L_1)(\omega L_2)X_{22}}{R_{22}^2 + X_{22}^2} = \omega L_1\left(1 - \frac{\omega L_2 X_{22}}{R_{22}^2 + X_{22}^2}\right), \tag{9.70}$$

where we recognize that, when $k = 1$, $M^2 = L_1 L_2$. Putting the term multiplying ωL_1 over a common denominator gives

$$X_{ab} = \omega L_1\left(\frac{R_{22}^2 + \omega L_2 X_L + X_L^2}{R_{22}^2 + X_{22}^2}\right). \tag{9.71}$$

Factoring ωL_2 out of the numerator and denominator of Eq. 9.71 yields

$$X_{ab} = \frac{L_1}{L_2}\frac{X_L + (R_{22}^2 + X_L^2)/\omega L_2}{(R_{22}/\omega L_2)^2 + [1 + (X_1/\omega L_2)]^2}. \tag{9.72}$$

As k approaches 1.0, the ratio L_1/L_2 approaches the constant value of $(N_1/N_2)^2$, which follows from Eqs. 6.54 and 6.55. The reason is that, as the coupling becomes extremely tight, the two permeances $\mathcal{P}_1$ and $\mathcal{P}_2$ become equal. Equation 9.72 then reduces to

$$X_{ab} = \left(\frac{N_1}{N_2}\right)^2 X_L, \tag{9.73}$$

as $L_1 \to \infty$, $L_2 \to \infty$, and $k \to 1.0$.

The same reasoning leads to simplification of the reflected resistance in Eq. 9.69:

$$\frac{\omega^2 M^2 R_{22}}{R_{22}^2 + X_{22}^2} = \frac{L_1}{L_2}R_{22} = \left(\frac{N_1}{N_2}\right)^2 R_{22}. \tag{9.74}$$

Applying the results given by Eqs. 9.73 and 9.74 to Eq. 9.69 yields

$$Z_{ab} = R_1 + \left(\frac{N_1}{N_2}\right)^2 R_2 + \left(\frac{N_1}{N_2}\right)^2 (R_L + jX_L). \tag{9.75}$$

Compare this result with the result in Eq. 9.68. Here we see that when the coefficient of coupling approaches unity and the self-inductances of the coupled coils approach infinity, the transformer reflects the secondary winding resistance and the load impedance to the primary side by a scaling factor equal to the turns ratio (N_1/N_2) squared. Hence we may describe the terminal behavior of the ideal transformer in terms of two characteristics. First, the magnitude of the volts per turn is the same for each coil, or

$$\left|\frac{\mathbf{V}_1}{N_1}\right| = \left|\frac{\mathbf{V}_2}{N_2}\right|. \tag{9.76}$$

Second, the magnitude of the ampere-turns is the same for each coil, or

$$|\mathbf{I}_1 N_1| = |\mathbf{I}_2 N_2|. \tag{9.77}$$

We are forced to use magnitude signs in Eqs. 9.76 and 9.77, because we have not yet established reference polarities for the currents and voltages; we discuss the removal of the magnitude signs shortly.

Figure 9.41 shows two lossless $(R_1 = R_2 = 0)$ magnetically coupled coils. We use Fig. 9.41 to validate Eqs. 9.76 and 9.77. In Fig. 9.41(a), coil 2 is open; in Fig. 9.41(b), coil 2 is shorted. Although we carry out the following analysis in terms of sinusoidal steady-state operation, the results also apply to instantaneous values of v and i.

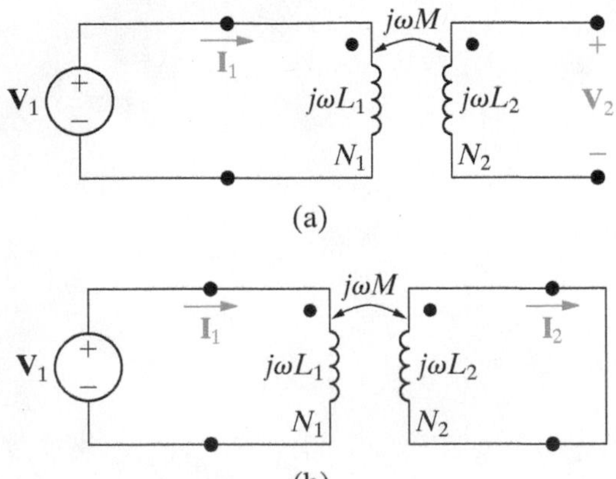

Determining the Voltage and Current Ratios

Note in Fig. 9.41(a) that the voltage at the terminals of the open-circuit coil is entirely the result of the current in coil 1; therefore

$$\mathbf{V}_2 = j\omega M \mathbf{I}_1. \tag{9.78}$$

The current in coil 1 is

$$\mathbf{I}_1 = \frac{\mathbf{V}_1}{j\omega L_1}. \tag{9.79}$$

From Eqs. 9.78 and 9.79,

$$\mathbf{V}_2 = \frac{M}{L_1}\mathbf{V}_1. \tag{9.80}$$

For unity coupling, the mutual inductance equals $\sqrt{L_1 L_2}$, so Eq. 9.80 becomes

$$\mathbf{V}_2 = \sqrt{\frac{L_2}{L_1}}\mathbf{V}_1. \tag{9.81}$$

For unity coupling, the flux linking coil 1 is the same as the flux linking coil 2, so we need only one permeance to describe the self-inductance of each coil. Thus Eq. 9.81 becomes

$$\mathbf{V}_2 = \sqrt{\frac{N_2^2 \mathcal{P}}{N_1^2 \mathcal{P}}}\mathbf{V}_1 = \frac{N_2}{N_1}\mathbf{V}_1 \tag{9.82}$$

or

Voltage relationship for an ideal transformer ▶

$$\frac{\mathbf{V}_1}{N_1} = \frac{\mathbf{V}_2}{N_2}. \tag{9.83}$$

Summing the voltages around the shorted coil of Fig. 9.41(b) yields

$$0 = -j\omega M \mathbf{I}_1 + j\omega L_2 \mathbf{I}_2, \tag{9.84}$$

Figure 9.41 ▲ The circuits used to verify the volts-per-turn and ampere-turn relationships for an ideal transformer.

from which, for $k = 1$,

$$\frac{\mathbf{I}_1}{\mathbf{I}_2} = \frac{L_2}{M} = \frac{L_2}{\sqrt{L_1 L_2}} = \sqrt{\frac{L_2}{L_1}} = \frac{N_2}{N_1}. \qquad (9.85)$$

Equation 9.85 is equivalent to

$$\mathbf{I}_1 N_1 = \mathbf{I}_2 N_2. \qquad (9.86)$$

◀ **Current relationship for an ideal transformer**

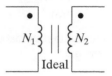

Figure 9.42 ▲ The graphic symbol for an ideal transformer.

Figure 9.42 shows the graphic symbol for an ideal transformer. The vertical lines in the symbol represent the layers of magnetic material from which ferromagnetic cores are often made. Thus, the symbol reminds us that coils wound on a ferromagnetic core behave very much like an ideal transformer.

There are several reasons for this. The ferromagnetic material creates a space with high permeance. Thus most of the magnetic flux is trapped inside the core material, establishing tight magnetic coupling between coils that share the same core. High permeance also means high self-inductance, because $L = N^2 \mathcal{P}$. Finally, ferromagnetically coupled coils efficiently transfer power from one coil to the other. Efficiencies in excess of 95% are common, so neglecting losses is not a crippling approximation for many applications.

Determining the Polarity of the Voltage and Current Ratios

We now turn to the removal of the magnitude signs from Eqs. 9.76 and 9.77. Note that magnitude signs did not show up in the derivations of Eqs. 9.83 and 9.86. We did not need them there because we had established reference polarities for voltages and reference directions for currents. In addition, we knew the magnetic polarity dots of the two coupled coils.

The rules for assigning the proper algebraic sign to Eqs. 9.76 and 9.77 are as follows:

> If the coil voltages $\mathbf{V}_1$ and $\mathbf{V}_2$ are both positive or negative at the dot-marked terminal, use a plus sign in Eq. 9.76. Otherwise, use a negative sign.
>
> If the coil currents $\mathbf{I}_1$ and $\mathbf{I}_2$ are both directed into or out of the dot-marked terminal, use a minus sign in Eq. 9.77. Otherwise, use a plus sign.

◀ **Dot convention for ideal transformers**

The four circuits shown in Fig. 9.43 illustrate these rules.

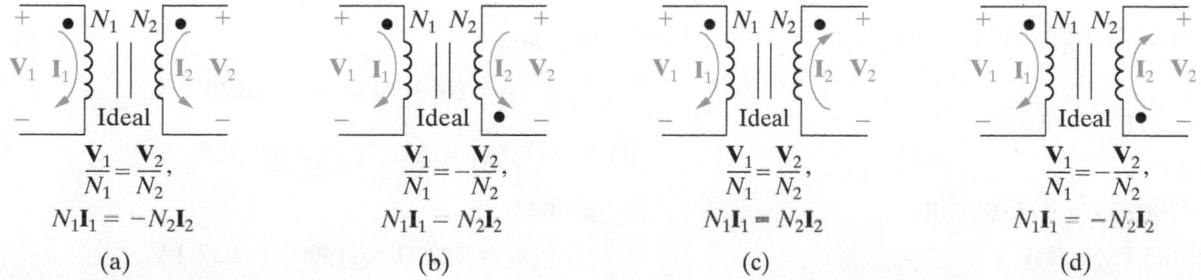

$$\frac{\mathbf{V}_1}{N_1} = \frac{\mathbf{V}_2}{N_2},$$
$$N_1 \mathbf{I}_1 = -N_2 \mathbf{I}_2$$

(a)

$$\frac{\mathbf{V}_1}{N_1} = -\frac{\mathbf{V}_2}{N_2},$$
$$N_1 \mathbf{I}_1 = N_2 \mathbf{I}_2$$

(b)

$$\frac{\mathbf{V}_1}{N_1} = \frac{\mathbf{V}_2}{N_2},$$
$$N_1 \mathbf{I}_1 = N_2 \mathbf{I}_2$$

(c)

$$\frac{\mathbf{V}_1}{N_1} = -\frac{\mathbf{V}_2}{N_2},$$
$$N_1 \mathbf{I}_1 = -N_2 \mathbf{I}_2$$

(d)

Figure 9.43 ▲ Circuits that show the proper algebraic signs for relating the terminal voltages and currents of an ideal transformer.

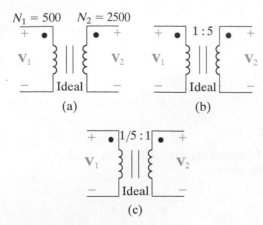

Figure 9.44 ▲ Three ways to show that the turns ratio of an ideal transformer is 5.

The ratio of the turns on the two windings is an important parameter of the ideal transformer. The turns ratio is defined as either N_1/N_2 or N_2/N_1; both ratios appear in various writings. In this text, we use a to denote the ratio N_2/N_1, or

$$a = \frac{N_2}{N_1}. \qquad (9.87)$$

Figure 9.44 shows three ways to represent the turns ratio of an ideal transformer. Figure 9.44(a) shows the number of turns in each coil explicitly. Figure 9.44(b) shows that the ratio N_2/N_1 is 5 to 1, and Fig. 9.44(c) shows that the ratio N_2/N_1 is 1 to $\frac{1}{5}$.

Example 9.14 illustrates the analysis of a circuit containing an ideal transformer.

Example 9.14 — Analyzing an Ideal Transformer Circuit in the Frequency Domain

The load impedance connected to the secondary winding of the ideal transformer in Fig. 9.45 consists of a 237.5 mΩ resistor in series with a 125 μH inductor.

If the sinusoidal voltage source (v_g) is generating the voltage $2500 \cos 400t$ V, find the steady-state expressions for: (a) i_1; (b) v_1; (c) i_2; and (d) v_2.

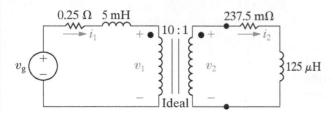

Figure 9.45 ▲ The circuit for Example 9.14.

Solution

a) We begin by constructing the phasor domain equivalent circuit. The voltage source becomes $2500 \underline{/0°}$ V; the 5 mH inductor converts to an impedance of $j2 \ \Omega$; and the 125 μH inductor converts to an impedance of $j0.05 \ \Omega$. The phasor domain equivalent circuit is shown in Fig. 9.46.

It follows directly from Fig. 9.46 that

$$2500 \underline{/0°} = (0.25 + j2)\mathbf{I}_1 + \mathbf{V}_1,$$

and

$$\mathbf{V}_1 = 10\mathbf{V}_2 = 10[(0.2375 + j0.05)\mathbf{I}_2].$$

Because

$$\mathbf{I}_2 = 10\mathbf{I}_1$$

we have

$$\mathbf{V}_1 = 10(0.2375 + j0.05)10\mathbf{I}_1$$
$$= (23.75 + j5)\mathbf{I}_1.$$

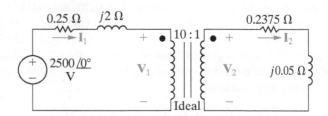

Figure 9.46 ▲ Phasor domain circuit for Example 9.14.

Therefore

$$2500 \underline{/0°} = (24 + j7)\mathbf{I}_1,$$

or

$$\mathbf{I}_1 = 100 \underline{/-16.26°} \text{ A}.$$

Thus the steady-state expression for i_1 is

$$i_1 = 100 \cos(400t - 16.26°) \text{ A}.$$

b) $\mathbf{V}_1 = 2500\underline{/0°} - (100 \underline{/-16.26°})(0.25 + j2)$
$$= 2500 - 80 - j185$$
$$= 2420 - j185 = 2427.06 \underline{/-4.37°} \text{ V}.$$

Hence

$$v_1 = 2427.06 \cos(400t - 4.37°) \text{ V}.$$

c) $\mathbf{I}_2 = 10\mathbf{I}_1 = 1000 \underline{/-16.26°}$ A.

Therefore

$$i_2 = 1000 \cos(400t - 16.26°) \text{ A}.$$

d) $\mathbf{V}_2 = 0.1\mathbf{V}_1 = 242.71 \underline{/-4.37°}$ V,

giving

$$v_2 = 242.71 \cos(400t - 4.37°) \text{ V}.$$

The Use of an Ideal Transformer for Impedance Matching

Ideal transformers can also be used to raise or lower the impedance level of a load. The circuit shown in Fig. 9.47 illustrates this. The impedance seen by the practical voltage source ($\mathbf{V}_s$ in series with Z_s) is $\mathbf{V}_1/\mathbf{I}_1$. The voltage and current at the terminals of the load impedance ($\mathbf{V}_2$ and $\mathbf{I}_2$) are related to $\mathbf{V}_1$ and $\mathbf{I}_1$ by the transformer turns ratio; thus

$$\mathbf{V}_1 = \frac{\mathbf{V}_2}{a}, \tag{9.88}$$

and

$$\mathbf{I}_1 = a\mathbf{I}_2. \tag{9.89}$$

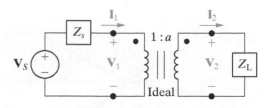

Figure 9.47 ▲ Using an ideal transformer to couple a load to a source.

Therefore the impedance seen by the practical source is

$$Z_{IN} = \frac{\mathbf{V}_1}{\mathbf{I}_1} = \frac{1}{a^2}\frac{\mathbf{V}_2}{\mathbf{I}_2}, \tag{9.90}$$

but the ratio $\mathbf{V}_2/\mathbf{I}_2$ is the load impedance Z_L, so Eq. 9.90 becomes

$$Z_{IN} = \frac{1}{a^2}Z_L. \tag{9.91}$$

Thus, the ideal transformer's secondary coil reflects the load impedance back to the primary coil, with the scaling factor $1/a^2$.

Note that the ideal transformer changes the magnitude of Z_L but does not affect its phase angle. Whether Z_{IN} is greater or less than Z_L depends on the turns ratio a.

The ideal transformer—or its practical counterpart, the ferromagnetic core transformer—can be used to match the magnitude of Z_L to the magnitude of Z_s. We will discuss why this may be desirable in Chapter 10.

✓ASSESSMENT PROBLEM

Objective 5—Be able to analyze circuits with ideal transformers

9.15   The source voltage in the phasor domain circuit in the accompanying figure is 25 $\underline{/0°}$ kV. Find the amplitude and phase angle of $\mathbf{V}_2$ and $\mathbf{I}_2$.

Answer: $\mathbf{V}_2 = 1868.15 \underline{/142.39°}$ V;

$\mathbf{I}_2 = 125 \underline{/216.87°}$ A.

NOTE: Also try Chapter Problem 9.82.

As we shall see, ideal transformers are used to increase or decrease voltages from a source to a load. Thus, ideal transformers are used widely in the electric utility industry, where it is desirable to decrease, or step down, the voltage level at the power line to safer residential voltage levels.

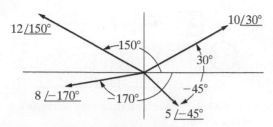

12 $\underline{/150°}$

10 $\underline{/30°}$

−150°

30°

−45°

8 $\underline{/−170°}$ −170°

5 $\underline{/−45°}$

Figure 9.48 ▲ A graphic representation of phasors.

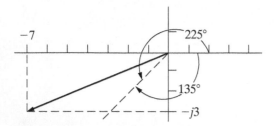

−7

225°

−135°

−j3

Figure 9.49 ▲ The complex number
$-7 - j3 = 7.62 \underline{/−156.80°}$.

9.12 Phasor Diagrams

When we are using the phasor method to analyze the steady-state sinusoidal operation of a circuit, a diagram of the phasor currents and voltages may give further insight into the behavior of the circuit. A phasor diagram shows the magnitude and phase angle of each phasor quantity in the complex-number plane. Phase angles are measured counterclockwise from the positive real axis, and magnitudes are measured from the origin of the axes. For example, Fig. 9.48 shows the phasor quantities 10 $\underline{/30°}$, 12 $\underline{/150°}$, 5 $\underline{/−45°}$, and 8 $\underline{/−170°}$.

Constructing phasor diagrams of circuit quantities generally involves both currents and voltages. As a result, two different magnitude scales are necessary, one for currents and one for voltages. The ability to visualize a phasor quantity on the complex-number plane can be useful when you are checking pocket calculator calculations. The typical pocket calculator doesn't offer a printout of the data entered. But when the calculated angle is displayed, you can compare it to your mental image as a check on whether you keyed in the appropriate values. For example, suppose that you are to compute the polar form of $-7 - j3$. Without making any calculations, you should anticipate a magnitude greater than 7 and an angle in the third quadrant that is more negative than $-135°$ or less positive than $225°$, as illustrated in Fig. 9.49.

Examples 9.15 and 9.16 illustrate the construction and use of phasor diagrams. We use such diagrams in subsequent chapters whenever they give additional insight into the steady-state sinusoidal operation of the circuit under investigation. Problem 9.84 shows how a phasor diagram can help explain the operation of a phase-shifting circuit.

Example 9.15   Using Phasor Diagrams to Analyze a Circuit

For the circuit in Fig. 9.50, use a phasor diagram to find the value of R that will cause the current through that resistor, i_R, to lag the source current, i_s, by 45° when $\omega = 5$ krad/s.

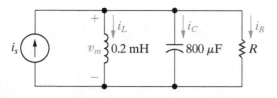

Figure 9.50 ▲ The circuit for Example 9.15.

Solution

By Kirchhoff's current law, the sum of the currents $\mathbf{I}_R$, $\mathbf{I}_L$, and $\mathbf{I}_C$ must equal the source current $\mathbf{I}_s$. If we assume that the phase angle of the voltage $\mathbf{V}_m$ is zero, we can draw the current phasors for each of the components. The current phasor for the inductor is given by

$$\mathbf{I}_L = \frac{V_m \underline{/0°}}{j(5000)(0.2 \times 10^{-3})} = V_m \underline{/−90°},$$

whereas the current phasor for the capacitor is given by

$$\mathbf{I}_C = \frac{V_m \underline{/0°}}{-j/(5000)(800 \times 10^{-6})} = 4V_m \underline{/90°},$$

and the current phasor for the resistor is given by

$$\mathbf{I}_R = \frac{V_m \underline{/0°}}{R} = \frac{V_m}{R} \underline{/0°}.$$

These phasors are shown in Fig. 9.51. The phasor diagram also shows the source current phasor, sketched as a dotted line, which must be the sum of the current phasors of the three circuit components and must be at an angle that is 45° more positive than the current phasor for the resistor. As you can see, summing the phasors makes an isosceles triangle, so the length of the current phasor for the resistor must equal $3V_m$. Therefore, the value of the resistor is $\frac{1}{3}$ Ω.

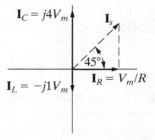

$\mathbf{I}_C = j4V_m$

$\mathbf{I}_s$

45°

$\mathbf{I}_R = V_m/R$

$\mathbf{I}_L = -j1V_m$

Figure 9.51 ▲ The phasor diagram for the currents in Fig. 9.50.

Example 9.16   Using Phasor Diagrams to Analyze Capacitive Loading Effects

The circuit in Fig. 9.52 has a load consisting of the parallel combination of the resistor and inductor. Use phasor diagrams to explore the effect of adding a capacitor across the terminals of the load on the amplitude of $\mathbf{V}_s$ if we adjust $\mathbf{V}_s$ so that the amplitude of $\mathbf{V}_L$ remains constant. Utility companies use this technique to control the voltage drop on their lines.

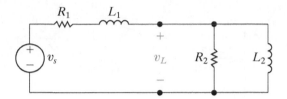

Figure 9.52 ▲ The circuit for Example 9.16.

Solution

We begin by assuming zero capacitance across the load. After constructing the phasor diagram for the zero-capacitance case, we can add the capacitor and study its effect on the amplitude of $\mathbf{V}_s$, holding the amplitude of $\mathbf{V}_L$ constant. Figure 9.53 shows the frequency-domain equivalent of the circuit shown in Fig. 9.52. We added the phasor branch currents $\mathbf{I}, \mathbf{I}_a$, and $\mathbf{I}_b$ to Fig. 9.53 to aid discussion.

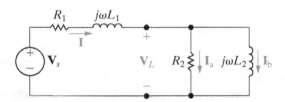

Figure 9.53 ▲ The frequency-domain equivalent of the circuit in Fig. 9.52.

Figure 9.54 shows the stepwise evolution of the phasor diagram. Keep in mind that we are not interested in specific phasor values and positions in this example, but rather in the general effect of adding a capacitor across the terminals of the load. Thus, we want to develop the relative positions of the phasors before and after the capacitor has been added.

Relating the phasor diagram to the circuit shown in Fig. 9.53 reveals the following points:

a) Because we are holding the amplitude of the load voltage constant, we choose $\mathbf{V}_L$ as our reference.

For convenience, we place this phasor on the positive real axis.

b) We know that $\mathbf{I}_a$ is in phase with $\mathbf{V}_L$ and that its magnitude is $|\mathbf{V}_L|/R_2$. (On the phasor diagram, the magnitude scale for the current phasors is independent of the magnitude scale for the voltage phasors.)

c) We know that $\mathbf{I}_b$ lags behind $\mathbf{V}_L$ by 90° and that its magnitude is $|\mathbf{V}_L|/\omega L_2$.

d) The line current $\mathbf{I}$ is equal to the sum of $\mathbf{I}_a$ and $\mathbf{I}_b$.

e) The voltage drop across R_1 is in phase with the line current, and the voltage drop across $j\omega L_1$ leads the line current by 90°.

f) The source voltage is the sum of the load voltage and the drop along the line; that is, $\mathbf{V}_s = \mathbf{V}_L + (R_1 + j\omega L_1)\mathbf{I}$.

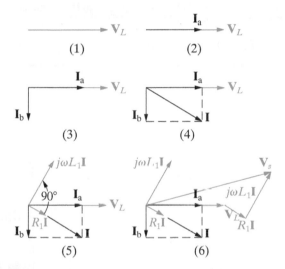

Figure 9.54 ▲ The step-by-step evolution of the phasor diagram for the circuit in Fig. 9.53.

Note that the completed phasor diagram shown in step 6 of Fig. 9.54 clearly shows the amplitude and phase angle relationships among all the currents and voltages in Fig. 9.53.

Now add the capacitor branch shown in Fig. 9.55. We are holding $\mathbf{V}_L$ constant, so we construct the phasor diagram for the circuit in Fig. 9.55 following the same steps as those in Fig. 9.54, except that, in step 4, we add the capacitor current $\mathbf{I}_c$ to the diagram. In so doing, $\mathbf{I}_c$ leads $\mathbf{V}_L$ by 90°, with its magnitude being $|\mathbf{V}_L\omega C|$. Figure 9.56 shows the effect of $\mathbf{I}_c$ on the line current: Both the magnitude and phase angle of the line current $\mathbf{I}$ change with changes in the magnitude of $\mathbf{I}_c$. As $\mathbf{I}$ changes, so do the magnitude and phase angle of the voltage drop along the line. As the drop along the line changes, the magnitude and phase angle of $\mathbf{V}_s$ change. The phasor diagram shown in Fig. 9.57 depicts these observations. The dotted phasors represent the pertinent currents and voltages before the addition of the capacitor.

Thus, comparing the dotted phasors of $\mathbf{I}$, $R_1\mathbf{I}$, $j\omega L_1\mathbf{I}$, and $\mathbf{V}_s$ with their solid counterparts clearly shows the effect of adding C to the circuit. In particular, note that this reduces the amplitude of the source voltage and still maintains the amplitude of the load voltage. Practically, this result means that, as the load increases (i.e., as $\mathbf{I}_a$ and $\mathbf{I}_b$ increase), we can add capacitors to the system (i.e., increase $\mathbf{I}_c$) so that under heavy load conditions we can maintain $\mathbf{V}_L$ without increasing the amplitude of the source voltage.

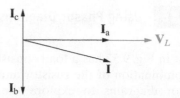

Figure 9.56 ▲ The effect of the capacitor current $\mathbf{I}_c$ on the line current $\mathbf{I}$.

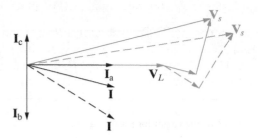

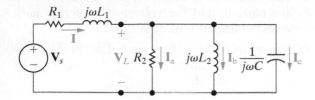

Figure 9.55 ▲ The addition of a capacitor to the circuit shown in Fig. 9.53.

Figure 9.57 ▲ The effect of adding a load-shunting capacitor to the circuit shown in Fig. 9.53 if $\mathbf{V}_L$ is held constant.

NOTE: Assess your understanding of this material by trying Chapter Problems 9.83 and 9.84.

Practical Perspective

A Household Distribution Circuit
Let us return to the household distribution circuit introduced at the beginning of the chapter. We will modify the circuit slightly by adding resistance to each conductor on the secondary side of the transformer to simulate more accurately the residential wiring conductors. The modified circuit is shown in Fig. 9.58. In Problem 9.88 you will calculate the six branch currents on the secondary side of the distribution transformer and then show how to calculate the current in the primary winding.

NOTE: Assess your understanding of this Practical Perspective by trying Chapter Problems 9.87 and 9.88.

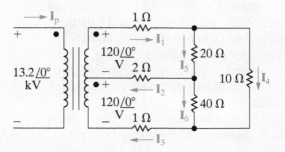

Figure 9.58 ▲ Distribution circuit.

Summary

- The general equation for a **sinusoidal source** is

$$v = V_m \cos(\omega t + \phi) \text{ (voltage source)},$$

or

$$i = I_m \cos(\omega t + \phi) \text{ (current source)},$$

where V_m (or I_m) is the maximum amplitude, ω is the frequency, and ϕ is the phase angle. (See page 306.)

- The frequency, ω, of a sinusoidal response is the same as the frequency of the sinusoidal source driving the circuit. The amplitude and phase angle of the response are usually different from those of the source. (See page 309.)

- The best way to find the steady-state voltages and currents in a circuit driven by sinusoidal sources is to perform the analysis in the frequency domain. The following mathematical transforms allow us to move between the time and frequency domains.

  - The phasor transform (from the time domain to the frequency domain):

  $$\mathbf{V} = V_m e^{j\phi} = \mathscr{P}\{V_m \cos(\omega t + \phi)\}.$$

  - The inverse phasor transform (from the frequency domain to the time domain):

  $$\mathscr{P}^{-1}\{V_m e^{j\phi} = \Re\{V_m e^{j\phi} e^{j\omega t}\}.$$

  (See pages 310–311.)

- When working with sinusoidally varying signals, remember that voltage leads current by 90° at the terminals of an inductor, and current leads voltage by 90° at the terminals of a capacitor. (See pages 315–318.)

- **Impedance** (Z) plays the same role in the frequency domain as resistance, inductance, and capacitance play in the time domain. Specifically, the relationship between phasor current and phasor voltage for resistors, inductors, and capacitors is

$$\mathbf{V} = Z\mathbf{I},$$

where the reference direction for $\mathbf{I}$ obeys the passive sign convention. The reciprocal of impedance is **admittance** (Y), so another way to express the current-voltage relationship for resistors, inductors, and capacitors in the frequency domain is

$$\mathbf{V} = \mathbf{I}/Y.$$

(See pages 318 and 322.)

- All of the circuit analysis techniques developed in Chapters 2–4 for resistive circuits also apply to sinusoidal steady-state circuits in the frequency domain. These techniques include KVL, KCL, series, and parallel combinations of impedances, voltage and current division, node voltage and mesh current methods, source transformations and Thévenin and Norton equivalents.

- The two-winding **linear transformer** is a coupling device made up of two coils wound on the same nonmagnetic core. **Reflected impedance** is the impedance of the secondary circuit as seen from the terminals of the primary circuit or vice versa. The reflected impedance of a linear transformer seen from the primary side is the conjugate of the self-impedance of the secondary circuit scaled by the factor $(\omega M/|Z_{22}|)^2$. (See pages 333 and 334.)

- The two-winding **ideal transformer** is a linear transformer with the following special properties: perfect coupling ($k = 1$), infinite self-inductance in each coil ($L_1 = L_2 = \infty$), and lossless coils ($R_1 = R_2 = 0$). The circuit behavior is governed by the turns ratio $a = N_2/N_1$. In particular, the volts per turn is the same for each winding, or

$$\frac{\mathbf{V}_1}{N_1} = \pm \frac{\mathbf{V}_2}{N_2},$$

and the ampere turns are the same for each winding, or

$$N_1\mathbf{I}_1 = \pm N_2\mathbf{I}_2.$$

(See page 338.)

TABLE 9.3 **Impedance and Related Values**

Element	Impedance (Z)	Reactance	Admittance (Y)	Susceptance
Resistor	R (resistance)	—	G (conductance)	—
Capacitor	$j(-1/\omega C)$	$-1/\omega C$	$j\omega C$	ωC
Inductor	$j\omega L$	ωL	$j(-1/\omega L)$	$-1/\omega L$

Problems

Section 9.1

9.1 A sinusoidal current is given by the expression

$$i = 125 \cos(800t + 36.87°) \text{ mA.}$$

Find (a) f in hertz; (b) T in milliseconds; (c) I_m; (d) $i(0)$; (e) ϕ in degrees and radians; (f) the smallest positive value of t at which $i = 0$; and (g) the smallest positive value of t at which $di/dt = 0$.

9.2 In a single graph, sketch $v = 100 \cos(\omega t + \phi)$ versus ωt for $\phi = 90°, 45°, 0°, -45°$, and $-90°$.

  a) State whether the voltage function is shifting to the right or left as ϕ becomes more negative.

  b) What is the direction of shift if ϕ changes from 0 to 45°?

9.3 Consider the sinusoidal voltage

$$v(t) = 25 \cos(400\pi t + 60°) \text{ V.}$$

  a) What is the maximum amplitude of the voltage?

  b) What is the frequency in hertz?

  c) What is the frequency in radians per second?

  d) What is the phase angle in radians?

  e) What is the phase angle in degrees?

  f) What is the period in milliseconds?

  g) What is the first time after $t = 0$ that $v = 0$ V?

  h) The sinusoidal function is shifted 5/6 ms to the right along the time axis. What is the expression for $v(t)$?

  i) What is the minimum number of milliseconds that the function must be shifted to the left if the expression for $v(t)$ is $25 \sin 400\pi t$ V?

9.4 A sinusoidal voltage is zero at $t = (40/3)$ ms and increasing at a rate of 750π V/s. The maximum amplitude of the voltage is 50 V.

  a) What is the frequency of v in radians per second?

  b) What is the expression for v?

9.5 At $t = 5$ ms, a sinusoidal current is known to be zero and going negative. The current is next zero at $t = 25$ ms. It is also known that the current is 50 mA at $t = 0$.

  a) What is the frequency of i in hertz?

  b) What is the expression for i?

9.6 The rms value of the sinusoidal voltage supplied to the convenience outlet of a home in Scotland is 240 V. What is the maximum value of the voltage at the outlet?

9.7 Find the rms value of the half-wave rectified sinusoidal voltage shown in Fig. P9.7.

Figure P9.7

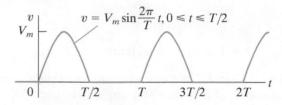

9.8 Show that

$$\int_{t_0}^{t_0+T} V_m^2 \cos^2(\omega t + \phi)\,dt = \frac{V_m^2 T}{2}$$

Section 9.2

9.9 The voltage applied to the circuit shown in Fig. 9.5 at $t = 0$ is $75 \cos(4000t - 60°)$ V. The circuit resistance is 400 Ω and the initial current in the 75 mH inductor is zero.

  a) Find $i(t)$ for $t \geq 0$.

  b) Write the expressions for the transient and steady-state components of $i(t)$.

  c) Find the numerical value of i after the switch has been closed for 750 μs.

  d) What are the maximum amplitude, frequency (in radians per second), and phase angle of the steady-state current?

  e) By how many degrees are the voltage and the steady-state current out of phase?

9.10 a) Verify that Eq. 9.9 is the solution of Eq. 9.8. This can be done by substituting Eq. 9.9 into the left-hand side of Eq. 9.8 and then noting that it equals the right-hand side for all values of $t > 0$. At $t = 0$, Eq. 9.9 should reduce to the initial value of the current.

  b) Because the transient component vanishes as time elapses and because our solution must satisfy the differential equation for all values of t, the steady-state component, by itself, must also satisfy the differential equation. Verify this observation by showing that the steady-state component of Eq. 9.9 satisfies Eq. 9.8.

Sections 9.3–9.4

9.11 Use the concept of the phasor to combine the following sinusoidal functions into a single trigonometric expression:

  a) $y = 30 \cos(200t - 160°) + 15 \cos(200t + 70°)$,

  b) $y = 90 \sin(50t - 20°) + 60 \cos(200t - 70°)$,

c) $y = 50 \cos(5000t - 60°) + 25 \sin(5000t + 110°)$
   $- 75 \cos(5000t - 30°),$

d) $y = 10 \cos(\omega t + 30°) + 10 \sin \omega t$
   $+ 10 \cos(\omega t + 150°).$

9.12 A 400 Hz sinusoidal voltage with a maximum amplitude of 100 V at $t = 0$ is applied across the terminals of an inductor. The maximum amplitude of the steady state current in the inductor is 20 A.

a) What is the frequency of the inductor current?

b) If the phase angle of the voltage is zero, what is the phase angle of the current?

c) What is the inductive reactance of the inductor?

d) What is the inductance of the inductor in millihenrys?

e) What is the impedance of the inductor?

9.13 A 80 kHz sinusoidal voltage has zero phase angle and a maximum amplitude of 25 mV. When this voltage is applied across the terminals of a capacitor, the resulting steady-state current has a maximum amplitude of 628.32 μA.

a) What is the frequency of the current in radians per second?

b) What is the phase angle of the current?

c) What is the capacitive reactance of the capacitor?

d) What is the capacitance of the capacitor in microfarads?

e) What is the impedance of the capacitor?

9.14 The expressions for the steady-state voltage and current at the terminals of the circuit seen in Fig. P9.14 are

$$v_g = 300 \cos (5000\pi t + 78°) \text{ V},$$

$$i_g = 6 \sin (5000\pi t + 123°) \text{ A}$$

a) What is the impedance seen by the source?

b) By how many microseconds is the current out of phase with the voltage?

Figure P9.14

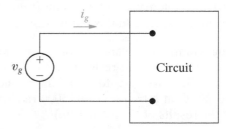

Sections 9.5 and 9.6

9.15 A 25 Ω resistor, a 50 mH inductor, and a 32 μF
capacitor are connected in series. The series-connected

elements are energized by a sinusoidal voltage source whose voltage is 25 cos ($500t - 60°$)V.

a) Draw the frequency-domain equivalent circuit.

b) Reference the current in the direction of the voltage rise across the source, and find the phasor current.

c) Find the steady-state expression for $i(t)$.

9.16 A 25 Ω resistor and a 10 mH inductor are con-
nected in parallel. This parallel combination is also in parallel with the series combination of a 30 Ω resistor and a 10 μF capacitor. These three parallel branches are driven by a sinusoidal current source whose current is 125 sin($2500t + 60°$) A.

a) Draw the frequency-domain equivalent circuit.

b) Reference the voltage across the current source as a rise in the direction of the source current, and find the phasor voltage.

c) Find the steady-state expression for $v(t)$.

9.17 Three branches having impedances of $3 + j4$ Ω, $16 - j12$ Ω, and $-j4$ Ω, respectively, are connected in parallel. What are the equivalent (a) admittance, (b) conductance, and (c) susceptance of the parallel connection in millisiemens? (d) If the parallel branches are excited from a sinusoidal current source where $i = 8 \cos \omega t$ A, what is the maximum amplitude of the current in the purely capacitive branch?

9.18 a) Show that, at a given frequency ω, the circuits in Fig. P9.18(a) and (b) will have the same impedance between the terminals a,b if

$$R_1 = \frac{\omega^2 L_2^2 R_2}{R_2^2 + \omega^2 L_2^2}, \quad L_1 = \frac{R_2^2 L_2}{R_2^2 + \omega^2 L_2^2}.$$

b) Find the values of resistance and inductance that when connected in series will have the same impedance at 4 krad/s as that of a 5 kΩ resistor connected in parallel with a 1.25 H inductor.

Figure P9.18

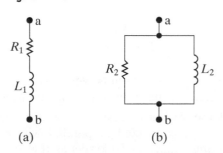

(a)　　　　(b)

9.19 a) Show that at a given frequency ω, the circuits in Fig. P9.19(a) and (b) will have the same impedance between the terminals a,b if

$$R_2 = \frac{R_1^2 + \omega^2 L_1^2}{R_1}, \quad L_2 = \frac{R_1^2 + \omega^2 L_1^2}{\omega^2 L_1}.$$

(*Hint:* The two circuits will have the same impedance if they have the same admittance.)

b) Find the values of resistance and inductance that when connected in parallel will have the same impedance at 1 krad/s as an 8 kΩ resistor connected in series with a 4 H inductor.

9.20 a) Show that at a given frequency ω, the circuits in Fig. P9.20(a) and (b) will have the same impedance between the terminals a,b if

$$R_1 = \frac{R_2}{1 + \omega^2 R_2^2 C_2^2},$$

$$C_1 = \frac{1 + \omega^2 R_2^2 C_2^2}{\omega^2 R_2^2 C_2}.$$

b) Find the values of resistance and capacitance that when connected in series will have the same impedance at 40 krad/s as that of a 1000 Ω resistor connected in parallel with a 50 nF capacitor.

Figure P9.20

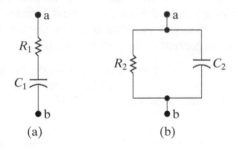

(a)   (b)

9.21 a) Show that at a given frequency ω, the circuits in Fig 9.20(a) and (b) will have the same impedance between the terminals a,b if

$$R_2 = \frac{1 + \omega^2 R_1^2 C_1^2}{\omega^2 R_1 C_1^2},$$

$$C_2 = \frac{C_1}{1 + \omega^2 R_1^2 C_1^2}.$$

(*Hint:* The two circuits will have the same impedance if they have the same admittance.)

b) Find the values of resistance and capacitance that when connected in parallel will give the same impedance at 50 krad/s as that of a 1 kΩ resistor connected in series with a capacitance of 40 nF.

9.22 Find the impedance Z_{ab} in the circuit seen in Fig. P9.22. Express Z_{ab} in both polar and rectangular form.

Figure P9.22

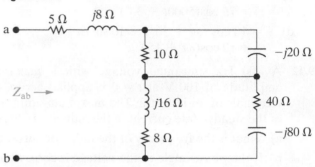

9.23 Find the admittance Y_{ab} in the circuit seen in Fig. P9.23. Express Y_{ab} in both polar and rectangular form. Give the value of Y_{ab} in millisiemens.

Figure P9.23

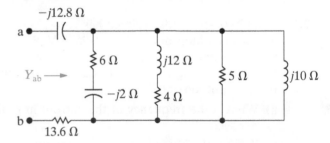

9.24 a) For the circuit shown in Fig. P9.24, find the frequency (in radians per second) at which the impedance Z_{ab} is purely resistive.

b) Find the value of Z_{ab} at the frequency of (a).

Figure P9.24

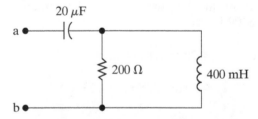

9.25 a) Using component values from Appendix H, combine at least one resistor, inductor, and capacitor in series to create an impedance of $300 - j400\ \Omega$ at a frequency of 10,000 rad/s.

b) At what frequency does the circuit from part (a) have an impedance that is purely resistive?

9.26 a) Using component values from Appendix H, combine at least one resistor and one inductor in parallel to create an impedance of $40 + j20\ \Omega$ at a frequency of 5000 rad/s. (*Hint:* Use the results of Problem 9.19.)

b) Using component values from Appendix H, combine at least one resistor and one capacitor in parallel to create an impedance of $40 - j20\ \Omega$ at a frequency of 5000 rad/s. (*Hint:* Use the result of Problem 9.21.)

9.27 a) Using component values from Appendix H, find a single capacitor or a network of capacitors that, when combined in parallel with the *RL* circuit from Problem 9.26(a), gives an equivalent impedance that is purely resistive at a frequency of 5000 rad/s.

b) Using component values from Appendix H, find a single inductor or a network of inductors that, when combined in parallel with the *RC* circuit from Problem 9.26(b), gives an equivalent impedance that is purely resistive at a frequency of 5000 rad/s.

9.28 Find the steady-state expression for $i_o(t)$ in the circuit
PSPICE in Fig. P9.28 if $v_s = 80 \cos 2000t$ V.
MULTISIM

Figure P9.28

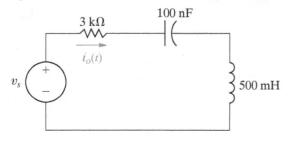

9.29 The circuit in Fig. P9.29 is operating in the sinusoidal
PSPICE steady state. Find the steady-state expression for $v_o(t)$
MULTISIM if $v_g = 60 \sin 8000t$ V.

Figure P9.29

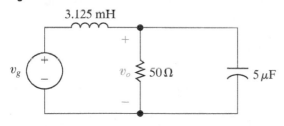

9.30 The circuit in Fig. P9.30 is operating in the sinusoidal
PSPICE steady state. Find $i_o(t)$ if $v_s(t) = 25 \sin 4000t$ V.
MULTISIM

Figure P9.30

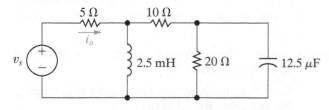

9.31 a) For the circuit shown in Fig. P9.31, find the steady-
PSPICE state expression for v_o if $i_g = 25 \cos 50,000t$ mA.
MULTISIM
b) By how many microseconds does v_o lead i_g?

Figure P9.31

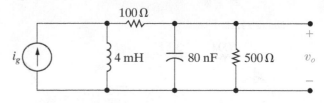

9.32 Find $\mathbf{I}_b$ and Z in the circuit shown in Fig. P9.32 if $\mathbf{V}_g = 25\ \underline{/0°}$ V and $\mathbf{I}_a = 5\ \underline{/90°}$ A.

Figure P9.32

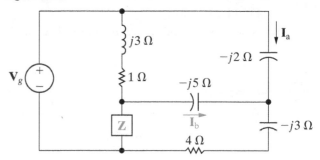

9.33 Find the value of Z in the circuit seen in Fig. P9.33 if $\mathbf{V}_g = 100 - j50$ V, $\mathbf{I}_g = 30 + j20$ A, and $\mathbf{V}_1 = 140 + j30$ V.

Figure P9.33

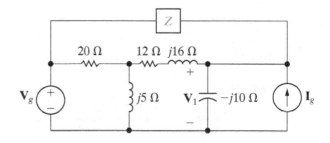

9.34 Find the steady-state expression for v_o in the circuit of Fig. P9.34 if $i_g = 60 \cos 10,000t$ mA.

Figure P9.34

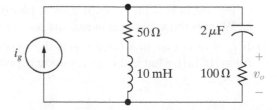

9.35 The circuit shown in Fig. P9.35 is operating in the sinusoidal steady state. Find the value of ω if

$$i_o = 40 \sin(\omega t + 21.87°) \text{ mA},$$

$$v_g = 40 \cos(\omega t - 15°) \text{ V}.$$

Figure P9.35

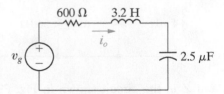

9.36 The phasor current $\mathbf{I}_b$ in the circuit shown in
PSPICE Fig. P9.36 is $25\underline{/0°}$ mA.
MULTISIM
a) Find $\mathbf{I}_a$, $\mathbf{I}_c$, and $\mathbf{I}_g$.
b) If $\omega = 1500$ rad/s, write expressions for $i_a(t)$, $i_c(t)$, and $i_g(t)$.

Figure P9.36

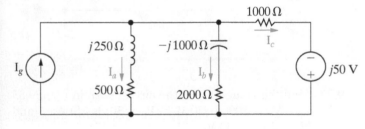

9.37 The frequency of the sinusoidal voltage source in
PSPICE the circuit in Fig. P9.37 is adjusted until the current
MULTISIM i_o is in phase with v_g.
a) Find the frequency in hertz.
b) Find the steady-state expression for i_g (at the frequency found in [a]) if $v_g = 90 \cos \omega t$ V.

Figure P9.37

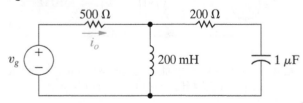

9.38 a) The frequency of the source voltage in the circuit
PSPICE in Fig. P9.38 is adjusted until v_g is in phase with
MULTISIM i_g. What is the value of ω in radians per second?
b) If $i_g = 60 \cos \omega t$ mA (where ω is the frequency found in [a]), what is the steady-state expression for v_g?

Figure P9.38

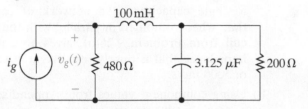

9.39 The frequency of the sinusoidal voltage source in
PSPICE the circuit in Fig. P9.39 is adjusted until i_g is in
MULTISIM phase with v_g.
a) What is the value of ω in radians per second?
b) If $v_g = 15 \cos \omega t$ V (where ω is the frequency found in [a]), what is the steady-state expression for i_g?

Figure P9.39

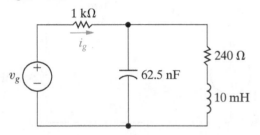

9.40 a) The source voltage in the circuit in Fig. P9.40 is
PSPICE $v_g = 40 \cos 1000t$ V. Find the values of L such
MULTISIM that i_g is in phase with v_g when the circuit is operating in the steady state.
b) For the values of L found in (a), find the steady-state expressions for i_g.

Figure P9.40

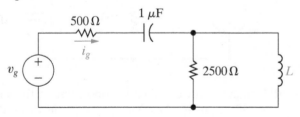

9.41 The circuit shown in Fig. P9.41 is operating in the
PSPICE sinusoidal steady state. The capacitor is adjusted
MULTISIM until the current i_g is in phase with the sinusoidal voltage v_g.
a) Specify the capacitance in microfarads if $v_g = 80 \cos 5000t$ V.
b) Give the steady-state expression for i_g when C has the value found in (a).

Figure P9.41

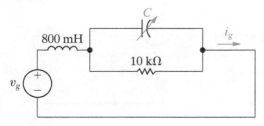

9.42 Find Z_{ab} for the circuit shown in Fig P9.42.

Figure P9.42

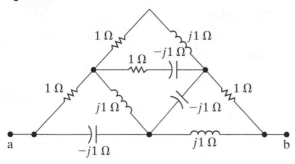

Section 9.7

9.43 The sinusoidal voltage source in the circuit in Fig. P9.43 is developing a voltage equal to $50 \sin 400t$ V.

a) Find the Thévenin voltage with respect to the terminals a,b.

b) Find the Thévenin impedance with respect to the terminals a,b.

c) Draw the Thévenin equivalent.

Figure P9.43

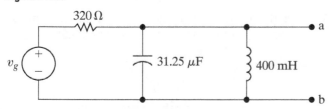

9.44 Use source transformations to find the Norton equivalent circuit with respect to the terminals a,b for the circuit shown in Fig. P9.44.

Figure P9.44

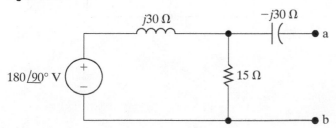

9.45 Use source transformations to find the Thévenin equivalent circuit with respect to the terminals a,b for the circuit shown in Fig. P9.45.

Figure P9.45

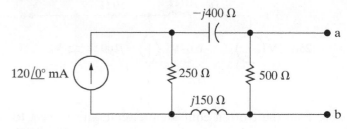

9.46 Find the Norton equivalent circuit with respect to the terminals a,b for the circuit shown in Fig. P9.46.

Figure P9.46

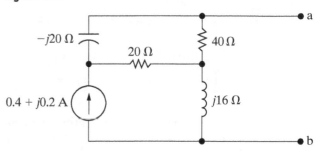

9.47 The device in Fig. P9.47 is represented in the frequency domain by a Thévenin equivalent. When a resistor having an impedance of 200 Ω is connected across the device, the value of $\mathbf{I}_0$ is $(-150 + j150)$ mA. When an inductor having an impedance of $j200$ Ω is connected across the device, the value of $\mathbf{V}_0$ is $(-40 - j40)$ V. Find the Thévenin volatge $\mathbf{V}_{Th}$ and the Thévenin impedance Z_{Th}.

Figure P9.47

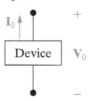

9.48 Find the Norton equivalent with respect to terminals a,b in the circuit of Fig. P9.48.

Figure P9.48

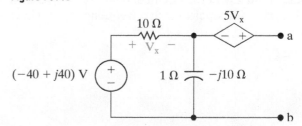

9.49 Find the Thévenin equivalent circuit with respect to the terminals a,b of the circuit shown in Fig. P9.49.

Figure P9.49

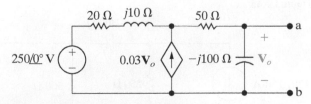

9.50 Find the Norton equivalent circuit with respect to the terminals a,b for the circuit shown in Fig. P9.50 when $\mathbf{V}_s = 5\underline{/0°}$ V.

Figure P9.50

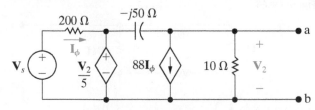

9.51 The circuit shown in Fig. P9.51 is operating at a frequency of 10 rad/s. Assume α is real and lies between -10 and $+10$, that is, $-10 \leq \alpha \leq 10$.

a) Find the value of α so that the Thévenin impedance looking into the terminals a,b is purely resistive.

b) What is the value of the Thévenin impedance for the α found in (a)?

c) Can α be adjusted so that the Thévenin impedance equals $500 - j500\ \Omega$? If so, what is the value of α?

d) For what values of α will the Thévenin impedance be inductive?

Figure P9.51

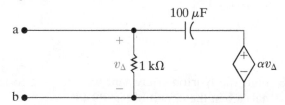

9.52 Find Z_{ab} in the circuit shown in Fig. P9.52 when the circuit is operating at a frequency of 100 krad/s.

Figure P9.52

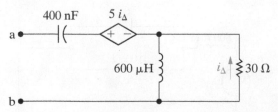

9.53 Find the Thévenin impedance seen looking into the terminals a,b of the circuit in Fig. P9.53 if the frequency of operation is $(25/\pi)$ kHz.

Figure P9.53

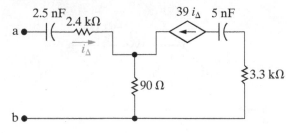

Section 9.8

9.54 Use the node-voltage method to find $\mathbf{V}_o$ in the circuit in Fig. P9.54.

Figure P9.54

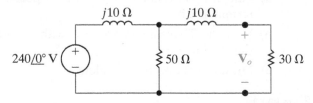

9.55 Use the node-voltage method to find the phasor voltage $\mathbf{V}_g$ in the circuit shown in Fig. P9.55.

Figure P9.55

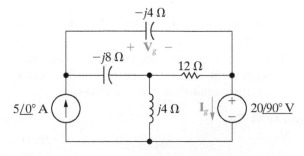

9.56 Use the node voltage method to find the steady-state
expression for i_o, in the circuit seen in Fig. P9.56 if
$i_g = 5 \cos 2500t$ A and $v_g = 20 \cos (2500t + 90°)$ V.

Figure P9.56

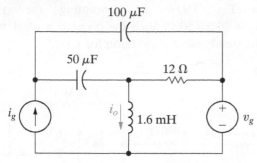

9.57 Use the node-voltage method to find the steady-
state expression for $v_o(t)$ in the circuit in Fig. P9.57 if

$$v_{g1} = 25 \sin (400t + 143.13°) \text{ V},$$

$$v_{g2} = 18.03 \cos (400t + 33.69°) \text{ V}.$$

Figure P9.57

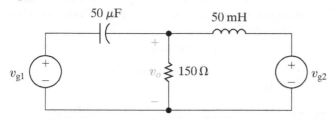

9.58 Use the node-voltage method to find the phasor
voltage $\mathbf{V}_o$ in the circuit shown in Fig. P9.58.
Express the voltage in both polar and rectangular
form.

Figure P9.58

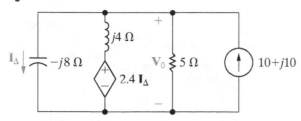

9.59 Use the node-voltage method to find $\mathbf{V}_o$ and $\mathbf{I}_o$ in
the circuit seen in Fig. P9.59.

Figure P9.59

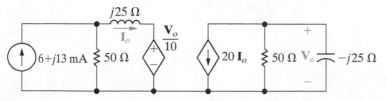

Section 9.9

9.60 Use the mesh-current method to find the phasor
current $\mathbf{I}_g$ in the circuit in Fig. P9.55.

9.61 Use the mesh-current method to find the steady-
state expression for $v_o(t)$ in the circuit in Fig. P9.57.

9.62 Use the mesh-current method to find the branch
currents $\mathbf{I}_a$, $\mathbf{I}_b$, $\mathbf{I}_c$, and $\mathbf{I}_d$ in the circuit shown in
Fig. P9.62.

Figure P9.62

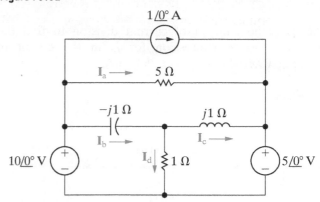

9.63 Use the mesh-current method to find the
steady-state expression for $v_o(t)$ in the circuit in
Fig. P9.63 if

$$v_a = 18 \sin 4000t \text{ V},$$

$$v_b = 12 \cos 4000t \text{ V}.$$

Figure P9.63

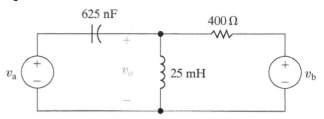

9.64 Use the mesh-current method to find the steady-
state expression for v_o in the circuit seen in
Fig. P9.64 if v_g equals $75 \cos 5000t$ V.

Figure P9.64

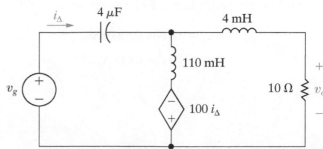

Sections 9.5–9.9

9.65 Use the concept of voltage division to find the steady-state expression for $v_o(t)$ in the circuit in Fig. P9.65 if $v_g = 120 \cos 100{,}000t$ V.

PSPICE
MULTISIM

Figure P9.65

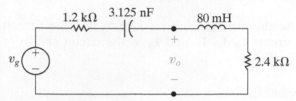

9.66 Use the concept of current division to find the steady-state expression for i_o in the circuit in Fig. P9.66 if $i_g = 60 \cos 250t$ mA.

PSPICE
MULTISIM

Figure P9.66

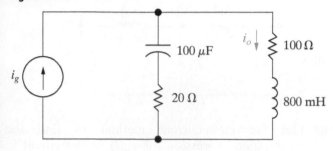

9.67 For the circuit in Fig. P9.67. Suppose

$$v_1 = 20 \cos(2000t - 36.87°) \text{ V}$$

$$v_2 = 10 \cos(5000t + 16.26°) \text{ V}$$

a) What circuit analysis technique must be used to find the steady-state expression for $v_o(t)$?

b) Find the steady-state expression for $v_o(t)$.

Figure P9.67

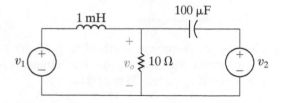

9.68 For the circuit in Fig. P9.63, suppose

$$v_a = 10 \cos 16{,}000t \text{ V}$$

$$v_b = 20 \cos 4000t \text{ V}$$

a) What circuit analysis technique must be used to find the steady-state expression for $i_o(t)$?

b) Find the steady-state expression for $i_o(t)$.

9.69 The sinusoidal voltage source in the circuit shown in Fig. P9.69 is generating the voltage $v_g = 20 \cos 5000t$ V. If the op amp is ideal, what is the steady-state expression for $v_o(t)$?

PSPICE
MULTISIM

Figure P9.69

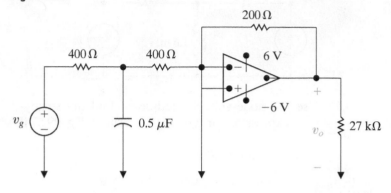

9.70 The 0.5 μF capacitor in the circuit seen in Fig. P9.69 is replaced with a variable capacitor. The capacitor is adjusted until the output voltage leads the input voltage by 135°.

PSPICE
MULTISIM

a) Find the value of C in microfarads.

b) Write the steady-state expression for $v_o(t)$ when C has the value found in (a).

9.71 The op amp in the circuit in Fig. P9.71 is ideal.

PSPICE
MULTISIM

a) Find the steady-state expression for $v_o(t)$.

b) How large can the amplitude of v_g be before the amplifier saturates?

Figure P9.71

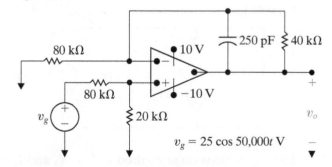

9.72 The op amp in the circuit seen in Fig. P9.72 is ideal. Find the steady-state expression for $v_o(t)$ when $v_g = 2 \cos 10^6 t$ V.

PSPICE
MULTISIM

Figure P9.72

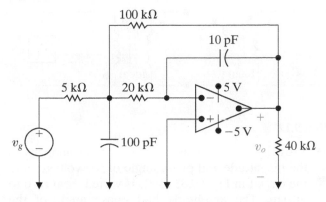

9.73 The operational amplifier in the circuit shown in
PSPICE Fig. P9.73 is ideal. The voltage of the ideal sinu-
MULTISIM soidal source is $v_g = 30 \cos 10^6 t$ V.

a) How small can C_o be before the steady-state
output voltage no longer has a pure sinusoidal
waveform?

b) For the value of C_o found in (a), write the
steady-state expression for v_o.

Figure P9.73

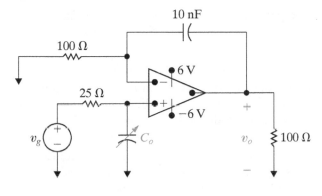

Section 9.10

9.74 The value of k in the circuit in Fig. P9.74 is adjusted
so that Z_{ab} is purely resistive when $\omega = 4$ krad/s.
Find Z_{ab}.

Figure P9.74

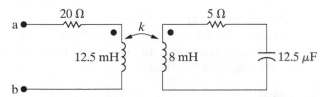

9.75 For the circuit in Fig. P9.75, find the Thévenin
equivalent with respect to the terminals c,d.

Figure P9.75

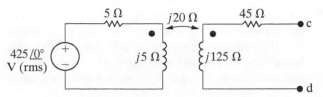

9.76 a) Find the steady-state expressions for the cur-
PSPICE rents i_g and i_L in the circuit in Fig. P9.76 when
MULTISIM $v_g = 168 \cos 800t$ V.

b) Find the coefficient of coupling.

c) Find the energy stored in the magnetically coupled coils at $t = 625\pi$ μs and $t = 1250\pi$ μs.

Figure P9.76

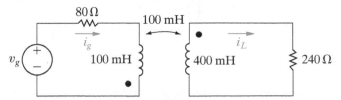

9.77 The sinusoidal voltage source in the circuit seen in
PSPICE Fig. P9.77 is operating at a frequency of 200 krad/s.
MULTISIM The coefficient of coupling is adjusted until the
peak amplitude of i_1 is maximum.

a) What is the value of k?

b) What is the peak amplitude of i_1 if
$v_g = 560 \cos(2 \times 10^5 t)$ V ?

Figure P9.77

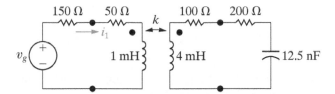

9.78 A series combination of a 60 Ω resistor and a
50 mH inductor is connected to a sinusoidal voltage
source by a linear transformer. The source is operating at a frequency of 400 rad/s. At this frequency,
the internal impedance of the source is
$(10 + j12.75)$ Ω. The rms voltage at the terminals of
the source is 75 V when it is not loaded. The parameters of the linear transformer are $R_1 = 8.34$ Ω,
$L_1 = 90$ mH, $R_2 = 100$ Ω, $L_2 = 250$ mH, and
$M = 135$ mH.

a) What is the value of the impedance reflected
into the primary?

b) What is the value of the impedance seen from
the terminals of the practical source?

Section 9.11

9.79 At first glance, it may appear from Eq. 9.69 that an inductive load could make the reactance seen looking into the primary terminals (i.e., X_{ab}) look capacitive. Intuitively, we know this is impossible. Show that X_{ab} can never be negative if X_L is an inductive reactance.

9.80 a) Show that the impedance seen looking into the terminals a,b in the circuit in Fig. P9.80 is given by the expression

$$Z_{ab} = \left(1 + \frac{N_1}{N_2}\right)^2 Z_L.$$

b) Show that if the polarity terminals of either one of the coils is reversed,

$$Z_{ab} = \left(1 - \frac{N_1}{N_2}\right)^2 Z_L.$$

Figure P9.80

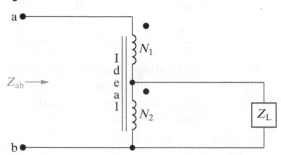

9.81 a) Show that the impedance seen looking into the terminals a,b in the circuit in Fig. P9.81 is given by the expression

$$Z_{ab} = \frac{Z_L}{\left(1 + \frac{N_1}{N_2}\right)^2}.$$

b) Show that if the polarity terminal of either one of the coils is reversed that

$$Z_{ab} = \frac{Z_L}{\left(1 - \frac{N_1}{N_2}\right)^2}.$$

Figure P9.81

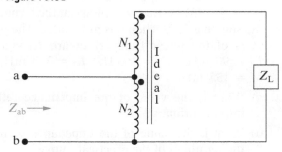

9.82 Find the impedance Z_{ab} in the circuit in Fig. P9.82 if $Z_L = 200 \angle -45° \ \Omega$.

Figure P9.82

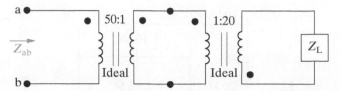

Section 9.12

9.83 Show by using a phasor diagram what happens to the magnitude and phase angle of the voltage v_o in the circuit in Fig. P9.83 as R_x is varied from zero to infinity. The amplitude and phase angle of the source voltage are held constant as R_x varies.

Figure P9.83

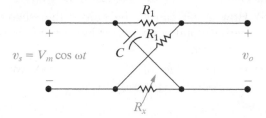

9.84 The parameters in the circuit shown in Fig. 9.53 are $R_1 = 0.1 \ \Omega, \omega L_1 = 0.8 \ \Omega, R_2 = 24 \ \Omega, \omega L_2 = 32 \ \Omega$, and $\mathbf{V}_L = 240 + j0$ V.

a) Calculate the phasor voltage $\mathbf{V}_s$.

b) Connect a capacitor in parallel with the inductor, hold $\mathbf{V}_L$ constant, and adjust the capacitor until the magnitude of $\mathbf{I}$ is a minimum. What is the capacitive reactance? What is the value of $\mathbf{V}_s$?

c) Find the value of the capacitive reactance that keeps the magnitude of $\mathbf{I}$ as small as possible and that at the same time makes

$$|\mathbf{V}_s| = |\mathbf{V}_L| = 240 \text{ V}.$$

9.85 a) For the circuit shown in Fig. P9.85, compute $\mathbf{V}_s$ and $\mathbf{V}_l$.

b) Construct a phasor diagram showing the relationship between $\mathbf{V}_s$, $\mathbf{V}_l$, and the load voltage of $240 \angle 0°$ V.

c) Repeat parts (a) and (b), given that the load voltage remains constant at $240 \angle 0°$ V, when a capacitive reactance of $-5 \ \Omega$ is connected across the load terminals.

Figure P9.85

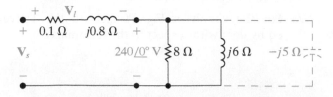

Sections 9.1–9.12

9.86 You may have the opportunity as an engineering graduate to serve as an expert witness in lawsuits involving either personal injury or property damage. As an example of the type of problem on which you may be asked to give an opinion, consider the following event. At the end of a day of fieldwork, a farmer returns to his farmstead, checks his hog confinement building, and finds to his dismay that the hogs are dead. The problem is traced to a blown fuse that caused a 240 V fan motor to stop. The loss of ventilation led to the suffocation of the livestock. The interrupted fuse is located in the main switch that connects the farmstead to the electrical service. Before the insurance company settles the claim, it wants to know if the electric circuit supplying the farmstead functioned properly. The lawyers for the insurance company are puzzled because the farmer's wife, who was in the house on the day of the accident convalescing from minor surgery, was able to watch TV during the afternoon. Furthermore, when she went to the kitchen to start preparing the evening meal, the electric clock indicated the correct time. The lawyers have hired you to explain (1) why the electric clock in the kitchen and the television set in the living room continued to operate after the fuse in the main switch blew and (2) why the second fuse in the main switch didn't blow after the fan motor stalled. After ascertaining the loads on the three-wire distribution circuit prior to the interruption of fuse A, you are able to construct the circuit model shown in Fig. P9.86. The impedances of the line conductors and the neutral conductor are assumed negligible.

a) Calculate the branch currents I_1, I_2, I_3, I_4, I_5, and I_6 prior to the interruption of fuse A.

b) Calculate the branch currents after the interruption of fuse A. Assume the stalled fan motor behaves as a short circuit.

c) Explain why the clock and television set were not affected by the momentary short circuit that interrupted fuse A.

d) Assume the fan motor is equipped with a thermal cutout designed to interrupt the motor circuit if the motor current becomes excessive. Would you expect the thermal cutout to operate? Explain.

e) Explain why fuse B is not interrupted when the fan motor stalls.

9.87 a) Calculate the branch currents I_1–I_6 in the circuit in Fig. 9.58.

PRACTICAL PERSPECTIVE

b) Find the primary current I_p.

9.88 Suppose the 40 Ω resistance in the distribution circuit in Fig. 9.58 is replaced by a 20 Ω resistance.

PRACTICAL PERSPECTIVE

a) Recalculate the branch current in the 2 Ω resistor, I_2.

b) Recalculate the primary current, I_p.

c) On the basis of your answers, is it desirable to have the resistance of the two 120 V loads be equal?

9.89 A residential wiring circuit is shown in Fig. P9.89. In this model, the resistor R_3 is used to model a 250 V appliance (such as an electric range), and the resistors R_1 and R_2 are used to model 125 V appliances (such as a lamp, toaster, and iron). The branches carrying I_1 and I_2 are modeling what electricians refer to as the hot conductors in the circuit, and the branch carrying I_n is modeling the neutral conductor. Our purpose in analyzing the circuit is to show the importance of the neutral conductor in the satisfactory operation of the circuit. You are to choose the method for analyzing the circuit.

PRACTICAL PERSPECTIVE

a) Show that I_n is zero if $R_1 = R_2$.

b) Show that $V_1 = V_2$ if $R_1 = R_2$.

c) Open the neutral branch and calculate V_1 and V_2 if $R_1 = 40 \ \Omega$, $R_2 = 400 \ \Omega$, and $R_3 = 8 \ \Omega$.

d) Close the neutral branch and repeat (c).

e) On the basis of your calculations, explain why the neutral conductor is never fused in such a manner that it could open while the hot conductors are energized.

Figure P9.89

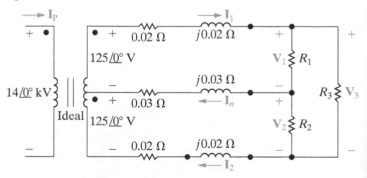

9.90 a) Find the primary current I_p for (c) and (d) in Problem 9.89.

PRACTICAL PERSPECTIVE

b) Do your answers make sense in terms of known circuit behavior?

Figure P9.86

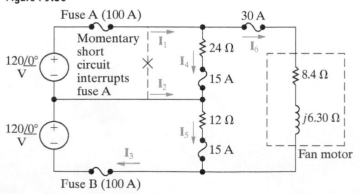

Sinusoidal Steady-State Power Calculations

✓ CHAPTER OBJECTIVES

1 Understand the following ac power concepts, their relationships to one another, and how to calculate them in a circuit:

  • Instantaneous power;

  • Average (real) power;

  • Reactive power;

  • Complex power; and

  • Power factor.

2 Understand the condition for maximum real power delivered to a load in an ac circuit and be able to calculate the load impedance required to deliver maximum real power to the load.

3 Be able to calculate all forms of ac power in ac circuits with linear transformers and in ac circuits with ideal transformers.

Power engineering has evolved into one of the important sub-disciplines within electrical engineering. The range of problems dealing with the delivery of energy to do work is considerable, from determining the power rating within which an appliance operates safely and efficiently, to designing the vast array of generators, transformers, and wires that provide electric energy to household and industrial consumers.

Nearly all electric energy is supplied in the form of sinusoidal voltages and currents. Thus, after our Chapter 9 discussion of sinusoidal circuits, this is the logical place to consider sinusoidal steady-state power calculations. We are primarily interested in the average power delivered to or supplied from a pair of terminals as a result of sinusoidal voltages and currents. Other measures, such as reactive power, complex power, and apparent power, will also be presented. The concept of the rms value of a sinusoid, briefly introduced in Chapter 9, is particularly pertinent to power calculations.

We begin and end this chapter with two concepts that should be very familiar to you from previous chapters: the basic equation for power (Section 10.1) and maximum power transfer (Section 10.6). In between, we discuss the general processes for analyzing power, which will be familiar from your studies in Chapters 1 and 4, although some additional mathematical techniques are required here to deal with sinusoidal, rather than dc, signals.

Practical Perspective

Vampire Power

In Chapter 9 we calculated the steady-state voltages and currents in electric circuits driven by sinusoidal sources. In this chapter we consider power in these circuits. The techniques we develop are useful for analyzing many of the electrical devices we encounter daily, because sinusoidal sources are the predominant means of providing electric power.

Even when we are not using many of the common electrical devices found in our homes, schools, and businesses, they may still be consuming power. This "standby power" may be used to run an internal clock, charge batteries, display time or other quantities, monitor temperature or other environmental measures, or search for signals to receive. Devices such as microwave ovens, DVRs, televisions, remote controls, and computers all consume power when not in use.

The ac adapters used to charge many portable devices are a common source of standby power. Even when the device is unplugged from the adapter, the adapter may continue to consume power if it is plugged into the wall outlet. The plug on the adapter looks like vampire fangs, so this standby power became known as "vampire power." It is power that is used even while we sleep.

How much vampire power is used by the electrical devices in our home over the course of a year? Is there a way to reduce or eliminate vampire power? These questions will be explored in the Practical Perspective example at the end of the chapter, and in the chapter problems.

borissos / fotolia

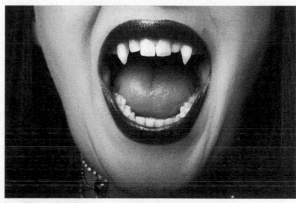

katalinks / fotolia

magraphics.eu / fotolia

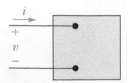

Figure 10.1 ▲ The black box representation of a circuit used for calculating power.

10.1 Instantaneous Power

We begin our investigation of sinusoidal power calculations with the familiar circuit in Fig. 10.1. Here, v and i are steady-state sinusoidal signals. Using the passive sign convention, the power at any instant of time is

$$p = vi. \tag{10.1}$$

This is **instantaneous power**. Remember that if the reference direction of the current is in the direction of the voltage rise, Eq. 10.1 must be written with a minus sign. Instantaneous power is measured in watts when the voltage is in volts and the current is in amperes. First, we write expressions for v and i:

$$v = V_m \cos(\omega t + \theta_v), \tag{10.2}$$

$$i = I_m \cos(\omega t + \theta_i), \tag{10.3}$$

where θ_v is the voltage phase angle, and θ_i is the current phase angle.

We are operating in the sinusoidal steady state, so we may choose any convenient reference for zero time. Engineers designing systems that transfer large blocks of power have found it convenient to use a zero time corresponding to the instant the current is passing through a positive maximum. This reference system requires a shift of both the voltage and current by θ_i. Thus Eqs. 10.2 and 10.3 become

$$v = V_m \cos(\omega t + \theta_v - \theta_i), \tag{10.4}$$

$$i = I_m \cos \omega t. \tag{10.5}$$

When we substitute Eqs. 10.4 and 10.5 into Eq. 10.1, the expression for the instantaneous power becomes

$$p = V_m I_m \cos(\omega t + \theta_v - \theta_i) \cos \omega t. \tag{10.6}$$

We could use Eq. 10.6 directly to find the average power; however, by simply applying a couple of trigonometric identities, we can put Eq. 10.6 into a much more informative form.

We begin with the trigonometric identity[1]

$$\cos \alpha \cos \beta = \frac{1}{2} \cos(\alpha - \beta) + \frac{1}{2} \cos(\alpha + \beta)$$

to expand Eq. 10.6; letting $\alpha = \omega t + \theta_v - \theta_i$ and $\beta = \omega t$ gives

$$p = \frac{V_m I_m}{2} \cos(\theta_v - \theta_i) + \frac{V_m I_m}{2} \cos(2\omega t + \theta_v - \theta_i). \tag{10.7}$$

Now use the trigonometric identity

$$\cos(\alpha + \beta) = \cos \alpha \cos \beta - \sin \alpha \sin \beta$$

---

[1] See entry 8 in Appendix F.

to expand the second term on the right-hand side of Eq. 10.7, which gives

$$p = \frac{V_m I_m}{2} \cos (\theta_v - \theta_i) + \frac{V_m I_m}{2} \cos (\theta_v - \theta_i) \cos 2\omega t$$

$$- \frac{V_m I_m}{2} \sin (\theta_v - \theta_i) \sin 2\omega t. \tag{10.8}$$

Figure 10.2 depicts a representative relationship among v, i, and p, based on the assumptions $\theta_v = 60°$ and $\theta_i = 0°$. You can see that the frequency of the instantaneous power is twice the frequency of the voltage or current. This observation also follows directly from the second two terms on the right-hand side of Eq. 10.8. Therefore, the instantaneous power goes through two complete cycles for every cycle of either the voltage or the current. Also note that the instantaneous power may be negative for a portion of each cycle, even if the network between the terminals is passive. In a completely passive network, negative power implies that energy stored in the inductors or capacitors is now being extracted. The fact that the instantaneous power varies with time in the sinusoidal steady-state operation of a circuit explains why some motor-driven appliances (such as refrigerators) experience vibration and require resilient motor mountings to prevent excessive vibration.

We are now ready to use Eq. 10.8 to find the average power at the terminals of the circuit represented by Fig. 10.1 and, at the same time, introduce the concept of reactive power.

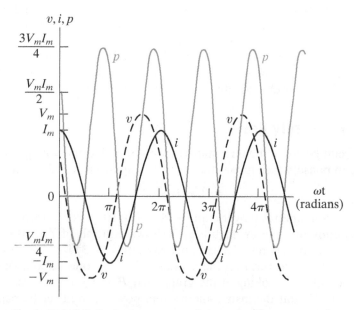

Figure 10.2 ▲ Instantaneous power, voltage, and current versus vt for steady-state sinusoidal operation.

10.2 Average and Reactive Power

We begin by noting that Eq. 10.8 has three terms, which we can rewrite as follows:

$$p = P + P \cos 2\omega t - Q \sin 2\omega t, \tag{10.9}$$

where

Average (real) power ▶

$$P = \frac{V_m I_m}{2} \cos(\theta_v - \theta_i), \qquad (10.10)$$

Reactive power ▶

$$Q = \frac{V_m I_m}{2} \sin(\theta_v - \theta_i). \qquad (10.11)$$

P is called the **average power**, and Q is called the **reactive power**. Average power is sometimes called **real power**, because it describes the power in a circuit that is transformed from electric to nonelectric energy. Although the two terms are interchangeable, we primarily use the term *average power* in this text.

It is easy to see why P is called the average power. The average power associated with sinusoidal signals is the average of the instantaneous power over one period, or, in equation form,

$$P = \frac{1}{T} \int_{t_0}^{t_0+T} p \, dt, \qquad (10.12)$$

where T is the period of the sinusoidal function. The limits on Eq. 10.12 imply that we can initiate the integration process at any convenient time t_0 but that we must terminate the integration exactly one period later. (We could integrate over nT periods, where n is an integer, provided we multiply the integral by $1/nT$.)

We could find the average power by substituting Eq. 10.9 directly into Eq. 10.12 and then performing the integration. But note that the average value of p is given by the first term on the right-hand side of Eq. 10.9, because the integral of both $\cos 2\omega t$ and $\sin 2\omega t$ over one period is zero. Thus the average power is given in Eq. 10.10.

We can develop a better understanding of all the terms in Eq. 10.9 and the relationships among them by examining the power in circuits that are purely resistive, purely inductive, or purely capacitive.

Power for Purely Resistive Circuits

If the circuit between the terminals is purely resistive, the voltage and current are in phase, which means that $\theta_v = \theta_i$. Equation 10.9 then reduces to

$$p = P + P \cos 2\omega t. \qquad (10.13)$$

The instantaneous power expressed in Eq. 10.13 is referred to as the **instantaneous real power**. Figure 10.3 shows a graph of Eq. 10.13 for a representative purely resistive circuit, assuming $\omega = 377$ rad/s. By definition, the average power, P, is the average of p over one period. Thus it is easy to see just by looking at the graph that $P = 1$ for this circuit. Note from Eq. 10.13 that the instantaneous real power can never be negative, which is also shown in Fig. 10.3. In other words, power cannot be extracted from a purely resistive network. Rather, all the electric energy is dissipated in the form of thermal energy.

Power for Purely Inductive Circuits

If the circuit between the terminals is purely inductive, the voltage and current are out of phase by precisely $90°$. In particular, the current lags the voltage by $90°$ (that is, $\theta_i = \theta_v - 90°$); therefore $\theta_v - \theta_i = +90°$. The expression for the instantaneous power then reduces to

$$p = -Q \sin 2\omega t. \qquad (10.14)$$

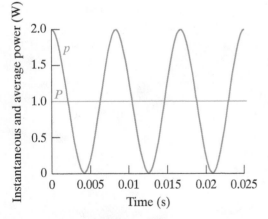

Figure 10.3 ▲ Instantaneous real power and average power for a purely resistive circuit.

In a purely inductive circuit, the average power is zero. Therefore no transformation of energy from electric to nonelectric form takes place. The instantaneous power at the terminals in a purely inductive circuit is continually exchanged between the circuit and the source driving the circuit, at a frequency of 2ω. In other words, when p is positive, energy is being stored in the magnetic fields associated with the inductive elements, and when p is negative, energy is being extracted from the magnetic fields.

A measure of the power associated with purely inductive circuits is the reactive power Q. The name *reactive power* comes from the characterization of an inductor as a reactive element; its impedance is purely reactive. Note that average power P and reactive power Q carry the same dimension. To distinguish between average and reactive power, we use the units *watt* (W) for average power and **var** (*volt-amp reactive*, or VAR) for reactive power. Figure 10.4 plots the instantaneous power for a representative purely inductive circuit, assuming $\omega = 377$ rad/s and $Q = 1$ VAR.

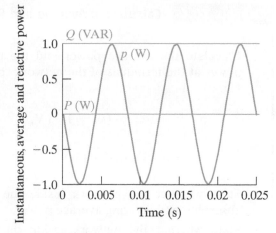

Figure 10.4 ▲ Instantaneous real power, average power, and reactive power for a purely inductive circuit.

Power for Purely Capacitive Circuits

If the circuit between the terminals is purely capacitive, the voltage and current are precisely 90° out of phase. In this case, the current leads the voltage by 90° (that is, $\theta_i = \theta_v + 90°$); thus, $\theta_v - \theta_i = -90°$. The expression for the instantaneous power then becomes

$$p = -Q\sin 2\omega t. \qquad (10.15)$$

Again, the average power is zero, so there is no transformation of energy from electric to nonelectric form. In a purely capacitive circuit, the power is continually exchanged between the source driving the circuit and the electric field associated with the capacitive elements. Figure 10.5 plots the instantaneous power for a representative purely capacitive circuit, assuming $\omega = 377$ rad/s and $Q = -1$ VAR.

Note that the decision to use the current as the reference leads to Q being positive for inductors (that is, $\theta_v - \theta_i = 90°$ and negative for capacitors (that is, $\theta_v - \theta_i = -90°$. Power engineers recognize this difference in the algebraic sign of Q by saying that inductors demand (or absorb) magnetizing vars, and capacitors furnish (or deliver) magnetizing vars. We say more about this convention later.

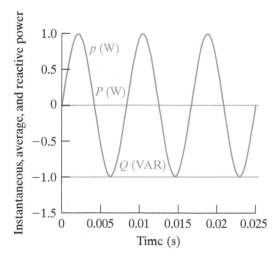

Figure 10.5 ▲ Instantaneous real power and average power for a purely capacitive circuit.

The Power Factor

The angle $\theta_v - \theta_i$ plays a role in the computation of both average and reactive power and is referred to as the **power factor angle**. The cosine of this angle is called the **power factor**, abbreviated pf, and the sine of this angle is called the **reactive factor**, abbreviated rf. Thus

$$pf = \cos(\theta_v - \theta_i), \qquad (10.16)$$

◄ **Power factor**

$$rf = \sin(\theta_v - \theta_i). \qquad (10.17)$$

Knowing the value of the power factor does not tell you the value of the power factor angle, because $\cos(\theta_v - \theta_i) = \cos(\theta_i - \theta_v)$. To completely describe this angle, we use the descriptive phrases **lagging power factor** and **leading power factor**. Lagging power factor implies that current lags voltage—hence an inductive load. Leading power factor implies that current leads voltage—hence a capacitive load. Both the power factor and the reactive factor are convenient quantities to use in describing electrical loads.

Example 10.1 illustrates the interpretation of P and Q on the basis of a numerical calculation.

Example 10.1   Calculating Average and Reactive Power

a) Calculate the average power and the reactive power at the terminals of the network shown in Fig. 10.6 if

$$v = 100 \cos (\omega t + 15°) \text{ V},$$

$$i = 4 \sin (\omega t - 15°) \text{ A}.$$

b) State whether the network inside the box is absorbing or delivering average power.

c) State whether the network inside the box is absorbing or supplying magnetizing vars.

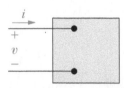

Figure 10.6 ▲ A pair of terminals used for calculating power.

Solution

a) Because i is expressed in terms of the sine function, the first step in the calculation for P and Q is to rewrite i as a cosine function:

$$i = 4 \cos (\omega t - 105°) \text{ A}.$$

We now calculate P and Q directly from Eqs. 10.10 and 10.11. Thus

$$P = \frac{1}{2}(100)(4) \cos [15 - (-105)] = -100 \text{ W},$$

$$Q = \frac{1}{2}100(4) \sin [15 - (-105)] = 173.21 \text{ VAR}.$$

b) Note from Fig. 10.6 the use of the passive sign convention. Because of this, the negative value of -100 W means that the network inside the box is delivering average power to the terminals.

c) The passive sign convention means that, because Q is positive, the network inside the box is absorbing magnetizing vars at its terminals.

✓ ASSESSMENT PROBLEMS

Objective 1—Understand ac power concepts, their relationships to one another, and how to calcuate them in a circuit

10.1 For each of the following sets of voltage and current, calculate the real and reactive power in the line between networks A and B in the circuit shown. In each case, state whether the power flow is from A to B or vice versa. Also state whether magnetizing vars are being transferred from A to B or vice versa.

a) $v = 100 \cos (\omega t - 45°)$ V;
$i = 20 \cos (\omega t + 15°)$ A.

b) $v = 100 \cos (\omega t - 45°)$ V;
$i = 20 \cos (\omega t + 165°)$ A.

c) $v = 100 \cos (\omega t - 45°)$ V;
$i = 20 \cos (\omega t - 105°)$ A.

d) $v = 100 \cos \omega t$ V;
$i = 20 \cos (\omega t + 120°)$ A.

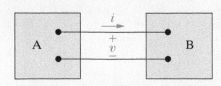

NOTE: Also try Chapter Problem 10.1.

Answer: (a) $P = 500$ W   (A to B),
$Q = -866.03$ VAR (B to A);

(b) $P = -866.03$ W   (B to A),
$Q = 500$ VAR   (A to B);

(c) $P = 500$ W   (A to B),
$Q = 866.03$ VAR   (A to B);

(d) $P = -500$ W   (B to A),
$Q = -866.03$ VAR (B to A).

10.2 Compute the power factor and the reactive factor for the network inside the box in Fig. 10.6, whose voltage and current are described in Example 10.1.

Hint: Use $-i$ to calculate the power and reactive factors.

Answer: pf $= 0.5$ leading; rf $= -0.866$.

365 Average and Reactive Power

Appliance Ratings

Average power is used to quantify the power needs of household appliances. The average power rating and estimated annual kilowatt-hour consumption of some common appliances are presented in Table 10.1. The energy consumption values are obtained by estimating the number of hours annually that the appliances are in use. For example, a coffeemaker has an estimated annual consumption of 140 kWh and an average power consumption during operation of 1.2 kW. Therefore a coffeemaker is assumed to be in operation 140/1.2, or 116.67, hours per year, or approximately 19 minutes per day.

Example 10.2 uses Table 10.1 to determine whether four common appliances can all be in operation without exceeding the current-carrying capacity of the household.

Example 10.2   **Making Power Calculations Involving Household Appliances**

The branch circuit supplying the outlets in a typical home kitchen is wired with #12 conductor and is protected by either a 20 A fuse or a 20 A circuit breaker. Assume that the following 120 V appliances are in operation at the same time: a coffeemaker, egg cooker, frying pan, and toaster. Will the circuit be interrupted by the protective device?

Solution

From Table 10.1, the total average power demanded by the four appliances is

$$P = 1200 + 516 + 1196 + 1146 = 4058 \text{ W}.$$

The total current in the protective device is

$$I_{\text{eff}} = \frac{4058}{120} \approx 33.82 \text{ A}.$$

Yes, the protective device will interrupt the circuit.

TABLE 10.1   Annual Energy Requirements of Electric Household Appliances

Appliance	Average Wattage	Est. kWh Consumed Annually[a]	Appliance	Average Wattage	Est. kWh Consumed Annually[a]
Food preparation			**Health and beauty**		
Coffeemaker	1200	140	Hair dryer	600	25
Dishwasher	1201	165	Shaver	15	0.5
Egg cooker	516	14	Sunlamp	279	16
Frying pan	1196	100	**Home entertainment**		
Mixer	127	2	Radio	71	86
Oven, microwave (only)	1450	190	Television, color, tube type	240	528
Range, with oven	12,200	596	Solid-state type	145	320
Toaster	1146	39	**Housewares**		
Laundry			Clock	2	17
Clothes dryer	4856	993	Vacuum cleaner	630	46
Washing machine, automatic	512	103			
Water heater	2475	4219			
Quick recovery type	4474	4811			
Comfort conditioning					
Air conditioner (room)	860	860[b]			
Dehumidifier	257	377			
Fan (circulating)	88	43			
Heater (portable)	1322	176			

a) Based on normal usage. When using these figures for projections, such factors as the size of the specific appliance, the geographical area of use, and individual usage should be taken into consideration. Note that the wattages are not additive, since all units are normally not in operation at the same time.

b) Based on 1000 hours of operation per year. This figure will vary widely depending on the area and the specific size of the unit. See EEI-Pub #76-2, "Air Conditioning Usage Study," for an estimate for your location.

Source: Edison Electric Institute.

NOTE: Assess your understanding of this material by trying Chapter Problem 10.2.

10.3 The rms Value and Power Calculations

In introducing the rms value of a sinusoidal voltage (or current) in Section 9.1, we mentioned that it would play an important role in power calculations. We can now discuss this role.

Assume that a sinusoidal voltage is applied to the terminals of a resistor, as shown in Fig. 10.7, and that we want to determine the average power delivered to the resistor. From Eq. 10.12,

$$P = \frac{1}{T}\int_{t_0}^{t_0+T} \frac{V_m^2 \cos^2(\omega t + \phi_v)}{R} dt$$

$$= \frac{1}{R}\left[\frac{1}{T}\int_{t_0}^{t_0+T} V_m^2 \cos^2(\omega t + \phi_v) dt\right]. \tag{10.18}$$

Comparing Eq. 10.18 with Eq. 9.5 reveals that the average power delivered to R is simply the rms value of the voltage squared divided by R, or

$$P = \frac{V_{rms}^2}{R}. \tag{10.19}$$

If the resistor is carrying a sinusoidal current, say, $I_m \cos(\omega t + \phi_i)$, the average power delivered to the resistor is

$$P = I_{rms}^2 R. \tag{10.20}$$

The rms value is also referred to as the **effective value** of the sinusoidal voltage (or current). The rms value has an interesting property: Given an equivalent resistive load, R, and an equivalent time period, T, the rms value of a sinusoidal source delivers the same energy to R as does a dc source of the same value. For example, a dc source of 100 V delivers the same energy in T seconds that a sinusoidal source of 100 V_{rms} delivers, assuming equivalent load resistances (see Problem 10.12). Figure 10.8 demonstrates this equivalence. Energywise, the effect of the two sources is identical. This has led to the term *effective value* being used interchangeably with *rms value*.

The average power given by Eq. 10.10 and the reactive power given by Eq. 10.11 can be written in terms of effective values:

$$P = \frac{V_m I_m}{2}\cos(\theta_v - \theta_i)$$

$$= \frac{V_m}{\sqrt{2}}\frac{I_m}{\sqrt{2}}\cos(\theta_v - \theta_i)$$

$$= V_{eff}I_{eff}\cos(\theta_v - \theta_i); \tag{10.21}$$

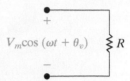

Figure 10.7 ▲ A sinusoidal voltage applied to the terminals of a resistor.

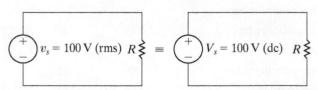

Figure 10.8 ▲ The effective value of v_s (100 V rms) delivers the same power to R as the dc voltage V_s (100 V dc).

and, by similar manipulation,

$$Q = V_{\text{eff}}I_{\text{eff}} \sin (\theta_v - \theta_i). \qquad (10.22)$$

The effective value of the sinusoidal signal in power calculations is so widely used that voltage and current ratings of circuits and equipment involved in power utilization are given in terms of rms values. For example, the voltage rating of residential electric wiring is often 240 V/120 V service. These voltage levels are the rms values of the sinusoidal voltages supplied by the utility company, which provides power at two voltage levels to accommodate low-voltage appliances (such as televisions) and higher voltage appliances (such as electric ranges). Appliances such as electric lamps, irons, and toasters all carry rms ratings on their nameplates. For example, a 120 V, 100 W lamp has a resistance of $120^2/100$, or 144 Ω, and draws an rms current of 120/144, or 0.833 A. The peak value of the lamp current is $0.833\sqrt{2}$, or 1.18 A.

The phasor transform of a sinusoidal function may also be expressed in terms of the rms value. The magnitude of the rms phasor is equal to the rms value of the sinusoidal function. If a phasor is based on the rms value, we indicate this by either an explicit statement, a parenthetical "rms" adjacent to the phasor quantity, or the subscript "eff," as in Eq. 10.21.

In Example 10.3, we illustrate the use of rms values for calculating power.

Example 10.3   Determining Average Power Delivered to a Resistor by Sinusoidal Voltage

a) A sinusoidal voltage having a maximum amplitude of 625 V is applied to the terminals of a 50 Ω resistor. Find the average power delivered to the resistor.

b) Repeat (a) by first finding the current in the resistor.

Solution

a) The rms value of the sinusoidal voltage is $625/\sqrt{2}$, or approximately 441.94 V. From Eq. 10.19, the average power delivered to the 50 Ω resistor is

$$P = \frac{(441.94)^2}{50} = 3906.25 \text{ W}.$$

b) The maximum amplitude of the current in the resistor is 625/50, or 12.5 A. The rms value of the current is $12.5/\sqrt{2}$, or approximately 8.84 A. Hence the average power delivered to the resistor is

$$P = (8.84)^2 50 = 3906.25 \text{ W}.$$

✓ ASSESSMENT PROBLEM

Objective 1—Understand ac power concepts, their relationships to one another, and how to calculate them in a circuit

10.3 The periodic triangular current in Example 9.4, repeated here, has a peak value of 180 mA. Find the average power that this current delivers to a 5 kΩ resistor.

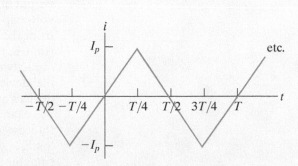

Answer: 54 W.

NOTE: Also try Chapter Problem 10.15.

10.4 Complex Power

Before proceeding to the various methods of calculating real and reactive power in circuits operating in the sinusoidal steady state, we need to introduce and define complex power. **Complex power** is the complex sum of real power and reactive power, or

Complex power ▶

$$S = P + jQ. \tag{10.23}$$

As you will see, we can compute the complex power directly from the voltage and current phasors for a circuit. Equation 10.23 can then be used to compute the average power and the reactive power, because $P = \Re\{S\}$ and $Q = \Im\{S\}$.

Dimensionally, complex power is the same as average or reactive power. However, to distinguish complex power from either average or reactive power, we use the units **volt-amps** (VA). Thus we use volt-amps for complex power, watts for average power, and vars for reactive power, as summarized in Table 10.2.

Another advantage of using complex power is the geometric interpretation it provides. When working with Eq. 10.23, think of P, Q, and $|S|$ as the sides of a right triangle, as shown in Fig. 10.9. It is easy to show that the angle θ in the power triangle is the power factor angle $\theta_v - \theta_i$. For the right triangle shown in Fig. 10.9,

$$\tan \theta = \frac{Q}{P}. \tag{10.24}$$

But from the definitions of P and Q (Eqs. [10.10] and [10.11], respectively),

$$\frac{Q}{P} = \frac{(V_m I_m/2) \sin (\theta_v - \theta_i)}{(V_m I_m/2) \cos (\theta_v - \theta_i)}$$

$$= \tan (\theta_v - \theta_i). \tag{10.25}$$

Therefore, $\theta = \theta_v - \theta_i$. The geometric relations for a right triangle mean also that the four power triangle dimensions (the three sides and the power factor angle) can be determined if any two of the four are known.

The magnitude of complex power is referred to as **apparent power**. Specifically,

Apparent power ▶

$$|S| = 2\ \overline{P^2 + Q^2}. \tag{10.26}$$

Apparent power, like complex power, is measured in volt-amps. The apparent power, or volt-amp, requirement of a device designed to convert electric energy to a nonelectric form is more important than the average power requirement. Although the average power represents the useful output of the energy-converting device, the apparent power represents the volt-amp capacity required to supply the average power. As you can see from the power triangle in Fig. 10.9, unless the power factor angle is 0° (that is, the device is purely resistive, pf = 1, and $Q = 0$), the volt-amp capacity required by the device is larger than the average power used by the device. As we will see in Example 10.6, it makes sense to operate devices at a power factor close to 1.

Many useful appliances (such as refrigerators, fans, air conditioners, fluorescent lighting fixtures, and washing machines) and most industrial loads operate at a lagging power factor. The power factor of these loads sometimes is corrected either by adding a capacitor to the device itself or

TABLE 10.2 Three Power Quantities and Their Units

Quantity	Units
Complex power	volt-amps
Average power	watts
Reactive power	var

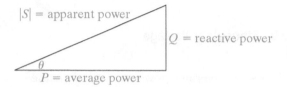

Figure 10.9 ▲ A power triangle.

by connecting capacitors across the line feeding the load; the latter method is often used for large industrial loads. Many of the Chapter Problems give you a chance to make some calculations that correct a lagging power factor load and improve the operation of a circuit.

Example 10.4 uses a power triangle to calculate several quantities associated with an electrical load.

Example 10.4   **Calculating Complex Power**

An electrical load operates at 240 V rms. The load absorbs an average power of 8 kW at a lagging power factor of 0.8.

a) Calculate the complex power of the load.

b) Calculate the impedance of the load.

Solution

a) The power factor is described as lagging, so we know that the load is inductive and that the algebraic sign of the reactive power is positive. From the power triangle shown in Fig. 10.10,

$$P = |S| \cos \theta,$$

$$Q = |S| \sin \theta.$$

Now, because $\cos \theta = 0.8$, $\sin \theta = 0.6$. Therefore

$$|S| = \frac{P}{\cos \theta} = \frac{8\ kW}{0.8} = 10\ kVA,$$

$$Q = 10 \sin \theta = 6\ kVAR,$$

and

$$S = 8 + j6\ kVA.$$

b) From the computation of the complex power of the load, we see that $P = 8$ kW. Using Eq. 10.21,

$$P = V_{eff}I_{eff} \cos (\theta_v - \theta_i)$$

$$= (240)I_{eff}(0.8)$$

$$= 8000\ W.$$

Solving for I_{eff},

$$I_{eff} = 41.67\ A.$$

We already know the angle of the load impedance, because it is the power factor angle:

$$\theta = \cos^{-1}(0.8) = 36.87°.$$

We also know that θ is positive because the power factor is lagging, indicating an inductive load. We compute the magnitude of the load impedance from its definition as the ratio of the magnitude of the voltage to the magnitude of the current:

$$|Z| = \frac{|V_{eff}|}{|I_{eff}|} = \frac{240}{41.67} = 5.76.$$

Hence,

$$Z = 5.76\ \underline{/36.87°}\ \Omega = 4.608 + j3.456\ \Omega.$$

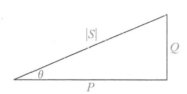

Figure 10.10 ▲ A power triangle.

10.5 Power Calculations

We are now ready to develop additional equations that can be used to calculate real, reactive, and complex power. We begin by combining Eqs. 10.10, 10.11, and 10.23 to get

$$S = \frac{V_m I_m}{2} \cos (\theta_v - \theta_i) + j\frac{V_m I_m}{2} \sin (\theta_v - \theta_i)$$

$$= \frac{V_m I_m}{2} [\cos (\theta_v - \theta_i) + j \sin (\theta_v - \theta_i)]$$

$$= \frac{V_m I_m}{2} e^{j(\theta_v - \theta_i)} = \frac{1}{2} V_m I_m \underline{/(\theta_v - \theta_i)}. \tag{10.27}$$

If we use the effective values of the sinusoidal voltage and current, Eq. 10.27 becomes

$$S = V_{\text{eff}}I_{\text{eff}}\underline{/(\theta_v - \theta_i)}. \tag{10.28}$$

Equations 10.27 and 10.28 are important relationships in power calculations because they show that if the phasor current and voltage are known at a pair of terminals, the complex power associated with that pair of terminals is either one half the product of the voltage and the conjugate of the current, or the product of the rms phasor voltage and the conjugate of the rms phasor current. We can show this for the rms phasor voltage and current in Fig. 10.11 as follows:

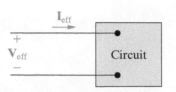

Figure 10.11 ▲ The phasor voltage and current associated with a pair of terminals.

$$S = V_{\text{eff}}I_{\text{eff}}\underline{/(\theta_v - \theta_i)}$$

$$= V_{\text{eff}}I_{\text{eff}}e^{j(\theta_v - \theta_i)}$$

$$= V_{\text{eff}}e^{j\theta_v}I_{\text{eff}}e^{-j\theta_i}$$

Complex power ▶

$$= \mathbf{V}_{\text{eff}}\mathbf{I}_{\text{eff}}^*. \tag{10.29}$$

Note that $\mathbf{I}_{\text{eff}}^* = I_{\text{eff}}e^{-j\theta_i}$ follows from Euler's identity and the trigonometric identities $\cos(-\theta) = \cos(\theta)$ and $\sin(-\theta) = -\sin(\theta)$:

$$I_{\text{eff}}e^{-j\theta_i} = I_{\text{eff}}\cos(-\theta_i) + jI_{\text{eff}}\sin(-\theta_i)$$

$$= I_{\text{eff}}\cos(\theta_i) - jI_{\text{eff}}\sin(\theta_i)$$

$$= \mathbf{I}_{\text{eff}}^*.$$

The same derivation technique could be applied to Eq. 10.27 to yield

$$S = \frac{1}{2}\mathbf{V}\mathbf{I}^*. \tag{10.30}$$

Both Eqs. 10.29 and 10.30 are based on the passive sign convention. If the current reference is in the direction of the voltage rise across the terminals, we insert a minus sign on the right-hand side of each equation.

To illustrate the use of Eq. 10.30 in a power calculation, let's use the same circuit that we used in Example 10.1. Expressed in terms of the phasor representation of the terminal voltage and current,

$$\mathbf{V} = 100\ \underline{/15°}\ \text{V},$$

$$\mathbf{I} = 4\underline{/-105°}\ \text{A}.$$

Therefore

$$S = \frac{1}{2}(100\ \underline{/15°})(4\ \underline{/+105°}) = 200\ \underline{/120°}$$

$$= -100 + j173.21\ \text{VA}.$$

Once we calculate the complex power, we can read off both the real and reactive powers, because $S = P + jQ$. Thus

$$P = -100 \text{ W},$$

$$Q = 173.21 \text{ VAR}.$$

The interpretations of the algebraic signs on P and Q are identical to those given in the solution of Example 10.1.

Alternate Forms for Complex Power

Equations 10.29 and 10.30 have several useful variations. Here, we use the rms value form of the equations, because rms values are the most common type of representation for voltages and currents in power computations.

The first variation of Eq. 10.29 is to replace the voltage with the product of the current times the impedance. In other words, we can always represent the circuit inside the box of Fig. 10.11 by an equivalent impedance, as shown in Fig. 10.12. Then,

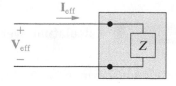

Figure 10.12 ▲ The general circuit of Fig. 10.11 replaced with an equivalent impedance.

$$\mathbf{V}_{\text{eff}} = Z\mathbf{I}_{\text{eff}}. \tag{10.31}$$

Substituting Eq. 10.31 into Eq. 10.29 yields

$$S = Z\mathbf{I}_{\text{eff}}\mathbf{I}_{\text{eff}}^{*}$$

$$= |\mathbf{I}_{\text{eff}}|^{2}Z$$

$$= |\mathbf{I}_{\text{eff}}|^{2}(R + jX)$$

$$= |\mathbf{I}_{\text{eff}}|^{2}R + j|\mathbf{I}_{\text{eff}}|^{2}X = P + jQ, \tag{10.32}$$

from which

$$P = |\mathbf{I}_{\text{eff}}|^{2}R = \frac{1}{2}I_{m}^{2}R, \tag{10.33}$$

$$Q = |\mathbf{I}_{\text{eff}}|^{2}X = \frac{1}{2}I_{m}^{2}X. \tag{10.34}$$

In Eq. 10.34, X is the reactance of either the equivalent inductance or equivalent capacitance of the circuit. Recall from our earlier discussion of reactance that it is positive for inductive circuits and negative for capacitive circuits.

A second useful variation of Eq. 10.29 comes from replacing the current with the voltage divided by the impedance:

$$S = \mathbf{V}_{\text{eff}}\left(\frac{\mathbf{V}_{\text{eff}}}{Z}\right)^{*} = \frac{|\mathbf{V}_{\text{eff}}|^{2}}{Z^{*}} = P + jQ. \tag{10.35}$$

Note that if Z is a pure resistive element,

$$P = \frac{|\mathbf{V}_{\text{eff}}|^2}{R}, \qquad (10.36)$$

and if Z is a pure reactive element,

$$Q = \frac{|\mathbf{V}_{\text{eff}}|^2}{X}. \qquad (10.37)$$

In Eq. 10.37, X is positive for an inductor and negative for a capacitor.

The following examples demonstrate various power calculations in circuits operating in the sinusoidal steady state.

Example 10.5   Calculating Average and Reactive Power

In the circuit shown in Fig. 10.13, a load having an impedance of $39 + j26 \ \Omega$ is fed from a voltage source through a line having an impedance of $1 + j4 \ \Omega$. The effective, or rms, value of the source voltage is 250 V.

a) Calculate the load current $\mathbf{I}_L$ and voltage $\mathbf{V}_L$.

b) Calculate the average and reactive power delivered to the load.

c) Calculate the average and reactive power delivered to the line.

d) Calculate the average and reactive power supplied by the source.

Thus the load is absorbing an average power of 975 W and a reactive power of 650 VAR.

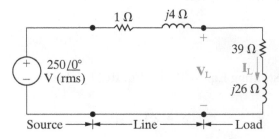

Figure 10.13 ▲ The circuit for Example 10.5.

Solution

a) The line and load impedances are in series across the voltage source, so the load current equals the voltage divided by the total impedance, or

$$\mathbf{I}_L = \frac{250 \ \underline{/0^\circ}}{40 + j30} = 4 - j3 = 5 \ \underline{/-36.87^\circ} \text{ A (rms).}$$

Because the voltage is given in terms of its rms value, the current also is rms. The load voltage is the product of the load current and load impedance:

$$\mathbf{V}_L = (39 + j26)\mathbf{I}_L = 234 - j13$$

$$= 234.36 \ \underline{/-3.18^\circ} \text{ V (rms).}$$

b) The average and reactive power delivered to the load can be computed using Eq. 10.29. Therefore

$$S = \mathbf{V}_L \mathbf{I}_L^* = (234 - j13)(4 + j3)$$

$$= 975 + j650 \text{ VA.}$$

c) The average and reactive power delivered to the line are most easily calculated from Eqs. 10.33 and 10.34 because the line current is known. Thus

$$P = (5)^2(1) = 25 \text{ W,}$$

$$Q = (5)^2(4) = 100 \text{ VAR.}$$

Note that the reactive power associated with the line is positive because the line reactance is inductive.

d) One way to calculate the average and reactive power delivered by the source is to add the complex power delivered to the line to that delivered to the load, or

$$S = 25 + j100 + 975 + j650$$

$$= 1000 + j750 \text{ VA.}$$

The complex power at the source can also be calculated from Eq. 10.29:

$$S_s = -250\mathbf{I}_L^*.$$

The minus sign is inserted in Eq. 10.29 whenever the current reference is in the direction of a voltage rise. Thus

$$S_s = -250(4 + j3) = -(1000 + j750) \text{ VA.}$$

The minus sign implies that both average power and magnetizing reactive power are being delivered by the source. Note that this result agrees with the previous calculation of S, as it must, because the source must furnish all the average and reactive power absorbed by the line and load.

Example 10.6   Calculating Power in Parallel Loads

The two loads in the circuit shown in Fig. 10.14 can be described as follows: Load 1 absorbs an average power of 8 kW at a leading power factor of 0.8. Load 2 absorbs 20 kVA at a lagging power factor of 0.6.

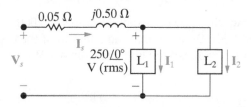

Figure 10.14 ▲ The circuit for Example 10.6.

a) Determine the power factor of the two loads in parallel.

b) Determine the apparent power required to supply the loads, the magnitude of the current, $\mathbf{I}_s$, and the average power loss in the transmission line.

c) Given that the frequency of the source is 60 Hz, compute the value of the capacitor that would correct the power factor to 1 if placed in parallel with the two loads. Recompute the values in (b) for the load with the corrected power factor.

Solution

a) All voltage and current phasors in this problem are assumed to represent effective values. Note from the circuit diagram in Fig. 10.14 that $\mathbf{I}_s = \mathbf{I}_1 + \mathbf{I}_2$. The total complex power absorbed by the two loads is

$$S = (250)\mathbf{I}_s^*$$

$$= (250)(\mathbf{I}_1 + \mathbf{I}_2)^*$$

$$= (250)\mathbf{I}_1^* + (250)\mathbf{I}_2^*$$

$$= S_1 + S_2.$$

We can sum the complex powers geometrically, using the power triangles for each load, as shown in Fig. 10.15. By hypothesis,

$$S_1 = 8000 - j\frac{8000(.6)}{(.8)}$$

$$= 8000 - j6000 \text{ VA,}$$

$$S_2 = 20,000(.6) + j20,000(.8)$$

$$= 12,000 + j16,000 \text{ VA.}$$

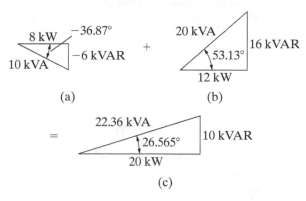

Figure 10.15 ▲ (a) The power triangle for load 1. (b) The power triangle for load 2. (c) The sum of the power triangles.

It follows that

$$S = 20,000 + j10,000 \text{ VA,}$$

and

$$\mathbf{I}_s^* = \frac{20,000 + j10,000}{250} = 80 + j40 \text{ A.}$$

Therefore

$$\mathbf{I}_s = 80 - j40 = 89.44 \underline{/-26.57°} \text{ A.}$$

Thus the power factor of the combined load is

$$\text{pf} = \cos(0 + 26.57°) = 0.8944 \text{ lagging.}$$

The power factor of the two loads in parallel is lagging because the net reactive power is positive.

b) The apparent power which must be supplied to these loads is

$$|S| = |20 + j10| = 22.36 \text{ kVA.}$$

The magnitude of the current that supplies this apparent power is

$$|\mathbf{I}_s| = |80 - j40| = 89.44 \text{ A.}$$

The average power lost in the line results from the current flowing through the line resistance:

$$P_{\text{line}} = |\mathbf{I}_s|^2 R = (89.44)^2 (0.05) = 400\ W$$

Note that the power supplied totals $20{,}000 + 400 = 20{,}400\ W$, even though the loads require a total of only $20{,}000\ W$.

c) As we can see from the power triangle in Fig. 10.15(c), we can correct the power factor to 1 if we place a capacitor in parallel with the existing loads such that the capacitor supplies 10 kVAR of magnetizing reactive power. The value of the capacitor is calculated as follows. First, find the capacitive reactance from Eq. 10.37:

$$X = \frac{|V_{\text{eff}}|^2}{Q}$$

$$= \frac{(250)^2}{-10{,}000}$$

$$= -6.25\ \Omega.$$

Recall that the reactive impedance of a capacitor is $-1/\omega C$, and $\omega = 2\pi(60) = 376.99\ \text{rad/s}$, if the source frequency is 60 Hz. Thus,

$$C = \frac{-1}{\omega X} = \frac{-1}{(376.99)(-6.25)} = 424.4\ \mu F.$$

The addition of the capacitor as the third load is represented in geometric form as the sum of the two power triangles shown in Fig. 10.16. When

the power factor is 1, the apparent power and the average power are the same, as seen from the power triangle in Fig. 10.16(c). Therefore, the apparent power once the power factor has been corrected is

$$|S| = P = 20\ \text{kVA}.$$

The magnitude of the current that supplies this apparent power is

$$|\mathbf{I}_s| = \frac{20{,}000}{250} = 80\ A.$$

The average power lost in the line is thus reduced to

$$P_{\text{line}} = |\mathbf{I}_s|^2 R = (80)^2 (0.05) = 320\ W.$$

Now, the power supplied totals $20{,}000 + 320 = 20{,}320\ W$. Note that the addition of the capacitor has reduced the line loss from 400 W to 320 W.

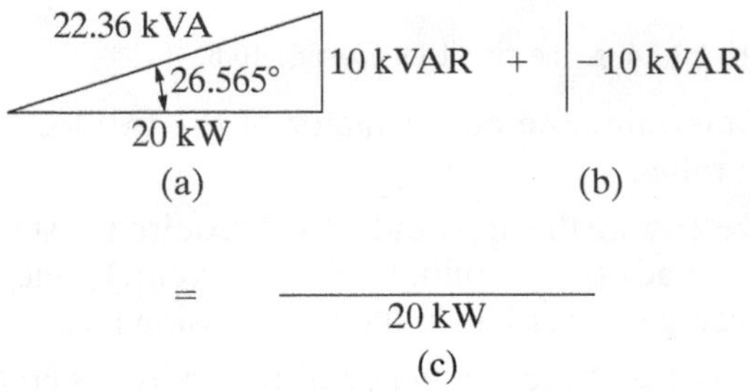

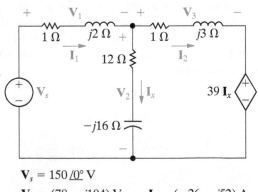

Figure 10.16 ▲ (a) The sum of the power triangles for loads 1 and 2. (b) The power triangle for a 424.4 μF capacitor at 60 Hz. (c) The sum of the power triangles in (a) and (b).

Example 10.7 **Balancing Power Delivered with Power Absorbed in an ac Circuit**

a) Calculate the total average and reactive power delivered to each impedance in the circuit shown in Fig. 10.17.

b) Calculate the average and reactive powers associated with each source in the circuit.

c) Verify that the average power delivered equals the average power absorbed, and that the magnetizing reactive power delivered equals the magnetizing reactive power absorbed.

$\mathbf{V}_s = 150\ \underline{/0^\circ}\ \text{V}$

$\mathbf{V}_1 = (78 - j104)\ \text{V}$ $\mathbf{I}_1 = (-26 - j52)\ \text{A}$

$\mathbf{V}_2 = (72 + j104)\ \text{V}$ $\mathbf{I}_x = (-2 + j6)\ \text{A}$

$\mathbf{V}_3 = (150 - j130)\ \text{V}$ $\mathbf{I}_2 = (-24 - j58)\ \text{A}$

Figure 10.17 ▲ The circuit, with solution, for Example 10.7.

Solution

a) The complex power delivered to the $(1 + j2)\ \Omega$ impedance is

$$S_1 = \frac{1}{2}\mathbf{V}_1\mathbf{I}_1^* = P_1 + jQ_1$$

$$= \frac{1}{2}(78 - j104)(-26 + j52)$$

$$= \frac{1}{2}(3380 + j6760)$$

$$= 1690 + j3380\ \text{VA}.$$

Thus this impedance is absorbing an average power of 1690 W and a reactive power of 3380 VAR. The complex power delivered to the $(12 - j16)\ \Omega$ impedance is

$$S_2 = \frac{1}{2}\mathbf{V}_2\mathbf{I}_x^* = P_2 + jQ_2$$

$$= \frac{1}{2}(72 + j104)(-2 - j6)$$

$$= 240 - j320\ \text{VA}.$$

Therefore the impedance in the vertical branch is absorbing 240 W and delivering 320 VAR. The complex power delivered to the $(1 + j3)\ \Omega$ impedance is

$$S_3 = \frac{1}{2}\mathbf{V}_3\mathbf{I}_2^* = P_3 + jQ_3$$

$$= \frac{1}{2}(150 - j130)(-24 + j58)$$

$$= 1970 + j5910\ \text{VA}.$$

This impedance is absorbing 1970 W and 5910 VAR.

b) The complex power associated with the independent voltage source is

$$S_s = -\frac{1}{2}\mathbf{V}_s\mathbf{I}_1^* = P_s + jQ_s$$

$$= -\frac{1}{2}(150)(-26 + j52)$$

$$= 1950 - j3900\ \text{VA}.$$

Note that the independent voltage source is absorbing an average power of 1950 W and delivering 3900 VAR. The complex power associated with the current-controlled voltage source is

$$S_x = \frac{1}{2}(39\mathbf{I}_x)(\mathbf{I}_2^*) = P_x + jQ_x$$

$$= \frac{1}{2}(-78 + j234)(-24 + j58)$$

$$= -5850 - j5070\ \text{VA}.$$

Both average power and magnetizing reactive power are being delivered by the dependent source.

c) The total power absorbed by the passive impedances and the independent voltage source is

$$P_{\text{absorbed}} = P_1 + P_2 + P_3 + P_s = 5850\ \text{W}.$$

The dependent voltage source is the only circuit element delivering average power. Thus

$$P_{\text{delivered}} = 5850\ \text{W}.$$

Magnetizing reactive power is being absorbed by the two horizontal branches. Thus

$$Q_{\text{absorbed}} = Q_1 + Q_3 = 9290\ \text{VAR}.$$

Magnetizing reactive power is being delivered by the independent voltage source, the capacitor in the vertical impedance branch, and the dependent voltage source. Therefore

$$Q_{\text{delivered}} = 9290\ \text{VAR}.$$

✓**ASSESSMENT PROBLEMS**

Objective 1—Understand ac power concepts, their relationships to one another, and how to calculate them in a circuit

10.4 The load impedance in the circuit shown is shunted by a capacitor having a capacitive reactance of $-52\ \Omega$. Calculate:

a) the rms phasors $\mathbf{V}_L$ and $\mathbf{I}_L$,

b) the average power and magnetizing reactive power absorbed by the $(39 + j26)\ \Omega$ load impedance,

c) the average power and magnetizing reactive power absorbed by the $(1 + j4)\ \Omega$ line impedance,

d) the average power and magnetizing reactive power delivered by the source, and

e) the magnetizing reactive power delivered by the shunting capacitor.

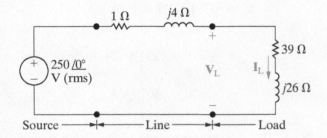

Answer: (a) $252.20\ \underline{/-4.54^\circ}$ V (rms),
$5.38\ \underline{/-38.23^\circ}$ A (rms);

(b) 1129.09 W, 752.73 VAR;

(c) 23.52 W, 94.09 VAR;

(d) 1152.62 W, -376.36 VAR;

(e) 1223.18 VAR.

10.5 The rms voltage at the terminals of a load is 250 V. The load is absorbing an average power of 40 kW and delivering a magnetizing reactive power of 30 kVAR. Derive two equivalent impedance models of the load.

Answer: 1 Ω in series with 0.75 Ω of capacitive reactance; 1.5625 Ω in parallel with 2.083 Ω of capacitive reactance.

10.6 Find the phasor voltage $\mathbf{V}_s$ (rms) in the circuit shown if loads L_1 and L_2 are absorbing 15 kVA at 0.6 pf lagging and 6 kVA at 0.8 pf leading, respectively. Express $\mathbf{V}_s$ in polar form.

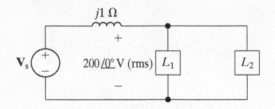

Answer: $251.64\ \underline{/15.91^\circ}$ V.

NOTE: Also try Chapter Problems 10.20, 10.28, and 10.30.

10.6 Maximum Power Transfer

Recall from Chapter 4 that certain systems—for example, those that transmit information via electric signals—depend on being able to transfer a maximum amount of power from the source to the load. We now reexamine maximum power transfer in the context of a sinusoidal steady-state network, beginning with Fig. 10.18. We must determine the load impedance Z_L that results in the delivery of maximum average power to terminals a and b. Any linear network may be viewed from the terminals of the load in terms of a Thévenin equivalent circuit. Thus the task reduces to finding the value of Z_L that results in maximum average power delivered to Z_L in the circuit shown in Fig. 10.19.

For maximum average power transfer, Z_L must equal the conjugate of the Thévenin impedance; that is,

Figure 10.18 ▲ A circuit describing maximum power transfer.

Condition for maximum average power transfer ▶

$$Z_L = Z_{Th}^*.$$

(10.38)

We derive Eq. 10.38 by a straightforward application of elementary calculus. We begin by expressing Z_{Th} and Z_L in rectangular form:

$$Z_{Th} = R_{Th} + jX_{Th}, \qquad (10.39)$$

$$Z_L = R_L + jX_L. \qquad (10.40)$$

In both Eqs. 10.39 and 10.40, the reactance term carries its own algebraic sign—positive for inductance and negative for capacitance. Because we are making an average-power calculation, we assume that the amplitude of the Thévenin voltage is expressed in terms of its rms value. We also use the Thévenin voltage as the reference phasor. Then, from Fig. 10.19, the rms value of the load current **I** is

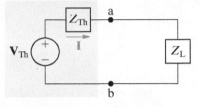

Figure 10.19 ▲ The circuit shown in Fig. 10.18, with the network replaced by its Thévenin equivalent.

$$\mathbf{I} = \frac{\mathbf{V}_{Th}}{(R_{Th} + R_L) + j(X_{Th} + X_L)}. \qquad (10.41)$$

The average power delivered to the load is

$$P = |\mathbf{I}|^2 R_L. \qquad (10.42)$$

Substituting Eq. 10.41 into Eq. 10.42 yields

$$P = \frac{|\mathbf{V}_{Th}|^2 R_L}{(R_{Th} + R_L)^2 + (X_{Th} + X_L)^2}. \qquad (10.43)$$

When working with Eq. 10.43, always remember that V_{Th}, R_{Th}, and X_{Th} are fixed quantities, whereas R_L and X_L are independent variables. Therefore, to maximize P, we must find the values of R_L and X_L where $\partial P/\partial R_L$ and $\partial P/\partial X_L$ are both zero. From Eq. 10.43,

$$\frac{\partial P}{\partial X_L} = \frac{-|\mathbf{V}_{Th}|^2 2R_L(X_L + X_{Th})}{[(R_L + R_{Th})^2 + (X_L + X_{Th})^2]^2}, \qquad (10.44)$$

$$\frac{\partial P}{\partial R_L} = \frac{|\mathbf{V}_{Th}|^2[(R_L + R_{Th})^2 + (X_L + X_{Th})^2 - 2R_L(R_L + R_{Th})]}{[(R_L + R_{Th})^2 + (X_L + X_{Th})^2]^2}. \qquad (10.45)$$

From Eq. 10.44, $\partial P/\partial X_L$ is zero when

$$X_L = -X_{Th}. \qquad (10.46)$$

From Eq. 10.45, $\partial P/\partial R_L$ is zero when

$$R_L = \sqrt{R_{Th}^2 + (X_L + X_{Th})^2}. \qquad (10.47)$$

Note that when we combine Eq. 10.46 with Eq. 10.47, both derivatives are zero when $Z_L = Z_{Th}^*$.

The Maximum Average Power Absorbed

The maximum average power that can be delivered to Z_L when it is set equal to the conjugate of Z_{Th} is calculated directly from the circuit in Fig. 10.19. When $Z_L = Z_{Th}^*$, the rms load current is $\mathbf{V}_{Th}/2R_L$, and the maximum average power delivered to the load is

$$P_{max} = \frac{|\mathbf{V}_{Th}|^2 R_L}{4R_L^2} = \frac{1}{4}\frac{|\mathbf{V}_{Th}|^2}{R_L}. \tag{10.48}$$

If the Thévenin voltage is expressed in terms of its maximum amplitude rather than its rms amplitude, Eq. 10.48 becomes

$$P_{max} = \frac{1}{8}\frac{\mathbf{V}_m^2}{R_L}. \tag{10.49}$$

Maximum Power Transfer When Z is Restricted

Maximum average power can be delivered to Z_L only if Z_L can be set equal to the conjugate of Z_{Th}. There are situations in which this is not possible. First, R_L and X_L may be restricted to a limited range of values. In this situation, the optimum condition for R_L and X_L is to adjust X_L as near to $-X_{Th}$ as possible and then adjust R_L as close to $\sqrt{R_{Th}^2 + (X_L + X_{Th})^2}$ as possible (see Example 10.9).

A second type of restriction occurs when the magnitude of Z_L can be varied but its phase angle cannot. Under this restriction, the greatest amount of power is transferred to the load when the magnitude of Z_L is set equal to the magnitude of Z_{Th}; that is, when

$$|Z_L| = |Z_{Th}|. \tag{10.50}$$

The proof of Eq. 10.50 is left to you as Problem 10.45.

For purely resistive networks, maximum power transfer occurs when the load resistance equals the Thévenin resistance. Note that we first derived this result in the introduction to maximum power transfer in Chapter 4.

Examples 10.8–10.11 illustrate the problem of obtaining maximum power transfer in the situations just discussed.

Example 10.8   Determining Maximum Power Transfer without Load Restrictions

a) For the circuit shown in Fig. 10.20, determine the impedance Z_L that results in maximum average power transferred to Z_L.

b) What is the maximum average power transferred to the load impedance determined in (a)?

Solution

a) We begin by determining the Thévenin equivalent with respect to the load terminals a, b. After two source transformations involving the 20 V source, the 5 Ω resistor, and the 20 Ω resistor, we simplify the circuit shown in Fig. 10.20 to the one shown in Fig. 10.21. Then,

$$\mathbf{V}_{Th} = \frac{16\ \underline{/0°}}{4 + j3 - j6}(-j6)$$

$$= 19.2\ \underline{/-53.13°} = 11.52 - j15.36\ \text{V}.$$

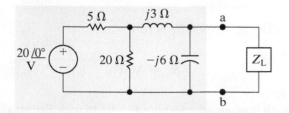

Figure 10.20 ▲ The circuit for Example 10.8.

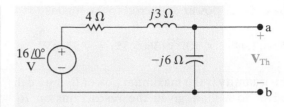

Figure 10.21 ▲ A simplification of Fig. 10.20 by source transformations.

We find the Thévenin impedance by deactivating the independent source and calculating the impedance seen looking into the terminals a and b. Thus,

$$Z_{Th} = \frac{(-j6)(4 + j3)}{4 + j3 - j6} = 5.76 - j1.68 \ \Omega.$$

For maximum average power transfer, the load impedance must be the conjugate of Z_{Th}, so

$$Z_L = 5.76 + j1.68 \ \Omega.$$

b) We calculate the maximum average power delivered to Z_L from the circuit shown in Fig. 10.22, in

which we replaced the original network with its Thévenin equivalent. From Fig. 10.22, the rms magnitude of the load current **I** is

$$I_{eff} = \frac{19.2/\sqrt{2}}{2(5.76)} = 1.1785 \ \text{A}.$$

The average power delivered to the load is

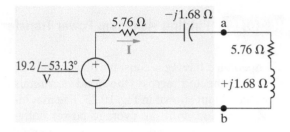

Figure 10.22 ▲ The circuit shown in Fig. 10.20, with the original network replaced by its Thévenin equivalent.

$$P = I_{eff}^2(5.76) - 8 \ \text{W}.$$

Example 10.9   **Determining Maximum Power Transfer with Load Impedance Restriction**

a) For the circuit shown in Fig. 10.23, what value of Z_L results in maximum average power transfer to Z_L? What is the maximum power in milliwatts?

b) Assume that the load resistance can be varied between 0 and 4000 Ω and that the capacitive reactance of the load can be varied between 0 and −2000 Ω. What settings of R_L and X_L transfer the most average power to the load? What is the maximum average power that can be transferred under these restrictions?

Solution

a) If there are no restrictions on R_L and X_L, the load impedance is set equal to the conjugate of the output or the Thévenin impedance. Therefore we set

$$R_L = 3000 \ \Omega \quad \text{and} \quad X_L = -4000 \ \Omega,$$

or

$$Z_L = 3000 - j4000 \ \Omega.$$

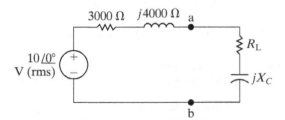

Figure 10.23 ▲ The circuit for Examples 10.9 and 10.10.

Because the source voltage is given in terms of its rms value, the average power delivered to Z_L is

$$P = \frac{1}{4}\frac{10^2}{3000} = \frac{25}{3} \ \text{mW} = 8.33 \ \text{mW}.$$

b) Because R_L and X_L are restricted, we first set X_L as close to −4000 Ω as possible; thus $X_L = -2000 \ \Omega$. Next, we set R_L as close to $\sqrt{R_{Th}^2 + (X_L + X_{Th})^2}$ as possible. Thus

$$R_L = \sqrt{3000^2 + (-2000 + 4000)^2} = 3605.55 \ \Omega.$$

Now, because R_L can be varied from 0 to 4000 Ω, we can set R_L to 3605.55 Ω. Therefore, the load impedance is adjusted to a value of

$$Z_L = 3605.55 - j2000 \ \Omega.$$

With Z_L set at this value, the value of the load current is

$$\mathbf{I}_{eff} = \frac{10 \ \underline{/0°}}{6605.55 + j2000} = 1.4489 \ \underline{/-16.85°} \ \text{mA}.$$

The average power delivered to the load is

$$P = (1.4489 \times 10^{-3})^2(3605.55) = 7.57 \ \text{mW}.$$

This quantity is the maximum power that we can deliver to a load, given the restrictions on R_L and X_L. Note that this is less than the power that can be delivered if there are no restrictions; in (a) we found that we can deliver 8.33 mW.

Example 10.10 **Finding Maximum Power Transfer with Impedance Angle Restrictions**

A load impedance having a constant phase angle of $-36.87°$ is connected across the load terminals a and b in the circuit shown in Fig. 10.23. The magnitude of Z_L is varied until the average power delivered is the most possible under the given restriction.

a) Specify Z_L in rectangular form.

b) Calculate the average power delivered to Z_L.

Solution

a) From Eq. 10.50, we know that the magnitude of Z_L must equal the magnitude of Z_{Th}. Therefore

$$|Z_L| = |Z_{Th}| = |3000 + j4000| = 5000 \ \Omega.$$

Now, as we know that the phase angle of Z_L is $-36.87°$, we have

$$Z_L = 5000 \ \underline{/-36.87°} = 4000 - j3000 \ \Omega.$$

b) With Z_L set equal to $4000 - j3000 \ \Omega$, the load current is

$$\mathbf{I}_{eff} = \frac{10}{7000 + j1000} = 1.4142 \ \underline{/-8.13°} \ \text{mA},$$

and the average power delivered to the load is

$$P = (1.4142 \times 10^{-3})^2(4000) = 8 \ \text{mW}.$$

This quantity is the maximum power that can be delivered by this circuit to a load impedance whose angle is constant at $-36.87°$. Again, this quantity is less than the maximum power that can be delivered if there are no restrictions on Z_L.

✓ ASSESSMENT PROBLEM

Objective 2—Understand the condition for maximum real power delivered to a load in an ac circuit

10.7 The source current in the circuit shown is $3 \cos 5000t$ A.

a) What impedance should be connected across terminals a,b for maximum average power transfer?

b) What is the average power transferred to the impedance in (a)?

c) Assume that the load is restricted to pure resistance. What size resistor connected across a,b will result in the maximum average power transferred?

d) What is the average power transferred to the resistor in (c)?

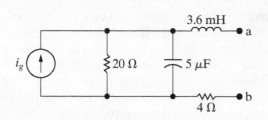

Answer: (a) $20 - j10 \ \Omega$;

(b) 18 W;

(c) 22.36 Ω;

(d) 17.00 W.

NOTE: Also try Chapter Problems 10.41, 10.48, and 10.62.

Example 10.11   **Finding Maximum Power Transfer in a Circuit with an Ideal Transformer**

The variable resistor in the circuit in Fig. 10.24 is adjusted until maximum average power is delivered to R_L.

a) What is the value of R_L in ohms?

b) What is the maximum average power (in watts) delivered to R_L?

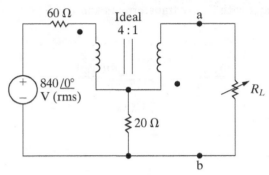

Figure 10.24 ▲ The circuit for Example 10.11.

Solution

a) We first find the Thévenin equivalent with respect to the terminals of R_L. The circuit for determining the open circuit voltage in shown in Fig. 10.25. The variables $\mathbf{V}_1$, $\mathbf{V}_2$, $\mathbf{I}_1$, and $\mathbf{I}_2$ have been added to expedite the discussion.

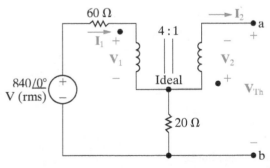

Figure 10.25 ▲ The circuit used to find the Thévenin voltage.

First we note the ideal transformer imposes the following constraints on the variables $\mathbf{V}_1$, $\mathbf{V}_2$, $\mathbf{I}_1$, and $\mathbf{I}_2$:

$$\mathbf{V}_2 = \frac{1}{4}\mathbf{V}_1, \qquad \mathbf{I}_1 = -\frac{1}{4}\mathbf{I}_2.$$

The open circuit value of $\mathbf{I}_2$ is zero, hence $\mathbf{I}_1$ is zero. It follows that

$$\mathbf{V}_1 = 840 \underline{/0°} \text{ V}, \qquad \mathbf{V}_2 = 210 \underline{/0°} \text{ V}.$$

From Fig. 10.25 we note that $\mathbf{V}_{\text{Th}}$ is the negative of $\mathbf{V}_2$, hence

$$\mathbf{V}_{\text{Th}} = -210 \underline{/0°} \text{ V}.$$

The circuit shown in Fig. 10.26 is used to determine the short circuit current. Viewing $\mathbf{I}_1$ and $\mathbf{I}_2$ as mesh currents, the two mesh equations are

$$840 \underline{/0°} = 80\mathbf{I}_1 - 20\mathbf{I}_2 + \mathbf{V}_1,$$

$$0 = 20\mathbf{I}_2 - 20\mathbf{I}_1 + \mathbf{V}_2.$$

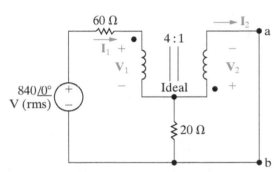

Figure 10.26 ▲ The circuit used to calculate the short circuit current.

When these two mesh current equations are combined with the constraint equations we get

$$840 \underline{/0°} = -40\mathbf{I}_2 + \mathbf{V}_1,$$

$$0 = 25\mathbf{I}_2 + \frac{\mathbf{V}_1}{4}.$$

Solving for the short circuit value of $\mathbf{I}_2$ yields

$$\mathbf{I}_2 = -6 \text{ A}.$$

Therefore the Thévenin resistance is

$$R_{\text{Th}} = \frac{-210}{-6} = 35 \ \Omega.$$

Maximum power will be delivered to R_L when R_L equals 35 Ω.

b) The maximum power delivered to R_L is most easily determined using the Thévenin equivalent. From the circuit shown in Fig. 10.27 we have

$$P_{\max} = \left(\frac{-210}{70}\right)^2 (35) = 315 \text{ W}.$$

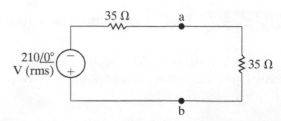

Figure 10.27 ▲ The Thévenin equivalent loaded for maximum power transfer.

✓ ASSESSMENT PROBLEMS

Objective 3—Be able to calculate all forms of ac power in ac circuits with linear transformers and ideal transformers

10.8 Find the average power delivered to the 100 Ω resistor in the circuit shown if $v_g = 660 \cos 5000t$ V.

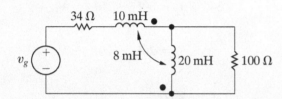

Answer: 612.5 W.

10.9 a) Find the average power delivered to the 400 Ω resistor in the circuit shown if $v_g = 248 \cos 10{,}000t$ V.

b) Find the average power delivered to the 375 Ω resistor.

c) Find the power developed by the ideal voltage source. Check your result by showing the power absorbed equals the power developed.

NOTE: Also try Chapter Problems 10.61 and 10.62.

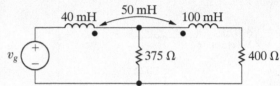

Answer: (a) 50 W;

(b) 49.2 W;

(c) 99.2 W, 50 + 49.2 = 99.2 W.

10.10 Solve Example 10.11 if the polarity dot on the coil connected to terminal a is at the top.

Answer: (a) 15 Ω;

(b) 735 W.

10.11 Solve Example 10.11 if the voltage source is reduced to 146 $\underline{/0°}$ V rms and the turns ratio is reversed to 1:4.

Answer: (a) 1460 Ω;

(b) 58.4 W.

Practical Perspective

Vampire Power

Vampire power, or standby power, may cost you more than you think. The average household has about 40 electrical products that draw power, even when turned off. Approximately 5% of typical residential power consumption can be attributed to standby power. Table 10.3 provides the power consumption of several different devices. Notice that when a device is considered to be off, it is often still consuming power.

Consider a typical mobile phone charger. According to the values given in Table 10.3, when the charger is detached from the phone it consumes only a fraction of the power that is used when the charger is attached to the phone and the phone is charging. Suppose you charge your phone for three hours each day, but leave the charger plugged into the wall outlet 24 hours a day. Recall that the electric company bills you based on the number of kilowatt-hours (kWh) you use in a given month. A device that uses 1000 W of power

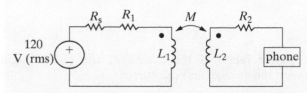

Figure 10.28 ▲ A linear transformed used in a phone charger.

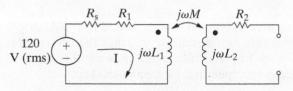

Figure 10.29 ▲ The phone charger circuit when the phone is not connected.

TABLE 10.3 Average power consumption of common electrical devices

Electrical device[+]	Power [W]*
Mobile phone charger	
Attached to phone, phone charging	3.68
Plugged into wall outlet but not into phone	0.26
Notebook computer AC adapter	
Attached to computer, computer charging	44.28
Attached to computer, computer sleeping	15.77
Attached to computer, computer off	8.9
Plugged into wall outlet but not into computer	4.42
DVD player	
On and playing	9.91
On and not playing	7.54
Off	1.55
Microwave oven	
Ready with door closed	3.08
Ready with door open	25.79
Cooking	1433.0
Inkjet multifunction printer	
On	9.16
Off	5.26

*Data in this table from Lawrence Berkeley National Laboratory report (http://standby.lbl.gov/standby.html)
[+]This value is the average of the power measured for many types of each device

continuously over one hour has consumed 1 kWh. Let's calculate the number of kilowatt-hours used by the phone charger in one month.

$$P[\text{kWh}] = \frac{30[3(3.68) + 21(0.26)]}{1000} = 1.8 \text{ kWh}$$

Now do the calculation again, this time assuming that you unplug the charger when it is not being used to charge the phone.

$$P[\text{kWh}] = \frac{30[3(3.68) + 21(0)]}{1000} = 0.33 \text{ kWh}$$

Keeping the charger plugged in when you are not using it causes the charger to consume more than 5 times the power needed to charge your phone every day. You can therefore minimize the cost of vampire power by unplugging electrical devices if they are not being used.

How can the phone charger consume power when not plugged into the phone? The electronic circuitry in your phone uses 5 V(dc) sources to supply power. The phone charger must transform the 120 V(rms) signal supplied by the wall outlet into a signal that can be used to charge the phone. Phone chargers can use linear transformers, together with other circuitry, to output a voltage suited to the phone.

Consider the circuit in Fig. 10.28. The linear transformer is part of the circuitry used to reduce the voltage supplied by the source to a level suited to the phone. The additional components needed to complete this task are not shown in the circuit. When the phone is unplugged from the circuit in Fig. 10.28, but the circuit is still connected to the 120 V(rms) source, there is still a path for the current, as shown in Fig. 10.29. The current is

$$I = \frac{120}{R_s + R_1 + j\omega L_1}.$$

The real power, delivered by the voltage source and supplied to the resistors, is

$$P = (R_s + R_1)|I|^2.$$

This is the vampire power being consumed by the phone charger even when it is not connected to the phone.

NOTE: Assess you understanding of this Practical Perspective by trying Chapter Problems 10.66–10.68.

Summary

- **Instantaneous power** is the product of the instantaneous terminal voltage and current, or $p = \pm vi$. The positive sign is used when the reference direction for the current is from the positive to the negative reference polarity of the voltage. The frequency of the instantaneous power is twice the frequency of the voltage (or current). (See page 360.)

- **Average power** is the average value of the instantaneous power over one period. It is the power converted from electric to nonelectric form and vice versa. This conversion is the reason that average power is also referred to as real power. Average power, with the passive sign convention, is expressed as

$$P = \frac{1}{2}V_m I_m \cos(\theta_v - \theta_i)$$

$$= V_{\text{eff}} I_{\text{eff}} \cos(\theta_v - \theta_i).$$

(See page 362.)

- **Reactive power** is the electric power exchanged between the magnetic field of an inductor and the source that drives it or between the electric field of a capacitor and the source that drives it. Reactive power is never converted to nonelectric power. Reactive power, with the passive sign convention, is expressed as

$$Q = \frac{1}{2}V_m I_m \sin(\theta_v - \theta_i)$$

$$= V_{\text{eff}} I_{\text{eff}} \sin(\theta_v - \theta_i).$$

Both average power and reactive power can be expressed in terms of either peak (V_m, I_m) or effective (V_{eff}, I_{eff}) current and voltage. Effective values are widely used in both household and industrial applications. *Effective value* and *rms value* are interchangeable terms for the same value. (See page 362.)

- The **power factor** is the cosine of the phase angle between the voltage and the current:

$$\text{pf} = \cos(\theta_v - \theta_i).$$

The terms *lagging* and *leading* added to the description of the power factor indicate whether the current is lagging or leading the voltage and thus whether the load is inductive or capacitive. (See page 363.)

- The **reactive factor** is the sine of the phase angle between the voltage and the current:

$$\text{rf} = \sin(\theta_v - \theta_i).$$

(See page 363.)

- **Complex power** is the complex sum of the real and reactive powers, or

$$S = P + jQ$$

$$= \frac{1}{2}\mathbf{VI}^* = \mathbf{V}_{\text{eff}}\mathbf{I}_{\text{eff}}^*$$

$$= I_{\text{eff}}^2 Z = \frac{V_{\text{eff}}^2}{Z^*}.$$

(See page 368.)

- **Apparent power** is the magnitude of the complex power:

$$|S| = \sqrt{P^2 + Q^2}.$$

(See page 368.)

- The **watt** is used as the unit for both instantaneous and real power. The **var** (volt amp reactive, or VAR) is used as the unit for reactive power. The **volt-amp** (VA) is used as the unit for complex and apparent power. (See page 368.)

- **Maximum power transfer** occurs in circuits operating in the sinusoidal steady state when the load impedance is the conjugate of the Thévenin impedance as viewed from the terminals of the load impedance. (See page 376.)

Problems

Sections 10.1–10.2

10.1 The following sets of values for v and i pertain to the circuit seen in Fig. 10.1. For each set of values, calculate P and Q and state whether the circuit inside the box is absorbing or delivering (1) average power and (2) magnetizing vars.

a) $v = 250\cos(\omega t + 45°)$ V,
   $i = 4\sin(\omega t + 60°)$ A.

b) $v = 18\cos(\omega t - 30°)$ V,
   $i = 5\cos(\omega t - 75°)$ A.

c) $v = 150\sin(\omega t + 25°)$ V,
   $i = 2\cos(\omega t + 50°)$ A.

d) $v = 80\cos(\omega t + 120°)$ V,
   $i = 10\cos(\omega t + 170°)$ A.

10.2 a) A college student wakes up hungry. He turns on the coffee maker, puts some oatmeal in the microwave oven to cook, puts a couple of slices of bread in the toaster, and starts making scrambled eggs in the electric frying pan. If all of these appliances in his dorm room are supplied by a 120 V branch circuit protected by a 50 A circuit breaker, will the breaker interrupt his breakfast?

b) The student's roommate wakes up and turns on the air conditioner. He realizes that the room is a mess, so starts to vacuum. Now does the circuit breaker interrupt breakfast?

10.3 Show that the maximum value of the instantaneous power given by Eq. 10.9 is $P + \sqrt{P^2 + Q^2}$ and that the minimum value is $P - \sqrt{P^2 + Q^2}$.

10.4 A load consisting of a 480 Ω resistor in parallel with a $(5/9)\,\mu$F capacitor is connected across the terminals of a sinusoidal voltage source v_g, where $v_g = 240\cos 5000t$ V.

a) What is the peak value of the instantaneous power delivered by the source?

b) What is the peak value of the instantaneous power absorbed by the source?

c) What is the average power delivered to the load?

d) What is the reactive power delivered to the load?

e) Does the load absorb or generate magnetizing vars?

f) What is the power factor of the load?

g) What is the reactive factor of the load?

10.5 Find the average power delivered by the ideal current source in the circuit in Fig. P10.5 if $i_g = 4\cos 5000t$ mA.

PSPICE
MULTISIM

Figure P10.5

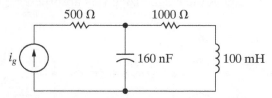

10.6 Find the average power dissipated in the 30 Ω resistor in the circuit seen in Fig. P10.6 if $i_g = 6\cos 20{,}000t$ A.

PSPICE
MULTISIM

Figure P10.6

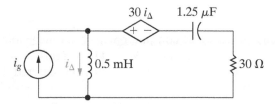

10.7 The op amp in the circuit shown in Fig. P10.7 is ideal. Calculate the average power delivered to the 1 kΩ resistor when $v_g = \cos 1000t$ V.

PSPICE
MULTISIM

Figure P10.7

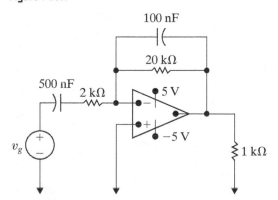

10.8 a) Calculate the real and reactive power associated with each circuit element in the circuit in Fig. P9.63.

b) Verify that the average power generated equals the average power absorbed.

c) Verify that the magnetizing vars generated equal the magnetizing vars absorbed.

10.9 Repeat Problem 10.8 for the circuit shown in Fig. P9.64.

10.10 The load impedance in Fig. P10.10 absorbs 6 kW and generates 8 kVAR. The sinusoidal voltage source develops 8 kW.

a) Find the values of inductive line reactance that will satisfy these constraints.

b) For each value of line reactance found in (a), show that the magnetizing vars developed equals the magnetizing vars absorbed.

Figure P10.10

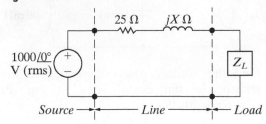

Section 10.3

10.11 a) A personal computer with a monitor and keyboard requires 40 W at 115 V (rms). Calculate the rms value of the current carried by its power cord.

b) A laser printer for the personal computer in (a) is rated at 90 W at 115 V (rms). If this printer is plugged into the same wall outlet as the computer, what is the rms value of the current drawn from the outlet?

10.12 Find the rms value of the periodic current shown in Fig. P10.12.

Figure P10.12

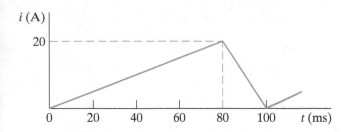

10.13 The periodic current shown in Fig. P10.12 dissipates an average power of 1280 W in a resistor. What is the value of the resistor?

10.14 a) Find the rms value of the periodic voltage shown in Fig. P10.14.

b) Suppose the voltage in part (a) is applied to the terminals of a 40 Ω resistor. Calculate the average power dissipated by the resistor.

c) When the voltage in part (a) is applied to a different resistor, that resistor dissipates 10 mW of average power. What is the value of the resistor?

Figure P10.14

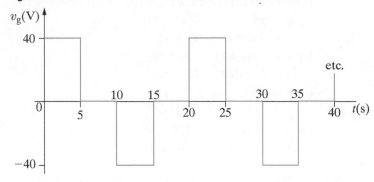

10.15 a) Find the rms value of the periodic voltage shown in Fig. P10.15.

b) If this voltage is applied to the terminals of a 4 Ω resistor, what is the average power dissipated in the resistor?

Figure P10.15

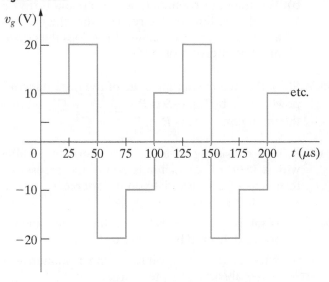

10.16 A dc voltage equal to V_{dc} V is applied to a resistor of R Ω. A sinusoidal voltage equal to v_s V is also applied to a resistor of R Ω. Show that the dc voltage will deliver the same amount of energy in T seconds (where T is the period of the sinusoidal voltage) as the sinusoidal voltage provided V_{dc} equals the rms value of v_s. (*Hint:* Equate the two expressions for the energy delivered to the resistor.)

Sections 10.4–10.5

10.17 The current $\mathbf{I}_g$ in the frequency-domain circuit shown in Fig. P10.17 is $50\underline{/0°}$ mA (rms).

a) Find the average and reactive power for the current source.

b) Is the current source absorbing or delivering average power?

c) Is the current source absorbing or delivering magnetizing vars?

d) Find the average and reactive powers associated with each impedance branch in the circuit.

e) Check the balance between delivered and absorbed average power.

f) Check the balance between delivered and absorbed magnetizing vars.

Figure P10.17

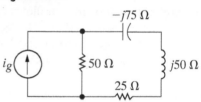

10.18 Find the average power, the reactive power, and the
PSPICE apparent power absorbed by the load in the circuit
MULTISIM in Fig. P10.18 if v_g equals $150 \cos 250t$ V.

Figure P10.18

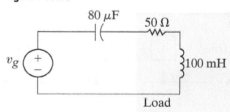

10.19 a) Find V_L (rms) and θ for the circuit in Fig. P10.19 if the load absorbs 2500 VA at a lagging power factor of 0.8.

b) Construct a phasor diagram of each solution obtained in (a).

Figure P10.19

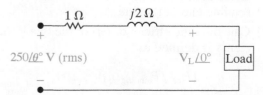

10.20 a) Find the average power, the reactive power, and
PSPICE the apparent power supplied by the voltage
MULTISIM source in the circuit in Fig. P10.20 if $v_g = 40 \cos 10^6 t$ V.

b) Check your answer in (a) by showing $P_{dev} = \sum P_{abs}$.

c) Check your answer in (a) by showing $Q_{dev} = \sum Q_{abs}$.

Figure P10.20

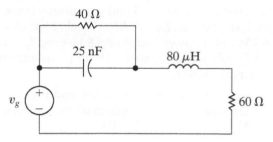

10.21 Two 480 V (rms) loads are connected in parallel. The two loads draw a total average power of 40,800 W at a power factor of 0.8 lagging. One of the loads draws 20 kVA at a power factor of 0.96 leading. What is the power factor of the other load?

10.22 The two loads shown in Fig. P10.22 can be described as follows: Load 1 absorbs an average power of 10 kW and delivers 4 kVAR of reactive power; Load 2 has an impedance of $(60 + j80)\Omega$. The voltage at the terminals of the loads is $1000\sqrt{2} \cos 100\pi t$ V.

a) Find the rms value of the source voltage.

b) By how many microseconds is the load voltage out of phase with the source voltage?

c) Does the load voltage lead or lag the source voltage?

Figure P10.22

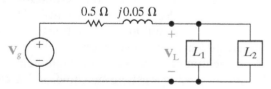

10.23 The three loads in the circuit seen in Fig. P10.23 are $S_1 = 6 + j3$ kVA, $S_2 = 7.5 - j4.5$ kVA, $S_3 = 12 + j9$ kVA.

a) Calculate the complex power associated with each voltage source, $\mathbf{V}_{g1}$ and $\mathbf{V}_{g2}$.

b) Verify that the total real and reactive power delivered by the sources equals the total real and reactive power absorbed by the network.

Figure P10.23

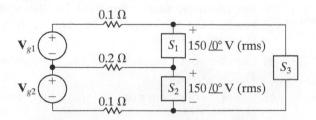

10.24 The three loads in the circuit seen in Fig. P10.24 are described as follows: Load 1 is absorbing 4.8 kW and delivering 2.4 kVAR; Load 2 is absorbing 6 kVA at a power factor of 0.8 lagging; Load 3 is a 24 Ω resistor in parallel with an inductance whose reactance is 6 Ω.

a) Calculate the average power and the magnetizing reactive power delivered by each source if $\mathbf{V}_{g1} = \mathbf{V}_{g2} = 120\underline{/0°}$ V (rms).

b) Check your calculations by showing your results are consistent with the requirements

$$\sum P_{dev} = \sum P_{abs}$$

$$\sum Q_{dev} = \sum Q_{abs}.$$

Figure P10.24

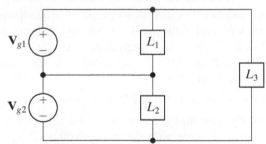

10.25 Suppose the circuit shown in Fig. P10.24 represents a residential distribution circuit in which the impedances of the service conductors are negligible and $\mathbf{V}_{g1} = \mathbf{V}_{g2} = 110\underline{/0°}$ V (rms). The three loads in the circuit are L_1 (a toaster, a coffee maker, and a microwave oven); L_2 (a solid-state TV, a vacuum cleaner, and a portable heater); and L_3 (an automatic washing machine and a clothes dryer). Assume that all of these appliances are in operation at the same time. The service conductors are protected with 50 A circuit breakers. Will the service to this residence be interrupted? Why or why not?

10.26 The three parallel loads in the circuit shown in Fig. 10.26 can be described as follows: Load 1 is absorbing an average power of 6 kW and delivering reactive power of 8 kvars; Load 2 is absorbing an

average power of 9 kW and reactive power of 3 kvars; Load 3 is a 25 Ω resistor in parallel with a capacitor whose reactance is -5 Ω. Find the rms magnitude and the phase angle of $\mathbf{V}_g$ if $\mathbf{V}_o = 250\underline{/0°}$ V.

Figure P10.26

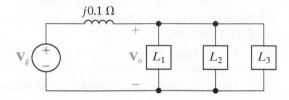

10.27 Consider the circuit described in Problem 9.78.

a) What is the rms magnitude of the voltage across the load impedance?

b) What percentage of the average power developed by the practical source is delivered to the load impedance?

10.28 Three loads are connected in parallel across a 300 V(rms) line, as shown in Fig. P10.28. Load 1 absorbs 3 kW at unity power factor; Load 2 absorbs 5 kVA at 0.8 leading; Load 3 absorbs 5 kW and delivers 6 kvars.

a) Find the impedance that is equivalent to the three parallel loads.

b) Find the power factor of the equivalent load as seen from the line's input terminals.

Figure P10.28

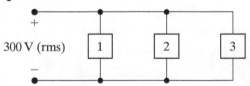

10.29 The three loads in Problem 10.28 are fed from a line having a series impedance $0.02 + j0.05$ Ω, as shown in Fig. P10.29.

a) Calculate the rms value of the voltage ($\mathbf{V}_s$) at the sending end of the line.

b) Calculate the average and reactive powers associated with the line impedance.

c) Calculate the average and reactive powers at the sending end of the line.

d) Calculate the efficiency (η) of the line if the efficiency is defined as

$$\eta = (P_{load}/P_{sending\ end}) \times 100.$$

Figure P10.29

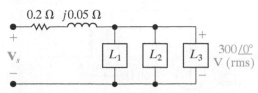

10.30 The three loads in the circuit in Fig. P10.30 can be described as follows: Load 1 is a 240 Ω resistor in series with an inductive reactance of 70 Ω; load 2 is a capacitive reactance of 120 Ω in series with a 160 Ω resistor; and load 3 is a 30 Ω resistor in series with a capacitive reactance of 40 Ω. The frequency of the voltage source is 60 Hz.

a) Give the power factor and reactive factor of each load.

b) Give the power factor and reactive factor of the composite load seen by the voltage source.

Figure P10.30

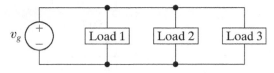

10.31 a) Find the average power dissipated in the line in Fig. P10.31.

b) Find the capacitive reactance that when connected in parallel with the load will make the load look purely resistive.

c) What is the equivalent impedance of the load in (b)?

d) Find the average power dissipated in the line when the capacitive reactance is connected across the load.

e) Express the power loss in (d) as a percentage of the power loss found in (a).

Figure P10.31

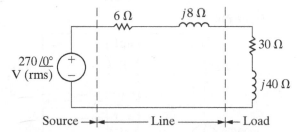

10.32 The steady-state voltage drop between the load and the sending end of the line seen in Fig. P10.32 is excessive. A capacitor is placed in parallel with the 150 kVA load and is adjusted until the steady-state voltage at the sending end of the line has the same magnitude as the voltage at the load end, that is, 4800 V (rms). The 150 kVA load is operating at a power factor of 0.8 lag. Calculate the size of the capacitor in microfarads if the circuit is operating at 60 Hz. In selecting the capacitor, keep in mind the need to keep the power loss in the line at a reasonable level.

Figure P10.32

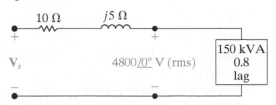

10.33 A group of small appliances on a 60 Hz system requires 20 kVA at 0.85 pf lagging when operated at 125 V (rms). The impedance of the feeder supplying the appliances is $0.01 + j0.08$ Ω. The voltage at the load end of the feeder is 125 V (rms).

a) What is the rms magnitude of the voltage at the source end of the feeder?

b) What is the average power loss in the feeder?

c) What size capacitor (in microfarads) across the load end of the feeder is needed to improve the load power factor to unity?

d) After the capacitor is installed, what is the rms magnitude of the voltage at the source end of the feeder if the load voltage is maintained at 125 V (rms)?

e) What is the average power loss in the feeder for (d)?

10.34 A factory has an electrical load of 1600 kW at a lagging power factor of 0.8. An additional variable power factor load is to be added to the factory. The new load will add 320 kW to the real power load of the factory. The power factor of the added load is to be adjusted so that the overall power factor of the factory is 0.96 lagging.

a) Specify the reactive power associated with the added load.

b) Does the added load absorb or deliver magnetizing vars?

c) What is the power factor of the additional load?

d) Assume that the voltage at the input to the factory is 2400 V (rms). What is the rms magnitude of the current into the factory before the variable power factor load is added?

e) What is the rms magnitude of the current into the factory after the variable power factor load has been added?

10.35 Assume the factory described in Problem 10.34 is fed from a line having an impedance of $0.25 + j0.1 \, \Omega$. The voltage at the factory is maintained at 2400 V (rms).

   a) Find the average power loss in the line before and after the load is added.

   b) Find the magnitude of the voltage at the sending end of the line before and after the load is added.

10.36 a) Find the six branch currents $\mathbf{I}_a - \mathbf{I}_f$ in the circuit in Fig. P10.36.

   b) Find the complex power in each branch of the circuit.

   c) Check your calculations by verifying that the average power developed equals the average power dissipated.

   d) Check your calculations by verifying that the magnetizing vars generated equal the magnetizing vars absorbed.

Figure P10.36

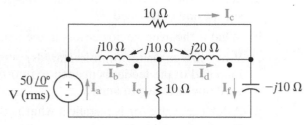

10.37 a) Find the average power delivered to the 8 Ω resistor in the circuit in Fig. P10.37.

   b) Find the average power developed by the ideal sinusoidal voltage source.

   c) Find Z_{ab}.

   d) Show that the average power developed equals the average power dissipated.

Figure P10.37

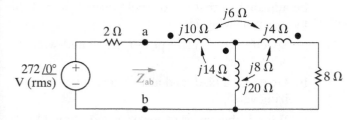

10.38 a) Find the average power delivered by the sinusoidal current source in the circuit of Fig. P10.38.

   b) Find the average power delivered to the 20 Ω resistor.

Figure P10.38

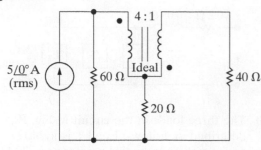

10.39 a) Find the average power dissipated in each resistor in the circuit in Fig. P10.39.

   b) Check your answer by showing that the total power developed equals the total power absorbed.

Figure P10.39

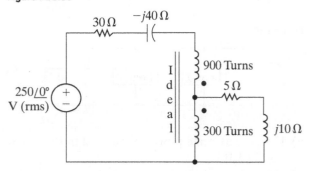

10.40 The sinusoidal voltage source in the circuit in Fig. P10.40 is developing an rms voltage of 2000 V. The 4 Ω load in the circuit is absorbing four times as much average power as the 25 Ω load. The two loads are matched to the sinusoidal source that has an internal impedance of $500 \underline{/0°} \, k\Omega$.

   a) Specify the numerical values of a_1 and a_2.

   b) Calculate the power delivered to the 25 Ω load.

   c) Calculate the rms value of the voltage across the 4 Ω resistor.

Figure P10.40

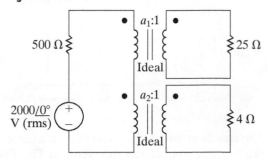

Section 10.6

10.41 a) Determine the load impedance for the circuit shown in Fig. P10.41 that will result in maximum average power being transferred to the load if $\omega = 8$ krad/s.

b) Determine the maximum average power delivered to the load from part (a) if $v_g = 10 \cos 8000t$ V.

c) Repeat part (a) when Z_L consists of two components from Appendix H whose values yield a maximum average power closest to the value calculated in part (b).

Figure P10.41

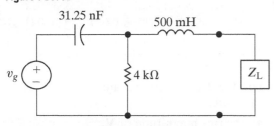

10.42 Suppose an impedance equal to the conjugate of the Thévenin impedance is connected to the terminals c, d of the circuit shown in Fig. P9.75.

a) Find the average power developed by the sinusoidal voltage source.

b) What percentage of the power developed by the source is lost in the linear transformer?

10.43 The phasor voltage $\mathbf{V}_{ab}$ in the circuit shown in Fig. P10.43 is $300\underline{/0°}$ V (rms) when no external load is connected to the terminals a, b. When a load having an impedance of $200 - j500$ Ω is connected across a, b, the value of $\mathbf{V}_{ab}$ is $156 - j42$ V (rms).

a) Find the impedance that should be connected across a, b for maximum average power transfer.

b) Find the maximum average power transferred to the load of (a).

c) Construct the impedance of part (a) using components from Appendix H if the source frequency is 50 Hz.

Figure P10.43

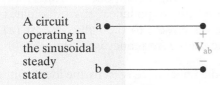

10.44 The load impedance Z_L for the circuit shown in Fig. P10.44 is adjusted until maximum average power is delivered to Z_L.

a) Find the maximum average power delivered to Z_L.

b) What percentage of the total power developed in the circuit is delivered to Z_L?

Figure P10.44

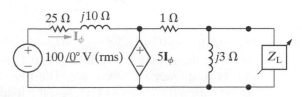

10.45 Prove that if only the magnitude of the load impedance can be varied, most average power is transferred to the load when $|Z_L| = |Z_{Th}|$. (*Hint:* In deriving the expression for the average load power, write the load impedance (Z_L) in the form $Z_L = |Z_L| \cos \theta + j|Z_L| \sin \theta$, and note that only $|Z_L|$ is variable.)

10.46 The variable resistor in the circuit shown in Fig. P10.46 is adjusted until the average power it absorbs is maximum.

a) Find R.

b) Find the maximum average power.

c) Find a resistor in Appendix H that would have the most average power delivered to it.

Figure P10.46

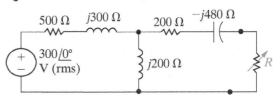

10.47 The variable resistor R_o in the circuit shown in Fig. P10.47 is adjusted until maximum average power is delivered to R_o.

a) What is the value of R_o in ohms?

b) Calculate the average power delivered to R_o.

c) If R_o is replaced with a variable impedance Z_o, what is the maximum average power that can be delivered to Z_o?

d) In (c), what percentage of the circuit's developed power is delivered to the load Z_o?

Figure P10.47

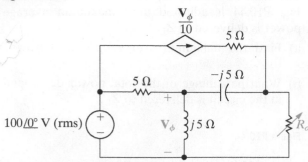

10.48 The peak amplitude of the sinusoidal voltage
PSPICE source in the circuit shown in Fig. P10.48 is 180 V,
MULTISIM and its frequency is 5000 rad/s. The load resistor
can be varied from 0 to 4000 Ω, and the load capacitor can be varied from 0.1 μF to 0.5 μF.

a) Calculate the average power delivered to the
load when $R_o = 2000\ \Omega$ and $C_o = 0.2\ \mu F$.

b) Determine the settings of R_o and C_o that will
result in the most average power being transferred to R_o.

c) What is the average power in (b)? Is it greater
than the power in (a)?

d) If there are no constraints on R_o and C_o, what is
the maximum average power that can be delivered to a load?

e) What are the values of R_o and C_o for the condition of (d)?

f) Is the average power calculated in (d) larger
than that calculated in (c)?

Figure P10.48

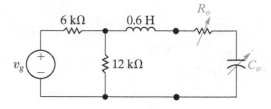

10.49 a) Assume that R_o in Fig. P10.48 can be varied
PSPICE between 0 and 10 kΩ. Repeat (b) and (c) of
MULTISIM Problem 10.48.

b) Is the new average power calculated in (a)
greater than that found in Problem 10.48(a)?

c) Is the new average power calculated in (a) less
than that found in 10.48(d)?

10.50 The sending-end voltage in the circuit seen in
Fig. P10.50 is adjusted so that the rms value of
the load voltage is always 4000 V. The variable

capacitor is adjusted until the average power dissipated in the line resistance is minimum.

a) If the frequency of the sinusoidal source is
60 Hz, what is the value of the capacitance in
microfarads?

b) If the capacitor is removed from the circuit,
what percentage increase in the magnitude of V_s
is necessary to maintain 4000 V at the load?

c) If the capacitor is removed from the circuit,
what is the percentage increase in line loss?

Figure P10.50

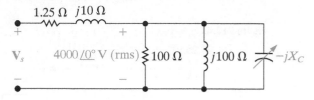

10.51 For the frequency-domain circuit in Fig. P10.51,
calculate:

a) the rms magnitude of V_o.

b) the average power dissipated in the 160 Ω
resistor.

c) the percentage of the average power generated
by the ideal voltage source that is delivered to
the 9 Ω load resistor.

Figure P10.51

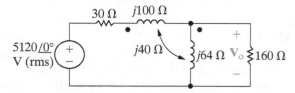

10.52 The 160 Ω resistor in the circuit in Fig. P10.51 is
replaced with a variable impedance Z_o. Assume Z_o
is adjusted for maximum average power transfer
to Z_o.

a) What is the maximum average power that can
be delivered to Z_o?

b) What is the average power developed by the
ideal voltage source when maximum average
power is delivered to Z_o?

c) Choose single components from Appendix H to
form an impedance that dissipates average
power closest to the value in part (a). Assume
the source frequency is 60 Hz.

10.53 Find the impedance seen by the ideal voltage source
in the circuit in Fig. P10.53 when Z_o is adjusted for
maximum average power transfer to Z_o.

Figure P10.53

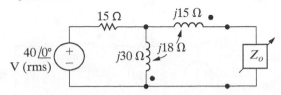

10.54 The impedance Z_L in the circuit in Fig. P10.54 is adjusted for maximum average power transfer to Z_L. The internal impedance of the sinusoidal voltage source is $4 + j7\ \Omega$.

a) What is the maximum average power delivered to Z_L?

b) What percentage of the average power delivered to the linear transformer is delivered to Z_L?

Figure P10.54

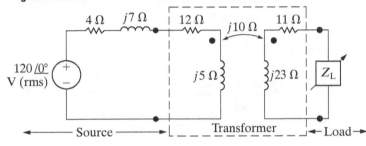

10.55 a) Find the steady-state expression for the currents i_g and i_L in the circuit in Fig. P10.55 when $v_g = 400 \cos 400t$ V.

PSPICE
MULTISIM

b) Find the coefficient of coupling.

c) Find the energy stored in the magnetically coupled coils at $t = 1.25\pi$ ms and $t = 2.5\pi$ ms.

d) Find the power delivered to the 375 Ω resistor.

e) If the 375 Ω resistor is replaced by a variable resistor R_L, what value of R_L will yield maximum average power transfer to R_L?

f) What is the maximum average power in (e)?

g) Assume the 375 Ω resistor is replaced by a variable impedance Z_L. What value of Z_L will result in maximum average power transfer to Z_L?

h) What is the maximum average power in (g)?

Figure P10.55

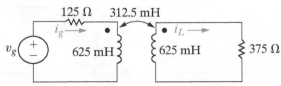

10.56 The values of the parameters in the circuit shown in Fig. P10.56 are $L_1 = 8$ mH; $L_2 = 2$ mH; $k = 0.75$; $R_g = 1\ \Omega$; and $R_L = 7\ \Omega$. If $v_g = 54\sqrt{2} \cos 1000t$ V, find

a) the rms magnitude of v_o

b) the average power delivered to R_L

c) the percentage of the average power generated by the ideal voltage source that is delivered to R_L.

Figure P10.56

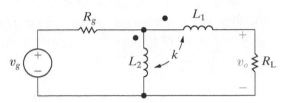

10.57 Assume the coefficient of coupling in the circuit in Fig. P10.56 is adjustable.

a) Find the value of k that makes v_o equal to zero.

b) Find the power developed by the source when k has the value found in (a).

10.58 Assume the load resistor (R_L) in the circuit in Fig. P10.56 is adjustable.

a) What value of R_L will result in the maximum average power being transferred to R_L?

b) What is the value of the maximum power transferred?

10.59 The load impedance Z_L in the circuit in Fig. P10.59 is adjusted until maximum average power is transferred to Z_L.

a) Specify the value of Z_L if $N_1 = 3600$ turns and $N_2 = 600$ turns.

b) Specify the values of $\mathbf{I}_L$ and $\mathbf{V}_L$ when Z_L is absorbing maximum average power.

Figure P10.59

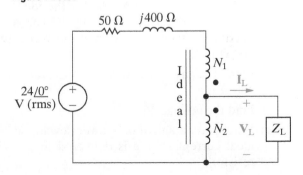

10.60 The sinusoidal voltage source in the circuit in Fig. P10.60 is operating at a frequency of 20 krad/s. The variable capacitive reactance in the circuit is adjusted until the average power delivered to the 100 Ω resistor is as large as possible.

a) Find the value of C in microfarads.

b) When C has the value found in (a), what is the average power delivered to the 100 Ω resistor?

c) Replace the 100 Ω resistor with a variable resistor R_o. Specify the value of R_o so that maximum average power is delivered to R_o.

d) What is the maximum average power that can be delivered to R_o?

Figure P10.60

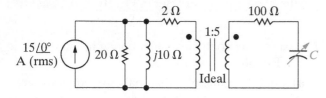

10.61 Find the average power delivered to the 5 kΩ resistor in the circuit of Fig. P10.61.

Figure P10.61

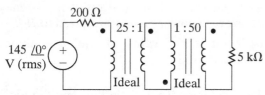

10.62 The ideal transformer connected to the 5 kΩ load in Problem 10.61 is replaced with an ideal transformer that has a turns ratio of 1:a.

a) What value of a results in maximum average power being delivered to the 5 kΩ resistor?

b) What is the maximum average power?

10.63 a) Find the turns ratio N_1/N_2 for the ideal transformer in the circuit in Fig. P10.63 so that maximum average power is delivered to the 400 Ω load.

b) Find the average power delivered to the 400 Ω load.

c) Find the voltage $\mathbf{V}_1$.

d) What percentage of the power developed by the ideal current source is delivered to the 400 Ω resistor?

Figure P10.63

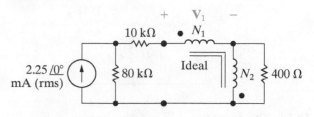

10.64 a) If N_1 equals 1000 turns, how many turns should be placed on the N_2 winding of the ideal transformer in the circuit seen in Fig. P10.64 so that maximum average power is delivered to the 6800 Ω load?

b) Find the average power delivered to the 6800 Ω resistor.

c) What percentage of the average power delivered by the ideal voltage source is dissipated in the linear transformer?

Figure P10.64

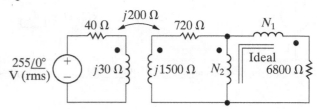

10.65 The variable load resistor R_L in the circuit shown in Fig. P10.65 is adjusted for maximum average power transfer to R_L.

PSPICE
MULTISIM

a) Find the maximum average power.

b) What percentage of the average power developed by the ideal voltage source is delivered to R_L when R_L is absorbing maximum average power?

c) Test your solution by showing that the power developed by the ideal voltage source equals the power dissipated in the circuit.

Figure P10.65

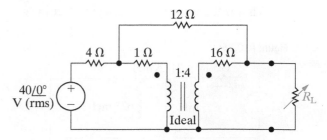

10.66 Repeat Problem 10.65 for the circuit shown in Fig. P10.66.

PSPICE
MULTISIM

Figure P10.66

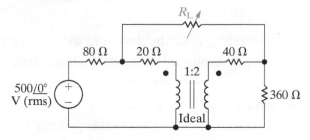

Sections 10.1–10.6

10.67 a) Use the values in Table 10.3 to calculate the number of kilowatt-hours consumed in one month by a notebook computer AC adapter if every day the computer is charging for 5 hours and sleeping for 19 hours..

b) Repeat the calculation in part (a) assuming that the computer is charging for 5 hours and off for 19 hours.

c) Repeat the calculation in part (a) assuming that the computer is charging for 5 hours and disconnected from the AC adapter for 19 hours, but the AC adapter remains plugged into the wall outlet.

d) Repeat the calculation in part (a) assuming that the computer is charging for 5 hours and the AC adapter is unplugged from the wall outlet for 19 hours.

10.68 a) Suppose you use your microwave oven for 12 minutes each day. The remaining time, the oven is ready with the door closed. Use the values in Table 10.3 to calculate the total number of kilowatt-hours used by the microwave oven in one month.

b) What percentage of the power used by the microwave oven in one month is consumed when the oven is ready with the door closed?

10.69 Determine the amount of power, in watts, consumed by the transformer in Fig. 10.29. Assume that the voltage source is ideal ($R_s = 0\ \Omega$), $R_1 = 5\ \Omega$, and $L_1 = 250$ mH. The frequency of the 120 V(rms) source is 60 Hz.

10.70 Repeat Problem 10.69, but assume that the linear transformer has been improved so that $R_s = 50$ mΩ. All other values are unchanged.

10.71 Repeat Problem 10.69 assuming that the linear transformer in Fig. 10.29 has been replaced by an ideal transformer with a turns ratio of 30:1. (*Hint* – you shouldn't need to make any calculations to determine the amount of power consumed.)

Balanced Three-Phase Circuits

✓ CHAPTER OBJECTIVES

1 Know how to analyze a balanced, three-phase wye-wye connected circuit.

2 Know how to analyze a balanced, three-phase wye-delta connected circuit.

3 Be able to calculate power (average, reactive, and complex) in any three-phase circuit.

Generating, transmitting, distributing, and using large blocks of electric power is accomplished with three-phase circuits. The comprehensive analysis of such systems is a field of study in its own right; we cannot hope to cover it in a single chapter. Fortunately, an understanding of only the steady-state sinusoidal behavior of balanced three-phase circuits is sufficient for engineers who do not specialize in power systems. We define what we mean by a balanced circuit later in the discussion. The same circuit analysis techniques discussed in earlier chapters can be applied to either unbalanced or balanced three-phase circuits. Here we use these familiar techniques to develop several shortcuts to the analysis of balanced three-phase circuits.

For economic reasons, three-phase systems are usually designed to operate in the balanced state. Thus, in this introductory treatment, we can justify considering only balanced circuits. The analysis of unbalanced three-phase circuits, which you will encounter if you study electric power in later courses, relies heavily on an understanding of balanced circuits.

The basic structure of a three-phase system consists of voltage sources connected to loads by means of transformers and transmission lines. To analyze such a circuit, we can reduce it to a voltage source connected to a load via a line. The omission of the transformer simplifies the discussion without jeopardizing a basic understanding of the calculations involved. Figure 11.1 on page 398 shows a basic circuit. A defining characteristic of a balanced three-phase circuit is that it contains a set of balanced three-phase voltages at its source. We begin by considering these voltages, and then we move to the voltage and current relationships for the Y-Y and Y-Δ circuits. After considering voltage and current in such circuits, we conclude with sections on power and power measurement.

Practical Perspective

Transmission and Distribution of Electric Power

In this chapter we introduce circuits that are designed to handle large blocks of electric power. These are the circuits that are used to transport electric power from the generating plants to both industrial and residential customers. We introduced the typical residential customer circuit as used in the United States as the design perspective in Chapter 9. Now we introduce the type of circuit used to deliver electric power to an entire residential subdivision.

One of the constraints imposed on the design and operation of an electric utility is the requirement that the utility maintain the rms voltage level at the customer's premises. Whether lightly loaded, as at 3:00 am, or heavily loaded, as at midafternoon on a hot, humid day, the utility is obligated to supply the same rms voltage. Recall from Chapter 10 that a capacitor can be thought of as a source of magnetizing vars. Therefore, one technique for maintaining voltage levels on a utility system is to place capacitors at strategic locations in the distribution network. The idea behind this technique is to use the capacitors to supply magnetizing vars close to the loads requiring them, as opposed to sending them over the lines from the generator. We shall illustrate this concept after we have introduced the analysis of balanced three-phase circuits.

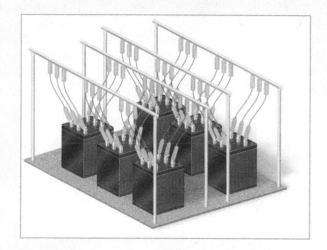

Rolf Vennenbernd/dpa/Corbis

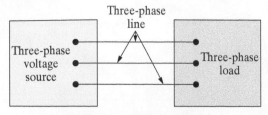

Figure 11.1 ▲ A basic three-phase circuit.

11.1 Balanced Three-Phase Voltages

A set of balanced three-phase voltages consists of three sinusoidal voltages that have identical amplitudes and frequencies but are out of phase with each other by exactly 120°. Standard practice is to refer to the three phases as a, b, and c, and to use the a-phase as the reference phase. The three voltages are referred to as the **a-phase voltage**, the **b-phase voltage**, and the **c-phase voltage**.

Only two possible phase relationships can exist between the a-phase voltage and the b- and c-phase voltages. One possibility is for the b-phase voltage to lag the a-phase voltage by 120°, in which case the c-phase voltage must lead the a-phase voltage by 120°. This phase relationship is known as the **abc** (or **positive**) **phase sequence**. The only other possibility is for the b-phase voltage to lead the a-phase voltage by 120°, in which case the c-phase voltage must lag the a-phase voltage by 120°. This phase relationship is known as the **acb** (or **negative**) **phase sequence**. In phasor notation, the two possible sets of balanced phase voltages are

$$\mathbf{V}_a = V_m \,\underline{/0°},$$

$$\mathbf{V}_b = V_m \,\underline{/-120°},$$

$$\mathbf{V}_c = V_m \,\underline{/+120°}, \tag{11.1}$$

and

$$\mathbf{V}_a = V_m \,\underline{/0°},$$

$$\mathbf{V}_b = V_m \,\underline{/+120°},$$

$$\mathbf{V}_c = V_m \,\underline{/-120°}. \tag{11.2}$$

Equations 11.1 are for the abc, or positive, sequence. Equations 11.2 are for the acb, or negative, sequence. Figure 11.2 shows the phasor diagrams of the voltage sets in Eqs. 11.1 and 11.2. The phase sequence is the clockwise order of the subscripts around the diagram from $\mathbf{V}_a$. The fact that a three-phase circuit can have one of two phase sequences must be taken into account whenever two such circuits operate in parallel. The circuits can operate in parallel only if they have the same phase sequence.

Another important characteristic of a set of balanced three-phase voltages is that the sum of the voltages is zero. Thus, from either Eqs. 11.1 or Eqs. 11.2,

$$\mathbf{V}_a + \mathbf{V}_b + \mathbf{V}_c = 0. \tag{11.3}$$

Because the sum of the phasor voltages is zero, the sum of the instantaneous voltages also is zero; that is,

$$v_a + v_b + v_c = 0. \tag{11.4}$$

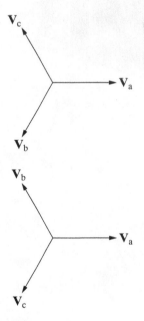

Figure 11.2 ▲ Phasor diagrams of a balanced set of three-phase voltages. (a) The abc (positive) sequence. (b) The acb (negative) sequence.

Now that we know the nature of a balanced set of three-phase voltages, we can state the first of the analytical shortcuts alluded to in the introduction to this chapter: If we know the phase sequence and one voltage in the set, we know the entire set. Thus for a balanced three-phase system, we can focus on determining the voltage (or current) in one phase, because once we know one phase quantity, we know the others.

NOTE: Assess your understanding of three-phase voltages by trying Chapter Problems 11.1 and 11.2.

11.2 Three-Phase Voltage Sources

A three-phase voltage source is a generator with three separate windings distributed around the periphery of the stator. Each winding comprises one phase of the generator. The rotor of the generator is an electromagnet driven at synchronous speed by a prime mover, such as a steam or gas turbine. Rotation of the electromagnet induces a sinusoidal voltage in each winding. The phase windings are designed so that the sinusoidal voltages induced in them are equal in amplitude and out of phase with each other by 120°. The phase windings are stationary with respect to the rotating electromagnet, so the frequency of the voltage induced in each winding is the same. Figure 11.3 shows a sketch of a two-pole three-phase source.

There are two ways of interconnecting the separate phase windings to form a three-phase source: in either a wye (Y) or a delta (Δ) configuration. Figure 11.4 shows both, with ideal voltage sources used to model the phase windings of the three-phase generator. The common terminal in the Y-connected source, labeled *n* in Fig. 11.4(a), is called the **neutral terminal** of the source. The neutral terminal may or may not be available for external connections.

Sometimes, the impedance of each phase winding is so small (compared with other impedances in the circuit) that we need not account for it in modeling the generator; the model consists solely of ideal voltage sources, as in Fig. 11.4. However, if the impedance of each phase winding is not negligible, we place the winding impedance in series with an ideal sinusoidal voltage source. All windings on the machine are of the same construction, so we assume the winding impedances to be identical. The winding impedance of a three-phase generator is inductive. Figure 11.5 shows a model of such a machine, in which is the winding resistance, and X_w is the inductive reactance of the winding.

Because three-phase sources and loads can be either Y-connected or Δ-connected, the basic circuit in Fig. 11.1 represents four different configurations:

Source	Load
Y	Y
Y	Δ
Δ	Y
Δ	Δ

We begin by analyzing the Y-Y circuit. The remaining three arrangements can be reduced to a Y-Y equivalent circuit, so analysis of the Y-Y circuit is the key to solving all balanced three-phase arrangements. We then illustrate the reduction of the Y-Δ arrangement and leave the analysis of the Δ-Y and Δ-Δ arrangements to you in the Problems.

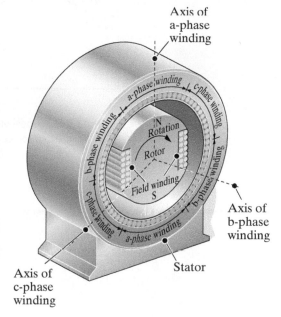

Figure 11.3 ▲ A sketch of a three-phase voltage source.

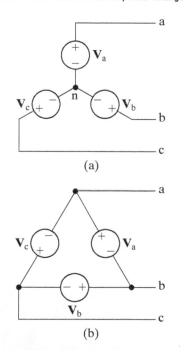

(a)

(b)

Figure 11.4 ▲ The two basic connections of an ideal three-phase source. (a) A Y-connected source. (b) A Δ-connected source.

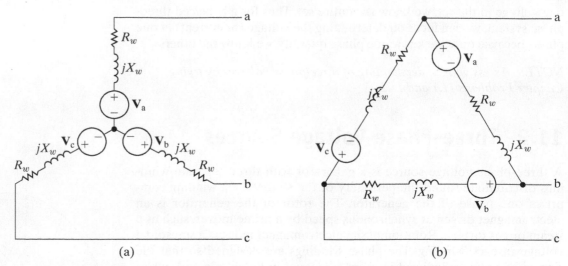

Figure 11.5 ▲ A model of a three-phase source with winding impedance: (a) a Y-connected source; and (b) a Δ-connected source.

11.3 Analysis of the Wye-Wye Circuit

Figure 11.6 illustrates a general Y-Y circuit, in which we included a fourth conductor that connects the source neutral to the load neutral. A fourth conductor is possible only in the Y-Y arrangement. (More about this later.) For convenience, we transformed the Y connections into "tipped-over tees." In Fig. 11.6, Z_{ga}, Z_{gb}, and Z_{gc} represent the internal impedance associated with each phase winding of the voltage generator; Z_{1a}, Z_{1b}, and Z_{1c} represent the impedance of the lines connecting a phase of the source to a phase of the load; Z_0 is the impedance of the neutral conductor connecting the source neutral to the load neutral; and Z_A, Z_B, and Z_C represent the impedance of each phase of the load.

We can describe this circuit with a single node-voltage equation. Using the source neutral as the reference node and letting $\mathbf{V}_N$ denote the node voltage between the nodes N and n, we find that the node-voltage equation is

$$\frac{\mathbf{V}_N}{Z_0} + \frac{\mathbf{V}_N - \mathbf{V}_{a'n}}{Z_A + Z_{1a} + Z_{ga}} + \frac{\mathbf{V}_N - \mathbf{V}_{b'n}}{Z_B + Z_{1b} + Z_{gb}} + \frac{\mathbf{V}_N - \mathbf{V}_{c'n}}{Z_C + Z_{1c} + Z_{gc}} = 0.$$

(11.5)

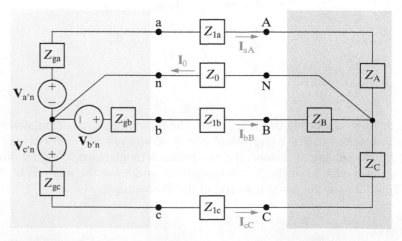

Figure 11.6 ▲ A three-phase Y-Y system.

This is the general equation for any circuit of the Y-Y configuration depicted in Fig. 11.6. But we can simplify Eq. 11.5 significantly if we now consider the formal definition of a balanced three-phase circuit. Such a circuit satisfies the following criteria:

1. The voltage sources form a set of balanced three-phase voltages. In Fig. 11.6, this means that $\mathbf{V}_{a'n}$, $\mathbf{V}_{b'n}$, and $\mathbf{V}_{c'n}$ are a set of balanced three-phase voltages.
2. The impedance of each phase of the voltage source is the same. In Fig. 11.6, this means that $Z_{ga} = Z_{gb} = Z_{gc}$.
3. The impedance of each line (or phase) conductor is the same. In Fig. 11.6, this means that $Z_{1a} = Z_{1b} = Z_{1c}$.
4. The impedance of each phase of the load is the same. In Fig. 11.6, this means that $Z_A = Z_B = Z_C$.

◀ **Conditions for a balanced three-phase circuit**

There is no restriction on the impedance of a neutral conductor; its value has no effect on whether the system is balanced.

If the circuit in Fig. 11.6 is balanced, we may rewrite Eq. 11.5 as

$$\mathbf{V}_N\left(\frac{1}{Z_0} + \frac{3}{Z_\phi}\right) = \frac{\mathbf{V}_{a'n} + \mathbf{V}_{b'n} + \mathbf{V}_{c'n}}{Z_\phi}, \tag{11.6}$$

where

$$Z_\phi = Z_A + Z_{1a} + Z_{ga} = Z_B + Z_{1b} + Z_{gb} = Z_C + Z_{1c} + Z_{gc}.$$

The right-hand side of Eq. 11.6 is zero, because by hypothesis the numerator is a set of balanced three-phase voltages and Z_ϕ is not zero. The only value of $\mathbf{V}_N$ that satisfies Eq. 11.6 is zero. Therefore, for a balanced three-phase circuit,

$$\mathbf{V}_N = 0. \tag{11.7}$$

Equation 11.7 is extremely important. If $\mathbf{V}_N$ is zero, there is no difference in potential between the source neutral, n, and the load neutral, N; consequently, the current in the neutral conductor is zero. Hence we may either remove the neutral conductor from a balanced Y-Y configuration ($\mathbf{I}_0 = 0$) or replace it with a perfect short circuit between the nodes n and N ($\mathbf{V}_N = 0$). Both equivalents are convenient to use when modeling balanced three-phase circuits.

We now turn to the effect that balanced conditions have on the three line currents. With reference to Fig. 11.6, when the system is balanced, the three line currents are

$$\mathbf{I}_{aA} = \frac{\mathbf{V}_{a'n} - \mathbf{V}_N}{Z_A + Z_{1a} + Z_{ga}} = \frac{\mathbf{V}_{a'n}}{Z_\phi}, \tag{11.8}$$

$$\mathbf{I}_{bB} = \frac{\mathbf{V}_{b'n} - \mathbf{V}_N}{Z_B + Z_{1b} + Z_{gb}} = \frac{\mathbf{V}_{b'n}}{Z_\phi}, \tag{11.9}$$

$$\mathbf{I}_{cC} = \frac{\mathbf{V}_{c'n} - \mathbf{V}_N}{Z_C + Z_{1c} + Z_{gc}} = \frac{\mathbf{V}_{c'n}}{Z_\phi}. \tag{11.10}$$

We see that the three line currents form a balanced set of three-phase currents; that is, the current in each line is equal in amplitude and frequency and is 120° out of phase with the other two line currents. Thus, if we calculate the current $\mathbf{I}_{aA}$ and we know the phase sequence, we have a shortcut

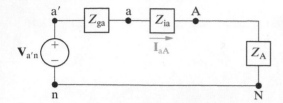

Figure 11.7 ▲ A single-phase equivalent circuit.

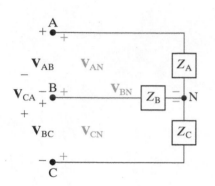

Figure 11.8 ▲ Line-to-line and line-to-neutral voltages.

for finding $\mathbf{I}_{bB}$ and $\mathbf{I}_{cC}$. This procedure parallels the shortcut used to find the b- and c-phase source voltages from the a-phase source voltage.

We can use Eq. 11.8 to construct an equivalent circuit for the a-phase of the balanced Y-Y circuit. From this equation, the current in the a-phase conductor line is simply the voltage generated in the a-phase winding of the generator divided by the total impedance in the a-phase of the circuit. Thus Eq. 11.8 describes the simple circuit shown in Fig. 11.7, in which the neutral conductor has been replaced by a perfect short circuit. The circuit in Fig. 11.7 is referred to as the **single-phase equivalent circuit** of a balanced three-phase circuit. Because of the established relationships between phases, once we solve this circuit, we can easily write down the voltages and currents in the other two phases. Thus, drawing a single-phase equivalent circuit is an important first step in analyzing a three-phase circuit.

A word of caution here. The current in the neutral conductor in Fig. 11.7 is $\mathbf{I}_{aA}$, which is not the same as the current in the neutral conductor of the balanced three-phase circuit, which is

$$\mathbf{I}_o = \mathbf{I}_{aA} + \mathbf{I}_{bB} + \mathbf{I}_{cC}. \tag{11.11}$$

Thus the circuit shown in Fig. 11.7 gives the correct value of the line current but only the a-phase component of the neutral current. Whenever this single-phase equivalent circuit is applicable, the line currents form a balanced three-phase set, and the right-hand side of Eq. 11.11 sums to zero.

Once we know the line current in Fig. 11.7, calculating any voltages of interest is relatively simple. Of particular interest is the relationship between the line-to-line voltages and the line-to-neutral voltages. We establish this relationship at the load terminals, but our observations also apply at the source terminals. The line-to-line voltages at the load terminals can be seen in Fig. 11.8. They are $\mathbf{V}_{AB}$, $\mathbf{V}_{BC}$, and $\mathbf{V}_{CA}$, where the double subscript notation indicates a voltage drop from the first-named node to the second. (Because we are interested in the balanced state, we have omitted the neutral conductor from Fig. 11.8.)

The line-to-neutral voltages are $\mathbf{V}_{AN}$, $\mathbf{V}_{BN}$, and $\mathbf{V}_{CN}$. We can now describe the line-to-line voltages in terms of the line-to-neutral voltages, using Kirchhoff's voltage law:

$$\mathbf{V}_{AB} = \mathbf{V}_{AN} - \mathbf{V}_{BN}, \tag{11.12}$$

$$\mathbf{V}_{BC} = \mathbf{V}_{BN} - \mathbf{V}_{CN}, \tag{11.13}$$

$$\mathbf{V}_{CA} = \mathbf{V}_{CN} - \mathbf{V}_{AN}. \tag{11.14}$$

To show the relationship between the line-to-line voltages and the line-to-neutral voltages, we assume a positive, or abc, sequence. Using the line-to-neutral voltage of the a-phase as the reference,

$$\mathbf{V}_{AN} = V_\phi \underline{/0°}, \tag{11.15}$$

$$\mathbf{V}_{BN} = V_\phi \underline{/-120°}, \tag{11.16}$$

$$\mathbf{V}_{CN} = V_\phi \underline{/+120°}, \tag{11.17}$$

where V_ϕ represents the magnitude of the line-to-neutral voltage. Substituting Eqs. 11.15–11.17 into Eqs. 11.12–11.14, respectively, yields

$$\mathbf{V}_{AB} = V_\phi \underline{/0°} - V_\phi \underline{/-120°} = \sqrt{3}V_\phi \underline{/30°}, \qquad (11.18)$$

$$\mathbf{V}_{BC} = V_\phi \underline{/-120°} - V_\phi \underline{/120°} = \sqrt{3}V_\phi \underline{/-90°}, \qquad (11.19)$$

$$\mathbf{V}_{CA} = V_\phi \underline{/120°} - V_\phi \underline{/0°} = \sqrt{3}V_\phi \underline{/150°}. \qquad (11.20)$$

Equations 11.18–11.20 reveal that

1. The magnitude of the line-to-line voltage is $\sqrt{3}$ times the magnitude of the line-to-neutral voltage.
2. The line-to-line voltages form a balanced three-phase set of voltages.
3. The set of line-to-line voltages leads the set of line-to-neutral voltages by 30°.

We leave to you the demonstration that for a negative sequence, the only change is that the set of line-to-line voltages lags the set of line-to-neutral voltages by 30°. The phasor diagrams shown in Fig. 11.9 summarize these observations. Here, again, is a shortcut in the analysis of a balanced system: If you know the line-to-neutral voltage at some point in the circuit, you can easily determine the line-to-line voltage at the same point and vice versa.

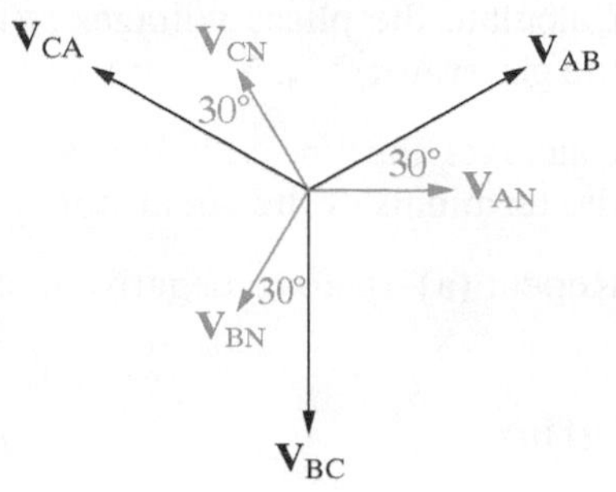

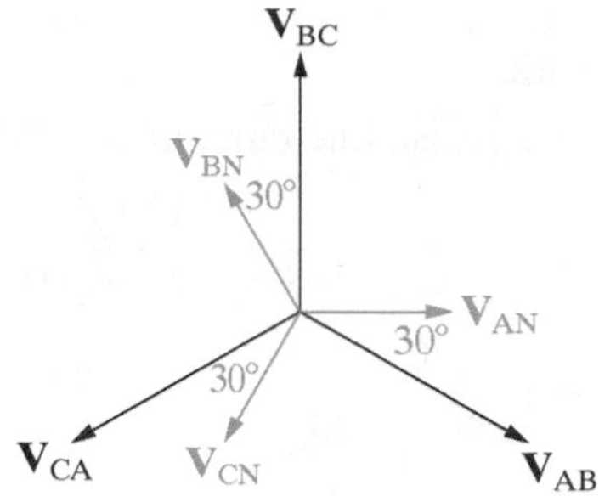

We now pause to elaborate on terminology. **Line voltage** refers to the voltage across any pair of lines; **phase voltage** refers to the voltage across a single phase. **Line current** refers to the current in a single line; **phase current** refers to current in a single phase. Observe that in a Δ connection, line voltage and phase voltage are identical, and in a Y connection, line current and phase current are identical.

Because three-phase systems are designed to handle large blocks of electric power, all voltage and current specifications are given as rms values. When voltage ratings are given, they refer specifically to the rating of the line voltage. Thus when a three-phase transmission line is rated at 345 kV, the nominal value of the rms line-to-line voltage is 345,000 V. In this chapter we express all voltages and currents as rms values.

Finally, the Greek letter phi (ϕ) is widely used in the literature to denote a per-phase quantity. Thus $\mathbf{V}_\phi$, $\mathbf{I}_\phi$, Z_ϕ, P_ϕ, and Q_ϕ are interpreted as voltage/phase, current/phase, impedance/phase, power/phase, and reactive power/phase, respectively.

Example 11.1 shows how to use the observations made so far to solve a balanced three-phase Y-Y circuit.

Figure 11.9 ▲ Phasor diagrams showing the relationship between line-to-line and line-to-neutral voltages in a balanced system. (a) The abc sequence. (b) The acb sequence.

Example 11.1   Analyzing a Wye-Wye Circuit

A balanced three-phase Y-connected generator with positive sequence has an impedance of $0.2 + j0.5 \ \Omega/\phi$ and an internal voltage of $120 \ V/\phi$. The generator feeds a balanced three-phase Y-connected load having an impedance of $39 + j28 \ \Omega/\phi$. The impedance of the line connecting the generator to the load is $0.8 + j1.5 \ \Omega/\phi$. The a-phase internal voltage of the generator is specified as the reference phasor.

a) Construct the a-phase equivalent circuit of the system.

b) Calculate the three line currents $\mathbf{I}_{aA}$, $\mathbf{I}_{bB}$, and $\mathbf{I}_{cC}$.

c) Calculate the three phase voltages at the load, $\mathbf{V}_{AN}$, $\mathbf{V}_{BN}$, and $\mathbf{V}_{CN}$.

d) Calculate the line voltages $\mathbf{V}_{AB}$, $\mathbf{V}_{BC}$, and $\mathbf{V}_{CA}$ at the terminals of the load.

e) Calculate the phase voltages at the terminals of the generator, $\mathbf{V}_{an}$, $\mathbf{V}_{bn}$, and $\mathbf{V}_{cn}$.

f) Calculate the line voltages $\mathbf{V}_{ab}$, $\mathbf{V}_{bc}$, and $\mathbf{V}_{ca}$ at the terminals of the generator.

g) Repeat (a)–(f) for a negative phase sequence.

Solution

a) Figure 11.10 shows the single-phase equivalent circuit.

b) The a-phase line current is

$$\mathbf{I}_{aA} = \frac{120\ \underline{/0^\circ}}{(0.2 + 0.8 + 39) + j(0.5 + 1.5 + 28)}$$

$$= \frac{120\ \underline{/0^\circ}}{40 + j30}$$

$$= 2.4\ \underline{/-36.87^\circ}\ \text{A}.$$

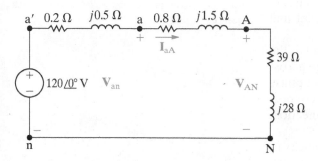

Figure 11.10 ▲ The single-phase equivalent circuit for Example 11.1.

For a positive phase sequence,

$$\mathbf{I}_{bB} = 2.4\ \underline{/-156.87^\circ}\ \text{A},$$

$$\mathbf{I}_{cC} = 2.4\ \underline{/83.13^\circ}\ \text{A}.$$

c) The phase voltage at the A terminal of the load is

$$\mathbf{V}_{AN} = (39 + j28)(2.4\ \underline{/-36.87^\circ})$$

$$= 115.22\ \underline{/-1.19^\circ}\ \text{V}.$$

For a positive phase sequence,

$$\mathbf{V}_{BN} = 115.22\ \underline{/-121.19^\circ}\ \text{V},$$

$$\mathbf{V}_{CN} = 115.22\ \underline{/118.81^\circ}\ \text{V}.$$

d) For a positive phase sequence, the line voltages lead the phase voltages by 30°; thus

$$\mathbf{V}_{AB} = (\sqrt{3}\ \underline{/30^\circ})\mathbf{V}_{AN}$$

$$= 199.58\ \underline{/28.81^\circ}\ \text{V},$$

$$\mathbf{V}_{BC} = 199.58\ \underline{/-91.19^\circ}\ \text{V},$$

$$\mathbf{V}_{CA} = 199.58\ \underline{/148.81^\circ}\ \text{V}.$$

e) The phase voltage at the a terminal of the source is

$$\mathbf{V}_{an} = 120 - (0.2 + j0.5)(2.4\ \underline{/-36.87^\circ})$$

$$= 120 - 1.29\ \underline{/31.33^\circ}$$

$$= 118.90 - j0.67$$

$$= 118.90\ \underline{/-0.32^\circ}\ \text{V}.$$

For a positive phase sequence,

$$\mathbf{V}_{bn} = 118.90\ \underline{/-120.32^\circ}\ \text{V},$$

$$\mathbf{V}_{cn} = 118.90\ \underline{/119.68^\circ}\ \text{V}.$$

f) The line voltages at the source terminals are

$$\mathbf{V}_{ab} = (\sqrt{3}\ \underline{/30^\circ})\mathbf{V}_{an}$$

$$= 205.94\ \underline{/29.68^\circ}\ \text{V},$$

$$\mathbf{V}_{bc} = 205.94\ \underline{/-90.32^\circ}\ \text{V},$$

$$\mathbf{V}_{ca} = 205.94\ \underline{/149.68^\circ}\ \text{V}.$$

g) Changing the phase sequence has no effect on the single-phase equivalent circuit. The three line currents are

$$\mathbf{I}_{aA} = 2.4\ \underline{/-36.87^\circ}\ \text{A},$$

$$\mathbf{I}_{bB} = 2.4\ \underline{/83.13^\circ}\ \text{A},$$

$$\mathbf{I}_{cC} = 2.4\ \underline{/-156.87^\circ}\ \text{A}.$$

The phase voltages at the load are

$$\mathbf{V}_{AN} = 115.22\ \underline{/-1.19^\circ}\ \text{V},$$

$$\mathbf{V}_{BN} = 115.22\ \underline{/118.81^\circ}\ \text{V},$$

$$\mathbf{V}_{CN} = 115.22\ \underline{/-121.19^\circ}\ \text{V}.$$

For a negative phase sequence, the line voltages lag the phase voltages by 30°:

$$\mathbf{V}_{AB} = (\sqrt{3}\ \underline{/-30^\circ})\mathbf{V}_{AN}$$

$$= 199.58\ \underline{/-31.19^\circ}\ \text{V},$$

$$\mathbf{V}_{BC} = 199.58\ \underline{/88.81^\circ}\ \text{V},$$

$$\mathbf{V}_{CA} = 199.58\ \underline{/-151.19^\circ}\ \text{V}.$$

The phase voltages at the terminals of the generator are

$$\mathbf{V}_{an} = 118.90\ \underline{/-0.32^\circ}\ \text{V},$$

$$\mathbf{V}_{bn} = 118.90\ \underline{/119.68^\circ}\ \text{V},$$

$$\mathbf{V}_{cn} = 118.90\ \underline{/-120.32^\circ}\ \text{V}.$$

The line voltages at the terminals of the generator are

$$\mathbf{V}_{ab} = (\sqrt{3}\ \underline{/-30^\circ})\mathbf{V}_{an}$$

$$= 205.94\ \underline{/-30.32^\circ}\ \text{V},$$

$$\mathbf{V}_{bc} = 205.94\ \underline{/89.68^\circ}\ \text{V},$$

$$\mathbf{V}_{ca} = 205.94\ \underline{/-150.32^\circ}\ \text{V}.$$

✔ASSESSMENT PROBLEMS

Objective 1—Know how to analyze a balanced, three-phase wye-wye circuit

11.1 The voltage from A to N in a balanced three-phase circuit is $240\ \underline{/-30^\circ}$ V. If the phase sequence is positive, what is the value of $\mathbf{V}_{BC}$?

Answer: $415.69\ \underline{/-120^\circ}$ V.

11.2 The c-phase voltage of a balanced three-phase Y-connected system is $450\ \underline{/-25^\circ}$ V. If the phase sequence is negative, what is the value of $\mathbf{V}_{AB}$?

Answer: $779.42\ \underline{/65^\circ}$ V.

11.3 The phase voltage at the terminals of a balanced three-phase Y-connected load is 2400 V. The load has an impedance of $16 + j12\ \Omega/\phi$ and is fed from a line having an impedance of $0.10 + j0.80\ \Omega/\phi$. The Y-connected source at the sending end of the line has a phase

sequence of acb and an internal impedance of $0.02 + j0.16\ \Omega/\phi$. Use the a-phase voltage at the load as the reference and calculate (a) the line currents $\mathbf{I}_{aA}$, $\mathbf{I}_{bB}$, and $\mathbf{I}_{cC}$; (b) the line voltages at the source, $\mathbf{V}_{ab}$, $\mathbf{V}_{bc}$, and $\mathbf{V}_{ca}$; and (c) the internal phase-to-neutral voltages at the source, $\mathbf{V}_{a'n}$, $\mathbf{V}_{b'n}$, and $\mathbf{V}_{c'n}$.

Answer: (a) $\mathbf{I}_{aA} = 120\ \underline{/-36.87^\circ}$ A,
$\mathbf{I}_{bB} = 120\ \underline{/83.13^\circ}$ A, and
$\mathbf{I}_{cC} = 120\ \underline{/-156.87^\circ}$ A;

(b) $\mathbf{V}_{ab} = 4275.02\ \underline{/-28.38^\circ}$ V,
$\mathbf{V}_{bc} = 4275.02\ \underline{/91.62^\circ}$ V, and
$\mathbf{V}_{ca} = 4275.02\ \underline{/-148.38^\circ}$ V;

(c) $\mathbf{V}_{a'n} = 2482.05\ \underline{/1.93^\circ}$ V,
$\mathbf{V}_{b'n} = 2482.05\ \underline{/121.93^\circ}$ V, and
$\mathbf{V}_{c'n} = 2482.05\ \underline{/-118.07^\circ}$ V.

NOTE: Also try Chapter Problems 11.9, 11.11, and 11.12.

11.4 Analysis of the Wye-Delta Circuit

If the load in a three-phase circuit is connected in a delta, it can be transformed into a wye by using the delta-to-wye transformation discussed in Section 9.6. When the load is balanced, the impedance of each leg of the wye is one third the impedance of each leg of the delta, or

Relationship between three-phase delta-connected and wye-connected ◀ impedance

$$Z_Y = \frac{Z_\Delta}{3}, \tag{11.21}$$

which follows directly from Eqs. 9.51–9.53. After the Δ load has been replaced by its Y equivalent, the a-phase can be modeled by the single-phase equivalent circuit shown in Fig. 11.11.

We use this circuit to calculate the line currents, and we then use the line currents to find the currents in each leg of the original Δ load. The relationship between the line currents and the currents in each leg of the delta can be derived using the circuit shown in Fig. 11.12.

When a load (or source) is connected in a delta, the current in each leg of the delta is the phase current, and the voltage across each leg is the phase voltage. Figure 11.12 shows that, in the Δ configuration, the phase voltage is identical to the line voltage.

To demonstrate the relationship between the phase currents and line currents, we assume a positive phase sequence and let I_ϕ represent the magnitude of the phase current. Then

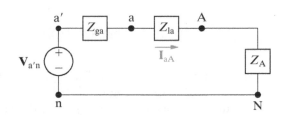

Figure 11.11 ▲ A single-phase equivalent circuit.

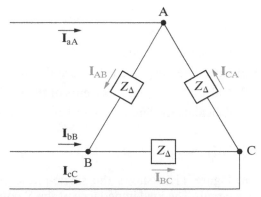

$$\mathbf{I}_{AB} = I_\phi\ \underline{/0^\circ}, \tag{11.22}$$

$$\mathbf{I}_{BC} = I_\phi\ \underline{/-120^\circ}, \tag{11.23}$$

$$\mathbf{I}_{CA} = I_\phi\ \underline{/120^\circ}. \tag{11.24}$$

Figure 11.12 ▲ A circuit used to establish the relationship between line currents and phase currents in a balanced Δ load.

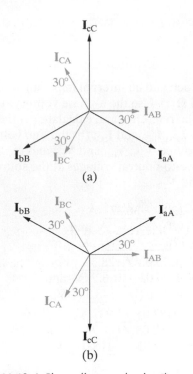

Figure 11.13 ▲ Phasor diagrams showing the relationship between line currents and phase currents in a Δ-connected load. (a) The positive sequence. (b) The negative sequence.

In writing these equations, we arbitrarily selected $\mathbf{I}_{AB}$ as the reference phasor.

We can write the line currents in terms of the phase currents by direct application of Kirchhoff's current law:

$$\mathbf{I}_{aA} = \mathbf{I}_{AB} - \mathbf{I}_{CA}$$

$$= I_\phi \underline{/0°} - I_\phi \underline{/120°}$$

$$= \sqrt{3}I_\phi \underline{/-30°}, \tag{11.25}$$

$$\mathbf{I}_{bB} = \mathbf{I}_{BC} - \mathbf{I}_{AB}$$

$$= I_\phi \underline{/-120°} - I_\phi \underline{/0°}$$

$$= \sqrt{3}I_\phi \underline{/-150°}, \tag{11.26}$$

$$\mathbf{I}_{cC} = \mathbf{I}_{CA} - \mathbf{I}_{BC}$$

$$= I_\phi \underline{/120°} - I_\phi \underline{/-120°}$$

$$= \sqrt{3}I_\phi \underline{/90°}. \tag{11.27}$$

Comparing Eqs. 11.25–11.27 with Eqs. 11.22–11.24 reveals that the magnitude of the line currents is $\sqrt{3}$ times the magnitude of the phase currents and that the set of line currents lags the set of phase currents by 30°.

We leave to you to verify that, for a negative phase sequence, the line currents are $\sqrt{3}$ times larger than the phase currents and lead the phase currents by 30°. Thus, we have a shortcut for calculating line currents from phase currents (or vice versa) for a balanced three-phase Δ-connected load. Figure 11.13 summarizes this shortcut graphically. Example 11.2 illustrates the calculations involved in analyzing a balanced three-phase circuit having a Y-connected source and a Δ-connected load.

Example 11.2 | Analyzing a Wye-Delta Circuit

The Y-connected source in Example 11.1 feeds a Δ-connected load through a distribution line having an impedance of $0.3 + j0.9 \ \Omega/\phi$. The load impedance is $118.5 + j85.8 \ \Omega/\phi$. Use the a-phase internal voltage of the generator as the reference.

a) Construct a single-phase equivalent circuit of the three-phase system.

b) Calculate the line currents $\mathbf{I}_{aA}$, $\mathbf{I}_{bB}$, and $\mathbf{I}_{cC}$.

c) Calculate the phase voltages at the load terminals.

d) Calculate the phase currents of the load.

e) Calculate the line voltages at the source terminals.

Solution

a) Figure 11.14 shows the single-phase equivalent circuit. The load impedance of the Y equivalent is

$$\frac{118.5 + j85.8}{3} = 39.5 + j28.6 \ \Omega/\phi.$$

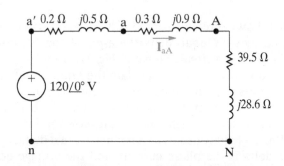

Figure 11.14 ▲ The single-phase equivalent circuit for Example 11.2.

b) The a-phase line current is

$$\mathbf{I}_{aA} = \frac{120 \ \underline{/0°}}{(0.2 + 0.3 + 39.5) + j(0.5 + 0.9 + 28.6)}$$

$$= \frac{120 \ \underline{/0°}}{40 + j30} = 2.4 \ \underline{/-36.87°} \ \text{A}.$$

Hence

$$\mathbf{I}_{bB} = 2.4 \underline{/-156.87^\circ} \text{ A,}$$

$$\mathbf{I}_{cC} = 2.4 \underline{/83.13^\circ} \text{ A.}$$

c) Because the load is Δ connected, the phase voltages are the same as the line voltages. To calculate the line voltages, we first calculate $\mathbf{V}_{AN}$:

$$\mathbf{V}_{AN} = (39.5 + j28.6)(2.4 \underline{/-36.87^\circ})$$

$$= 117.04 \underline{/-0.96^\circ} \text{ V.}$$

Because the phase sequence is positive, the line voltage $\mathbf{V}_{AB}$ is

$$\mathbf{V}_{AB} = (\sqrt{3} \underline{/30^\circ}) \mathbf{V}_{AN}$$

$$= 202.72 \underline{/29.04^\circ} \text{ V.}$$

Therefore

$$\mathbf{V}_{BC} = 202.72 \underline{/-90.96^\circ} \text{ V,}$$

$$\mathbf{V}_{CA} = 202.72 \underline{/149.04^\circ} \text{ V.}$$

d) The phase currents of the load may be calculated directly from the line currents:

$$\mathbf{I}_{AB} = \left(\frac{1}{\sqrt{3}} \underline{/30^\circ}\right) \mathbf{I}_{aA}$$

$$= 1.39 \underline{/-6.87^\circ} \text{ A.}$$

Once we know $\mathbf{I}_{AB}$, we also know the other load phase currents:

$$\mathbf{I}_{BC} = 1.39 \underline{/-126.87^\circ} \text{ A,}$$

$$\mathbf{I}_{CA} = 1.39 \underline{/113.13^\circ} \text{ A.}$$

Note that we can check the calculation of $\mathbf{I}_{AB}$ by using the previously calculated $\mathbf{V}_{AB}$ and the impedance of the Δ-connected load; that is,

$$\mathbf{I}_{AB} = \frac{\mathbf{V}_{AB}}{Z_\phi} = \frac{202.72 \underline{/29.04^\circ}}{118.5 + j85.8}$$

$$= 1.39 \underline{/-6.87^\circ} \text{ A.}$$

e) To calculate the line voltage at the terminals of the source, we first calculate $\mathbf{V}_{an}$. Figure 11.14 shows that $\mathbf{V}_{an}$ is the voltage drop across the line impedance plus the load impedance, so

$$\mathbf{V}_{an} = (39.8 + j29.5)(2.4 \underline{/-36.87^\circ})$$

$$= 118.90 \underline{/-0.32^\circ} \text{ V.}$$

The line voltage $\mathbf{V}_{ab}$ is

$$\mathbf{V}_{ab} = (\sqrt{3} \underline{/30^\circ})\mathbf{V}_{an},$$

or

$$\mathbf{V}_{ab} = 205.94 \underline{/29.68^\circ} \text{ V.}$$

Therefore

$$\mathbf{V}_{bc} = 205.94 \underline{/-90.32^\circ} \text{ V,}$$

$$\mathbf{V}_{ca} = 205.94 \underline{/149.68^\circ} \text{ V.}$$

✓ ASSESSMENT PROBLEMS

Objective 2—Know how to analyze a balanced, three-phase wye-delta connected circuit

11.4   The current $\mathbf{I}_{CA}$ in a balanced three-phase Δ-connected load is $8 \underline{/-15^\circ}$ A. If the phase sequence is positive, what is the value of $\mathbf{I}_{cC}$?

Answer: $13.86 \underline{/-45^\circ}$ A.

11.5   A balanced three-phase Δ-connected load is fed from a balanced three-phase circuit. The reference for the b-phase line current is toward the load. The value of the current in the b-phase is $12 \underline{/65^\circ}$ A. If the phase sequence is negative, what is the value of $\mathbf{I}_{AB}$?

Answer: $6.93 \underline{/-85^\circ}$ A.

NOTE: Also try Chapter Problems 11.14–11.16.

11.6   The line voltage $\mathbf{V}_{AB}$ at the terminals of a balanced three-phase Δ-connected load is $4160 \underline{/0^\circ}$ V. The line current $\mathbf{I}_{aA}$ is $69.28 \underline{/-10^\circ}$ A.

a) Calculate the per-phase impedance of the load if the phase sequence is positive.

b) Repeat (a) for a negative phase sequence.

Answer: (a) $104 \underline{/-20^\circ}$ Ω;
   (b) $104 \underline{/+40^\circ}$ Ω.

11.7   The line voltage at the terminals of a balanced Δ-connected load is 110 V. Each phase of the load consists of a 3.667 Ω resistor in parallel with a 2.75 Ω inductive impedance. What is the magnitude of the current in the line feeding the load?

Answer: 86.60 A.

11.5 Power Calculations in Balanced Three-Phase Circuits

So far, we have limited our analysis of balanced three-phase circuits to determining currents and voltages. We now discuss three-phase power calculations. We begin by considering the average power delivered to a balanced Y-connected load.

Average Power in a Balanced Wye Load

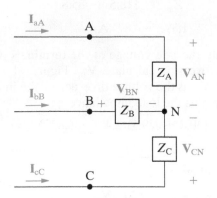

Figure 11.15 ▲ A balanced Y load used to introduce average power calculations in three-phase circuits.

Figure 11.15 shows a Y-connected load, along with its pertinent currents and voltages. We calculate the average power associated with any one phase by using the techniques introduced in Chapter 10. With Eq. 10.21 as a starting point, we express the average power associated with the a-phase as

$$P_A = |\mathbf{V}_{AN}||\mathbf{I}_{aA}| \cos(\theta_{vA} - \theta_{iA}), \qquad (11.28)$$

where θ_{vA} and θ_{iA} denote the phase angles of $\mathbf{V}_{AN}$ and $\mathbf{I}_{aA}$, respectively. Using the notation introduced in Eq. 11.28, we can find the power associated with the b- and c-phases:

$$P_B = |\mathbf{V}_{BN}||\mathbf{I}_{bB}| \cos(\theta_{vB} - \theta_{iB}), \qquad (11.29)$$

$$P_C = |\mathbf{V}_{CN}||\mathbf{I}_{cC}| \cos(\theta_{vC} - \theta_{iC}). \qquad (11.30)$$

In Eqs. 11.28–11.30, all phasor currents and voltages are written in terms of the rms value of the sinusoidal function they represent.

In a balanced three-phase system, the magnitude of each line-to-neutral voltage is the same, as is the magnitude of each phase current. The argument of the cosine functions is also the same for all three phases. We emphasize these observations by introducing the following notation:

$$V_\phi = |\mathbf{V}_{AN}| = |\mathbf{V}_{BN}| = |\mathbf{V}_{CN}|, \qquad (11.31)$$

$$I_\phi = |\mathbf{I}_{aA}| = |\mathbf{I}_{bB}| = |\mathbf{I}_{cC}|, \qquad (11.32)$$

and

$$\theta_\phi = \theta_{vA} - \theta_{iA} = \theta_{vB} - \theta_{iB} = \theta_{vC} - \theta_{iC}. \qquad (11.33)$$

Moreover, for a balanced system, the power delivered to each phase of the load is the same, so

$$P_A = P_B = P_C = P_\phi = V_\phi I_\phi \cos\theta_\phi, \qquad (11.34)$$

where P_ϕ represents the average power per phase.

The total average power delivered to the balanced Y-connected load is simply three times the power per phase, or

$$P_T = 3P_\phi = 3V_\phi I_\phi \cos\theta_\phi. \qquad (11.35)$$

Expressing the total power in terms of the rms magnitudes of the line voltage and current is also desirable. If we let V_L and I_L represent the rms magnitudes of the line voltage and current, respectively, we can modify Eq. 11.35 as follows:

Total real power in a balanced three-phase load ▶

$$P_T = 3\left(\frac{V_L}{\sqrt{3}}\right)I_L \cos\theta_\phi$$

$$= \sqrt{3}V_L I_L \cos\theta_\phi. \qquad (11.36)$$

In deriving Eq. 11.36, we recognized that, for a balanced Y-connected load, the magnitude of the phase voltage is the magnitude of the line voltage divided by $\sqrt{3}$, and that the magnitude of the line current is equal to the magnitude of the phase current. When using Eq. 11.36 to calculate the total power delivered to the load, remember that θ_ϕ is the phase angle between the phase voltage and current.

Complex Power in a Balanced Wye Load

We can also calculate the reactive power and complex power associated with any one phase of a Y-connected load by using the techniques introduced in Chapter 10. For a balanced load, the expressions for the reactive power are

$$Q_\phi = V_\phi I_\phi \sin\theta_\phi, \tag{11.37}$$

$$Q_T = 3Q_\phi = \sqrt{3}V_L I_L \sin\theta_\phi. \tag{11.38}$$

◀ **Total reactive power in a balanced three-phase load**

Equation 10.29 is the basis for expressing the complex power associated with any phase. For a balanced load,

$$S_\phi = \mathbf{V}_{AN}\mathbf{I}_{aA}^* = \mathbf{V}_{BN}\mathbf{I}_{bB}^* = \mathbf{V}_{CN}\mathbf{I}_{cC}^* = \mathbf{V}_\phi\mathbf{I}_\phi^*, \tag{11.39}$$

where $\mathbf{V}_\phi$ and $\mathbf{I}_\phi$ represent a phase voltage and current taken from the same phase. Thus, in general,

$$S_\phi = P_\phi + jQ_\phi = \mathbf{V}_\phi\mathbf{I}_\phi^*, \tag{11.40}$$

$$S_T = 3S_\phi = \sqrt{3}V_L I_L \underline{/\theta_\phi^\circ}. \tag{11.41}$$

◀ **Total complex power in a balanced three-phase load**

Power Calculations in a Balanced Delta Load

If the load is Δ-connected, the calculation of power—reactive or complex— is basically the same as that for a Y-connected load. Figure 11.16 shows a Δ-connected load, along with its pertinent currents and voltages. The power associated with each phase is

$$P_A = |\mathbf{V}_{AB}||\mathbf{I}_{AB}|\cos(\theta_{vAB} - \theta_{iAB}), \tag{11.42}$$

$$P_B = |\mathbf{V}_{BC}||\mathbf{I}_{BC}|\cos(\theta_{vBC} - \theta_{iBC}), \tag{11.43}$$

$$P_C = |\mathbf{V}_{CA}||\mathbf{I}_{CA}|\cos(\theta_{vCA} - \theta_{iCA}). \tag{11.44}$$

For a balanced load,

$$|\mathbf{V}_{AB}| = |\mathbf{V}_{BC}| = |\mathbf{V}_{CA}| = V_\phi, \tag{11.45}$$

$$|\mathbf{I}_{AB}| = |\mathbf{I}_{BC}| = |\mathbf{I}_{CA}| = I_\phi, \tag{11.46}$$

$$\theta_{vAB} - \theta_{iAB} = \theta_{vBC} - \theta_{iBC} = \theta_{vCA} - \theta_{iCA} = \theta_\phi, \tag{11.47}$$

and

$$P_A = P_B = P_C = P_\phi = V_\phi I_\phi \cos\theta_\phi. \tag{11.48}$$

Note that Eq. 11.48 is the same as Eq. 11.34. Thus, in a balanced load, regardless of whether it is Y- or Δ-connected, the average power per phase is equal to the product of the rms magnitude of the phase voltage, the rms magnitude of the phase current, and the cosine of the angle between the phase voltage and current.

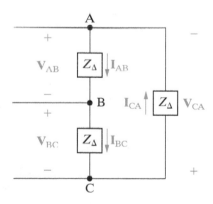

Figure 11.16 ▲ A Δ-connected load used to discuss power calculations.

The total power delivered to a balanced Δ-connected load is

$$P_T = 3P_\phi = 3V_\phi I_\phi \cos\theta_\phi$$

$$= 3V_L\left(\frac{I_L}{\sqrt{3}}\right)\cos\theta_\phi$$

$$= \sqrt{3}V_L I_L \cos\theta_\phi. \tag{11.49}$$

Note that Eq. 11.49 is the same as Eq. 11.36. The expressions for reactive power and complex power also have the same form as those developed for the Y load:

$$Q_\phi = V_\phi I_\phi \sin\theta_\phi; \tag{11.50}$$

$$Q_T = 3Q_\phi = 3V_\phi I_\phi \sin\theta_\phi; \tag{11.51}$$

$$S_\phi = P_\phi + jQ_\phi = \mathbf{V}_\phi \mathbf{I}_\phi^*; \tag{11.52}$$

$$S_T = 3S_\phi = \sqrt{3}V_L I_L \underline{/\theta_\phi}. \tag{11.53}$$

Instantaneous Power in Three-Phase Circuits

Although we are primarily interested in average, reactive, and complex power calculations, the computation of the total instantaneous power is also important. In a balanced three-phase circuit, this power has an interesting property: It is invariant with time! Thus the torque developed at the shaft of a three-phase motor is constant, which in turn means less vibration in machinery powered by three-phase motors.

Let the instantaneous line-to-neutral voltage v_{AN} be the reference, and, as before, θ_ϕ is the phase angle $\theta_{vA} - \theta_{iA}$. Then, for a positive phase sequence, the instantaneous power in each phase is

$$p_A = v_{AN}i_{aA} = V_m I_m \cos\omega t \cos(\omega t - \theta_\phi),$$

$$p_B = v_{BN}i_{bB} = V_m I_m \cos(\omega t - 120°)\cos(\omega t - \theta_\phi - 120°),$$

$$p_C = v_{CN}i_{cC} = V_m I_m \cos(\omega t + 120°)\cos(\omega t - \theta_\phi + 120°),$$

where V_m and I_m represent the maximum amplitude of the phase voltage and line current, respectively. The total instantaneous power is the sum of the instantaneous phase powers, which reduces to $1.5V_m I_m \cos\theta_\phi$; that is,

$$p_T = p_A + p_B + p_C = 1.5V_m I_m \cos\theta_\phi.$$

Note this result is consistent with Eq. 11.35 since $V_m = \sqrt{2}V_\phi$ and $I_m = \sqrt{2}I_\phi$ (see Problem 11.26).

Examples 11.3–11.5 illustrate power calculations in balanced three-phase circuits.

Example 11.3   Calculating Power in a Three-Phase Wye-Wye Circuit

a) Calculate the average power per phase delivered to the Y-connected load of Example 11.1.
b) Calculate the total average power delivered to the load.
c) Calculate the total average power lost in the line.
d) Calculate the total average power lost in the generator.
e) Calculate the total number of magnetizing vars absorbed by the load.
f) Calculate the total complex power delivered by the source.

Solution

a) From Example 11.1, $V_\phi = 115.22$ V, $I_\phi = 2.4$ A, and $\theta_\phi = -1.19 - (-36.87) = 35.68°$. Therefore

$$P_\phi = (115.22)(2.4)\cos 35.68°$$

$$= 224.64 \text{ W}.$$

The power per phase may also be calculated from $I_\phi^2 R_\phi$, or

$$P_\phi = (2.4)^2(39) = 224.64 \text{ W}.$$

b) The total average power delivered to the load is $P_T = 3P_\phi = 673.92$ W. We calculated the line voltage in Example 11.1, so we may also use Eq. 11.36:

$$P_T = \sqrt{3}(199.58)(2.4)\cos 35.68°$$

$$= 673.92 \text{ W}.$$

c) The total power lost in the line is

$$P_{\text{line}} = 3(2.4)^2(0.8) = 13.824 \text{ W}.$$

d) The total internal power lost in the generator is

$$P_{\text{gen}} = 3(2.4)^2(0.2) = 3.456 \text{ W}.$$

e) The total number of magnetizing vars absorbed by the load is

$$Q_T = \sqrt{3}(199.58)(2.4)\sin 35.68°$$

$$= 483.84 \text{ VAR}.$$

f) The total complex power associated with the source is

$$S_T = 3S_\phi = -3(120)(2.4) \underline{/36.87°}$$

$$= -691.20 - j518.40 \text{ VA}.$$

The minus sign indicates that the internal power and magnetizing reactive power are being delivered to the circuit. We check this result by calculating the total and reactive power absorbed by the circuit:

$$P = 673.92 + 13.824 + 3.456$$

$$= 691.20 \text{ W (check)},$$

$$Q = 483.84 + 3(2.4)^2(1.5) + 3(2.4)^2(0.5)$$

$$= 483.84 + 25.92 + 8.64$$

$$= 518.40 \text{ VAR(check)}.$$

Example 11.4   Calculating Power in a Three-Phase Wye-Delta Circuit

a) Calculate the total complex power delivered to the Δ-connected load of Example 11.2.
b) What percentage of the average power at the sending end of the line is delivered to the load?

Solution

a) Using the a-phase values from the solution of Example 11.2, we obtain

$$\mathbf{V}_\phi = \mathbf{V}_{AB} = 202.72 \underline{/29.04°} \text{ V},$$

$$\mathbf{I}_\phi = \mathbf{I}_{AB} = 1.39 \underline{/-6.87°} \text{ A}.$$

Using Eqs. 11.52 and 11.53, we have

$$S_T = 3(202.72 \underline{/29.04°})(1.39 \underline{/6.87°})$$

$$= 682.56 + j494.21 \text{ VA}.$$

b) The total power at the sending end of the distribution line equals the total power delivered to the load plus the total power lost in the line; therefore

$$P_{\text{input}} = 682.56 + 3(2.4)^2(0.3)$$

$$= 687.74 \text{ W}.$$

The percentage of the average power reaching the load is 682.56/687.74, or 99.25%. Nearly 100% of the average power at the input is delivered to the load because the impedance of the line is quite small compared to the load impedance.

Example 11.5 **Calculating Three-Phase Power with an Unspecified Load**

A balanced three-phase load requires 480 kW at a lagging power factor of 0.8. The load is fed from a line having an impedance of $0.005 + j0.025 \, \Omega/\phi$. The line voltage at the terminals of the load is 600 V.

a) Construct a single-phase equivalent circuit of the system.

b) Calculate the magnitude of the line current.

c) Calculate the magnitude of the line voltage at the sending end of the line.

d) Calculate the power factor at the sending end of the line.

Solution

a) Figure 11.17 shows the single-phase equivalent circuit. We arbitrarily selected the line-to-neutral voltage at the load as the reference.

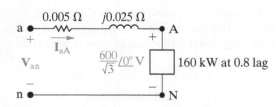

Figure 11.17 ▲ The single-phase equivalent circuit for Example 11.5.

b) The line current $\mathbf{I}^*_{aA}$ is given by

$$\left(\frac{600}{\sqrt{3}}\right)\mathbf{I}^*_{aA} = (160 + j120)10^3,$$

or

$$\mathbf{I}^*_{aA} = 577.35 \underline{/36.87^\circ} \text{ A}.$$

Therefore, $\mathbf{I}_{aA} = 577.35 \underline{/-36.87^\circ}$ A. The magnitude of the line current is the magnitude of $\mathbf{I}_{aA}$:

$$I_L = 577.35 \text{ A}.$$

We obtain an alternative solution for I_L from the expression

$$P_T = \sqrt{3}V_L I_L \cos\theta_p$$

$$= \sqrt{3}(600)I_L(0.8)$$

$$= 480,000 \text{ W};$$

$$I_L = \frac{480,000}{\sqrt{3}(600)(0.8)}$$

$$= \frac{1000}{\sqrt{3}}$$

$$= 577.35 \text{ A}.$$

c) To calculate the magnitude of the line voltage at the sending end, we first calculate $\mathbf{V}_{an}$. From Fig. 11.17,

$$\mathbf{V}_{an} = \mathbf{V}_{AN} + Z_\ell \mathbf{I}_{aA}$$

$$= \frac{600}{\sqrt{3}} + (0.005 + j0.025)(577.35 \underline{/-36.87^\circ})$$

$$= 357.51 \underline{/1.57^\circ} \text{ V}.$$

Thus

$$V_L = \sqrt{3}|\mathbf{V}_{an}|$$

$$= 619.23 \text{ V}.$$

d) The power factor at the sending end of the line is the cosine of the phase angle between $\mathbf{V}_{an}$ and $\mathbf{I}_{aA}$:

$$\text{pf} = \cos[1.57^\circ - (-36.87^\circ)]$$

$$= \cos 38.44^\circ$$

$$= 0.783 \text{ lagging}.$$

An alternative method for calculating the power factor is to first calculate the complex power at the sending end of the line:

$$S_\phi = (160 + j120)10^3 + (577.35)^2(0.005 + j0.025)$$

$$= 161.67 + j128.33 \text{ kVA}$$

$$= 206.41 \underline{/38.44^\circ} \text{ kVA}.$$

The power factor is

$$\text{pf} = \cos 38.44^\circ$$

$$= 0.783 \text{ lagging}.$$

Finally, if we calculate the total complex power at the sending end, after first calculating the magnitude of the line current, we may use this value to calculate V_L. That is,

$$\sqrt{3}V_L I_L = 3(206.41) \times 10^3,$$

$$V_L = \frac{3(206.41) \times 10^3}{\sqrt{3}(577.35)},$$

$$= 619.23 \text{ V}.$$

✓ ASSESSMENT PROBLEMS

Objective 3—Be able to calculate power (average, reactive, and complex) in any three-phase circuit

11.8 The three-phase average power rating of the central processing unit (CPU) on a mainframe digital computer is 22,659 W. The three-phase line supplying the computer has a line voltage rating of 208 V (rms). The line current is 73.8 A (rms). The computer absorbs magnetizing VARs.

    a) Calculate the total magnetizing reactive power absorbed by the CPU.

    b) Calculate the power factor.

Answer: (a) 13,909.50 VAR;

               (b) 0.852 lagging.

11.9 The complex power associated with each phase of a balanced load is $144 + j192$ kVA. The line voltage at the terminals of the load is 2450 V.

    a) What is the magnitude of the line current feeding the load?

    b) The load is delta connected, and the impedance of each phase consists of a resistance in parallel with a reactance. Calculate R and X.

    c) The load is wye connected, and the impedance of each phase consists of a resistance in series with a reactance. Calculate R and X.

Answer: (a) 169.67 A;

               (b) $R = 41.68\ \Omega$, $X = 31.26\ \Omega$;

               (c) $R = 5\ \Omega$, $X = 6.67\ \Omega$.

NOTE: Also try Chapter Problems 11.25 and 11.27.

11.6 Measuring Average Power in Three-Phase Circuits

The basic instrument used to measure power in three-phase circuits is the electrodynamometer wattmeter. It contains two coils. One coil, called the **current coil**, is stationary and is designed to carry a current proportional to the load current. The second coil, called the **potential coil**, is movable and carries a current proportional to the load voltage. The important features of the wattmeter are shown in Fig. 11.18.

    The average deflection of the pointer attached to the movable coil is proportional to the product of the effective value of the current in the current coil, the effective value of the voltage impressed on the potential coil, and the cosine of the phase angle between the voltage and current. The direction in which the pointer deflects depends on the instantaneous polarity of the current-coil current and the potential-coil voltage. Therefore each coil has one terminal with a polarity mark—usually a plus sign—but sometimes the double polarity mark ± is used. The wattmeter deflects upscale when (1) the polarity-marked terminal of the current coil is toward the source, and (2) the polarity-marked terminal of the potential coil is connected to the same line in which the current coil has been inserted.

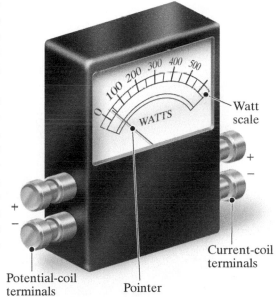

Figure 11.18 ▲ The key features of the electrodynamometer wattmeter.

The Two-Wattmeter Method

Consider a general network inside a box to which power is supplied by n conducting lines. Such a system is shown in Fig. 11.19.

    If we wish to measure the total power at the terminals of the box, we need to know $n - 1$ currents and voltages. This follows because if we choose one terminal as a reference, there are only $n - 1$ independent voltages. Likewise, only $n - 1$ independent currents can exist in the n conductors entering the box. Thus the total power is the sum of $n - 1$ product terms; that is, $p = v_1 i_1 + v_2 i_2 + \cdots + v_{n-1} i_{n-1}$.

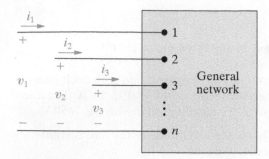

Figure 11.19 ▲ A general circuit whose power is supplied by n conductors.

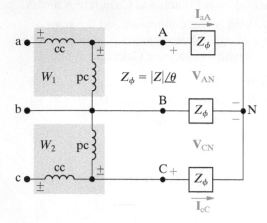

Figure 11.20 ▲ A circuit used to analyze the two-wattmeter method of measuring average power delivered to a balanced load.

Applying this general observation, we can see that for a three-conductor circuit, whether balanced or not, we need only two wattmeters to measure the total power. For a four-conductor circuit, we need three wattmeters if the three-phase circuit is unbalanced, but only two wattmeters if it is balanced, because in the latter case there is no current in the neutral line. Thus, only two wattmeters are needed to measure the total average power in any balanced three-phase system.

The two-wattmeter method reduces to determining the magnitude and algebraic sign of the average power indicated by each wattmeter. We can describe the basic problem in terms of the circuit shown in Fig. 11.20, where the two wattmeters are indicated by the shaded boxes and labeled W_1 and W_2. The coil notations cc and pc stand for current coil and potential coil, respectively. We have elected to insert the current coils of the wattmeters in lines aA and cC. Thus, line bB is the reference line for the two potential coils. The load is connected as a wye, and the per-phase load impedance is designated as $Z_\phi = |Z| \underline{/\theta}$. This is a general representation, as any Δ-connected load can be represented by its Y equivalent; furthermore, for the balanced case, the impedance angle θ is unaffected by the Δ-to-Y transformation.

We now develop general equations for the readings of the two wattmeters. We assume that the current drawn by the potential coil of the wattmeter is negligible compared with the line current measured by the current coil. We further assume that the loads can be modeled by passive circuit elements so that the phase angle of the load impedance (θ in Fig. 11.20) lies between $-90°$ (pure capacitance) and $+90°$ (pure inductance). Finally, we assume a positive phase sequence.

From our introductory discussion of the average deflection of the wattmeter, we can see that wattmeter 1 will respond to the product of $|\mathbf{V}_{AB}|$, $|\mathbf{I}_{aA}|$, and the cosine of the angle between $\mathbf{V}_{AB}$ and $\mathbf{I}_{aA}$. If we denote this wattmeter reading as W_1, we can write

$$W_1 = |\mathbf{V}_{AB}||\mathbf{I}_{aA}| \cos \theta_1$$

$$= V_L I_L \cos \theta_1. \tag{11.54}$$

It follows that

$$W_2 = |\mathbf{V}_{CB}||\mathbf{I}_{cC}| \cos \theta_2$$

$$= V_L I_L \cos \theta_2. \tag{11.55}$$

In Eq. 11.54, θ_1 is the phase angle between $\mathbf{V}_{AB}$ and $\mathbf{I}_{aA}$, and in Eq. 11.55, θ_2 is the phase angle between $\mathbf{V}_{CB}$ and $\mathbf{I}_{cC}$.

To calculate W_1 and W_2, we express θ_1 and θ_2 in terms of the impedance angle θ, which is also the same as the phase angle between the phase voltage and current. For a positive phase sequence,

$$\theta_1 = \theta + 30° = \theta_\phi + 30°, \tag{11.56}$$

$$\theta_2 = \theta - 30° = \theta_\phi - 30°. \tag{11.57}$$

The derivation of Eqs. 11.56 and 11.57 is left as an exercise (see Problem 11.35). When we substitute Eqs. 11.56 and 11.57 into Eqs. 11.54 and 11.55, respectively, we get

$$W_1 = V_L I_L \cos (\theta_\phi + 30°), \tag{11.58}$$

$$W_2 = V_L I_L \cos (\theta_\phi - 30°). \tag{11.59}$$

To find the total power, we add W_1 and W_2; thus

$$P_T = W_1 + W_2 = 2V_L I_L \cos \theta_\phi \cos 30°$$

$$= \sqrt{3} V_L I_L \cos \theta_\phi, \qquad (11.60)$$

which is the expression for the total power in a three-phase circuit. Therefore we have confirmed that the sum of the two wattmeter readings yields the total average power.

A closer look at Eqs. 11.58 and 11.59 reveals the following about the readings of the two wattmeters:

1. If the power factor is greater than 0.5, both wattmeters read positive.
2. If the power factor equals 0.5, one wattmeter reads zero.
3. If the power factor is less than 0.5, one wattmeter reads negative.
4. Reversing the phase sequence will interchange the readings on the two wattmeters.

These observations are illustrated in the following example and in Problems 11.41–11.52.

Example 11.6   Computing Wattmeter Readings in Three-Phase Circuits

Calculate the reading of each wattmeter in the circuit in Fig. 11.20 if the phase voltage at the load is 120 V and (a) $Z_\phi = 8 + j6\ \Omega$; (b) $Z_\phi = 8 - j6\ \Omega$; (c) $Z_\phi = 5 + j5\sqrt{3}\ \Omega$; and (d) $Z_\phi = 10\ \underline{/-75°}\ \Omega$. (e) Verify for (a)–(d) that the sum of the wattmeter readings equals the total power delivered to the load.

c) $Z_\phi = 5(1 + j\sqrt{3}) = 10\ \underline{/60°}\ \Omega, V_L = 120\sqrt{3}$ V, and $I_L = 12$ A.

$$W_1 = (120\sqrt{3})(12) \cos (60° + 30°) = 0,$$

$$W_2 = (120\sqrt{3})(12) \cos (60° - 30°)$$

$$= 2160 \text{ W}.$$

d) $Z_\phi = 10\ \underline{/-75°}\ \Omega, V_L = 120\sqrt{3}$ V, and $I_L = 12$ A.

$$W_1 = (120\sqrt{3})(12) \cos (-75° + 30°) = 1763.63 \text{ W},$$

$$W_2 = (120\sqrt{3})(12) \cos (-75° - 30°) = -645.53 \text{ W}.$$

Solution

a) $Z_\phi = 10\ \underline{/36.87°}\ \Omega, V_L = 120\sqrt{3}$ V, and $I_L = 120/10 = 12$ A.

$$W_1 = (120\sqrt{3})(12) \cos (36.87° + 30°)$$

$$= 979.75 \text{ W},$$

$$W_2 = (120\sqrt{3})(12) \cos (36.87° - 30°)$$

$$= 2476.25 \text{ W}.$$

b) $Z_\phi = 10\ \underline{/-36.87°}\ \Omega, V_L = 120\sqrt{3}$ V, and $I_L = 120/10 = 12$ A.

$$W_1 = (120\sqrt{3})(12) \cos (-36.87° + 30°)$$

$$= 2476.25 \text{ W},$$

$$W_2 = (120\sqrt{3})(12) \cos (-36.87° - 30°)$$

$$= 979.75 \text{ W}.$$

e) $P_T(a) = 3(12)^2(8) = 3456$ W,

$$W_1 + W_2 = 979.75 + 2476.25$$

$$= 3456 \text{ W},$$

$$P_T(b) = P_T(a) = 3456 \text{ W},$$

$$W_1 + W_2 = 2476.25 + 979.75$$

$$= 3456 \text{ W},$$

$$P_T(c) = 3(12)^2(5) = 2160 \text{ W},$$

$$W_1 + W_2 = 0 + 2160$$

$$= 2160 \text{ W},$$

$$P_T(d) = 3(12)^2(2.5882) = 1118.10 \text{ W},$$

$$W_1 + W_2 = 1763.63 - 645.53$$

$$= 1118.10 \text{ W}.$$

NOTE: Assess your understanding of the two-wattmeter method by trying Chapter Problems 11.41 and 11.45.

Practical Perspective

Transmission and Distribution of Electric Power

At the start of this chapter we pointed out the obligation utilities have to maintain the rms voltage level at their customer's premises. Although the acceptable deviation from a nominal level may vary among different utilities we will assume for purposes of discussion that an allowable tolerance is ± 5.8%. Thus a nominal rms voltage of 120 V could range from 113 to 127 V. We also pointed out that capacitors strategically located on the system could be used to support voltage levels.

The circuit shown in Fig. 11.21 represents a substation on a Midwestern municipal system. We will assume the system is balanced, the line-to-line voltage at the substation is 13.8 kV, the phase impedance of the distribution line is $0.6 + j4.8\,\Omega$, and the load at the substation at 3 PM on a hot, humid day in July is 3.6 MW and 3.6 magnetizing MVAR.

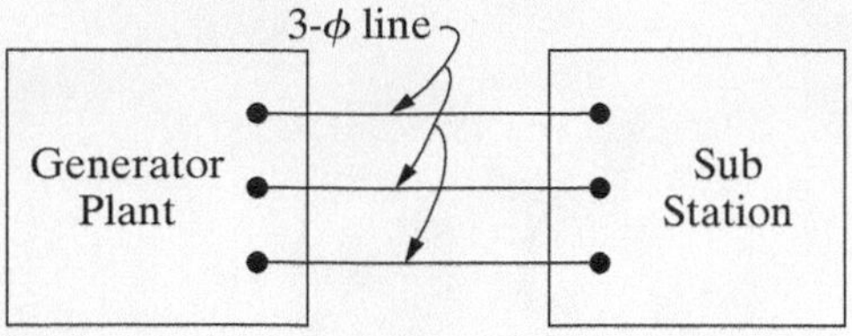

Using the line-to-neutral voltage at the substation as a reference, the single-phase equivalent circuit for the system in Fig. 11.21 is shown in Fig. 11.22. The line current can be calculated from the expression for the complex power at the substation. Thus,

$$\frac{13,800}{\sqrt{3}}\mathbf{I}_{aA}^{*} = (1.2 + j1.2)10^{6}.$$

It follows that

$$\mathbf{I}_{aA}^{*} = 150.61 + j150.61 \text{ A}$$

or

$$\mathbf{I}_{aA} = 150.61 - j150.61 \text{ A}.$$

The line-to-neutral voltage at the generating plant is

$$\mathbf{V}_{an} = \frac{13,800}{\sqrt{3}}\underline{/0^{\circ}} + (0.6 + j4.8)(150.61 - j150.61)$$

$$= 8780.74 + j632.58$$

$$= 8803.50\underline{/4.12^{\circ}} \text{ V}.$$

Therefore the magnitude of the line voltage at the generating plant is

$$|\mathbf{V}_{ab}| = \sqrt{3}(8803.50) = 15,248.11 \text{ V}.$$

We are assuming the utility is required to keep the voltage level within ± 5.8% of the nominal value. This means the magnitude of the line-to-line voltage at the power plant should not exceed 14.6 kV nor be less than 13 kV. Therefore, the magnitude of the line voltage at the generating plant could cause problems for customers.

When the magnetizing vars are supplied by a capacitor bank connected to the substation bus, the line current $\mathbf{I}_{aA}$ becomes

$$\mathbf{I}_{aA} = 150.61 + j0 \text{ A}.$$

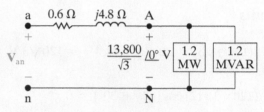

Figure 11.21 ▲ A substation connected to a power plant via a three-phase line.

Figure 11.22 ▲ A single phase equivalent circuit for the system in Fig. 11.21.

Therefore the voltage at the generating plant necessary to maintain a line-to-line voltage of 13,800 V at the substation is

$$\mathbf{V}_{an} = \frac{13,800}{\sqrt{3}} \underline{/0°} + (0.6 + j4.8)(150.61 + j0)$$

$$= 8057.80 + j722.94$$

$$= 8090.17 \underline{/5.13°} \text{ V}.$$

Hence

$$|\mathbf{V}_{ab}| = \sqrt{3}(8090.17) = 14,012.58 \, V.$$

This voltage level falls within the allowable range of 13 kV to 14.6 kV.

NOTE: Assess your understanding of this Practical Perspective by trying Chapter Problems 11.53(a)–(b) and 11.54, 11.57, and 11.58.

Summary

- When analyzing balanced three-phase circuits, the first step is to transform any Δ connections into Y connections, so that the overall circuit is of the Y-Y configuration. (See page 400.)

- A **single-phase equivalent circuit** is used to calculate the line current and the phase voltage in one phase of the Y-Y structure. The a-phase is normally chosen for this purpose. (See page 402.)

- Once we know the line current and phase voltage in the a-phase equivalent circuit, we can take analytical shortcuts to find any current or voltage in a balanced three-phase circuit, based on the following facts:

  - The b- and c-phase currents and voltages are identical to the a-phase current and voltage except for a 120° shift in phase. In a positive-sequence circuit, the b-phase quantity lags the a-phase quantity by 120°, and the c-phase quantity leads the a-phase quantity by 120°. For a negative sequence circuit, phases b and c are interchanged with respect to phase a.

  - The set of line voltages is out of phase with the set of phase voltages by ±30°. The plus or minus sign corresponds to positive and negative sequence, respectively.

  - In a Y-Y circuit the magnitude of a line voltage is √3 times the magnitude of a phase voltage.

- The set of line currents is out of phase with the set of phase currents in Δ-connected sources and loads by ∓30°. The minus or plus sign corresponds to positive and negative sequence, respectively.

- The magnitude of a line current is √3 times the magnitude of a phase current in a Δ-connected source or load.

(See pages 402–403 and 405–406.)

- The techniques for calculating per-phase average power, reactive power, and complex power are identical to those introduced in Chapter 10. (See page 408.)

- The total real, reactive, and complex power can be determined either by multiplying the corresponding per phase quantity by 3 or by using the expressions based on line current and line voltage, as given by Eqs. 11.36, 11.38, and 11.41. (See pages 408 and 409.)

- The total instantaneous power in a balanced three-phase circuit is constant and equals 1.5 times the average power per phase. (See page 410.)

- A wattmeter measures the average power delivered to a load by using a current coil connected in series with the load and a potential coil connected in parallel with the load. (See page 413.)

- The total average power in a balanced three-phase circuit can be measured by summing the readings of two wattmeters connected in two different phases of the circuit. (See page 413.)

Problems

All phasor voltages in the following Problems are stated in terms of the rms value.

Section 11.1

11.1 What is the phase sequence of each of the following sets of voltages?

a) $v_a = 137 \cos{(\omega t + 63°)}$ V,

$v_b = 137 \cos{(\omega t - 57°)}$ V,

$v_c = 137 \cos{(\omega t + 183°)}$ V.

b) $v_a = 820 \cos{(\omega t - 36°)}$ V,

$v_b = 820 \cos{(\omega t + 84°)}$ V,

$v_c = 820 \sin{(\omega t - 66°)}$ V.

11.2 For each set of voltages, state whether or not the voltages form a balanced three-phase set. If the set is balanced, state whether the phase sequence is positive or negative. If the set is not balanced, explain why.

PSPICE
MULTISIM

a) $v_a = 48 \cos(314t - 45°)$ V,

$v_b = 48 \cos{(314t - 165°)}$ V,

$v_c = 48 \cos{(314t + 75°)}$ V.

b) $v_a = 188 \cos(250t + 60°)$ V,

$v_b = -188 \cos 250t$ V,

$v_c = 188 \cos{(250t - 60°)}$ V.

c) $v_a = 426 \ \cos 100t$ V,

$v_b = 462 \cos(100t + 120°)$ V,

$v_c = 426 \cos(100t - 120°)$ V.

d) $v_a = 1121 \cos{(2000t - 20°)}$ V,

$v_b = 1121 \sin{(2000t - 50°)}$ V,

$v_c = 1121 \cos{(2000t + 100°)}$ V.

e) $v_a = 540 \sin 630t$ V,

$v_b = 540 \cos(630t - 120°)$ V,

$v_c = 540 \cos{(630t + 120°)}$ V.

f) $v_a = 144 \cos{(800t + 80°)}$ V,

$v_b = 144 \sin{(800t - 70°)}$ V,

$v_c = 144 \sin{(800t + 50°)}$ V.

11.3 Verify that Eq. 11.3 is true for either Eq. 11.1 or Eq. 11.2.

Section 11.2

11.4 Refer to the circuit in Fig. 11.5(b). Assume that there are no external connections to the terminals a, b, c. Assume further that the three windings are from a three-phase generator whose voltages are those described in Problem 11.2(b). Determine the current circulating in the Δ-connected generator.

11.5 Repeat Problem 11.4 but assume that the three-phase voltages are those described in Problem 11.2(c).

Section 11.3

11.6 a) Is the circuit in Fig. P11.6 a balanced or unbalanced three-phase system? Explain.

PSPICE
MULTISIM

b) Find $\mathbf{I}_o$.

Figure P11.6

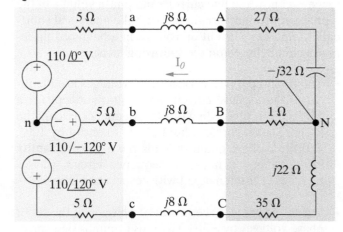

11.7 a) Find $\mathbf{I}_o$ in the circuit in Fig. P11.7.

PSPICE
MULTISIM

b) Find $\mathbf{V}_{AN}$.

c) Find $\mathbf{V}_{AB}$.

d) Is the circuit a balanced or unbalanced three-phase system?

11.8 Find the rms value of $\mathbf{I}_o$ in the unbalanced three-phase circuit seen in Fig. P11.8.

Figure P11.8

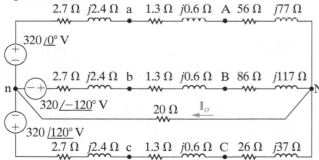

11.9 The time-domain expressions for three line-to-neutral voltages at the terminals of a Y-connected load are

$$v_{AN} = 288 \cos{(\omega t - 45°)} \text{ V},$$

$$v_{BN} = 288 \cos{(\omega t - 165°)} \text{ V},$$

$$v_{CN} = 288 \cos{(\omega t + 75°)} \text{ V}.$$

What are the time-domain expressions for the three line-to-line voltages v_{AB}, v_{BC}, and v_{CA}?

11.10 A balanced three-phase circuit has the following characteristics:

• Y-Y connected;

• The line voltage at the source, $\mathbf{V}_{ab}$, is $110\sqrt{3}\,\underline{/-60°}$ V;

• The phase sequence is positive;

• The line impedance is $3 + j2\ \Omega/\phi$;

• The load impedance is $37 + j28\ \Omega/\phi$;

a) Draw the single phase equivalent circuit for the a-phase.

b) Calculated the line current in the a-phase.

c) Calculated the line voltage at the load in the a-phase.

11.11 The magnitude of the line voltage at the terminals of a balanced Y-connected load is 6600 V. The load impedance is $240 - j70\ \Omega/\phi$. The load is fed from a line that has an impedance of $0.5 + j4\ \Omega/\phi$.

a) What is the magnitude of the line current?

b) What is the magnitude of the line voltage at the source?

11.12 The magnitude of the phase voltage of an ideal balanced three-phase Y-connected source is 125 V. The source is connected to a balanced Y-connected load by a distribution line that has an impedance of $0.1 + j0.8\ \Omega/\phi$. The load impedance is $19.9 + j14.2\ \Omega/\phi$. The phase sequence of the source is acb. Use the a-phase voltage of the source as the reference. Specify the magnitude and phase angle of the following quantities: (a) the three line currents, (b) the three line voltages at the source, (c) the three phase voltages at the load, and (d) the three line voltages at the load.

Section 11.4

11.13 A balanced Δ-connected load has an impedance of $216 - j288\ \Omega/\phi$. The load is fed through a line having an impedance of $3 + j5\ \Omega/\phi$. The phase voltage at the terminals of the load is 7.2 kV. The phase sequence is negative. Use $\mathbf{V}_{AB}$ as the reference.

a) Calculate the three phase currents of the load.

b) Calculate the three line currents.

c) Calculate the three line voltages at the sending end of the line.

11.14 A balanced, three-phase circuit is characterized as follows:

• Y-Δ connected;

• Source voltage in the b-phase is $150\underline{/135°}$ V;

• Source phase sequence is acb;

• Line impedance is $2 + j3\ \Omega/\phi$;

• Load impedance is $129 + j171\ \Omega/\phi$.

Figure P11.7

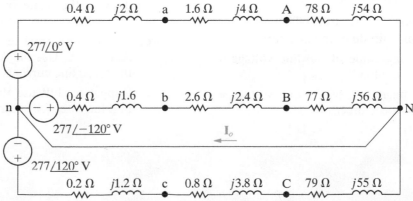

a) Draw the single phase equivalent for the a-phase.

b) Calculate the a-phase line current.

c) Calculate the a-phase line voltage for the three-phase load.

11.15 An acb sequence balanced three-phase Y-connected source supplies power to a balanced, three-phase Δ-connected load with an impedance of $12 + j9 \, \Omega/\phi$. The source voltage in the b-phase is $240\underline{/-50°}$ V. The line impedance is $1 + j1 \, \Omega/\phi$. Draw the single phase equivalent circuit for the a-phase and use it to find the current in the a-phase of the load.

11.16 In a balanced three-phase system, the source is a balanced Y with an abc phase sequence and a line voltage $\mathbf{V}_{ab} = 208\underline{/50°}$ V. The load is a balanced Y in parallel with a balanced Δ. The phase impedance of the Y is $4 + j3 \, \Omega/\phi$ and the phase impedance of the Δ is $3 - j9 \, \Omega/\phi$. The line impedance is $1.4 + j0.8 \, \Omega/\phi$. Draw the single phase equivalent circuit and use it to calculate the line voltage at the load in the a-phase.

11.17 A balanced Y-connected load having an impedance of $60 - j45 \, \Omega/\phi$ is connected in parallel with a balanced Δ-connected load having an impedance of $90\sqrt{2}\underline{/45°} \, \Omega/\phi$. The paralleled loads are fed from a line having an impedance of $2 + j2 \, \Omega/\phi$. The magnitude of the line-to-line voltage of the Δ-load is $300\sqrt{3}$ V.

a) Calculate the magnitude of the phase current in the Y-connected load.

b) Calculate the magnitude of the phase current in the Δ-connected load.

c) Calculate the magnitude of the current in the line feeding the loads.

d) Calculate the magnitude of the line voltage at the sending end of the line.

11.18 A three-phase Δ-connected generator has an internal impedance of $9 + j90 \, \text{m}\Omega/\phi$. When the load is removed from the generator, the magnitude of the terminal voltage is 13,800 V. The generator feeds a Δ-connected load through a transmission line with an impedance of $20 + j180 \, \text{m}\Omega/\phi$. The per-phase impedance of the load is $7.056 + j3.417 \, \Omega$.

a) Construct a single-phase equivalent circuit.

b) Calculate the magnitude of the line current.

c) Calculate the magnitude of the line voltage at the terminals of the load.

d) Calculate the magnitude of the line voltage at the terminals of the source.

e) Calculate the magnitude of the phase current in the load.

f) Calculate the magnitude of the phase current in the source.

11.19 The impedance Z in the balanced three-phase circuit in Fig. P11.19 is $100 - j75 \, \Omega$. Find

a) $\mathbf{I}_{AB}$, $\mathbf{I}_{BC}$, and $\mathbf{I}_{CA}$,

b) $\mathbf{I}_{aA}$, $\mathbf{I}_{bB}$, and $\mathbf{I}_{cC}$,

c) $\mathbf{I}_{ba}$, $\mathbf{I}_{cb}$, and $\mathbf{I}_{ac}$.

Figure P11.19

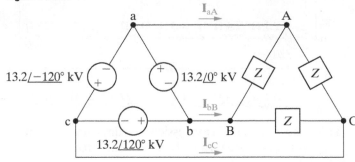

11.20 For the circuit shown in Fig. P11.20, find

a) the phase currents $\mathbf{I}_{AB}$, $\mathbf{I}_{BC}$, and $\mathbf{I}_{CA}$

b) the line currents $\mathbf{I}_{aA}$, $\mathbf{I}_{bB}$, and $\mathbf{I}_{cC}$

when $Z_1 = 2.4 - j0.7 \, \Omega$, $Z_2 = 8 + j6 \, \Omega$, and $Z_3 = 20 + j0 \, \Omega$.

Figure P11.20

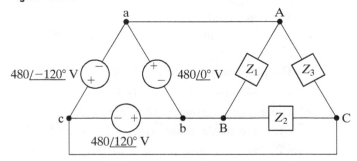

11.21 A balanced three-phase Δ-connected source is shown in Fig. P11.21.

a) Find the Y-connected equivalent circuit.

b) Show that the Y-connected equivalent circuit delivers the same open-circuit voltage as the original Δ-connected source.

c) Apply an external short circuit to the terminals A, B, and C. Use the Δ-connected source to find the three line currents $\mathbf{I}_{aA}$, $\mathbf{I}_{bB}$, and $\mathbf{I}_{cC}$.

d) Repeat (c) but use the Y-equivalent source to find the three line currents.

Figure P11.21

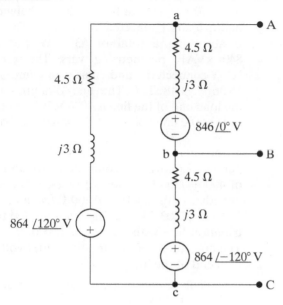

11.22 The Δ-connected source of Problem 11.21 is connected to a Y-connected load by means of a balanced three-phase distribution line. The load impedance is $1192 + j1584\ \Omega/\phi$. and the line impedance is $6.5 + j15\ \Omega/\phi$.

a) Construct a single-phase equivalent circuit of the system.

b) Determine the magnitude of the line voltage at the terminals of the load.

c) Determine the magnitude of the phase current in the Δ-source.

d) Determine the magnitude of the line voltage at the terminals of the source.

Section 11.5

11.23 a) Find the rms magnitude and the phase angle of $\mathbf{I}_{CA}$ in the circuit shown in Fig. P11.23.

b) What percent of the average power delivered by the three-phase source is dissipated in the three-phase load?

Figure P11.23

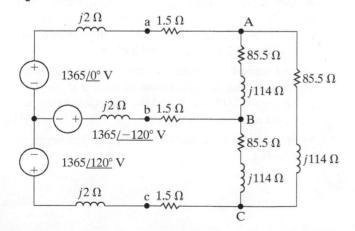

11.24 A balanced three-phase source is supplying 60 kVA at 0.6 lagging to two balanced Y-connected parallel loads. The distribution line connecting the source to the load has negligible impedance. Load 1 is purely resistive and absorbs 30 kW. Find the per-phase impedance of Load 2 if the line voltage is $120\sqrt{3}$ V and the impedance components are in series.

11.25 In a balanced three-phase system, the source has an abc sequence, is Y-connected, and $\mathbf{V}_{an} = 120\underline{/20°}$ V. The source feeds two loads, both of which are Y-connected. The impedance of load 1 is $8 + j6\ \Omega/\phi$. The complex power for the a-phase of load 2 is $600\underline{/36°}$ VA. Find the total complex power supplied by the source.

11.26 The line-to-neutral voltage at the terminals of the balanced three-phase load in the circuit shown in Fig. P11.26 is 1600 V. At this voltage, the load is absorbing 480 kVA at 0.8 pf lag.

a) Use $\mathbf{V}_{AN}$ as the reference and express $\mathbf{I}_{na}$ in polar form.

b) Calculate the complex power associated with the ideal three-phase source.

c) Check that the total average power delivered equals the total average power absorbed.

d) Check that the total magnetizing reactive power delivered equals the total magnetizing reactive power absorbed.

Figure P11.26

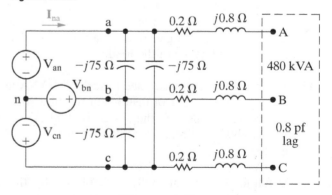

11.27 A three-phase positive sequence Y-connected source supplies 14 kVA with a power factor of 0.75 lagging to a parallel combination of a Y-connected load and a Δ-connected load. The Y-connected load uses 9 kVA at a power factor of 0.6 lagging and has an a-phase current of $10\underline{/-30°}$ A.

a) Find the complex power per phase of the Δ-connected load.

b) Find the magnitude of the line voltage.

11.28 A balanced three-phase distribution line has an impedance of $5 + j10\ \Omega/\phi$. This line is used to supply three balanced three-phase loads that are connected in parallel. The three loads are $L_1 = 180\ \text{kVA}$ at 0.866 pf lag, $L_2 = 150\ \text{kVA}$ at 0.28 pf lead, and $L_3 = 72.12\ \text{kW}$ at unity pf. The magnitude of the line voltage at the terminals of the loads is $1800\sqrt{3}\ \text{V}$.

  a) What is the magnitude of the line voltage at the sending end of the line?

  b) What is the percent efficiency of the distribution line with respect to average power?

11.29 The three tools described below are part of a university's machine shop. Each piece of equipment is a balanced three-phase load rated at 220 V(rms). Calculate (a) the magnitude of the line current supplying these three tools and (b) the power factor of the combined load.

  • Drill press: 10.2 kVA at 0.87 pf lag.
  • Lathe: 4.2 kW at 0.91 pf lag.
  • Band saw: line current 36.8 A(rms), 7.25 kVAR.

11.30 Calculate the complex power in each phase of the unbalanced load in Problem 11.20.

11.31 Show that the total instantaneous power in a balanced three-phase circuit is constant and equal to $1.5 V_m I_m \cos\theta_\phi$, where V_m and I_m represent the maximum amplitudes of the phase voltage and phase current, respectively.

11.32 The total apparent power supplied in a balanced, three-phase Y-Δ system is 4800 VA. The line voltage is 240 V. If the line impedance is negligible and the power factor angle of the load is $-50°$, determine the impedance of the load.

11.33 A balanced three-phase load absorbs 150 kVA at a leading power factor of 0.96 when the line voltage at the terminals of the load is 600 V. Find four equivalent circuits that can be used to model this load.

11.34 At full load, a commercially available 100 hp, three-phase induction motor operates at an efficiency of 97% and a power factor of 0.88 lag. The motor is supplied from a three-phase outlet with a line-voltage rating of 208 V.

  a) What is the magnitude of the line current drawn from the 208 V outlet? (1 hp = 746 W.)

  b) Calculate the reactive power supplied to the motor.

11.35 A three-phase line has an impedance of $0.1 + j0.8\ \Omega/\phi$. The line feeds two balanced three-phase loads connected in parallel. The first load is absorbing a total of 630 kW and absorbing 840 kVAR magnetizing vars. The second load is Y-connected and has an impedance of $15.36 - j4.48\ \Omega/\phi$. The line-to-neutral voltage at the load end of the line is 4000 V. What is the magnitude of the line voltage at the source end of the line?

11.36 Three balanced three-phase loads are connected in parallel. Load 1 is Y-connected with an impedance of $400 + j300\ \Omega/\phi$; load 2 is Δ-connected with an impedance of $2400 - j1800\ \Omega/\phi$; and load 3 is $172.8 + j2203.2\ \text{kVA}$. The loads are fed from a distribution line with an impedance of $2 + j16\ \Omega/\phi$. The magnitude of the line-to-neutral voltage at the load end of the line is $24\sqrt{3}\ \text{kV}$.

  a) Calculate the total complex power at the sending end of the line.

  b) What percentage of the average power at the sending end of the line is delivered to the loads?

11.37 The output of the balanced positive-sequence three-phase source in Fig. P11.37 is 41.6 kVA at a lagging power factor of 0.707. The line voltage at the source is 240 V.

  a) Find the magnitude of the line voltage at the load.

  b) Find the total complex power at the terminals of the load.

Figure P11.37

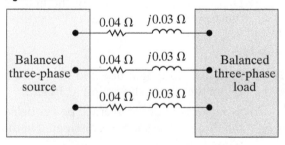

11.38 A balanced three-phase source is supplying 540 kVA at 0.96 pf lag to two balanced Δ-connected parallel loads. The distribution line connecting the source to the load has negligible impedance. The power associated with load 1 is $38.4 - j208.8\ \text{kVA}$.

  a) Determine the types of components and their impedances in each phase of load 2 if the line voltage is $1600\sqrt{3}\ \text{V}$ and the impedance components are in series.

  b) Repeat (a) with the impedance components in parallel.

11.39 The total power delivered to a balanced three-phase load when operating at a line voltage of $2500\sqrt{3}$ V is 900 kW at a lagging power factor of 0.6. The impedance of the distribution line supplying the load is $1 + j3$ Ω/ϕ. Under these operating conditions, the drop in the magnitude of the line voltage between the sending end and the load end of the line is excessive. To compensate, a bank of Y-connected capacitors is placed in parallel with the load. The capacitor bank is designed to furnish 1125 kVAR of magnetizing reactive power when operated at a line voltage of $2500\sqrt{3}$ V.

  a) What is the magnitude of the voltage at the sending end of the line when the load is operating at a line voltage of $2500\sqrt{3}$ V and the capacitor bank is disconnected?

  b) Repeat (a) with the capacitor bank connected.

  c) What is the average power efficiency of the line in (a)?

  d) What is the average power efficiency in (b)?

  e) If the system is operating at a frequency of 60 Hz, what is the size of each capacitor in microfarads?

11.40 A balanced bank of delta-connected capacitors is connected in parallel with the load described in Assessment Problem 11.9. The effect is to place a capacitor in parallel with the load in each phase. The line voltage at the terminals of the load thus remains at 2450 V. The circuit is operating at a frequency of 60 Hz. The capacitors are adjusted so that the magnitude of the line current feeding the parallel combination of the load and capacitor bank is at its minimum.

  a) What is the size of each capacitor in microfarads?

  b) Repeat (a) for wye-connected capacitors.

  c) What is the magnitude of the line current?

Section 11.6

11.41 The two-wattmeter method is used to measure the power at the load end of the line in Example 11.1. Calculate the reading of each wattmeter.

11.42 The wattmeters in the circuit in Fig. 11.20 read as follows: $W_1 = 40,823.09$ W, and $W_2 = 103,176.91$ W. The magnitude of the line voltage is $2400\sqrt{3}$ V. The phase sequence is positive. Find Z_ϕ.

11.43 In the balanced three-phase circuit shown in Fig. P11.43, the current coil of the wattmeter is connected in line aA, and the potential coil of the wattmeter is connected across lines b and c. Show that the wattmeter reading multiplied by $\sqrt{3}$ equals the total reactive power associated with the load. The phase sequence is positive.

Figure P11.43

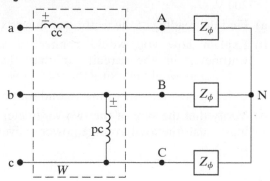

11.44 The line-to-neutral voltage in the circuit in Fig. P11.43 is 680 V, the phase sequence is positive, and the load impedance is $16 - j12$ Ω/ϕ.

  a) Calculate the wattmeter reading.

  b) Calculate the total reactive power associated with the load.

11.45 The two wattmeters in Fig. 11.20 can be used to compute the total reactive power of the load.

  a) Prove this statement by showing that $\sqrt{3}(W_2 - W_1) = \sqrt{3}V_L I_L \sin\theta_\phi$.

  b) Compute the total reactive power from the wattmeter readings for each of the loads in Example 11.6. Check your computations by calculating the total reactive power directly from the given voltage and impedance.

11.46 Derive Eqs. 11.56 and 11.57.

11.47 a) Calculate the complex power associated with each phase of the balanced load in Problem 11.19.

  b) If the two-wattmeter method is used to measure the average power delivered to the load, specify the reading of each meter.

11.48 The two-wattmeter method is used to measure the power delivered to the unbalanced load in Problem 11.20. The current coil of wattmeter 1 is placed in line aA and that of wattmeter 2 is placed in line bB.

  a) Calculate the reading of wattmeter 1.

  b) Calculate the reading of wattmeter 2.

  c) Show that the sum of the two wattmeter readings equals the total power delivered to the unbalanced load.

11.49 The balanced three-phase load shown in Fig. P11.49 is fed from a balanced, positive-sequence, three-phase Y-connected source. The impedance of the line connecting the source to the load is negligible. The line-to-neutral voltage of the source is 7200 V.

a) Find the reading of the wattmeter in watts.

b) Explain how you would connect a second wattmeter in the circuit so that the two wattmeters would measure the total power.

c) Calculate the reading of the second wattmeter.

d) Verify that the sum of the two wattmeter readings equals the total average power delivered to the load.

Figure P11.49

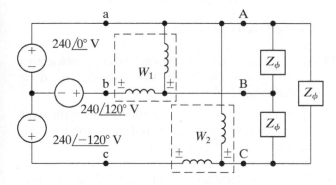

11.50 a) Calculate the reading of each wattmeter in the circuit shown in Fig. P11.50. The value of Z_ϕ is $40 \underline{/-30°}\ \Omega$.

b) Verify that the sum of the wattmeter readings equals the total average power delivered to the Δ-connected load.

Figure P11.50

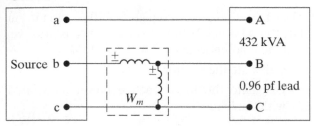

11.51 a) Calculate the reading of each wattmeter in the circuit shown in Fig. P11.51 when $Z = 13.44 + j46.08\ \Omega$.

b) Check that the sum of the two wattmeter readings equals the total power delivered to the load.

c) Check that $\sqrt{3}(W_1 - W_2)$ equals the total magnetizing vars delivered to the load.

Figure P11.51

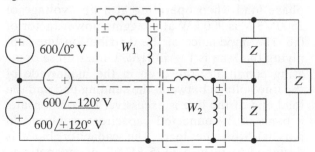

11.52 a) Find the reading of each wattmeter in the circuit shown in Fig. P11.52 if $Z_A = 20 \underline{/30°}\ \Omega$, $Z_B = 60 \underline{/0°}\ \Omega$, and $Z_C = 40 \underline{/-30°}\ \Omega$.

b) Show that the sum of the wattmeter readings equals the total average power delivered to the unbalanced three-phase load.

Figure P11.52

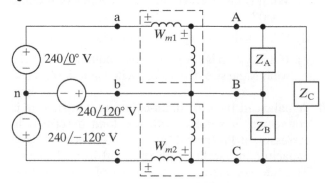

Sections 11.1–11.6

11.53 Refer to the Practical Perspective example:

PRACTICAL PERSPECTIVE a) Construct a power triangle for the substation load before the capacitors are connected to the bus.

b) Repeat (a) after the capacitors are connected to the bus.

c) Using the line-to-neutral voltage at the substation as a reference, construct a phasor diagram that depicts the relationship between $\mathbf{V}_{AN}$ and $\mathbf{V}_{an}$ before the capacitors are added.

d) Assume a positive phase sequence and construct a phasor diagram that depicts the relationship between $\mathbf{V}_{AB}$ and $\mathbf{V}_{ab}$.

11.54 Refer to the Practical Perspective example. Assume the frequency of the utility is 60 Hz.

PRACTICAL PERSPECTIVE a) What is the μF rating of each capacitor if the capacitors are delta-connected?

b) What is the μF rating of each capacitor if the capacitors are wye-connected?

11.55 Choose a single capacitor from Appendix H that is closest to the μF rating of the wye-connected capacitor from Problem 11.54(b).

  a) How much reactive power will a capacitor bank using this new value supply?

  b) What line-to-line voltage at the generating plant will be required when this new capacitor bank is connected to the substation bus?

11.56 Choose a single capacitor from Appendix H that is closest to the μF rating of the delta-connected capacitor from Problem 11.54(a).

  a) How much reactive power will a capacitor bank using this new value supply?

  b) What line-to-line voltage at the generating plant will be required when this new capacitor bank is connected to the substation bus?

11.57 In the Practical Perspective example, what happens
PRACTICAL to the voltage level at the generating plant if the
PERSPECTIVE substation is maintained at 13.8 kV, the substation load is removed, and the added capacitor bank remains connected?

11.58 In the Practical Perspective example, calculate the
PRACTICAL total line loss in kW before and after the capacitors
PERSPECTIVE are connected to the substation bus.

11.59 Assume the load on the substation bus in the
PRACTICAL Practical Perspective example drops to 180 kW and
PERSPECTIVE 480 magnetizing kVAR. Also assume the capacitors remain connected to the substation.

  a) What is the magnitude of the line-to-line voltage at the generating plant that is required to maintain a line-to-line voltage of 13.8 kV at the substation?

  b) Will this power plant voltage level cause problems for other customers?

11.60 Assume in Problem 11.59 that when the load drops
PRACTICAL to 180 kW and 480 magnetizing kVAR the capaci-
PERSPECTIVE tor bank at the substation is disconnected. Also assume that the line-to-line voltage at the substation is maintained at 13.8 kV.

  a) What is the magnitude of the line-to-line voltage at the generating plant?

  b) Is the voltage level found in (a) within the acceptable range of variation?

  c) What is the total line loss in kW when the capacitors stay on line after the load drops to $180 + j480 \, \text{kVA}$?

  d) What is the total line loss in kW when the capacitors are removed after the load drops to $180 + j480 \, \text{kVA}$?

  e) Based on your calculations, would you recommend disconnecting the capacitors after the load drops to $180 + j480 \, \text{kVA}$? Explain.

Introduction to Frequency Selective Circuits

✓ CHAPTER OBJECTIVES

1 Know the RL and RC circuit configurations that act as low-pass filters and be able to design RL and RC circuit component values to meet a specified cutoff frequency.

2 Know the *RL* and *RC* circuit configurations that act as high-pass filters and be able to design *RL* and *RC* circuit component values to meet a specified cutoff frequency.

3 Know the *RLC* circuit configurations that act as bandpass filters, understand the definition of and relationship among the center frequency, cutoff frequencies, bandwidth, and quality factor of a bandpass filter, and be able to design *RLC* circuit component values to meet design specifications.

4 Know the *RLC* circuit configurations that act as bandreject filters, understand the definition of and relationship among the center frequency, cutoff frequencies, bandwidth, and quality factor of a bandreject filter, and be able to design *RLC* circuit component values to meet design specifications.

Up to this point in our analysis of circuits with sinusoidal sources, the source frequency was held constant. In this chapter, we analyze the effect of varying source frequency on circuit voltages and currents. The result of this analysis is the **frequency response** of a circuit.

We've seen in previous chapters that a circuit's response depends on the types of elements in the circuit, the way the elements are connected, and the impedance of the elements. Although varying the frequency of a sinusoidal source does not change the element types or their connections, it does alter the impedance of capacitors and inductors, because the impedance of these elements is a function of frequency. As we will see, the careful choice of circuit elements, their values, and their connections to other elements enables us to construct circuits that pass to the output only those input signals that reside in a desired range of frequencies. Such circuits are called **frequency-selective circuits**. Many devices that communicate via electric signals, such as telephones, radios, televisions, and satellites, employ frequency-selective circuits.

Frequency-selective circuits are also called **filters** because of their ability to filter out certain input signals on the basis of frequency. Figure 14.1 on page 522 represents this ability in a simplistic way. To be more accurate, we should note that no practical frequency-selective circuit can perfectly or completely filter out selected frequencies. Rather, filters **attenuate**—that is, weaken or lessen the effect of—any input signals with frequencies outside frequencies outside a particular frequency band. Your home stereo system may have a graphic equalizer, which is an excellent example of a collection of filter circuits. Each band in the graphic equalizer is a filter that amplifies sounds (audible frequencies) in the frequency range of the band and attenuates frequencies outside of that band. Thus the graphic equalizer enables you to change the sound volume in each frequency band.

Practical Perspective

Pushbutton Telephone Circuits

In this chapter, we examine circuits in which the source frequency varies. The behavior of these circuits varies as the source frequency varies, because the impedance of the reactive components is a function of the source frequency. These frequency-dependent circuits are called **filters** and are used in many common electrical devices. In radios, filters are used to select one radio station's signal while rejecting the signals from others transmitting at different frequencies. In stereo systems, filters are used to adjust the relative strengths of the low- and high-frequency components of the audio signal. Filters are also used throughout telephone systems.

A pushbutton telephone produces tones that you hear when you press a button. You may have wondered about these tones. How are they used to tell the telephone system which button was pushed? Why are tones used at all? Why do the tones sound musical? How does the phone system tell the difference between button tones and the normal sounds of people talking or singing?

The telephone system was designed to handle audio signals—those with frequencies between 300 Hz and 3 kHz. Thus, all signals from the system to the user have to be audible—including the dial tone and the busy signal. Similarly, all signals from the user to the system have to be audible, including the signal that the user has pressed a button. It is important to distinguish button signals from the normal audio signal, so a dual-tone-multiple-frequency (DTMF) design is employed. When a number button is pressed, a unique pair of sinusoidal tones with very precise frequencies is sent by the phone to the telephone system. The DTMF frequency and timing specifications make it unlikely that a human voice could produce the exact tone pairs, even if the person were trying. In the central telephone facility, electric circuits monitor the audio signal, listening for the tone pairs that signal a number. In the Practical Perspective example at the end of the chapter, we will examine the design of the DTMF filters used to determine which button has been pushed.

Tom Grill / Corbis

Figure 14.1 ▲ The action of a filter on an input signal results in an output signal.

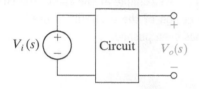

Figure 14.2 ▲ A circuit with voltage input and output.

We begin this chapter by analyzing circuits from each of the four major categories of filters: low pass, high pass, band pass, and band reject. The transfer function of a circuit is the starting point for the frequency response analysis. Pay close attention to the similarities among the transfer functions of circuits that perform the same filtering function. We will employ these similarities when designing filter circuits in Chapter 15.

14.1 Some Preliminaries

Recall from Section 13.7 that the transfer function of a circuit provides an easy way to compute the steady-state response to a sinusoidal input. There, we considered only fixed-frequency sources. To study the frequency response of a circuit, we replace a fixed-frequency sinusoidal source with a varying-frequency sinusoidal source. The transfer function is still an immensely useful tool because the magnitude and phase of the output signal depend only on the magnitude and phase of the transfer function $H(j\omega)$.

Note that the approach just outlined assumes that we can vary the frequency of a sinusoidal source without changing its magnitude or phase angle. Therefore, the amplitude and phase of the output will vary only if those of the transfer function vary as the frequency of the sinusoidal source is changed.

To further simplify this first look at frequency-selective circuits, we will also restrict our attention to cases where both the input and output signals are sinusoidal voltages, as illustrated in Fig. 14.2. Thus, the transfer function of interest to us will be the ratio of the Laplace transform of the output voltage to the Laplace transform of the input voltage, or $H(s) = V_o(s)/V_i(s)$. We should keep in mind, however, that for a particular application, a current may be either the input signal or output signal of interest.

The signals passed from the input to the output fall within a band of frequencies called the **passband**. Input voltages outside this band have their magnitudes attenuated by the circuit and are thus effectively prevented from reaching the output terminals of the circuit. Frequencies not in a circuit's passband are in its **stopband**. Frequency-selective circuits are categorized by the location of the passband.

One way of identifying the type of frequency-selective circuit is to examine a **frequency response plot**. A frequency response plot shows how a circuit's transfer function (both amplitude and phase) changes as the source frequency changes. A frequency response plot has two parts. One is a graph of $|H(j\omega)|$ versus frequency ω. This part of the plot is called the **magnitude plot**. The other part is a graph of $\theta(j\omega)$ versus frequency ω. This part is called the **phase angle plot**.

The ideal frequency response plots for the four major categories of filters are shown in Fig. 14.3. Parts (a) and (b) illustrate the ideal plots for a low-pass and a high-pass filter, respectively. Both filters have one passband and one stopband, which are defined by the **cutoff frequency** that separates them. The names *low pass* and *high pass* are derived from the magnitude plots: a **low-pass filter** passes signals at frequencies lower than the cutoff frequency from the input to the output, and a **high-pass filter** passes signals at frequencies higher than the cutoff frequency. Thus the terms *low* and *high* as used here do not refer to any absolute values of frequency, but rather to relative values with respect to the cutoff frequency.

Note from the graphs for both these filters (as well as those for the bandpass and bandreject filters) that the phase angle plot for an ideal filter varies linearly in the passband. It is of no interest outside the passband because there the magnitude is zero. Linear phase variation is necessary to avoid phase distortion.

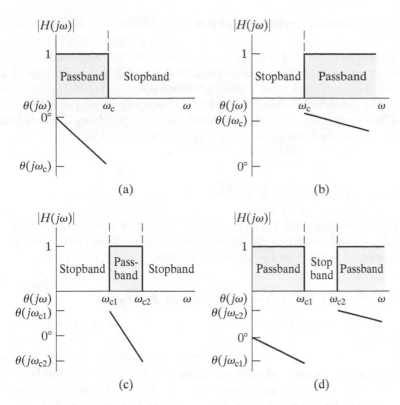

Figure 14.3 ▲ Ideal frequency response plots of the four types of filter circuits. (a) An ideal low-pass filter. (b) An ideal high-pass filter. (c) An ideal bandpass filter. (d) An ideal bandreject filter.

The two remaining categories of filters each have two cutoff frequencies. Figure 14.3(c) illustrates the ideal frequency response plot of a **bandpass filter**, which passes a source voltage to the output only when the source frequency is within the band defined by the two cutoff frequencies. Figure 14.3(d) shows the ideal plot of a **bandreject filter**, which passes a source voltage to the output only when the source frequency is outside the band defined by the two cutoff frequencies. The bandreject filter thus rejects, or stops, the source voltage from reaching the output when its frequency is within the band defined by the cutoff frequencies.

In specifying a realizable filter using any of the circuits from this chapter, it is important to note that the magnitude and phase angle characteristics are not independent. In other words, the characteristics of a circuit that result in a particular magnitude plot will also dictate the form of the phase angle plot and vice versa. For example, once we select a desired form for the magnitude response of a circuit, the phase angle response is also determined. Alternatively, if we select a desired form for the phase angle response, the magnitude response is also determined. Although there are some frequency-selective circuits for which the magnitude and phase angle behavior can be independently specified, these circuits are not presented here.

The next sections present examples of circuits from each of the four filter categories. They are a few of the many circuits that act as filters. You should focus your attention on trying to identify what properties of a circuit determine its behavior as a filter. Look closely at the form of the transfer function for circuits that perform the same filtering functions. Identifying the form of a filter's transfer function will ultimately help you in designing filtering circuits for particular applications.

All of the filters we will consider in this chapter are **passive filters**, so called because their filtering capabilities depend only on the passive elements: resistors, capacitors, and inductors. The largest output amplitude such filters can achieve is usually 1, and placing an impedance in series with the source or in parallel with the load will decrease this amplitude. Because many practical filter applications require increasing the amplitude of the output, passive filters have some significant disadvantages. The only passive filter described in this chapter that can amplify its output is the series *RLC* resonant filter. A much greater selection of amplifying filters is found among the active filter circuits, the subject of Chapter 15.

14.2 Low-Pass Filters

Here, we examine two circuits that behave as low-pass filters, the series *RL* circuit and the series *RC* circuit, and discover what characteristics of these circuits determine the cutoff frequency.

The Series *RL* Circuit—Qualitative Analysis

A series *RL* circuit is shown in Fig. 14.4(a). The circuit's input is a sinusoidal voltage source with varying frequency. The circuit's output is defined as the voltage across the resistor. Suppose the frequency of the source starts very low and increases gradually. We know that the behavior of the ideal resistor will not change, because its impedance is independent of frequency. But consider how the behavior of the inductor changes.

Recall that the impedance of an inductor is $j\omega L$. At low frequencies, the inductor's impedance is very small compared with the resistor's impedance, and the inductor effectively functions as a short circuit. The term *low frequencies* thus refers to any frequencies for which $\omega L \ll R$. The equivalent circuit for $\omega = 0$ is shown in Fig. 14.4(b). In this equivalent circuit, the output voltage and the input voltage are equal both in magnitude and in phase angle.

As the frequency increases, the impedance of the inductor increases relative to that of the resistor. Increasing the inductor's impedance causes a corresponding increase in the magnitude of the voltage drop across the inductor and a corresponding decrease in the output voltage magnitude. Increasing the inductor's impedance also introduces a shift in phase angle between the inductor's voltage and current. This results in a phase angle difference between the input and output voltage. The output voltage lags the input voltage, and as the frequency increases, this phase lag approaches 90°.

At high frequencies, the inductor's impedance is very large compared with the resistor's impedance, and the inductor thus functions as an open circuit, effectively blocking the flow of current in the circuit. The term *high frequencies* thus refers to any frequencies for which $\omega L \gg R$. The equivalent circuit for $\omega = \infty$ is shown in Fig. 14.4(c), where the output voltage magnitude is zero. The phase angle of the output voltage is 90° more negative than that of the input voltage.

Based on the behavior of the output voltage magnitude, this series *RL* circuit selectively passes low-frequency inputs to the output, and it blocks high-frequency inputs from reaching the output. This circuit's response to varying input frequency thus has the shape shown in Fig. 14.5. These two plots comprise the frequency response plots of the series *RL* circuit in Fig. 14.4(a). The upper plot shows how $|H(j\omega)|$ varies with frequency. The lower plot shows how $\theta(j\omega)$ varies as a function of frequency. We present a more formal method for constructing these plots in Appendix E.

We have also superimposed the ideal magnitude plot for a low-pass filter from Fig. 14.3(a) on the magnitude plot of the *RL* filter in Fig. 14.5. There is obviously a difference between the magnitude plots of an ideal

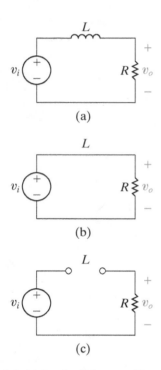

Figure 14.4 ▲ (a) A series *RL* low-pass filter. (b) The equivalent circuit at $\omega = 0$. and (c) The equivalent circuit at $\omega = \infty$.

filter and the frequency response of an actual *RL* filter. The ideal filter exhibits a discontinuity in magnitude at the cutoff frequency, ω_c, which creates an abrupt transition into and out of the passband. While this is, ideally, how we would like our filters to perform, it is not possible to use real components to construct a circuit that has this abrupt transition in magnitude. Circuits acting as low-pass filters have a magnitude response that changes gradually from the passband to the stopband. Hence the magnitude plot of a real circuit requires us to define what we mean by the cutoff frequency, ω_c.

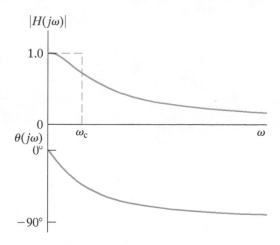

Figure 14.5 ▲ The frequency response plot for the series *RL* circuit in Fig. 14.4(a).

Defining the Cutoff Frequency

We need to define the cutoff frequency, ω_c, for realistic filter circuits when the magnitude plot does not allow us to identify a single frequency that divides the passband and the stopband. The definition for cutoff frequency widely used by electrical engineers is the frequency for which the transfer function magnitude is decreased by the factor $1/\sqrt{2}$ from its maximum value:

$$|H(j\omega_c)| = \frac{1}{\sqrt{2}}H_{max},\tag{14.1}$$

◀ **Cutoff frequency definition**

where H_{max} is the maximum magnitude of the transfer function. It follows from Eq. 14.1 that the passband of a realizable filter is defined as the range of frequencies in which the amplitude of the output voltage is at least 70.7% of the maximum possible amplitude.

The constant $1/\sqrt{2}$ used in defining the cutoff frequency may seem like an arbitrary choice. Examining another consequence of the cutoff frequency will make this choice seem more reasonable. Recall from Section 10.5 that the average power delivered by any circuit to a load is proportional to V_L^2, where V_L is the amplitude of the voltage drop across the load:

$$P = \frac{1}{2}\frac{V_L^2}{R}.\tag{14.2}$$

If the circuit has a sinusoidal voltage source, $V_i(j\omega)$, then the load voltage is also a sinusoid, and its amplitude is a function of the frequency ω. Define P_{max} as the value of the average power delivered to a load when the magnitude of the load voltage is maximum:

$$P_{max} = \frac{1}{2}\frac{V_{Lmax}^2}{R}.\tag{14.3}$$

If we vary the frequency of the sinusoidal voltage source, $V_i(j\omega)$, the load voltage is a maximum when the magnitude of the circuit's transfer function is also a maximum:

$$V_{Lmax} = H_{max}|V_i|.\tag{14.4}$$

Now consider what happens to the average power when the frequency of the voltage source is ω_c. Using Eq. 14.1, we determine the magnitude of the load voltage at ω_c to be

$$
\begin{aligned}
|V_L(j\omega_c)| &= |H(j\omega_c)||V_i| \\
&= \frac{1}{\sqrt{2}}H_{max}|V_i| \\
&= \frac{1}{\sqrt{2}}V_{Lmax}.
\end{aligned}\tag{14.5}
$$

Substituting Eq. 14.5 into Eq. 14.2,

$$P(j\omega_c) = \frac{1}{2}\frac{|V_L^2(j\omega_c)|}{R}$$

$$= \frac{1}{2}\frac{\left(\frac{1}{\sqrt{2}}V_{L\max}\right)^2}{R}$$

$$= \frac{1}{2}\frac{V_{L\max}^2/2}{R}$$

$$= \frac{P_{\max}}{2}. \tag{14.6}$$

Equation 14.6 shows that at the cutoff frequency ω_c, the average power delivered by the circuit is one half the maximum average power. Thus, ω_c is also called the **half-power frequency**. Therefore, in the passband, the average power delivered to a load is at least 50% of the maximum average power.

The Series *RL* Circuit—Quantitative Analysis

Now that we have defined the cutoff frequency for real filter circuits, we can analyze the series *RL* circuit to discover the relationship between the component values and the cutoff frequency for this low-pass filter. We begin by constructing the *s*-domain equivalent of the circuit in Fig. 14.4(a), assuming initial conditions of zero. The resulting equivalent circuit is shown in Fig. 14.6.

The voltage transfer function for this circuit is

$$H(s) = \frac{R/L}{s + R/L}. \tag{14.7}$$

To study the frequency response, we make the substitution $s = j\omega$ in Eq. 14.7:

$$H(j\omega) = \frac{R/L}{j\omega + R/L}. \tag{14.8}$$

We can now separate Eq. 14.8 into two equations. The first defines the transfer function magnitude as a function of frequency; the second defines the transfer function phase angle as a function of frequency:

$$|H(j\omega)| = \frac{R/L}{\sqrt{\omega^2 + (R/L)^2}}, \tag{14.9}$$

$$\theta(j\omega) = -\tan^{-1}\left(\frac{\omega L}{R}\right). \tag{14.10}$$

Close examination of Eq. 14.9 provides the quantitative support for the magnitude plot shown in Fig. 14.5. When $\omega = 0$, the denominator and the numerator are equal and $|H(j0)| = 1$. This means that at $\omega = 0$, the input voltage is passed to the output terminals without a change in the voltage magnitude.

As the frequency increases, the numerator of Eq. 14.9 is unchanged, but the denominator gets larger. Thus $|H(j\omega)|$ decreases as the frequency increases, as shown in the plot in Fig. 14.5. Likewise, as the frequency increases, the phase angle changes from its dc value of $0°$, becoming more negative, as seen from Eq. 14.10.

When $\omega = \infty$, the denominator of Eq. 14.9 is infinite and $|H(j\infty)| = 0$, as seen in Fig. 14.5. At $\omega = \infty$, the phase angle reaches a limit of $-90°$, as seen from Eq. 14.10 and the phase angle plot in Fig. 14.5.

Using Eq. 14.9, we can compute the cutoff frequency, ω_c. Remember that ω_c is defined as the frequency at which $|H(j\omega_c)| = (1/\sqrt{2})H_{\max}$. For

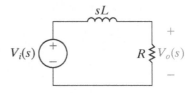

$V_i(s)$ sL $R \gtrless V_o(s)$

Figure 14.6 ▲ The *s*-domain equivalent for the circuit in Fig. 14.4(a).

the low-pass filter, $H_{max} = |H(j0)|$, as seen in Fig. 14.5. Thus, for the circuit in Fig. 14.4(a),

$$|H(j\omega_c)| = \frac{1}{\sqrt{2}}|1| = \frac{R/L}{\sqrt{\omega_c^2 + (R/L)^2}}. \qquad (14.11)$$

Solving Eq. 14.11 for ω_c, we get

$$\omega_c = \frac{R}{L}. \qquad (14.12)$$

◀ **Cutoff frequency for *RL* filters**

Equation 14.12 provides an important result. The cutoff frequency, ω_c, can be set to any desired value by appropriately selecting values for R and L. We can therefore design a low-pass filter with whatever cutoff frequency is needed. Example 14.1 demonstrates the design potential of Eq. 14.12.

Example 14.1   Designing a Low-Pass Filter

Electrocardiology is the study of the electric signals produced by the heart. These signals maintain the heart's rhythmic beat, and they are measured by an instrument called an electrocardiograph. This instrument must be capable of detecting periodic signals whose frequency is about 1 Hz (the normal heart rate is 72 beats per minute). The instrument must operate in the presence of sinusoidal noise consisting of signals from the surrounding electrical environment, whose fundamental frequency is 60 Hz—the frequency at which electric power is supplied.

Choose values for R and L in the circuit of Fig. 14.4(a) such that the resulting circuit could be used in an electrocardiograph to filter out any noise above 10 Hz and pass the electric signals from the heart at or near 1 Hz. Then compute the magnitude of V_o at 1 Hz, 10 Hz, and 60 Hz to see how well the filter performs.

Solution

The problem is to select values for R and L that yield a low-pass filter with a cutoff frequency of 10 Hz. From Eq. 14.12, we see that R and L cannot be specified independently to generate a value for ω_c. Therefore, let's choose a commonly available value of L, 100 mH. Before we use Eq. 14.12 to compute the value of R needed to obtain the desired cutoff frequency, we need to convert the cutoff frequency from hertz to radians per second:

$$\omega_c = 2\pi(10) = 20\pi \text{ rad/s}.$$

Now, solve for the value of R which, together with $L = 100$ mH, will yield a low-pass filter with a cutoff frequency of 10 Hz:

$$R = \omega_c L$$
$$= (20\pi)(100 \times 10^{-3})$$
$$= 6.28 \ \Omega.$$

We can compute the magnitude of V_o using the equation $|V_o| = |H(j\omega)| \cdot |V_i|$:

$$|V_o(\omega)| = \frac{R/L}{\sqrt{\omega^2 + (R/L)^2}}|V_i|$$

$$= \frac{20\pi}{\sqrt{\omega^2 + 400\pi^2}}|V_i|.$$

Table 14.1 summarizes the computed magnitude values for the frequencies 1 Hz, 10 Hz, and 60 Hz. As expected, the input and output voltages have the same magnitudes at the low frequency, because the circuit is a low-pass filter. At the cutoff frequency, the output voltage magnitude has been reduced by $1/\sqrt{2}$ from the unity passband magnitude. At 60 Hz, the output voltage magnitude has been reduced by a factor of about 6, achieving the desired attenuation of the noise that could corrupt the signal the electrocardiograph is designed to measure.

TABLE 14.1   Input and Output Voltage Magnitudes for Several Frequencies

f(Hz)	$|V_i|$ (V)	$|V_o|$ (V)
1	1.0	0.995
10	1.0	0.707
60	1.0	0.164

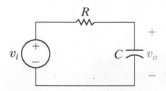

Figure 14.7 ▲ A series RC low-pass filter.

A Series RC Circuit

The series RC circuit shown in Fig. 14.7 also behaves as a low-pass filter. We can verify this via the same qualitative analysis we used previously. In fact, such a qualitative examination is an important problem-solving step that you should get in the habit of performing when analyzing filters. Doing so will enable you to predict the filtering characteristics (low pass, high pass, etc.) and thus also predict the general form of the transfer function. If the calculated transfer function matches the qualitatively predicted form, you have an important accuracy check.

Note that the circuit's output is defined as the output across the capacitor. As we did in the previous qualitative analysis, we use three frequency regions to develop the behavior of the series RC circuit in Fig. 14.7:

1. *Zero frequency* ($\omega = 0$): The impedance of the capacitor is infinite, and the capacitor acts as an open circuit. The input and output voltages are thus the same.

2. *Frequencies increasing from zero*: The impedance of the capacitor decreases relative to the impedance of the resistor, and the source voltage divides between the resistive impedance and the capacitive impedance. The output voltage is thus smaller than the source voltage.

3. *Infinite frequency* ($\omega = \infty$): The impedance of the capacitor is zero, and the capacitor acts as a short circuit. The output voltage is thus zero.

Based on this analysis of how the output voltage changes as a function of frequency, the series RC circuit functions as a low-pass filter. Example 14.2 explores this circuit quantitatively.

Example 14.2   **Designing a Series RC Low-Pass Filter**

For the series RC circuit in Fig. 14.7:

a) Find the transfer function between the source voltage and the output voltage.

b) Determine an equation for the cutoff frequency in the series RC circuit.

c) Choose values for R and C that will yield a low-pass filter with a cutoff frequency of 3 kHz.

Solution

a) To derive an expression for the transfer function, we first construct the s-domain equivalent of the circuit in Fig. 14.7, as shown in Fig. 14.8.

Using s-domain voltage division on the equivalent circuit, we find

$$H(s) = \frac{\frac{1}{RC}}{s + \frac{1}{RC}}.$$

Now, substitute $s = j\omega$ and compute the magnitude of the resulting complex expression:

$$|H(j\omega)| = \frac{\frac{1}{RC}}{\sqrt{\omega^2 + \left(\frac{1}{RC}\right)^2}}.$$

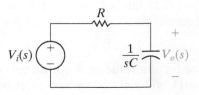

Figure 14.8 ▲ The s-domain equivalent for the circuit in Fig. 14.7.

b) At the cutoff frequency ω_c, $|H(j\omega)|$ is equal to $(1/\sqrt{2})H_{\max}$. For a low-pass filter,

$H_{max} = H(j0)$, and for the circuit in Fig. 14.8, $H(j0) = 1$. We can then describe the relationship among the quantities R, C, and ω_c:

$$|H(j\omega_c)| = \frac{1}{\sqrt{2}}(1) = \frac{\dfrac{1}{RC}}{\sqrt{\omega_c^2 + \left(\dfrac{1}{RC}\right)^2}}.$$

Solving this equation for ω_c, we get

$$\omega_c = \frac{1}{RC}.$$

▶ **Cutoff frequency of *RC* filters**

c) From the results in (b), we see that the cutoff frequency is determined by the values of R and C. Because R and C cannot be computed independently, let's choose $C = 1\ \mu F$. Given a choice, we will usually specify a value for C first, rather than for R or L, because the number of available capacitor values is much smaller than the number of resistor or inductor values. Remember that we have to convert the specified cutoff frequency from 3 kHz to $(2\pi)(3)$ krad/s:

$$\begin{aligned} R &= \frac{1}{\omega_c C} \\[6pt] &= \frac{1}{(2\pi)(3 \times 10^3)(1 \times 10^{-6})} \\[6pt] &= 53.05\ \Omega. \end{aligned}$$

Figure 14.9 summarizes the two low-pass filter circuits we have examined. Look carefully at the transfer functions. Notice how similar in form they are—they differ only in the terms that specify the cutoff frequency. In fact, we can state a general form for the transfer functions of these two low-pass filters:

$$H(s) = \frac{\omega_c}{s + \omega_c}. \tag{14.13}$$

◀ **Transfer function for a low-pass filter**

Any circuit with the voltage ratio in Eq. 14.13 would behave as a low-pass filter with a cutoff frequency of ω_c. The problems at the end of the chapter give you other examples of circuits with this voltage ratio.

Relating the Frequency Domain to the Time Domain

Finally, you might have noticed one other important relationship. Remember our discussion of the natural responses of the first-order RL and RC circuits in Chapter 6. An important parameter for these circuits is the time constant, τ, which characterizes the shape of the time response. For the RL circuit, the time constant has the value L/R (Eq. 7.14); for the RC circuit, the time constant is RC (Eq. 7.24). Compare the time constants to the cutoff frequencies for these circuits and notice that

$$\tau = 1/\omega_c. \tag{14.14}$$

This result is a direct consequence of the relationship between the time response of a circuit and its frequency response, as revealed by the Laplace transform. The discussion of memory and weighting as represented in the convolution integral of Section 13.6 shows that as $\omega_c \rightarrow \infty$, the filter has no memory, and the output approaches a scaled replica of the input; that is, no filtering has occurred. As $\omega_c \rightarrow 0$, the filter has increased memory and the output voltage is a distortion of the input, because filtering has occurred.

$$H(s) = \frac{R/L}{s + R/L}$$

$$\omega_c = R/L$$

$$H(s) = \frac{1/RC}{s + 1/RC}$$

$$\omega_c = 1/RC$$

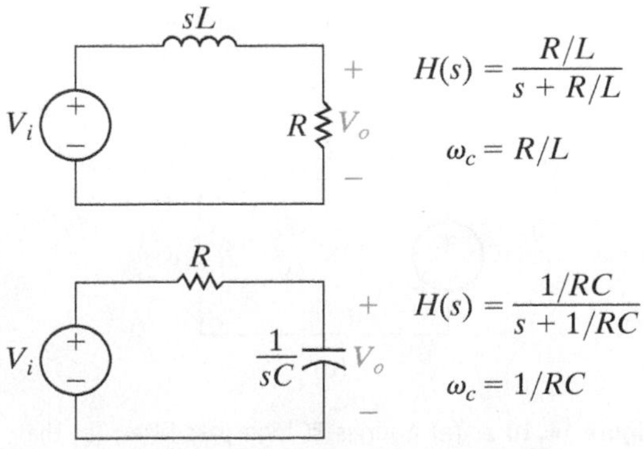

Figure 14.9 ▲ Two low-pass filters, the series RL and the series RC, together with their transfer functions and cutoff frequencies.

✓ASSESSMENT PROBLEMS

Objective 1—Know the *RL* and *RC* circuit configurations that act as low-pass filters

14.1 A series *RC* low-pass filter requires a cutoff frequency of 8 kHz. Use $R = 10\,\text{k}\Omega$ and compute the value of *C* required.

Answer: 1.99 nF.

14.2 A series *RL* low-pass filter with a cutoff frequency of 2 kHz is needed. Using $R = 5\,\text{k}\Omega$, compute (a) *L*; (b) $|H(j\omega)|$ at 50 kHz; and (c) $\theta(j\omega)$ at 50 kHz.

Answer: (a) 0.40 H;
(b) 0.04;
(c) $-87.71°$.

NOTE: Also try Chapter Problems 14.1 and 14.7.

14.3 High-Pass Filters

We next examine two circuits that function as high-pass filters. Once again, they are the series *RL* circuit and the series *RC* circuit. We will see that the same series circuit can act as either a low-pass or a high-pass filter, depending on where the output voltage is defined. We will also determine the relationship between the component values and the cutoff frequency of these filters.

The Series *RC* Circuit—Qualitative Analysis

A series *RC* circuit is shown in Fig. 14.10(a). In contrast to its low-pass counterpart in Fig. 14.7, the output voltage here is defined across the resistor, not the capacitor. Because of this, the effect of the changing capacitive impedance is different than it was in the low-pass configuration.

At $\omega = 0$, the capacitor behaves like an open circuit, so there is no current flowing in the resistor. This is illustrated in the equivalent circuit in Fig. 14.10(b). In this circuit, there is no voltage across the resistor, and the circuit filters out the low-frequency source voltage before it reaches the circuit's output.

As the frequency of the voltage source increases, the impedance of the capacitor decreases relative to the impedance of the resistor, and the source voltage is now divided between the capacitor and the resistor. The output voltage magnitude thus begins to increase.

When the frequency of the source is infinite ($\omega = \infty$), the capacitor behaves as a short circuit, and thus there is no voltage across the capacitor. This is illustrated in the equivalent circuit in Fig. 14.10(c). In this circuit, the input voltage and output voltage are the same.

The phase angle difference between the source and output voltages also varies as the frequency of the source changes. For $\omega = \infty$, the output voltage is the same as the input voltage, so the phase angle difference is zero. As the frequency of the source decreases and the impedance of the capacitor increases, a phase shift is introduced between the voltage and the current in the capacitor. This creates a phase difference between the source and output voltages. The phase angle of the output voltage leads that of the source voltage. When $\omega = 0$, this phase angle difference reaches its maximum of $+90°$.

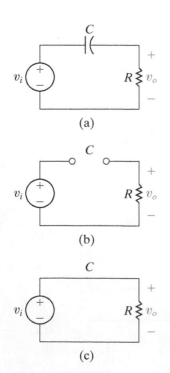

Figure 14.10 ▲ (a) A series *RC* high-pass filter; (b) the equivalent circuit at $\omega = 0$; and (c) the equivalent circuit at $\omega = \infty$.

Based on our qualitative analysis, we see that when the output is defined as the voltage across the resistor, the series RC circuit behaves as a high-pass filter. The components and connections are identical to the low-pass series RC circuit, but the choice of output is different. Thus, we have confirmed the earlier observation that the filtering characteristics of a circuit depend on the definition of the output as well as on circuit components, values, and connections.

Figure 14.11 shows the frequency response plot for the series RC high-pass filter. For reference, the dashed lines indicate the magnitude plot for an ideal high-pass filter. We now turn to a quantitative analysis of this same circuit.

The Series *RC* Circuit—Quantitative Analysis

To begin, we construct the s-domain equivalent of the circuit in Fig. 14.10(a). This equivalent is shown in Fig. 14.12. Applying s-domain voltage division to the circuit, we write the transfer function:

$$H(s) = \frac{s}{s + 1/RC}.$$

Making the substitution $s = j\omega$ results in

$$H(j\omega) = \frac{j\omega}{j\omega + 1/RC}. \tag{14.15}$$

Next, we separate Eq. 14.15 into two equations. The first is the equation describing the magnitude of the transfer function; the second is the equation describing the phase angle of the transfer function:

$$|H(j\omega)| = \frac{\omega}{\sqrt{\omega^2 + (1/RC)^2}}, \tag{14.16}$$

$$\theta(j\omega) = 90° - \tan^{-1}\omega RC. \tag{14.17}$$

A close look at Eqs. 14.16 and 14.17 confirms the shape of the frequency response plot in Fig. 14.11. Using Eq. 14.16, we can calculate the cutoff frequency for the series RC high-pass filter. Recall that at the cutoff frequency, the magnitude of the transfer function is $(1/\sqrt{2})H_{\max}$. For a high-pass filter, $H_{\max} = |H(j\omega)|_{\omega=\infty} = |H(j\infty)|$, as seen from Fig. 14.11. We can construct an equation for ω_c by setting the left-hand side of Eq. 14.16 to $(1/\sqrt{2})|H(j\infty)|$, noting that for this series RC circuit, $|H(j\infty)| = 1$:

$$\frac{1}{\sqrt{2}} = \frac{\omega_c}{\sqrt{\omega_c^2 + (1/RC)^2}}. \tag{14.18}$$

Solving Eq. 14.18 for ω_c, we get

$$\omega_c = \frac{1}{RC}. \tag{14.19}$$

Equation 14.19 presents a familiar result. The cutoff frequency for the series RC circuit has the value $1/RC$, whether the circuit is configured as a low-pass filter in Fig. 14.7 or as a high-pass filter in Fig. 14.10(a). This is perhaps not a surprising result, as we have already discovered a connection between the cutoff frequency, ω_c, and the time constant, τ, of a circuit.

Example 14.3 analyzes a series RL circuit, this time configured as a high-pass filter. Example 14.4 examines the effect of adding a load resistor in parallel with the inductor.

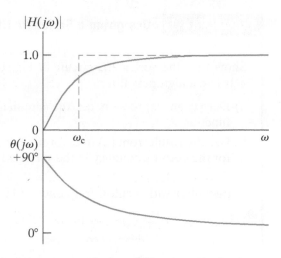

Figure 14.11 ▲ The frequency response plot for the series RC circuit in Fig. 14.10(a).

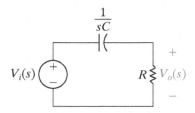

Figure 14.12 ▲ The s-domain equivalent of the circuit in Fig. 14.10(a).

Example 14.3   Designing a Series *RL* High-Pass Filter

Show that the series *RL* circuit in Fig. 14.13 also acts like a high-pass filter:

a) Derive an expression for the circuit's transfer function.

b) Use the result from (a) to determine an equation for the cutoff frequency in the series RL circuit.

c) Choose values for *R* and *L* that will yield a high-pass filter with a cutoff frequency of 15 kHz.

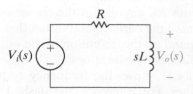

Figure 14.14 ▲ The *s*-domain equivalent of the circuit in Fig. 14.13.

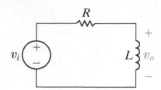

Figure 14.13 ▲ The circuit for Example 14.3.

Solution

a) Begin by constructing the *s*-domain equivalent of the series *RL* circuit, as shown in Fig. 14.14. Then use *s*-domain voltage division on the equivalent circuit to construct the transfer function:

$$H(s) = \frac{s}{s + R/L}.$$

Making the substitution $s = j\omega$, we get

$$H(j\omega) = \frac{j\omega}{j\omega + R/L}.$$

Notice that this equation has the same form as Eq. 14.15 for the series *RC* high-pass filter.

b) To find an equation for the cutoff frequency, first compute the magnitude of $H(j\omega)$:

$$|H(j\omega)| = \frac{\omega}{\sqrt{\omega^2 + (R/L)^2}}.$$

Then, as before, we set the left-hand side of this equation to $(1/\sqrt{2})H_{max}$, based on the definition of the cutoff frequency ω_c. Remember that $H_{max} = |H(j\infty)|$ for a high-pass filter, and for the series *RL* circuit, $|H(j\infty)| = 1$. We solve the resulting equation for the cutoff frequency:

$$\frac{1}{\sqrt{2}} = \frac{\omega_c}{\sqrt{\omega_c^2 + (R/L)^2}}, \quad \omega_c = \frac{R}{L}.$$

This is the same cutoff frequency we computed for the series *RL* low-pass filter.

c) Using the equation for ω_c computed in (b), we recognize that it is not possible to specify values for *R* and *L* independently. Therefore, let's arbitrarily select a value of 500 Ω for *R*. Remember to convert the cutoff frequency to radians per second:

$$L = \frac{R}{\omega_c} = \frac{500}{(2\pi)(15,000)} = 5.31 \text{ mH}.$$

Example 14.4   Loading the Series *RL* High-Pass Filter

Examine the effect of placing a load resistor in parallel with the inductor in the *RL* high-pass filter shown in Fig. 14.15:

a) Determine the transfer function for the circuit in Fig. 14.15.

b) Sketch the magnitude plot for the loaded *RL* high-pass filter, using the values for *R* and *L* from the circuit in Example 14.3(c) and letting $R_L = R$. On the same graph, sketch the magnitude plot for the unloaded *RL* high-pass filter of Example 14.3(c).

Solution

a) Begin by transforming the circuit in Fig. 14.15 to the *s*-domain, as shown in Fig. 14.16. Use voltage division across the parallel combination of inductor and load resistor to compute the transfer function:

$$H(s) = \frac{\dfrac{R_L s L}{R_L + s L}}{R + \dfrac{R_L s L}{R_L + s L}} = \frac{\left(\dfrac{R_L}{R + R_L}\right)s}{s + \left(\dfrac{R_L}{R + R_L}\right)\dfrac{R}{L}} = \frac{Ks}{s + \omega_c},$$

where

$$K = \frac{R_L}{R + R_L}, \quad \omega_c = KR/L.$$

Note that ω_c is the cutoff frequency of the loaded filter.

b) For the unloaded RL high-pass filter from Example 14.3(c), the passband magnitude is 1, and the cutoff frequency is 15 kHz. For the loaded RL high-pass filter, $R = R_L = 500\ \Omega$, so $K = 1/2$. Thus, for the loaded filter, the passband magnitude is $(1)(1/2) = 1/2$, and the cutoff frequency is $(15,000)(1/2) = 7.5$ kHz. A sketch of the magnitude plots of the loaded and unloaded circuits is shown in Fig. 14.17.

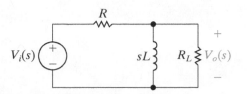

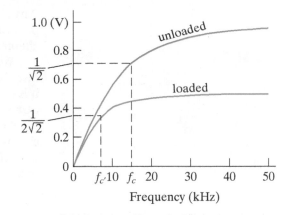

Figure 14.16 ▲ The s-domain equivalent of the circuit in Fig. 14.15.

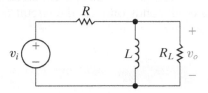

Figure 14.15 ▲ The circuit for Example 14.4.

Figure 14.17 ▲ The magnitude plots for the unloaded RL high-pass filter of Fig 14.13 and the loaded RL high-pass filter of Fig. 14.15.

Comparing the transfer functions of the unloaded filter in Example 14.3 and the loaded filter in Example 14.4 is useful at this point. Both transfer functions are in the form:

$$H(s) = \frac{Ks}{s + K(R/L)},$$

with $K = 1$ for the unloaded filter and $K = R_L/(R + R_L)$ for the loaded filter. Note that the value of K for the loaded circuit reduces to the value of K for the unloaded circuit when $R_L = \infty$; that is, when there is no load resistor. The cutoff frequencies for both filters can be seen directly from their transfer functions. In both cases, $\omega_c = K(R/L)$, where $K = 1$ for the unloaded circuit, and $K = R_L/(R + R_L)$ for the loaded circuit. Again, the cutoff frequency for the loaded circuit reduces to that of the unloaded circuit when $R_L = \infty$. Because $R_L/(R + R_L) < 1$, the effect of the load resistor is to reduce the passband magnitude by the factor K and to lower the cutoff frequency by the same factor. We predicted these results at the beginning of this chapter. The largest output amplitude a passive high-pass filter can achieve is 1, and placing a load across the filter, as we did in Example 14.4, has served to decrease the amplitude. When we need to amplify signals in the passband, we must turn to active filters, such as those discussed in Chapter 15.

The effect of a load on a filter's transfer function poses another dilemma in circuit design. We typically begin with a transfer function specification and then design a filter to produce that function. We may or may not know what the load on the filter will be, but in any event, we usually want the filter's transfer function to remain the same regardless of the load on it. This desired behavior cannot be achieved with the passive filters presented in this chapter.

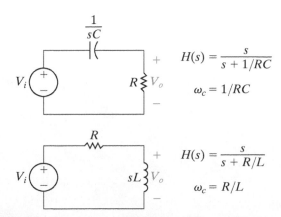

Figure 14.18 ▲ Two high-pass filters, the series RC and the series RL, together with their transfer functions and cutoff frequencies.

Figure 14.18 summarizes the high-pass filter circuits we have examined. Look carefully at the expressions for $H(s)$. Notice how similar in form these expressions are—they differ only in the denominator, which includes the cutoff frequency. As we did with the low-pass filters in Eq. 14.13, we state a general form for the transfer function of these two high-pass filters:

Transfer function for a high-pass filter ▶

$$H(s) = \frac{s}{s + \omega_c}.$$ (14.20)

Any circuit with the transfer function in Eq. 14.20 would behave as a high-pass filter with a cutoff frequency of ω_c. The problems at the end of the chapter give you other examples of circuits with this voltage ratio.

We have drawn attention to another important relationship. We have discovered that a series RC circuit has the same cutoff frequency whether it is configured as a low-pass filter or as a high-pass filter. The same is true of a series RL circuit. Having previously noted the connection between the cutoff frequency of a filter circuit and the time constant of that same circuit, we should expect the cutoff frequency to be a characteristic parameter of the circuit whose value depends only on the circuit components, their values, and the way they are connected.

✓ ASSESSMENT PROBLEMS

Objective 2—Know the RL and RC circuit configurations that act as high-pass filters

14.3   A series RL high-pass filter has $R = 5\ \text{k}\Omega$ and $L = 3.5\ \text{mH}$. What is ω_c for this filter?

Answer: 1.43 Mrad/s.

14.4   A series RC high-pass filter has $C = 1\ \mu\text{F}$. Compute the cutoff frequency for the following values of R: (a) 100 Ω; (b) 5 kΩ; and (c) 30 kΩ.

Answer: (a) 10 krad/s;
(b) 200 rad/s;
(c) 33.33 rad/s.

14.5   Compute the transfer function of a series RC low-pass filter that has a load resistor R_L in parallel with its capacitor.

Answer: $H(s) = \dfrac{\dfrac{1}{RC}}{s + \dfrac{1}{KRC}}$, where $K = \dfrac{R_L}{R + R_L}$.

NOTE: Also try ChapterProblems 14.13 and 14.17.

14.4 Bandpass Filters

The next filters we examine are those that pass voltages within a band of frequencies to the output while filtering out voltages at frequencies outside this band. These filters are somewhat more complicated than the low-pass and high-pass filters of the previous sections. As we have already seen in Fig. 14.3(c), ideal bandpass filters have two cutoff frequencies, ω_{c1} and ω_{c2}, which identify the passband. For realistic bandpass filters, these cutoff frequencies are again defined as the frequencies for which the magnitude of the transfer function equals $(1/\sqrt{2})H_{\text{max}}$.

Center Frequency, Bandwidth, and Quality Factor

There are three other important parameters that characterize a bandpass filter. The first is the **center frequency**, ω_o, defined as the frequency for which a circuit's transfer function is purely real. Another name for the center frequency is the **resonant frequency**. This is the same name given to the frequency that characterizes the natural response of the second-order circuits in Chapter 8, because they are the same frequencies! When a circuit is driven at the resonant frequency, we say that the circuit is *in resonance*, because the frequency of the forcing function is the same as the natural frequency of the circuit. The center frequency is the geometric center of the passband, that is, $\omega_o = \sqrt{\omega_{c1}\omega_{c2}}$. For bandpass filters, the magnitude of the transfer function is a maximum at the center frequency ($H_{\max} = |H(j\omega_o)|$).

The second parameter is the **bandwidth**, β, which is the width of the passband. The final parameter is the **quality factor**, which is the ratio of the center frequency to the bandwidth. The quality factor gives a measure of the width of the passband, independent of its location on the frequency axis. It also describes the shape of the magnitude plot, independent of frequency.

Although there are five different parameters that characterize the bandpass filter—ω_{c1}, ω_{c2}, ω_o, β, and Q—only two of the five can be specified independently. In other words, once we are able to solve for any two of these parameters, the other three can be calculated from the dependent relationships among them. We will define these quantities more specifically once we have analyzed a bandpass filter. In the next section, we examine two RLC circuits which act as bandpass filters, and then we derive expressions for all of their characteristic parameters.

The Series RLC Circuit—Qualitative Analysis

Figure 14.19(a) depicts a series RLC circuit. We want to consider the effect of changing the source frequency on the magnitude of the output voltage. As before, changes to the source frequency result in changes to the impedance of the capacitor and the inductor. This time, the qualitative analysis is somewhat more complicated, because the circuit has both an inductor and a capacitor.

At $\omega = 0$, the capacitor behaves like an open circuit, and the inductor behaves like a short circuit. The equivalent circuit is shown in Fig. 14.19(b). The open circuit representing the impedance of the capacitor prevents current from reaching the resistor, and the resulting output voltage is zero.

At $\omega = \infty$, the capacitor behaves like a short circuit, and the inductor behaves like an open circuit. The equivalent circuit is shown in Fig. 14.19(c). The inductor now prevents current from reaching the resistor, and again the output voltage is zero.

But what happens in the frequency region between $\omega = 0$ and $\omega = \infty$? Between these two extremes, both the capacitor and the inductor have finite impedances. In this region, voltage supplied by the source will drop across both the inductor and the capacitor, but some voltage will reach the resistor. Remember that the impedance of the capacitor is negative, whereas the impedance of the inductor is positive. Thus, at some frequency, the impedance of the capacitor and the impedance of the inductor have equal magnitudes and opposite signs; the two impedances cancel out, causing the output voltage to equal the source voltage. This special frequency is the center frequency, ω_o. On either side of ω_o, the output voltage is less than the source voltage. Note that at ω_o, the series combination of the inductor and capacitor appears as a short circuit.

The plot of the voltage magnitude ratio is shown in Fig. 14.20. Note that the ideal bandpass filter magnitude plot is overlaid on the plot of the series RLC transfer function magnitude.

Now consider what happens to the phase angle of the output voltage. At the frequency where the source and output voltage are the same, the phase angles are the same. As the frequency decreases, the phase angle contribution from the capacitor is larger than that from the inductor.

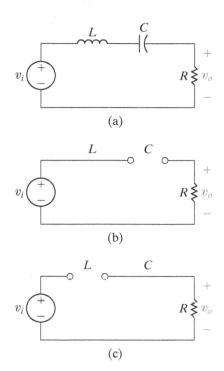

Figure 14.19 ▲ (a) A series RLC bandpass filter; (b) the equivalent circuit for $\omega = 0$; and (c) the equivalent circuit for $\omega = \infty$.

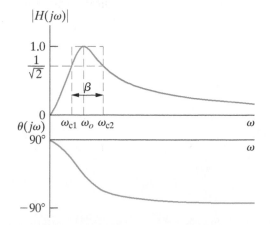

Figure 14.20 ▲ The frequency response plot for the series RLC bandpass filter circuit in Fig. 14.19.

Because the capacitor contributes positive phase shift, the net phase angle at the output is positive. At very low frequencies, the phase angle at the output maximizes at $+90°$.

Conversely, if the frequency increases from the frequency at which the source and the output voltage are in phase, the phase angle contribution from the inductor is larger than that from the capacitor. The inductor contributes negative phase shift, so the net phase angle at the output is negative. At very high frequencies, the phase angle at the output reaches its negative maximum of $-90°$. The plot of the phase angle difference thus has the shape shown in Fig. 14.20.

The Series *RLC* Circuit—Quantitative Analysis

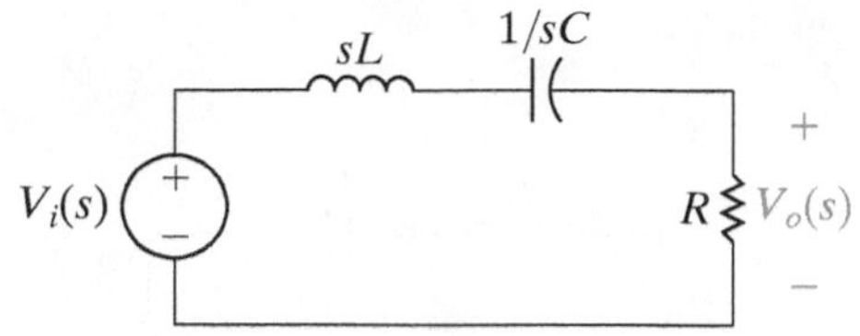

We begin by drawing the *s*-domain equivalent for the series *RLC* circuit, as shown in Fig. 14.21. Use *s*-domain voltage division to write an equation for the transfer function:

Figure 14.21 ▲ The *s*-domain equivalent for the circuit in Fig. 14.19(a).

$$H(s) = \frac{(R/L)s}{s^2 + (R/L)s + (1/LC)}. \tag{14.21}$$

As before, we substitute $s = j\omega$ into Eq. 14.21 and produce the equations for the magnitude and the phase angle of the transfer function:

$$|H(j\omega)| = \frac{\omega(R/L)}{\sqrt{[(1/LC) - \omega^2]^2 + [\omega(R/L)]^2}}, \tag{14.22}$$

$$\theta(j\omega) = 90° - \tan^{-1}\left[\frac{\omega(R/L)}{(1/LC) - \omega^2}\right]. \tag{14.23}$$

We now calculate the five parameters that characterize this *RLC* bandpass filter. Recall that the center frequency, ω_o, is defined as the frequency for which the circuit's transfer function is purely real. The transfer function for the *RLC* circuit in Fig. 14.19(a) will be real when the frequency of the voltage source makes the sum of the capacitor and inductor impedances zero:

$$j\omega_o L + \frac{1}{j\omega_o C} = 0. \tag{14.24}$$

Solving Eq. 14.24 for ω_o, we get

Center frequency ▶

$$\omega_o = \sqrt{\frac{1}{LC}}. \tag{14.25}$$

Next, calculate the cutoff frequencies, ω_{c1} and ω_{c2}. Remember that at the cutoff frequencies, the magnitude of the transfer function is $(1/\sqrt{2})H_{\max}$. Because $H_{\max} = |H(j\omega_o)|$, we can calculate $H_{\max}$ by substituting Eq. 14.25 into Eq. 14.22:

$$H_{\max} = |H(j\omega_o)|$$

$$= \frac{\omega_o(R/L)}{\sqrt{[(1/LC) - \omega_o^2]^2 + (\omega_o R/L)^2}}$$

$$= \frac{\sqrt{(1/LC)}(R/L)}{\sqrt{[(1/LC) - (1/LC)]^2 + \left[\sqrt{(1/LC)}(R/L)\right]^2}} = 1.$$

Now set the left-hand side of Eq. 14.22 to $(1/\sqrt{2})H_{max}$ (which equals $1/\sqrt{2}$) and prepare to solve for ω_c:

$$\frac{1}{\sqrt{2}} = \frac{\omega_c(R/L)}{\sqrt{[(1/LC) - \omega_c^2]^2 + (\omega_c R/L)^2}}$$

$$= \frac{1}{\sqrt{[(\omega_c L/R) - (1/\omega_c RC)]^2 + 1}}. \qquad (14.26)$$

We can equate the denominators of the two sides of Eq. 14.26 to get

$$\pm 1 = \omega_c \frac{L}{R} - \frac{1}{\omega_c RC}. \qquad (14.27)$$

Rearranging Eq. 14.27 results in the following quadratic equation:

$$\omega_c^2 L \pm \omega_c R - 1/C = 0. \qquad (14.28)$$

The solution of Eq. 14.28 yields four values for the cutoff frequency. Only two of these values are positive and have physical significance; they identify the passband of this filter:

$$\omega_{c1} = -\frac{R}{2L} + \sqrt{\left(\frac{R}{2L}\right)^2 + \left(\frac{1}{LC}\right)}, \qquad (14.29)$$

◀ **Cutoff frequencies, series *RLC* filters**

$$\omega_{c2} = \frac{R}{2L} + \sqrt{\left(\frac{R}{2L}\right)^2 + \left(\frac{1}{LC}\right)}. \qquad (14.30)$$

We can use Eqs. 14.29 and 14.30 to confirm that the center frequency, ω_o, is the geometric mean of the two cutoff frequencies:

$$\omega_o = \sqrt{\omega_{c1} \cdot \omega_{c2}}$$

◀ **Relationship between center frequency and cutoff frequencies**

$$= \sqrt{\left[-\frac{R}{2L} + \sqrt{\left(\frac{R}{2L}\right)^2 + \left(\frac{1}{LC}\right)}\right]\left[\frac{R}{2L} + \sqrt{\left(\frac{R}{2L}\right)^2 + \left(\frac{1}{LC}\right)}\right]}$$

$$= \sqrt{\frac{1}{LC}}. \qquad (14.31)$$

Recall that the bandwidth of a bandpass filter is defined as the difference between the two cutoff frequencies. Because $\omega_{c2} > \omega_{c1}$ we can compute the bandwidth by subtracting Eq. 14.29 from Eq. 14.30:

$$\beta = \omega_{c2} - \omega_{c1}$$

◀ **Relationship between bandwidth and cutoff frequencies**

$$= \left[\frac{R}{2L} + \sqrt{\left(\frac{R}{2L}\right)^2 + \left(\frac{1}{LC}\right)}\right] - \left[-\frac{R}{2L} + \sqrt{\left(\frac{R}{2L}\right)^2 + \left(\frac{1}{LC}\right)}\right]$$

$$= \frac{R}{L}. \qquad (14.32)$$

The quality factor, the last of the five characteristic parameters, is defined as the ratio of center frequency to bandwidth. Using Eqs. 14.25 and 14.32:

Quality factor ▶

$$Q = \omega_o/\beta$$

$$= \frac{(1/LC)}{(R/L)}$$

$$= \sqrt{\frac{L}{CR^2}}. \tag{14.33}$$

We now have five parameters that characterize the series RLC bandpass filter: two cutoff frequencies, ω_{c1} and ω_{c2}, which delimit the passband; the center frequency, ω_o, at which the magnitude of the transfer function is maximum; the bandwidth, β, a measure of the width of the passband; and the quality factor, Q, a second measure of passband width. As previously noted, only two of these parameters can be specified independently in a design. We have already observed that the quality factor is specified in terms of the center frequency and the bandwidth. We can also rewrite the equations for the cutoff frequencies in terms of the center frequency and the bandwidth:

$$\omega_{c1} = -\frac{\beta}{2} + \sqrt{\left(\frac{\beta}{2}\right)^2 + \omega_o^2}, \tag{14.34}$$

$$\omega_{c2} = \frac{\beta}{2} + \sqrt{\left(\frac{\beta}{2}\right)^2 + \omega_o^2}. \tag{14.35}$$

Alternative forms for these equations express the cutoff frequencies in terms of the quality factor and the center frequency:

$$\omega_{c1} = \omega_o \cdot \left[-\frac{1}{2Q} + \sqrt{1 + \left(\frac{1}{2Q}\right)^2} \right], \tag{14.36}$$

$$\omega_{c2} = \omega_o \cdot \left[\frac{1}{2Q} + \sqrt{1 + \left(\frac{1}{2Q}\right)^2} \right]. \tag{14.37}$$

Also see Problem 14.24 at the end of the chapter.

The examples that follow illustrate the design of bandpass filters, introduce another RLC circuit that behaves as a bandpass filter, and examine the effects of source resistance on the characteristic parameters of a series RLC bandpass filter.

Example 14.5   **Designing a Bandpass Filter**

A graphic equalizer is an audio amplifier that allows you to select different levels of amplification within different frequency regions. Using the series RLC circuit in Fig. 14.19(a), choose values for R, L, and C that yield a bandpass circuit able to select inputs within the 1–10 kHz frequency band. Such a circuit might be used in a graphic equalizer to select this frequency band from the larger audio band (generally 0–20 kHz) prior to amplification.

Solution

We need to compute values for R, L, and C that produce a bandpass filter with cutoff frequencies of 1 kHz and 10 kHz. There are many possible approaches to a solution. For instance, we could use Eqs. 14.29 and 14.30, which specify ω_{c1} and ω_{c2} in terms of R, L, and C. Because of the form of these equations, the algebraic manipulations might get complicated. Instead, we will use the fact that the center frequency is the geometric mean of the cutoff frequencies to compute ω_o, and we will then use Eq. 14.31 to compute L and C from ω_o. Next we will use the definition of quality factor to compute Q, and last we will use Eq. 14.33 to compute R. Even though this approach involves more individual computational steps, each calculation is fairly simple.

Any approach we choose will provide only two equations—insufficient to solve for the three unknowns—because of the dependencies among the bandpass filter characteristics. Thus, we need to select a value for either R, L, or C and use the two equations we've chosen to calculate the remaining component values. Here, we choose 1 μF as the capacitor value, because there are stricter limitations on commercially available capacitors than on inductors or resistors.

We compute the center frequency as the geometric mean of the cutoff frequencies:

$$f_o = \sqrt{f_{c1}f_{c2}} = \sqrt{(1000)(10,000)} = 3162.28 \text{ Hz.}$$

Next, compute the value of L using the computed center frequency and the selected value for C. We must remember to convert the center frequency to radians per second before we can use Eq. 14.31:

$$L = \frac{1}{\omega_o^2 C} = \frac{1}{[2\pi(3162.28)]^2(10^{-6})} = 2.533 \text{ mH.}$$

The quality factor, Q, is defined as the ratio of the center frequency to the bandwidth. The bandwidth is the difference between the two cutoff frequency values. Thus,

$$Q = \frac{f_o}{f_{c2} - f_{c1}} = \frac{3162.28}{10,000 - 1000} = 0.3514.$$

Now use Eq. 14.33 to calculate R:

$$R = \sqrt{\frac{L}{CQ^2}} = \sqrt{\frac{0.0025}{(10^{-6})(0.3514)^2}} = 143.24 \text{ }\Omega.$$

To check whether these component values produce the bandpass filter we want, substitute them into Eqs. 14.29 and 14.30. We find that

$$\omega_{c1} = 6283.19 \text{ rad/s (1000 Hz),}$$

$$\omega_{c2} = 62,831.85 \text{ rad/s (10,000 Hz),}$$

which are the cutoff frequencies specified for the filter.

This example reminds us that only two of the five bandpass filter parameters can be specified independently. The other three parameters can always be computed from the two that are specified. In turn, these five parameter values depend on the three component values, R, L, and C, of which only two can be specified independently.

Example 14.6   Designing a Parallel *RLC* Bandpass Filter

a) Show that the RLC circuit in Fig. 14.22 is also a bandpass filter by deriving an expression for the transfer function $H(s)$.
b) Compute the center frequency, ω_o.
c) Calculate the cutoff frequencies, ω_{c1} and ω_{c2}, the bandwidth, β, and the quality factor, Q.
d) Compute values for R and L to yield a bandpass filter with a center frequency of 5 kHz and a bandwidth of 200 Hz, using a 5 μF capacitor.

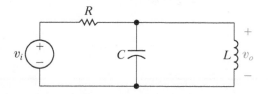

Figure 14.22 ▲ The circuit for Example 14.6.

Solution

a) Begin by drawing the s-domain equivalent of the circuit in Fig. 14.22, as shown in Fig. 14.23. Using voltage division, we can compute the transfer function for the equivalent circuit if we

first compute the equivalent impedance of the parallel combination of L and C, identified as $Z_{\text{eq}}(s)$ in Fig. 14.23:

$$Z_{\text{eq}}(s) = \frac{\frac{L}{C}}{sL + \frac{1}{sC}}.$$

Now,

$$H(s) = \frac{\frac{s}{RC}}{s^2 + \frac{s}{RC} + \frac{1}{LC}}.$$

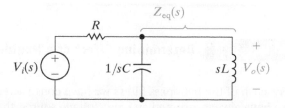

Figure 14.23 ▲ The s-domain equivalent of the circuit in Fig. 14.22.

b) To find the center frequency, , we need to calculate where the transfer function magnitude is maximum. Substituting $s = j\omega$ in $H(s)$,

$$|H(j\omega)| = \frac{\dfrac{\omega}{RC}}{\sqrt{\left(\dfrac{1}{LC} - \omega^2\right)^2 + \left(\dfrac{\omega}{RC}\right)^2}}$$

$$= \frac{1}{\sqrt{1 + \left(\omega RC - \dfrac{1}{\omega \dfrac{L}{R}}\right)^2}}.$$

The magnitude of this transfer function is maximum when the term

$$\left(\frac{1}{LC} - \omega^2\right)^2$$

is zero. Thus,

$$\omega_o = \sqrt{\frac{1}{LC}}$$

and

$$H_{max} = |H(j\omega_o)| = 1.$$

c) At the cutoff frequencies, the magnitude of the transfer function is $(1/\sqrt{2})H_{max} = 1/\sqrt{2}$. Substituting this constant on the left-hand side of the magnitude equation and then simplifying, we get

$$\left[\omega_c RC - \frac{1}{\omega_c \dfrac{L}{R}}\right] = \pm 1.$$

Squaring the left-hand side of this equation once again produces two quadratic equations for the cutoff frequencies, with four solutions. Only two of them are positive and therefore have physical significance:

$$\omega_{c1} = -\frac{1}{2RC} + \sqrt{\left(\frac{1}{2RC}\right)^2 + \frac{1}{LC}},$$

$$\omega_{c2} = \frac{1}{2RC} + \sqrt{\left(\frac{1}{2RC}\right)^2 + \frac{1}{LC}}.$$

▲ Cutoff frequencies for parallel *RLC* filters

We compute the bandwidth from the cutoff frequencies:

$$\beta = \omega_{c2} - \omega_{c1}$$

$$= \frac{1}{RC}.$$

Finally, use the definition of quality factor to calculate Q:

$$Q = \omega_o/\beta$$

$$= \sqrt{\frac{R^2C}{L}}.$$

Notice that once again we can specify the cutoff frequencies for this bandpass filter in terms of its center frequency and bandwidth:

$$\omega_{c1} = -\frac{\beta}{2} + \sqrt{\left(\frac{\beta}{2}\right)^2 + \omega_o^2},$$

$$\omega_{c2} = \frac{\beta}{2} + \sqrt{\left(\frac{\beta}{2}\right)^2 + \omega_o^2}.$$

d) Use the equation for bandwidth in (c) to compute a value for R, given a capacitance of $5\ \mu F$. Remember to convert the bandwidth to the appropriate units:

$$R = \frac{1}{\beta C}$$

$$= \frac{1}{(2\pi)(200)(5 \times 10^{-6})}$$

$$= 159.15\ \Omega.$$

Using the value of capacitance and the equation for center frequency in (c), compute the inductor value:

$$L = \frac{1}{\omega_o^2 C}$$

$$= \frac{1}{[2\pi(5000)]^2(5 \times 10^{-6})}$$

$$= 202.64\ \mu H.$$

Example 14.7 Determining Effect of a Nonideal Voltage Source on a *RLC* Bandpass Filter

For each of the bandpass filters we have constructed, we have always assumed an ideal voltage source, that is, a voltage source with no series resistance. Even though this assumption is often valid, sometimes it is not, as in the case where the filter design can be achieved only with values of R, L, and C whose equivalent impedance has a magnitude close to the actual impedance of the voltage source. Examine the effect of assuming a nonzero source resistance, R_i, on the characteristics of a series RLC bandpass filter.

a) Determine the transfer function for the circuit in Fig. 14.24.

b) Sketch the magnitude plot for the circuit in Fig. 14.24, using the values for R, L, and C from Example 14.5 and setting $R_i = R$. On the same graph, sketch the magnitude plot for the circuit in Example 14.5, where $R_i = 0$.

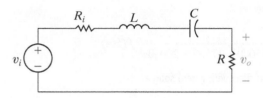

Figure 14.24 ▲ The circuit for Example 14.7.

Solution

a) Begin by transforming the circuit in Fig. 14.24 to its s-domain equivalent, as shown in Fig. 14.25. Now use voltage division to construct the transfer function:

$$H(s) = \frac{\frac{R}{L}s}{s^2 + \left(\frac{R + R_i}{L}\right)s + \frac{1}{LC}}.$$

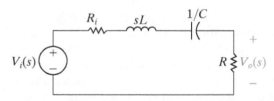

Figure 14.25 ▲ The s-domain equivalent of the circuit in Fig. 14.24.

Substitute $s = j\omega$ and calculate the transfer function magnitude:

$$|H(j\omega)| = \frac{\frac{R}{L}\omega}{\sqrt{\left(\frac{1}{LC} - \omega^2\right)^2 + \left(\omega\frac{R + R_i}{L}\right)^2}}.$$

The center frequency, ω_o, is the frequency at which this transfer function magnitude is maximum, which is

$$\omega_o = \sqrt{\frac{1}{LC}}.$$

At the center frequency, the maximum magnitude is

$$H_{\max} = |H(j\omega_o)| = \frac{R}{R_i + R}.$$

The cutoff frequencies can be computed by setting the transfer function magnitude equal to $(1/\sqrt{2})H_{\max}$:

$$\omega_{c1} = -\frac{R + R_i}{2L} + \sqrt{\left(\frac{R + R_i}{2L}\right)^2 + \frac{1}{LC}},$$

$$\omega_{c2} = \frac{R + R_i}{2L} + \sqrt{\left(\frac{R + R_i}{2L}\right)^2 + \frac{1}{LC}}.$$

The bandwidth is calculated from the cutoff frequencies:

$$\beta = \frac{R + R_i}{L}.$$

Finally, the quality factor is computed from the center frequency and the bandwidth:

$$Q = \frac{\sqrt{L/C}}{R + R_i}.$$

From this analysis, note that we can write the transfer function of the series RLC bandpass filter with nonzero source resistance as

$$H(s) = \frac{K\beta s}{s^2 + \beta s + \omega_o^2},$$

where

$$K = \frac{R}{R + R_i}.$$

Note that when $R_i = 0$, $K = 1$ and the transfer function is

$$H(s) = \frac{\beta s}{s^2 + \beta s + \omega_o^2}$$

b) The circuit in Example 14.5 has a center frequency of 3162.28 Hz and a bandwidth of 9 kHz, and $H_{\max} = 1$. If we use the same values for R, L, and C in the circuit in Fig. 14.24 and let $R_i = R$, then the center frequency remains at

3162.28 kHz, but $\beta = (R + R_i)/L = 18\,\text{kHz}$, and $H_{max} = R/(R + R_i) = 1/2$. The transfer

function magnitudes for these two bandpass filters are plotted on the same graph in Fig. 14.26.

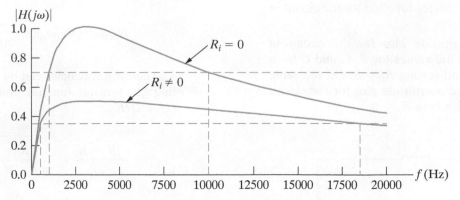

Figure 14.26 ▲ The magnitude plots for a series *RLC* bandpass filter with a zero source resistance and a nonzero source resistance.

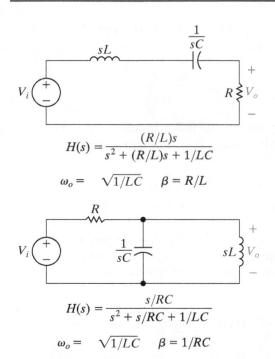

$$H(s) = \frac{(R/L)s}{s^2 + (R/L)s + 1/LC}$$

$$\omega_o = \sqrt{1/LC} \quad \beta = R/L$$

$$H(s) = \frac{s/RC}{s^2 + s/RC + 1/LC}$$

$$\omega_o = \sqrt{1/LC} \quad \beta = 1/RC$$

Figure 14.27 ▲ Two *RLC* bandpass filters, together with equations for the transfer function, center frequency, and bandwidth of each.

Transfer function for *RLC* bandpass filter ▶

If we compare the characteristic parameter values for the filter with $R_i = 0$ to the values for the filter with $R_i \neq 0$, we see the following:

- The center frequencies are the same.
- The maximum transfer function magnitude for the filter with $R_i \neq 0$ is smaller than for the filter with $R_i = 0$.
- The bandwidth for the filter with $R_i \neq 0$ is larger than that for the filter with $R_i = 0$. Thus, the cutoff frequencies and the quality factors for the two circuits are also different.

The addition of a nonzero source resistance to a series *RLC* bandpass filter leaves the center frequency unchanged but widens the passband and reduces the passband magnitude.

Here we see the same design challenge we saw with the addition of a load resistor to the high-pass filter, that is, we would like to design a bandpass filter that will have the same filtering properties regardless of any internal resistance associated with the voltage source. Unfortunately, filters constructed from passive elements have their filtering action altered with the addition of source resistance. In Chapter 15, we will discover that active filters are insensitive to changes in source resistance and thus are better suited to designs in which this is an important issue.

Figure 14.27 summarizes the two *RLC* bandpass filters we have studied. Note that the expressions for the circuit transfer functions have the same form. As we have done previously, we can create a general form for the transfer functions of these two bandpass filters:

$$H(s) = \frac{\beta s}{s^2 + \beta s + \omega_o^2}. \tag{14.38}$$

Any circuit with the transfer function in Eq. 14.38 acts as a bandpass filter with a center frequency ω_o and a bandwidth β.

In Example 14.7, we saw that the transfer function can also be written in the form

$$H(s) = \frac{K\beta s}{s^2 + \beta s + \omega_o^2}, \tag{14.39}$$

where the values for K and β depend on whether the series resistance of the voltage source is zero or nonzero.

Relating the Frequency Domain to the Time Domain

We can identify a relationship between the parameters that characterize the frequency response of RLC bandpass filters and the parameters that characterize the time response of RLC circuits. Consider the series RLC circuit in Fig. 14.19(a). In Chapter 8 we discovered that the natural response of this circuit is characterized by the neper frequency (α) and the resonant frequency (ω_o). These parameters were expressed in terms of the circuit components in Eqs. 8.58 and 8.59, which are repeated here for convenience:

$$\alpha = \frac{R}{2L} \text{ rad/s}, \tag{14.40}$$

$$\omega_o = \sqrt{\frac{1}{LC}} \text{ rad/s}. \tag{14.41}$$

We see that the same parameter ω_o is used to characterize both the time response and the frequency response. That's why the center frequency is also called the resonant frequency. The bandwidth and the neper frequency are related by the equation

$$\beta = 2\alpha. \tag{14.42}$$

Recall that the natural response of a series RLC circuit may be underdamped, overdamped, or critically damped. The transition from overdamped to underdamped occurs when $\omega_o^2 = \alpha^2$. Consider the relationship between α and β from Eq. 14.42 and the definition of the quality factor Q. The transition from an overdamped to an underdamped response occurs when $Q = 1/2$. Thus, a circuit whose frequency response contains a sharp peak at ω_o, indicating a high Q and a narrow bandwidth, will have an underdamped natural response. Conversely, a circuit whose frequency response has a broad bandwidth and a low Q will have an overdamped natural response.

✓ ASSESSMENT PROBLEMS

Objective 3—Know the *RLC* circuit configurations that act as bandpass filters

14.6   Using the circuit in Fig. 14.19(a), compute the values of R and L to give a bandpass filter with a center frequency of 12 kHz and a quality factor of 6. Use a 0.1 μF capacitor.

Answer: $L = 1.76$ mH, $R = 22.10 \ \Omega$.

14.7   Using the circuit in Fig. 14.22, compute the values of L and C to give a bandpass filter with a center frequency of 2 kHz and a bandwidth of 500 Hz. Use a 250 Ω resistor.

Answer: $L = 4.97$ mH, $C = 1.27 \ \mu$F.

NOTE: Also try Chapter Problems 14.18 and 14.25.

14.8   Recalculate the component values for the circuit in Example 14.6(d) so that the frequency response of the resulting circuit is unchanged using a 0.2 μF capacitor.

Answer: $L = 5.07$ mH, $R = 3.98$ kΩ.

14.9   Recalculate the component values for the circuit in Example 14.6(d) so that the quality factor of the resulting circuit is unchanged but the center frequency has been moved to 2 kHz. Use a 0.2 μF capacitor.

Answer: $R = 9.95$ kΩ, $L = 31.66$ mH.

14.5 Bandreject Filters

We turn now to the last of the four filter categories—the bandreject filter. This filter passes source voltages outside the band between the two cutoff frequencies to the output (the passband), and attenuates source voltages

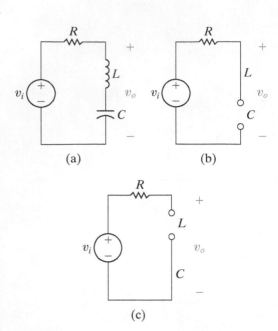

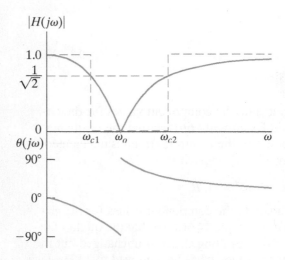

Figure 14.28 ▲ (a) A series RLC bandreject filter. (b) The equivalent circuit for $\omega = 0$. (c) The equivalent circuit for $\omega = \infty$.

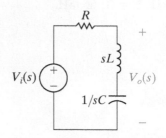

Figure 14.29 ▲ The frequency response plot for the series RLC bandreject filter circuit in Fig. 14.28(a).

Figure 14.30 ▲ The s-domain equivalent of the circuit in Fig. 14.28(a).

before they reach the output at frequencies between the two cutoff frequencies (the stopband). Bandpass filters and bandreject filters thus perform complementary functions in the frequency domain.

Bandreject filters are characterized by the same parameters as bandpass filters: the two cutoff frequencies, the center frequency, the bandwidth, and the quality factor. Again, only two of these five parameters can be specified independently.

In the next sections, we examine two circuits that function as bandreject filters and then compute equations that relate the circuit component values to the characteristic parameters for each circuit.

The Series RLC Circuit—Qualitative Analysis

Figure 14.28(a) shows a series RLC circuit. Although the circuit components and connections are identical to those in the series RLC bandpass filter in Fig. 14.19(a), the circuit in Fig. 14.28(a) has an important difference: the output voltage is now defined across the inductor-capacitor pair. As we saw in the case of low- and high-pass filters, the same circuit may perform two different filtering functions, depending on the definition of the output voltage.

We have already noted that at $\omega = 0$, the inductor behaves like a short circuit and the capacitor behaves like an open circuit, but at $\omega = \infty$, these roles switch. Figure 14.28(b) presents the equivalent circuit for $\omega = 0$; Fig. 14.28(c) presents the equivalent circuit for $\omega = \infty$. In both equivalent circuits, the output voltage is defined over an effective open circuit, and thus the output and input voltages have the same magnitude. This series RLC bandreject filter circuit then has two passbands—one below a lower cutoff frequency, and the other above an upper cutoff frequency.

Between these two passbands, both the inductor and the capacitor have finite impedances of opposite signs. As the frequency is increased from zero, the impedance of the inductor increases and that of the capacitor decreases. Therefore the phase shift between the input and the output approaches $-90°$ as ωL approaches $1/\omega C$. As soon as ωL exceeds $1/\omega C$, the phase shift jumps to $+90°$ and then approaches zero as ω continues to increase.

At some frequency between the two passbands, the impedances of the inductor and capacitor are equal but of opposite sign. At this frequency, the series combination of the inductor and capacitor is that of a short circuit, so the magnitude of the output voltage must be zero. This is the center frequency of this series RLC bandreject filter.

Figure 14.29 presents a sketch of the frequency response of the series RLC bandreject filter from Fig. 14.28(a). Note that the magnitude plot is overlaid with that of the ideal bandreject filter from Fig. 14.3(d). Our qualitative analysis has confirmed the shape of the magnitude and phase angle plots. We now turn to a quantitative analysis of the circuit to confirm this frequency response and to compute values for the parameters that characterize this response.

The Series RLC Circuit—Quantitative Analysis

After transforming to the s-domain, as shown in Fig. 14.30, we use voltage division to construct an equation for the transfer function:

$$H(s) = \frac{sL + \dfrac{1}{sC}}{R + sL + \dfrac{1}{sC}} = \frac{s^2 + \dfrac{1}{LC}}{s^2 + \dfrac{R}{L}s + \dfrac{1}{LC}}. \tag{14.43}$$

Substitute $j\omega$ for s in Eq. 14.43 and generate equations for the transfer function magnitude and the phase angle:

$$|H(j\omega)| = \frac{\left|\dfrac{1}{LC} - \omega^2\right|}{\sqrt{\left(\dfrac{1}{LC} - \omega^2\right)^2 + \left(\dfrac{\omega R}{L}\right)^2}}, \qquad (14.44)$$

$$\theta(j\omega) = -\tan^{-1}\left(\frac{\dfrac{\omega R}{L}}{\dfrac{1}{LC} - \omega^2}\right). \qquad (14.45)$$

Note that Eqs. 14.44 and 14.45 confirm the frequency response shape pictured in Fig. 14.29, which we developed based on the qualitative analysis.

We use the circuit in Fig. 14.30 to calculate the center frequency. For the bandreject filter, the center frequency is still defined as the frequency for which the sum of the impedances of the capacitor and inductor is zero. In the bandpass filter, the magnitude at the center frequency was a maximum, but in the bandreject filter, this magnitude is a minimum. This is because in the bandreject filter, the center frequency is not in the passband; rather, it is in the stopband. It is easy to show that the center frequency is given by

$$\omega_o = \sqrt{\frac{1}{LC}}. \qquad (14.46)$$

Substituting Eq. 14.46 into Eq. 14.44 shows that $|H(j\omega_o)| = 0$.

The cutoff frequencies, the bandwidth, and the quality factor are defined for the bandreject filter in exactly the way they were for the bandpass filters. Compute the cutoff frequencies by substituting the constant $(1/\sqrt{2})H_{max}$ for the left-hand side of Eq. 14.44 and then solving for ω_{c1} and ω_{c2}. Note that for the bandreject filter, $H_{max} = |H(j0)| = |H(j\infty)|$, and for the series RLC bandreject filter in Fig. 14.28(a), $H_{max} = 1$. Thus,

$$\omega_{c1} = -\frac{R}{2L} + \sqrt{\left(\frac{R}{2L}\right)^2 + \frac{1}{LC}}, \qquad (14.47)$$

$$\omega_{c2} = \frac{R}{2L} + \sqrt{\left(\frac{R}{2L}\right)^2 + \frac{1}{LC}}. \qquad (14.48)$$

Use the cutoff frequencies to generate an expression for the bandwidth, β:

$$\beta = R/L. \qquad (14.49)$$

Finally, the center frequency and the bandwidth produce an equation for the quality factor, Q:

$$Q = \sqrt{\frac{L}{R^2 C}}. \qquad (14.50)$$

Again, we can represent the expressions for the two cutoff frequencies in terms of the bandwidth and center frequency, as we did for the band-pass filter:

$$\omega_{c1} = -\frac{\beta}{2} + \sqrt{\left(\frac{\beta}{2}\right)^2 + \omega_o^2}, \tag{14.51}$$

$$\omega_{c2} = \frac{\beta}{2} + \sqrt{\left(\frac{\beta}{2}\right)^2 + \omega_o^2}. \tag{14.52}$$

Alternative forms for these equations express the cutoff frequencies in terms of the quality factor and the center frequency:

$$\omega_{c1} = \omega_o \cdot \left[-\frac{1}{2Q} + \sqrt{1 + \left(\frac{1}{2Q}\right)^2} \right], \tag{14.53}$$

$$\omega_{c2} = \omega_o \cdot \left[\frac{1}{2Q} + \sqrt{1 + \left(\frac{1}{2Q}\right)^2} \right]. \tag{14.54}$$

Example 14.8 presents the design of a series RLC bandreject filter.

Example 14.8 **Designing a Series RLC Bandreject Filter**

Using the series RLC circuit in Fig. 14.28(a), compute the component values that yield a bandreject filter with a bandwidth of 250 Hz and a center frequency of 750 Hz. Use a 100 nF capacitor. Compute values for $R, L, \omega_{c1}, \omega_{c2}$, and Q.

Solution

We begin by using the definition of quality factor to compute its value for this filter:

$$Q = \omega_o / \beta = 3.$$

Use Eq. 14.46 to compute L, remembering to convert ω_o to radians per second:

$$L = \frac{1}{\omega_o^2 C}$$

$$= \frac{1}{[2\pi(750)]^2(100 \times 10^{-9})}$$

$$= 450 \text{ mH}.$$

Use Eq. 14.49 to calculate R:

$$R = \beta L$$

$$= 2\pi(250)(450 \times 10^{-3})$$

$$= 707 \ \Omega.$$

The values for the center frequency and bandwidth can be used in Eqs. 14.51 and 14.52 to compute the two cutoff frequencies:

$$\omega_{c1} = -\frac{\beta}{2} + \sqrt{\left(\frac{\beta}{2}\right)^2 + \omega_o^2}$$

$$= 3992.0 \text{ rad/s},$$

$$\omega_{c2} = \frac{\beta}{2} + \sqrt{\left(\frac{\beta}{2}\right)^2 + \omega_o^2}$$

$$= 5562.8 \text{ rad/s}.$$

The cutoff frequencies are at 635.3 Hz and 885.3 Hz. Their difference is $885.3 - 635.3 = 250$ Hz, confirming the specified bandwidth. The geometric mean is $\sqrt{(635.3)(885.3)} = 750$ Hz, confirming the specified center frequency.

As you might suspect by now, another configuration that produces a bandreject filter is a parallel *RLC* circuit. Whereas the analysis details of the parallel *RLC* circuit are left to Problem 14.37, the results are summarized in Fig. 14.31, along with the series *RLC* bandreject filter. As we did for other categories of filters, we can state a general form for the transfer functions of bandreject filters, replacing the constant terms with β and ω_o:

$$H(s) = \frac{s^2 + \omega_o^2}{s^2 + \beta s + \omega_o^2}.$$ (14.55) ◀ **Transfer function for *RLC* bandreject filter**

Equation 14.55 is useful in filter design, because any circuit with a transfer function in this form can be used as a bandreject filter.

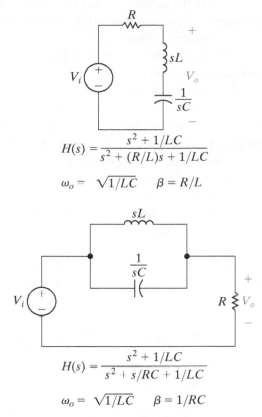

$$H(s) = \frac{s^2 + 1/LC}{s^2 + (R/L)s + 1/LC}$$

$$\omega_o = \sqrt{1/LC} \quad \beta = R/L$$

$$H(s) = \frac{s^2 + 1/LC}{s^2 + s/RC + 1/LC}$$

$$\omega_o = \sqrt{1/LC} \quad \beta = 1/RC$$

Figure 14.31 ▲ Two *RLC* bandreject filters, together with equations for the transfer function, center frequency, and bandwidth of each.

✓ ASSESSMENT PROBLEMS

Objective 4—Know the *RLC* circuit configurations that act as bandreject filters

14.10 Design the component values for the series *RLC* bandreject filter shown in Fig. 14.28(a) so that the center frequency is 4 kHz and the quality factor is 5. Use a 500 nF capacitor.

Answer: $L = 3.17\,\text{mH}$,

$R = 15.92\,\Omega$.

14.11 Recompute the component values for Assessment Problem 14.10 to achieve a bandreject filter with a center frequency of 20 kHz. The filter has a 100 Ω resistor. The quality factor remains at 5.

Answer: $L = 3.98\,\text{mH}$,

$C = 15.92\,\text{nF}$.

NOTE: Also try Chapter Problems 14.38 and 14.42.

Practical Perspective

Pushbutton Telephone Circuits

In the Practical Perspective at the start of this chapter, we described the dual-tone-multiple-frequency (DTMF) system used to signal that a button has been pushed on a pushbutton telephone. A key element of the DTMF system is the DTMF receiver—a circuit that decodes the tones produced by pushing a button and determines which button was pushed.

In order to design a DTMF reciever, we need a better understanding of the DTMF system. As you can see from Fig. 14.32, the buttons on the telephone are organized into rows and columns. The pair of tones generated by pushing a button depends on the button's row and column. The button's row determines its low-frequency tone, and the button's column determines its high-frequency tone.[1] For example, pressing the "6" button produces sinusoidal tones with the frequencies 770 Hz and 1477 Hz.

At the telephone switching facility, bandpass filters in the DTMF receiver first detect whether tones from both the low-frequency and high-frequency groups are simultaneously present. This test rejects many extraneous audio signals that are not DTMF. If tones are present in both bands, other filters are used to select among the possible tones in each band so that the frequencies can be decoded into a unique button signal. Additional tests are performed to prevent false button detection. For example, only one tone per frequency band is allowed; the high- and low-band frequencies must start and stop within a few milliseconds of one another to be considered valid; and the high- and low-band signal amplitudes must be sufficiently close to each other.

You may wonder why bandpass filters are used instead of a high-pass filter for the high-frequency group of DTMF tones and a low-pass filter for the low-frequency group of DTMF tones. The reason is that the telephone system uses frequencies outside of the 300–3 kHz band for other signaling purposes, such as ringing the phone's bell. Bandpass filters prevent the DTMF receiver from erroneously detecting these other signals.

NOTE: Assess your understanding of this Practical Perspective by trying Chapter Problems 14.51–14.53.

---

[1] A fourth high-frequency tone is reserved at 1633 Hz. This tone is used infrequently and is not produced by a standard 12-button telephone.

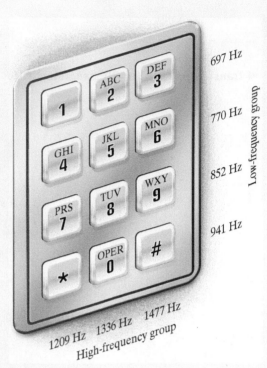

Figure 14.32 ▲ Tones generated by the rows and columns of telephone pushbuttons.

Summary

- A **frequency selective circuit**, or **filter**, enables signals at certain frequencies to reach the output, and it attenuates signals at other frequencies to prevent them from reaching the output. The **passband** contains the frequencies of those signals that are passed; the **stopband** contains the frequencies of those signals that are attenuated. (See page 522.)

- The **cutoff frequency**, ω_c, identifies the location on the frequency axis that separates the stopband from the passband. At the cutoff frequency, the magnitude of the transfer function equals $(1/\sqrt{2})H_{\max}$. (See page 525.)

- A **low-pass filter** passes voltages at frequencies below ω_c and attenuates frequencies above ω_c. Any circuit with the transfer function

$$H(s) = \frac{\omega_c}{s + \omega_c}$$

functions as a low-pass filter. (See page 529.)

• A **high-pass filter** passes voltages at frequencies above and attenuates voltages at frequencies below Any circuit with the transfer function

$$H(s) = \frac{s}{s + \omega_c}$$

functions as a high-pass filter. (See page 534.)

• Bandpass filters and bandreject filters each have two cutoff frequencies, ω_{c1} and ω_{c2}. These filters are further characterized by their **center frequency** (ω_o), **bandwidth** (β), and **quality factor** (Q). These quantities are defined as

$$\omega_o = \sqrt{\omega_{c1} \cdot \omega_{c2}},$$

$$\beta = \omega_{c2} - \omega_{c1},$$

$$Q = \omega_o/\beta.$$

(See pages 537–538.)

• A **bandpass filter** passes voltages at frequencies within the passband, which is between ω_{c1} and ω_{c2}. It attenuates frequencies outside of the passband. Any circuit with the transfer function

$$H(s) = \frac{\beta s}{s^2 + \beta s + \omega_o^2}$$

functions as a bandpass filter. (See page 542.)

• A **bandreject filter** attenuates voltages at frequencies within the stopband, which is between ω_{c1} and ω_{c2}. It passes frequencies outside of the stopband. Any circuit with the transfer function

$$H(s) = \frac{s^2 + \omega_o^2}{s^2 + \beta s + \omega_o^2}$$

functions as a bandreject filter. (See page 549.)

• Adding a load to the output of a passive filter changes its filtering properties by altering the location and magnitude of the passband. Replacing an ideal voltage source with one whose source resistance is nonzero also changes the filtering properties of the rest of the circuit, again by altering the location and magnitude of the passband. (See page 540.)

Problems

Section 14.2

14.1 a) Find the cutoff frequency in hertz for the *RL* filter shown in Fig. P14.1.

b) Calculate $H(j\omega)$ at ω_c, $0.125\omega_c$, and $8\omega_c$.

c) If $v_i = 20 \cos \omega t$ V, write the steady-state expression for v_o when $\omega = \omega_c$, $\omega = 0.125\omega_c$, and $\omega = 8\omega_c$.

Figure P14.1

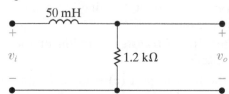

14.2 a) Find the cutoff frequency (in hertz) of the low-pass filter shown in Fig. P14.2.

b) Calculate $H(j\omega)$ at ω_c, $0.1\omega_c$, and $10\omega_c$.

c) If $v_i = 25 \cos \omega t$ mV, write the steady-state expression for v_o when $\omega = \omega_c$, $0.1\omega_c$, and $10\omega_c$.

Figure P14.2

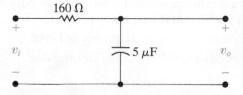

14.3 A resistor, denoted as R_l, is added in series with the inductor in the circuit in Fig. 14.4(a). The new low-pass filter circuit is shown in Fig. P14.3.

a) Derive the expression for $H(s)$ where $H(s) = V_o/V_i$.

b) At what frequency will the magnitude of $H(j\omega)$ be maximum?

c) What is the maximum value of the magnitude of $H(j\omega)$?

d) At what frequency will the magnitude of $H(j\omega)$ equal its maximum value divided by $\sqrt{2}$?

e) Assume a resistance of 300 Ω is added in series with the 50 mH inductor in the circuit in Fig. P14.1. Find ω_c, $H(j0)$, $H(j\omega_c)$, $H(j0.2\omega_c)$, and $H(j5\omega_c)$.

Figure P14.3

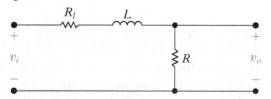

14.4 A resistor denoted as R_L is connected in parallel with the capacitor in the circuit in Fig. 14.7. The loaded low-pass filter circuit is shown in Fig. P14.7.

a) Derive the expression for the voltage transfer function V_o/V_i.

b) At what frequency will the magnitude of $H(j\omega)$ be maximum?

c) What is the maximum value of the magnitude of $H(j\omega)$?

d) At what frequency will the magnitude of $H(j\omega)$ equal its maximum value divided by $\sqrt{2}$?

e) Assume a resistance of 320 Ω is added in parallel with the 5 μF capacitor in the circuit in Fig. P14.4. Find ω_c, $H(j0)$, $H(j\omega_c)$, $H(j0.2\omega_c)$, and $H(j5\omega_c)$.

Figure P14.4

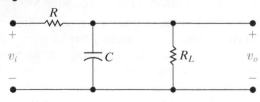

14.5 Study the circuit shown in Fig. P14.5 (without the load resistor).

a) As $\omega \rightarrow 0$, the inductor behaves like what circuit component? What value will the output voltage v_0 have?

b) As $\omega \rightarrow \infty$, the inductor behaves like what circuit component? What value will the output voltage v_0 have?

c) Based on parts (a) and (b), what type of filtering does this circuit exhibit?

d) What is the transfer function of the unloaded filter?

e) If $R = 330$ Ω and $L = 10$ mH, what is the cutoff frequency of the filter in rad/s?

Figure P14.5

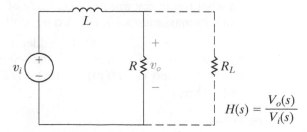

$$H(s) = \frac{V_o(s)}{V_i(s)}$$

14.6 Suppose we wish to add a load resistor in parallel with the resistor in the circuit shown in Fig. P14.5.

a) What is the transfer function of the loaded filter?

b) Compare the transfer function of the unloaded filter (part (d) of Problem 14.5) and the transfer function of the loaded filter (part (a) of Problem 14.6). Are the cutoff frequencies different? Are the passband gains different?

c) What is the smallest value of load resistance that can be used with the filter from Problem 14.5(e) such that the cutoff frequency of the resulting filter is no more than 5% different from the unloaded filter?

14.7 Use a 1 mH inductor to design a low-pass, RL, passive filter with a cutoff frequency of 5 kHz.

a) Specify the value of the resistor.

b) A load having a resistance of 68 Ω is connected across the output terminals of the filter. What is the corner, or cutoff, frequency of the loaded filter in hertz?

c) If you must use a single resistor from Appendix H for part (a), what resistor should you use? What is the resulting cutoff frequency of the filter?

Section 14.3

14.8 Use a 10 mH inductor to design a low-pass passive filter with a cutoff frequency of 1600 rad/s.

a) Specify the cutoff frequency in hertz.

b) Specify the value of the filter resistor.

c) Assume the cutoff frequency cannot decrease by more than 10%. What is the smallest value of load resistance that can be connected across the output terminals of the filter?

d) If the resistor found in (c) is connected across the output terminals, what is the magnitude of $H(j\omega)$ when $\omega = 0$?

14.9 Design a passive RC low pass filter (see Fig. 14.7) with a cutoff frequency of 100 Hz using a 4.7 μF capacitor.

a) What is the cutoff frequency in rad/s?

b) What is the value of the resistor?

c) Draw your circuit, labeling the component values and output voltage.

d) What is the transfer function of the filter in part (c)?

e) If the filter in part (c) is loaded with a resistor whose value is the same as the resistor part (b), what is the transfer function of this loaded filter?

f) What is the cutoff frequency of the loaded filter from part (e)?

g) What is the gain in the pass band of the loaded filter from part (e)?

14.10 Use a 500 nF capacitor to design a low-pass passive filter with a cutoff frequency of 50 krad/s.

a) Specify the cutoff frequency in hertz.

b) Specify the value of the filter resistor.

c) Assume the cutoff frequency cannot increase by more than 5%. What is the smallest value of load resistance that can be connected across the output terminals of the filter?

d) If the resistor found in (c) is connected across the output terminals, what is the magnitude of $H(j\omega)$ when $\omega = 0$?

Section 14.3

14.11 a) Find the cutoff frequency (in hertz) for the high-pass filter shown in Fig. P14.11.

b) Find $H(j\omega)$ at ω_c, $0.125\omega_c$, and $8\omega_c$.

c) If $v_i = 75 \cos \omega t$ V, write the steady-state expression for v_o when $\omega = \omega_c$, $\omega = 0.125\omega_c$, and $\omega = 8\omega_c$.

Figure P14.11

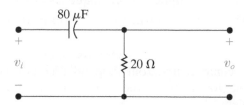

14.12 A resistor, denoted as R_c, is connected in series with the capacitor in the circuit in Fig. 14.11(a). The new high-pass filter circuit is shown in Fig. P14.12.

a) Derive the expression for $H(s)$ where $H(s) = V_o/V_i$.

b) At what frequency will the magnitude of $H(j\omega)$ be maximum?

c) What is the maximum value of the magnitude of $H(j\omega)$?

d) At what frequency will the magnitude of $H(j\omega)$ equal its maximum value divided by $\sqrt{2}$?

e) Assume a resistance of 5 Ω is connected in series with the 80 μF capacitor in the circuit in Fig. P14.11. Calculate ω_c, $H(j\omega_c)$, $H(j0.125\omega_c)$, and $H(j8\omega_c)$.

Figure P14.12

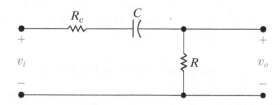

14.13 Using a 100 nF capacitor, design a high-pass passive filter with a cutoff frequency of 300 Hz.

DESIGN
PROBLEM
PSPICE
MULTISIM

a) Specify the value of R in kilohms.

b) A 47 kΩ resistor is connected across the output terminals of the filter. What is the cutoff frequency, in hertz, of the loaded filter?

14.14 Consider the circuit shown in Fig. P14.14.

a) With the input and output voltages shown in the figure, this circuit behaves like what type of filter?

b) What is the transfer function, $H(s) = V_o(s)/V_i(s)$, of this filter?

c) What is the cutoff frequency of this filter?

d) What is the magnitude of the filter's transfer function at $s = j\omega_c$?

Figure P14.14

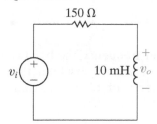

14.15 Suppose a 150 Ω load resistor is attached to the filter in Fig. P14.14.

a) What is the transfer function, $H(s) = V_o(s)/V_i(s)$, of this filter?

b) What is the cutoff frequency of this filter?

c) How does the cutoff frequency of the loaded filter compare with the cutoff frequency of the unloaded filter in Fig. P14.14?

d) What else is different for these two filters?

14.16 Design a passive RC high pass filter (see Fig. 14.10[a]) with a cutoff frequency of 500 Hz using a 220 pF capacitor.

a) What is the cutoff frequency in rad/s?

b) What is the value of the resistor?

c) Draw your circuit, labeling the component values and output voltage.

d) What is the transfer function of the filter in part (c)?

e) If the filter in part (c) is loaded with a resistor whose value is the same as the resistor in (b), what is the transfer function of this loaded filter?

f) What is the cutoff frequency of the loaded filter from part (e)?

g) What is the gain in the pass band of the loaded filter from part (e)?

14.17 Using a 100 μH inductor, design a high-pass, RL, passive filter with a cutoff frequency of 1500 krad/s.

DESIGN
PROBLEM
PSPICE
MULTISIM

a) Specify the value of the resistance, selecting from the components in Appendix H.

b) Assume the filter is connected to a pure resistive load. The cutoff frequency is not to drop below 1200 krad/s. What is the smallest load resistor from Appendix H that can be connected across the output terminals of the filter?

Section 14.4

14.18 For the bandpass filter shown in Fig. P14.18, find
PSPICE (a) ω_o, (b) f_o, (c) Q, (d) ω_{c1}, (e) f_{c1}, (f) ω_{c2}, (g) f_{c2},
MULTISIM and (h) β.

Figure P14.18

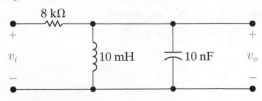

14.19 Calculate the center frequency, the bandwidth, and the quality factor of a bandpass filter that has an upper cutoff frequency of 121 krad/s and a lower cutoff frequency of 100 krad/s.

14.20 A bandpass filter has a center, or resonant, frequency of 50 krad/s and a quality factor of 4. Find the bandwidth, the upper cutoff frequency, and the lower cutoff frequency. Express all answers in kilohertz.

14.21 Design a series RLC bandpass filter (see Fig. 14.19[a]) with a quality of 8 and a center frequency of 50 krad/s, using a 0.01 μF capacitor.

a) Draw your circuit, labeling the component values and output voltage.

b) For the filter in part (a), calculate the bandwidth and the values of the two cutoff frequencies.

14.22 The input to the series RLC bandpass filter designed in Problem 14.21 is 5cosωt V. Find the voltage drop across the resistor when (a) $\omega = \omega_o$; (b) $\omega = \omega_{c1}$; (c) $\omega = \omega_{c2}$; (d) $\omega = 0.1\omega_o$; (e) $\omega = 10\omega_o$.

14.23 The input to the series RLC bandpass filter designed in Problem 14.21 is 5cosωt V. Find the voltage drop across the series combination of the inductor and capacitor when (a) $\omega = \omega_o$; (b) $\omega = \omega_{c1}$; (c) $\omega = \omega_{c2}$; (d) $\omega = 0.1\omega_o$; (e) $\omega = 10\omega_o$.

14.24 Show that the alternative forms for the cutoff frequencies of a bandpass filter, given in Eqs. 14.36 and 14.37, can be derived from Eqs. 14.34 and 14.35.

14.25 Using a 50 nF capacitor in the bandpass circuit
DESIGN shown in Fig. 14.22, design a filter with a quality fac-
PROBLEM tor of 5 and a center frequency of 20 krad/s.
PSPICE
MULTISIM a) Specify the numerical values of R and L.

b) Calculate the upper and lower cutoff frequencies in kilohertz.

c) Calculate the bandwidth in hertz.

14.26 Design a series RLC bandpass filter using only three components from Appendix H that comes closest to meeting the filter specifications in Problem 14.25.

a) Draw your filter, labeling all component values and the input and output voltages.

b) Calculate the percent error in this new filter's center frequency and quality factor when compared to the values specified in Problem 14.25.

14.27 Use a 5 nF capacitor to design a series RLC band-
DESIGN pass filter, as shown at the top of Fig. 14.27. The cen-
PROBLEM ter frequency of the filter is 8 kHz, and the quality
PSPICE factor is 2.
MULTISIM

a) Specify the values of R and L.

b) What is the lower cutoff frequency in kilohertz?

c) What is the upper cutoff frequency in kilohertz?

d) What is the bandwidth of the filter in kilohertz?

14.28 Design a series RLC bandpass filter using only three components from Appendix H that comes closest to meeting the filter specifications in Problem 14.27.

a) Draw your filter, labeling all component values and the input and output voltages.

b) Calculate the percent error in this new filter's center frequency and quality factor when compared to the values specified in Problem 14.27.

14.29 For the bandpass filter shown in Fig. P14.29, calculate
PSPICE the following: (a) f_o; (b) Q; (c) f_{c1}; (d) f_{c2}; and (e) β.
MULTISIM

Figure P14.29

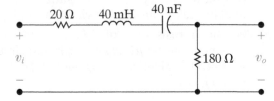

14.30 The input voltage in the circuit in Fig. P14.29 is 10 cos ωt V. Calculate the output voltage when (a) $\omega = \omega_o$; (b) $\omega = \omega_{c1}$; and (c) $\omega = \omega_{c2}$.

14.31 Consider the circuit shown in Fig. P14.31.
PSPICE
MULTISIM a) Find ω_o.

b) Find β.

c) Find Q.

d) Find the steady-state expression for v_o when $v_i = 250 \cos \omega_o t$ mV.

e) Show that if R_L is expressed in kilohms the Q of the circuit in Fig. P14.31 is

$$Q = \frac{20}{1 + 100/R_L}$$

f) Plot Q versus R_L for $20 \text{ k}\Omega \leq R_L \leq 2 \text{ M}\Omega$.

Figure P14.31

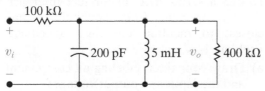
100 kΩ

14.32 A block diagram of a system consisting of a sinusoidal voltage source, an RLC series bandpass filter, and a load is shown in Fig. P14.32. The internal impedance of the sinusoidal source is $80 + j0 \ \Omega$, and the impedance of the load is $480 + j0 \ \Omega$.

The RLC series bandpass filter has a 20 nF capacitor, a center frequency of 50 krad/s, and a quality factor of 6.25.

a) Draw a circuit diagram of the system.

b) Specify the numerical values of L and R for the filter section of the system.

c) What is the quality factor of the interconnected system?

d) What is the bandwidth (in hertz) of the interconnected system?

Figure P14.32

14.33 The purpose of this problem is to investigate how a resistive load connected across the output terminals of the bandpass filter shown in Fig. 14.19 affects the quality factor and hence the bandwidth of the filtering system. The loaded filter circuit is shown in Fig. P14.33.

a) Calculate the transfer function V_o/V_i for the circuit shown in Fig. P14.33.

b) What is the expression for the bandwidth of the system?

c) What is the expression for the loaded bandwidth (β_L) as a function of the unloaded bandwidth (β_U)?

d) What is the expression for the quality factor of the system?

e) What is the expression for the loaded quality factor (Q_L) as a function of the unloaded quality factor (Q_U)?

f) What are the expressions for the cutoff frequencies ω_{c1} and ω_{c2}?

Figure P14.33

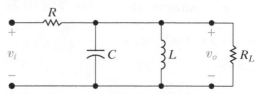

14.34 The parameters in the circuit in Fig. P14.33 are $R = 2.4 \text{ k}\Omega$, $C = 50 \text{ pF}$, and $L = 2 \ \mu\text{H}$. The quality factor of the circuit is not to drop below 7.5. What is the smallest permissible value of the load resistor R_L?

Section 14.5

14.35 For the bandreject filter in Fig. P14.35, calculate (a) ω_o; (b) f_o; (c) Q; (d) β in hertz; (e) ω_{c1}; (f) f_{c1}; (g) ω_{c2}; and (h) f_{c2}.

Figure P14.35

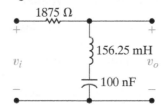
1875 Ω
156.25 mH
100 nF

14.36 For the bandreject filter in Fig. P14.35,

a) Find $H(j\omega)$ at ω_o, ω_{c1}, ω_{c2}, $0.1\omega_o$, and $10\omega_o$.

b) If $v_i = 80 \cos \omega t$ V, write the steady-state expression for v_o when $\omega = \omega_o$, $\omega = \omega_{c1}$, $\omega = \omega_{c2}$, $\omega = 0.1\omega_o$, and $\omega = 10\omega_o$.

14.37 a) Show (via a qualitative analysis) that the circuit in Fig. P14.37 is a bandreject filter.

b) Support the qualitative analysis of (a) by finding the voltage transfer function of the filter.

c) Derive the expression for the center frequency of the filter.

d) Derive the expressions for the cutoff frequencies ω_{c1} and ω_{c2}.

e) What is the expression for the bandwidth of the filter?

f) What is the expression for the quality factor of the circuit?

Figure P14.37

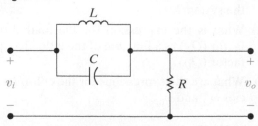

14.38 For the bandreject filter in Fig. P14.38, calculate
(a) ω_o; (b) f_o; (c) Q; (d) ω_{c1}; (e) f_{c1}; (f) ω_{c2}; (g) f_{c2};
and (h) β in kilohertz.

Figure P14.38

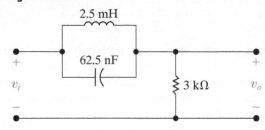

14.39 Design an RLC bandreject filter (see Fig. 14.28[a])
with a quality of 2.5 and a center frequency of
25 krad/s, using a 200 nF capacitor.

   a) Draw your circuit, labeling the component values and output voltage.

   b) For the filter in part (a), calculate the bandwidth and the values of the two cutoff frequencies.

14.40 The input to the RLC bandreject filter designed in
Problem 14.39 is $10\cos\omega t$ V. Find the voltage drop
across the series combination of the inductor and
capacitor when (a) $\omega = \omega_o$; (b) $\omega = \omega_{c1}$;
(c) $\omega = \omega_{c2}$; (d) $\omega = 0.125\omega_o$; (e) $\omega = 8\omega_o$.

14.41 The input to the RLC bandreject filter designed in
Problem 14.39 is $10\cos\omega t$ V. Find the voltage drop
across the resistor when (a) $\omega = \omega_o$; (b) $\omega = \omega_{c1}$;
(c) $\omega = \omega_{c2}$; (d) $\omega = 0.125\omega_o$; (e) $\omega = 8\omega_o$.

14.42 Use a 500 nF capacitor to design a bandreject filter,
as shown in Fig. P14.42. The filter has a center frequency of 4 kHz and a quality factor of 5.

   a) Specify the numerical values of R and L.

   b) Calculate the upper and lower corner, or cutoff, frequencies in kilohertz.

   c) Calculate the filter bandwidth in kilohertz.

Figure P14.42

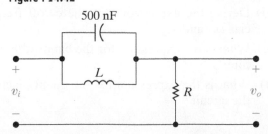

14.43 Assume the bandreject filter in Problem 14.42 is
loaded with a 1 kΩ resistor.

   a) What is the quality factor of the loaded circuit?

   b) What is the bandwidth (in kilohertz) of the loaded circuit?

   c) What is the upper cutoff frequency in kilohertz?

   d) What is the lower cutoff frequency in kilohertz?

14.44 Design a series RLC bandreject filter using only
three components from Appendix H that comes
closest to meeting the filter specifications in
Problem 14.42.

   a) Draw your filter, labeling all component values
   and the input and output voltages.

   b) Calculate the percent error in this new filter's
   center frequency and quality factor when compared to the values specified in Problem 14.42.

14.45 The purpose of this problem is to investigate how a
resistive load connected across the output terminals
of the bandreject filter shown in Fig. 14.28(a) affects
the behavior of the filter. The loaded filter circuit is
shown in Fig. P14.45.

   a) Find the voltage transfer function V_o/V_i.

   b) What is the expression for the center frequency?

   c) What is the expression for the bandwidth?

   d) What is the expression for the quality factor?

   e) Evaluate $H(j\omega_o)$.

   f) Evaluate $H(j0)$.

   g) Evaluate $H(j\infty)$.

   h) What are the expressions for the corner frequencies ω_{c1} and ω_{c2}?

Figure P14.45

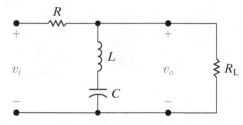

14.46 The parameters in the circuit in Fig. P14.45
are $R = 30\ \Omega$, $L = 1\ \mu H$, $C = 4\ pF$, and
$R_L = 150\ \Omega$.

   a) Find ω_o, β (in kilohertz), and Q.

   b) Find $H(j0)$ and $H(j\infty)$.

   c) Find f_{c2} and f_{c1}.

   d) Show that if R_L is expressed in ohms the Q of
   the circuit is

$$Q = \frac{50}{3}[1 + (30/R_L)].$$

   e) Plot Q versus R_L for $10\ \Omega \le R_L \le 300\ \Omega$.

14.47 The load in the bandreject filter circuit shown in
Fig. P14.42 is 500 Ω. The center frequency of the fil-

PSPICE
MULTISIM

ter is 25 krad/s, and the capacitor is 25 nF. At very
low and very high frequencies, the amplitude of the
sinusoidal output voltage should be at least 90% of
the amplitude of the sinusoidal input voltage.

a) Specify the numerical values of R and L.

b) What is the quality factor of the circuit?

Sections 14.1–14.5

14.48 Given the following voltage transfer function:

$$H(s) = \frac{V_o}{V_i}$$

$$= \frac{25 \times 10^6}{s^2 + 1000s + 25 \times 10^6}.$$

a) At what frequencies (in radians per second) is
the magnitude of the transfer function equal to
unity?

b) At what frequency is the magnitude of the transfer function maximum?

c) What is the maximum value of the transfer function magnitude?

14.49 Consider the series RLC circuit shown in
Fig. P14.49. When the output is the voltage
across the resistor, we know this circuit is a
bandpass filter. When the output is the voltage
across the series combination of the inductor
and capacitor, we know this circuit is a bandreject filter. This problem investigates the
behavior of this circuit when the output is across
the inductor.

a) Find the transfer function, $H(s) = V_o(s)/V_i(s)$
when $V_o(s)$ is the voltage across the inductor.

b) Find the magnitude of the transfer function in
part (a) for very low frequencies.

c) Find the magnitude of the transfer function in
part (a) for very high frequencies.

d) Based on your answers in parts (b) and (c), what
type of filter is this?

e) Suppose $R = 600\ \Omega$, $L = 400\ \text{mH}$, $C = 2.5\ \mu\text{F}$.
Calculate the cutoff frequency of this filter, that
is, the frequency at which the magnitude of the
transfer function is $1/\sqrt{2}$.

Figure P14.49

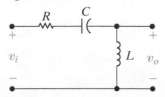

14.50 Repeat parts (a) – (d) from Problem 14.49 for the
circuit shown in Fig. P14.50. Note that the output
voltage is now the voltage across the capacitor.

Figure P14.50

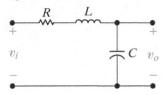

14.51 Design a series RLC bandpass filter (see

PRACTICAL
PERSPECTIVE

Fig. 14.27) for detecting the low-frequency tone
generated by pushing a telephone button as shown

DESIGN
PROBLEM

in Fig. 14.32.

a) Calculate the values of L and C that place
the cutoff frequencies at the edges of the
DTMF low-frequency band. Note that the
resistance in standard telephone circuits is
always $R = 600\ \Omega$.

b) What is the output amplitude of this circuit at
each of the low-band frequencies, relative to the
peak amplitude of the bandpass filter?

c) What is the output amplitude of this circuit at
the lowest of the high-band frequencies?

14.52 Design a DTMF high-band bandpass filter similar

PRACTICAL
PERSPECTIVE

to the low-band filter design in Problem 14.51. Be
sure to include the fourth high-frequency tone,

DESIGN
PROBLEM

1633 Hz, in your design. What is the response amplitude of your filter to the highest of the low-
frequency DTMF tones?

14.53 The 20 Hz signal that rings a telephone's bell has to

PRACTICAL
PERSPECTIVE

have a very large amplitude to produce a loud
enough bell signal. How much larger can the ring-

DESIGN
PROBLEM

ing signal amplitude be, relative to the low-bank
DTMF signal, so that the response of the filter in
Problem 14.51 is no more than half as large as the
largest of the DTMF tones?

The Solution of Linear Simultaneous Equations

Circuit analysis frequently involves the solution of linear simultaneous equations. Our purpose here is to review the use of determinants to solve such a set of equations. The theory of determinants (with applications) can be found in most intermediate-level algebra texts. (A particularly good reference for engineering students is Chapter 1 of E.A. Guillemin's *The Mathematics of Circuit Analysis* [New York: Wiley, 1949]. In our review here, we will limit our discussion to the mechanics of solving simultaneous equations with determinants.

A.1 Preliminary Steps

The first step in solving a set of simultaneous equations by determinants is to write the equations in a rectangular (square) format. In other words, we arrange the equations in a vertical stack such that each variable occupies the same horizontal position in every equation. For example, in Eqs. A.1, the variables i_1, i_2, and i_3 occupy the first, second, and third position, respectively, on the left-hand side of each equation:

$$21i_1 - 9i_2 - 12i_3 = -33,$$

$$-3i_1 + 6i_2 - 2i_3 = 3, \qquad \text{(A.1)}$$

$$-8i_1 - 4i_2 + 22i_3 = 50.$$

Alternatively, one can describe this set of equations by saying that i_1 occupies the first column in the array, i_2 the second column, and i_3 the third column.

If one or more variables are missing from a given equation, they can be inserted by simply making their coefficient zero. Thus Eqs. A.2 can be "squared up" as shown by Eqs. A.3:

$$2v_1 - v_2 = 4,$$

$$4v_2 + 3v_3 = 16, \qquad \text{(A.2)}$$

$$7v_1 + 2v_3 = 5;$$

$$2v_1 - v_2 + 0v_3 = 4,$$

$$0v_1 + 4v_2 + 3v_3 = 16, \qquad \text{(A.3)}$$

$$7v_1 + 0v_2 + 2v_3 = 5.$$

A.2 Cramer's Method

The value of each unknown variable in the set of equations is expressed as the ratio of two determinants. If we let N, with an appropriate subscript, represent the numerator determinant and Δ represent the denominator determinant, then the kth unknown x_k is

$$x_k = \frac{N_k}{\Delta}. \tag{A.4}$$

The denominator determinant Δ is the same for every unknown variable and is called the **characteristic determinant** of the set of equations. The numerator determinant N_k varies with each unknown. Equation A.4 is referred to as **Cramer's method** for solving simultaneous equations.

A.3 The Characteristic Determinant

Once we have organized the set of simultaneous equations into an ordered array, as illustrated by Eqs. A.1 and A.3, it is a simple matter to form the characteristic determinant. This determinant is the square array made up from the coefficients of the unknown variables. For example, the characteristic determinants of Eqs. A.1 and A.3 are

$$\Delta = \begin{vmatrix} 21 & -9 & -12 \\ -3 & 6 & -2 \\ -8 & -4 & 22 \end{vmatrix} \tag{A.5}$$

and

$$\Delta = \begin{vmatrix} 2 & -1 & 0 \\ 0 & 4 & 3 \\ 7 & 0 & 2 \end{vmatrix}, \tag{A.6}$$

respectively.

A.4 The Numerator Determinant

The numerator determinant N_k is formed from the characteristic determinant by replacing the kth column in the characteristic determinant with the column of values appearing on the right-hand side of the equations. For example, the numerator determinants for evaluating i_1, i_2, and i_3 in Eqs. A.1 are

$$N_1 = \begin{vmatrix} -33 & -9 & -12 \\ 3 & 6 & -2 \\ 50 & -4 & 22 \end{vmatrix}, \tag{A.7}$$

$$N_2 = \begin{vmatrix} 21 & -33 & -12 \\ -3 & 3 & -2 \\ -8 & 50 & 22 \end{vmatrix}, \tag{A.8}$$

and

$$N_3 = \begin{vmatrix} 21 & -9 & -33 \\ -3 & 6 & 3 \\ -8 & -4 & 50 \end{vmatrix}. \tag{A.9}$$

The numerator determinants for the evaluation of v_1, v_2, and v_3 in Eqs. A.3 are

$$N_1 = \begin{vmatrix} 4 & -1 & 0 \\ 16 & 4 & 3 \\ 5 & 0 & 2 \end{vmatrix}, \tag{A.10}$$

$$N_2 = \begin{vmatrix} 2 & 4 & 0 \\ 0 & 16 & 3 \\ 7 & 5 & 2 \end{vmatrix}, \tag{A.11}$$

and

$$N_3 = \begin{vmatrix} 2 & -1 & 4 \\ 0 & 4 & 16 \\ 7 & 0 & 5 \end{vmatrix}. \tag{A.12}$$

A.5 The Evaluation of a Determinant

The value of a determinant is found by expanding it in terms of its minors. The **minor** of any element in a determinant is the determinant that remains after the row and column occupied by the element have been deleted. For example, the minor of the element 6 in Eq. A.7 is

$$\begin{vmatrix} -33 & -12 \\ 50 & 22 \end{vmatrix},$$

while the minor of the element 22 in Eq. A.7 is

$$\begin{vmatrix} -33 & -9 \\ 3 & 6 \end{vmatrix}.$$

The **cofactor** of an element is its minor multiplied by the sign-controlling factor

$$-1^{(i+j)},$$

where i and j denote the row and column, respectively, occupied by the element. Thus the cofactor of the element 6 in Eq. A.7 is

$$-1^{(2+2)} \begin{vmatrix} -33 & -12 \\ 50 & 22 \end{vmatrix},$$

and the cofactor of the element 22 is

$$-1^{(3+3)} \begin{vmatrix} -33 & -9 \\ 3 & 6 \end{vmatrix}.$$

The cofactor of an element is also referred to as its **signed minor**.

The sign-controlling factor $-1^{(i+j)}$ will equal $+1$ or -1 depending on whether $i + j$ is an even or odd integer. Thus the algebraic sign of a cofactor alternates between $+1$ and -1 as we move along a row or column. For a 3×3 determinant, the plus and minus signs form the checkerboard pattern illustrated here:

$$\begin{vmatrix} + & - & + \\ - & + & - \\ + & - & + \end{vmatrix}$$

A determinant can be expanded along any row or column. Thus the first step in making an expansion is to select a row i or a column j. Once a row or column has been selected, each element in that row or column is multiplied by its signed minor, or cofactor. The value of the determinant is the sum of these products. As an example, let us evaluate the determinant in Eq. A.5 by expanding it along its first column. Following the rules just explained, we write the expansion as

$$\Delta = 21(1) \begin{vmatrix} 6 & -2 \\ -4 & 22 \end{vmatrix} - 3(-1) \begin{vmatrix} -9 & -12 \\ -4 & 22 \end{vmatrix} - 8(1) \begin{vmatrix} -9 & -12 \\ 6 & -2 \end{vmatrix} \quad \text{(A.13)}$$

The 2×2 determinants in Eq. A.13 can also be expanded by minors. The minor of an element in a 2×2 determinant is a single element. It follows that the expansion reduces to multiplying the upper-left element by the lower-right element and then subtracting from this product the product of the lower-left element times the upper-right element. Using this observation, we evaluate Eq. A.13 to

$$\Delta = 21(132 - 8) + 3(-198 - 48) - 8(18 + 72)$$

$$= 2604 - 738 - 720 = 1146. \quad \text{(A.14)}$$

Had we elected to expand the determinant along the second row of elements, we would have written

$$\Delta = -3(-1) \begin{vmatrix} -9 & -12 \\ -4 & 22 \end{vmatrix} + 6(+1) \begin{vmatrix} 21 & -12 \\ -8 & 22 \end{vmatrix} - 2(-1) \begin{vmatrix} 21 & -9 \\ -8 & -4 \end{vmatrix}$$

$$= 3(-198 - 48) + 6(462 - 96) + 2(-84 - 72)$$

$$= -738 + 2196 - 312 = 1146. \quad \text{(A.15)}$$

The numerical values of the determinants N_1, N_2, and N_3 given by Eqs. A.7, A.8, and A.9 are

$$N_1 = 1146, \quad \text{(A.16)}$$

$$N_2 = 2292, \tag{A.17}$$

and

$$N_3 = 3438. \tag{A.18}$$

It follows from Eqs. A.15 through A.18 that the solutions for $i_1, i_2,$ and i_3 in Eq. A.1 are

$$i_1 = \frac{N_1}{\Delta} = 1\text{ A},$$

$$i_2 = \frac{N_2}{\Delta} = 2\text{ A}, \tag{A.19}$$

and

$$i_3 = \frac{N_3}{\Delta} = 3\text{ A}.$$

We leave you to verify that the solutions for $v_1, v_2,$ and v_3 in Eqs. A.3 are

$$v_1 = \frac{49}{-5} = -9.8\text{ V},$$

$$v_2 = \frac{118}{-5} = -23.6\text{ V}, \tag{A.20}$$

and

$$v_3 = \frac{-184}{-5} = 36.8\text{ V}.$$

A.6 Matrices

A system of simultaneous linear equations can also be solved using matrices. In what follows, we briefly review matrix notation, algebra, and terminology.[1]

A **matrix** is by definition a rectangular array of elements; thus

$$\mathbf{A} = \begin{bmatrix} a_{11} & a_{12} & a_{13} & \cdots & a_{1n} \\ a_{21} & a_{22} & a_{23} & \cdots & a_{2n} \\ \cdots & \cdots & \cdots & \cdots & \cdots \\ a_{m1} & a_{m2} & a_{m3} & \cdots & a_{mn} \end{bmatrix} \tag{A.21}$$

is a matrix with m rows and n columns. We describe A as being a matrix of order m by n, or $m \times n$, where m equals the number of rows and n the

---

[1] An excellent introductory-level text in matrix applications to circuit analysis is Lawrence P. Huelsman, *Circuits, Matrices, and Linear Vector Spaces* (New York: McGraw-Hill, 1963).

number of columns. We always specify the rows first and the columns second. The elements of the matrix—$a_{11}, a_{12}, a_{13}, \ldots$—can be real numbers, complex numbers, or functions. We denote a matrix with a boldface capital letter.

The array in Eq. A.21 is frequently abbreviated by writing

$$\mathbf{A} = [a_{ij}]_{mn}, \tag{A.22}$$

where a_{ij} is the element in the ith row and the jth column.

If $m = 1$, $\mathbf{A}$ is called a **row matrix**, that is,

$$\mathbf{A} = [a_{11} \quad a_{12} \quad a_{13} \quad \cdots \quad a_{1n}]. \tag{A.23}$$

If $n = 1$, $\mathbf{A}$ is called a **column matrix**, that is,

$$\mathbf{A} = \begin{bmatrix} a_{11} \\ a_{21} \\ a_{31} \\ \vdots \\ a_{m1} \end{bmatrix}. \tag{A.24}$$

If $m = n$, $\mathbf{A}$ is called a **square matrix**. For example, if $m = n = 3$, the square 3 by 3 matrix is

$$\mathbf{A} = \begin{bmatrix} a_{11} & a_{12} & a_{13} \\ a_{21} & a_{22} & a_{23} \\ a_{31} & a_{32} & a_{33} \end{bmatrix}. \tag{A.25}$$

Also note that we use brackets [] to denote a matrix, whereas we use vertical lines || to denote a determinant. It is important to know the difference. A matrix is a rectangular array of elements. A **determinant** is a function of a square array of elements. Thus if a matrix $\mathbf{A}$ is square, we can define the determinant of $\mathbf{A}$. For example, if

$$\mathbf{A} = \begin{bmatrix} 2 & 1 \\ 6 & 15 \end{bmatrix},$$

then

$$\det \mathbf{A} = \begin{vmatrix} 2 & 1 \\ 6 & 15 \end{vmatrix} = 30 - 6 = 24.$$

A.7 Matrix Algebra

The equality, addition, and subtraction of matrices apply only to matrices of the same order. Two matrices are equal if, and only if, their corresponding elements are equal. In other words, $\mathbf{A} = \mathbf{B}$ if, and only if, $a_{ij} = b_{ij}$ for all i and j. For example, the two matrices in Eqs. A.26 and A.27 are equal because $a_{11} = b_{11}, a_{12} = b_{12}, a_{21} = b_{21}$, and $a_{22} = b_{22}$:

$$\mathbf{A} = \begin{bmatrix} 36 & -20 \\ 4 & 16 \end{bmatrix}, \tag{A.26}$$

$$\mathbf{B} = \begin{bmatrix} 36 & -20 \\ 4 & 16 \end{bmatrix}. \tag{A.27}$$

If $\mathbf{A}$ and $\mathbf{B}$ are of the same order, then

$$\mathbf{C} = \mathbf{A} + \mathbf{B} \tag{A.28}$$

implies

$$c_{ij} = a_{ij} + b_{ij}. \tag{A.29}$$

For example, if

$$\mathbf{A} = \begin{bmatrix} 4 & -6 & 10 \\ 8 & 12 & -4 \end{bmatrix}, \tag{A.30}$$

and

$$\mathbf{B} = \begin{bmatrix} 16 & 10 & -30 \\ -20 & 8 & 15 \end{bmatrix}, \tag{A.31}$$

then

$$\mathbf{C} = \begin{bmatrix} 20 & 4 & -20 \\ -12 & 20 & 11 \end{bmatrix}. \tag{A.32}$$

The equation

$$\mathbf{D} = \mathbf{A} - \mathbf{B} \tag{A.33}$$

implies

$$d_{ij} = a_{ij} - b_{ij}. \tag{A.34}$$

For the matrices in Eqs. A.30 and A.31, we would have

$$\mathbf{D} = \begin{bmatrix} -12 & -16 & 40 \\ 28 & 4 & -19 \end{bmatrix}. \tag{A.35}$$

Matrices of the same order are said to be **conformable** for addition and subtraction.

Multiplying a matrix by a scalar k is equivalent to multiplying each element by the scalar. Thus $\mathbf{A} = k\mathbf{B}$ if, and only if, $a_{ij} = kb_{ij}$. It should be noted that k may be real or complex. As an example, we will multiply the matrix $\mathbf{D}$ in Eq. A.35 by 5. The result is

$$5\mathbf{D} = \begin{bmatrix} -60 & -80 & 200 \\ 140 & 20 & -95 \end{bmatrix}. \tag{A.36}$$

Matrix multiplication can be performed only if the number of columns in the first matrix is equal to the number of rows in the second matrix. In other words, the product $\mathbf{AB}$ requires the number of columns in $\mathbf{A}$ to equal the number of rows in $\mathbf{B}$. The order of the resulting matrix will be the number of rows in $\mathbf{A}$ by the number of columns in $\mathbf{B}$. Thus if $\mathbf{C} = \mathbf{AB}$, where $\mathbf{A}$ is of order $m \times p$ and $\mathbf{B}$ is of order $p \times n$, then $\mathbf{C}$ will be a matrix of order $m \times n$. When the number of columns in $\mathbf{A}$ equals the number of rows in $\mathbf{B}$, we say $\mathbf{A}$ is conformable to $\mathbf{B}$ for multiplication.

An element in $\mathbf{C}$ is given by the formula

$$c_{ij} = \sum_{k=1}^{p} a_{ik}b_{kj}. \tag{A.37}$$

The formula given by Eq. A.37 is easy to use if one remembers that matrix multiplication is a row-by-column operation. Hence to get the ith, jth term in $\mathbf{C}$, each element in the ith row of $\mathbf{A}$ is multiplied by the corresponding element in the jth column of $\mathbf{B}$, and the resulting products are summed. The following example illustrates the procedure. We are asked to find the matrix $\mathbf{C}$ when

$$\mathbf{A} = \begin{bmatrix} 6 & 3 & 2 \\ 1 & 4 & 6 \end{bmatrix} \tag{A.38}$$

and

$$\mathbf{B} = \begin{bmatrix} 4 & 2 \\ 0 & 3 \\ 1 & -2 \end{bmatrix}. \tag{A.39}$$

First we note that $\mathbf{C}$ will be a 2×2 matrix and that each element in $\mathbf{C}$ will require summing three products.

To find C_{11} we multiply the corresponding elements in row 1 of matrix $\mathbf{A}$ with the elements in column 1 of matrix $\mathbf{B}$ and then sum the products. We can visualize this multiplication and summing process by extracting the corresponding row and column from each matrix and then lining them up element by element. So to find C_{11} we have

Row 1 of $\mathbf{A}$	6	3	2
Column 1 of $\mathbf{B}$	4	0	1

therefore

$$C_{11} = 6 \times 4 + 3 \times 0 + 2 \times 1 = 26.$$

To find C_{12} we visualize

Row 1 of $\mathbf{A}$	6	3	2
Column 2 of $\mathbf{B}$	2	3	-2

thus

$$C_{12} = 6 \times 2 + 3 \times 3 + 2 \times (-2) = 17.$$

For C_{21} we have

Row 2 of $\mathbf{A}$	1	4	6
Column 1 of $\mathbf{B}$	4	0	1

and

$$C_{21} = 1 \times 4 + 4 \times 0 + 6 \times 1 = 10.$$

Finally, for C_{22} we have

Row 2 of **A**	1	4	6
Column 2 of **B**	2	3	−2

from which

$$C_{22} = 1 \times 2 + 4 \times 3 + 6 \times (-2) = 2.$$

It follows that

$$\mathbf{C} = \mathbf{AB} = \begin{bmatrix} 26 & 17 \\ 10 & 2 \end{bmatrix}. \tag{A.40}$$

In general, matrix multiplication is not commutative, that is, $\mathbf{AB} \neq \mathbf{BA}$. As an example, consider the product **BA** for the matrices in Eqs. A.38 and A.39. The matrix generated by this multiplication is of order 3×3, and each term in the resulting matrix requires adding two products. Therefore if $\mathbf{D} = \mathbf{BA}$, we have

$$\mathbf{D} = \begin{bmatrix} 26 & 20 & 20 \\ 3 & 12 & 18 \\ 4 & -5 & -10 \end{bmatrix}. \tag{A.41}$$

Obviously, $\mathbf{C} \neq \mathbf{D}$. We leave you to verify the elements in Eq. A.41.

Matrix multiplication is associative and distributive. Thus

$$(\mathbf{AB})\mathbf{C} = \mathbf{A}(\mathbf{BC}), \tag{A.42}$$

$$\mathbf{A}(\mathbf{B} + \mathbf{C}) = \mathbf{AB} + \mathbf{AC}, \tag{A.43}$$

and

$$(\mathbf{A} + \mathbf{B})\mathbf{C} = \mathbf{AC} + \mathbf{BC}. \tag{A.44}$$

In Eqs. A.42, A.43, and A.44, we assume that the matrices are conformable for addition and multiplication.

We have already noted that matrix multiplication is not commutative. There are two other properties of multiplication in scalar algebra that do not carry over to matrix algebra.

First, the matrix product $\mathbf{AB} = 0$ does not imply either $\mathbf{A} = 0$ or $\mathbf{B} = 0$. (*Note:* A matrix is equal to zero when all its elements are zero.) For example, if

$$\mathbf{A} = \begin{bmatrix} 1 & 0 \\ 2 & 0 \end{bmatrix} \quad \text{and} \quad \mathbf{B} = \begin{bmatrix} 0 & 0 \\ 4 & 8 \end{bmatrix},$$

then

$$\mathbf{AB} = \begin{bmatrix} 0 & 0 \\ 0 & 0 \end{bmatrix} = 0.$$

Hence the product is zero, but neither **A** nor **B** is zero.

Second, the matrix equation **AB** = **AC** does not imply **B** = **C**. For example, if

$$\mathbf{A} = \begin{bmatrix} 1 & 0 \\ 2 & 0 \end{bmatrix}, \quad \mathbf{B} = \begin{bmatrix} 3 & 4 \\ 7 & 8 \end{bmatrix}, \quad \text{and} \quad \mathbf{C} = \begin{bmatrix} 3 & 4 \\ 5 & 6 \end{bmatrix},$$

then

$$\mathbf{AB} = \mathbf{AC} = \begin{bmatrix} 3 & 4 \\ 6 & 8 \end{bmatrix}, \quad \text{but } \mathbf{B} \neq \mathbf{C}.$$

The **transpose** of a matrix is formed by interchanging the rows and columns. For example, if

$$\mathbf{A} = \begin{bmatrix} 1 & 2 & 3 \\ 4 & 5 & 6 \\ 7 & 8 & 9 \end{bmatrix}, \quad \text{then } \mathbf{A}^T = \begin{bmatrix} 1 & 4 & 7 \\ 2 & 5 & 8 \\ 3 & 6 & 9 \end{bmatrix}.$$

The transpose of the sum of two matrices is equal to the sum of the transposes, that is,

$$(\mathbf{A} + \mathbf{B})^T = \mathbf{A}^T + \mathbf{B}^T. \tag{A.45}$$

The transpose of the product of two matrices is equal to the product of the transposes taken in reverse order. In other words,

$$[\mathbf{AB}]^T = \mathbf{B}^T \mathbf{A}^T. \tag{A.46}$$

Equation A.46 can be extended to a product of any number of matrices. For example,

$$[\mathbf{ABCD}]^T = \mathbf{D}^T \mathbf{C}^T \mathbf{B}^T \mathbf{A}^T. \tag{A.47}$$

If $\mathbf{A} = \mathbf{A}^T$, the matrix is said to be **symmetric**. Only square matrices can be symmetric.

A.8   Identity, Adjoint, and Inverse Matrices

An **identity matrix** is a square matrix where $a_{ij} = 0$ for $i \neq j$, and $a_{ij} = 1$ for $i = j$. In other words, all the elements in an identity matrix are zero except those along the main diagonal, where they are equal to 1. Thus

$$\begin{bmatrix} 1 & 0 \\ 0 & 1 \end{bmatrix}, \quad \begin{bmatrix} 1 & 0 & 0 \\ 0 & 1 & 0 \\ 0 & 0 & 1 \end{bmatrix}, \quad \text{and} \quad \begin{bmatrix} 1 & 0 & 0 & 0 \\ 0 & 1 & 0 & 0 \\ 0 & 0 & 1 & 0 \\ 0 & 0 & 0 & 1 \end{bmatrix}$$

are all identity matrices. Note that identity matrices are always square. We will use the symbol $\mathbf{U}$ for an identity matrix.

The **adjoint** of a matrix $\mathbf{A}$ of order $n \times n$ is defined as

$$\text{adj } \mathbf{A} = [\Delta_{ji}]_{n \times n}, \tag{A.48}$$

where Δ_{ij} is the cofactor of a_{ij}. (See Section A.5 for the definition of a cofactor.) It follows from Eq. A.48 that one can think of finding the adjoint of a square matrix as a two-step process. First construct a matrix made up of the cofactors of $\mathbf{A}$, and then transpose the matrix of cofactors. As an example we will find the adjoint of the 3×3 matrix

$$\mathbf{A} = \begin{bmatrix} 1 & 2 & 3 \\ 3 & 2 & 1 \\ -1 & 1 & 5 \end{bmatrix}.$$

The cofactors of the elements in $\mathbf{A}$ are

$$\begin{aligned}
\Delta_{11} &= 1(10 - 1) = 9, \\
\Delta_{12} &= -1(15 + 1) = -16, \\
\Delta_{13} &= 1(3 + 2) = 5, \\
\Delta_{21} &= -1(10 - 3) = -7, \\
\Delta_{22} &= 1(5 + 3) = 8, \\
\Delta_{23} &= -1(1 + 2) = -3, \\
\Delta_{31} &= 1(2 - 6) = -4, \\
\Delta_{32} &= -1(1 - 9) = 8, \\
\Delta_{33} &= 1(2 - 6) = -4.
\end{aligned}$$

The matrix of cofactors is

$$\mathbf{B} = \begin{bmatrix} 9 & -16 & 5 \\ -7 & 8 & -3 \\ -4 & 8 & -4 \end{bmatrix}.$$

It follows that the adjoint of $\mathbf{A}$ is

$$\text{adj } \mathbf{A} = \mathbf{B}^T = \begin{bmatrix} 9 & -7 & -4 \\ -16 & 8 & 8 \\ 5 & -3 & -4 \end{bmatrix}.$$

One can check the arithmetic of finding the adjoint of a matrix by using the theorem

$$\text{adj } \mathbf{A} \cdot \mathbf{A} = \det \mathbf{A} \cdot \mathbf{U}. \tag{A.49}$$

Equation A.49 tells us that the adjoint of $\mathbf{A}$ times $\mathbf{A}$ equals the determinant of $\mathbf{A}$ times the identity matrix, or for our example,

$$\det \mathbf{A} = 1(9) + 3(-7) - 1(-4) = -8.$$

If we let $\mathbf{C} = \text{adj }\mathbf{A} \cdot \mathbf{A}$ and use the technique illustrated in Section A.7, we find the elements of $\mathbf{C}$ to be

$$
\begin{aligned}
c_{11} &= 9 - 21 + 4 = -8, \\
c_{12} &= 18 - 14 - 4 = 0, \\
c_{13} &= 27 - 7 - 20 = 0, \\
c_{21} &= -16 + 24 - 8 = 0, \\
c_{22} &= -32 + 16 + 8 = -8, \\
c_{23} &= -48 + 8 + 40 = 0, \\
c_{31} &= 5 - 9 + 4 = 0, \\
c_{32} &= 10 - 6 - 4 = 0, \\
c_{33} &= 15 - 3 - 20 = -8.
\end{aligned}
$$

Therefore

$$
\mathbf{C} = \begin{bmatrix} -8 & 0 & 0 \\ 0 & -8 & 0 \\ 0 & 0 & -8 \end{bmatrix} = -8 \begin{bmatrix} 1 & 0 & 0 \\ 0 & 1 & 0 \\ 0 & 0 & 1 \end{bmatrix}
$$

$$
= \det \mathbf{A} \cdot \mathbf{U}.
$$

A square matrix $\mathbf{A}$ has an **inverse**, denoted as $\mathbf{A}^{-1}$, if

$$
\mathbf{A}^{-1}\mathbf{A} = \mathbf{A}\mathbf{A}^{-1} = \mathbf{U}. \tag{A.50}
$$

Equation A.50 tells us that a matrix either premultiplied or postmultiplied by its inverse generates the identity matrix $\mathbf{U}$. For the inverse matrix to exist, it is necessary that the determinant of $\mathbf{A}$ not equal zero. Only square matrices have inverses, and the inverse is also square.

A formula for finding the inverse of a matrix is

$$
\mathbf{A}^{-1} = \frac{\text{adj }\mathbf{A}}{\det \mathbf{A}}. \tag{A.51}
$$

The formula in Eq. A.51 becomes very cumbersome if $\mathbf{A}$ is of an order larger than 3 by 3.[2] Today the digital computer eliminates the drudgery of having to find the inverse of a matrix in numerical applications of matrix algebra.

It follows from Eq. A.51 that the inverse of the matrix $\mathbf{A}$ in the previous example is

$$
\mathbf{A}^{-1} = -1/8 \begin{bmatrix} 9 & -7 & -4 \\ -16 & 8 & 8 \\ 5 & -3 & -4 \end{bmatrix}
$$

$$
= \begin{bmatrix} -1.125 & 0.875 & 0.5 \\ 2 & -1 & -1 \\ -0.625 & 0.375 & 0.5 \end{bmatrix}.
$$

You should verify that $\mathbf{A}^{-1}\mathbf{A} = AA^{-1} = \mathbf{U}$.

---

[2] You can learn alternative methods for finding the inverse in any introductory text on matrix theory. See, for example, Franz E. Hohn, *Elementary Matrix Algebra* (New York: Macmillan, 1973).

A.9 Partitioned Matrices

It is often convenient in matrix manipulations to partition a given matrix into submatrices. The original algebraic operations are then carried out in terms of the submatrices. In partitioning a matrix, the placement of the partitions is completely arbitrary, with the one restriction that a partition must dissect the entire matrix. In selecting the partitions, it is also necessary to make sure the submatrices are conformable to the mathematical operations in which they are involved.

For example, consider using submatrices to find the product $\mathbf{C} = \mathbf{AB}$, where

$$\mathbf{A} = \begin{bmatrix} 1 & 2 & 3 & 4 & 5 \\ 5 & 4 & 3 & 2 & 1 \\ -1 & 0 & 2 & -3 & 1 \\ 0 & 1 & -1 & 0 & 1 \\ 0 & 2 & 1 & -2 & 0 \end{bmatrix}$$

and

$$\mathbf{B} = \begin{bmatrix} 2 \\ 0 \\ -1 \\ 3 \\ 0 \end{bmatrix}.$$

Assume that we decide to partition $\mathbf{B}$ into two submatrices, $\mathbf{B}_{11}$ and $\mathbf{B}_{21}$; thus

$$\mathbf{B} = \begin{bmatrix} \mathbf{B}_{11} \\ \mathbf{B}_{21} \end{bmatrix}.$$

Now since $\mathbf{B}$ has been partitioned into a two-row column matrix, $\mathbf{A}$ must be partitioned into at least a two-column matrix; otherwise the multiplication cannot be performed. The location of the vertical partitions of the $\mathbf{A}$ matrix will depend on the definitions of $\mathbf{B}_{11}$ and $\mathbf{B}_{21}$. For example, if

$$\mathbf{B}_{11} = \begin{bmatrix} 2 \\ 0 \\ -1 \end{bmatrix} \quad \text{and} \quad \mathbf{B}_{21} = \begin{bmatrix} 3 \\ 0 \end{bmatrix},$$

then $\mathbf{A}_{11}$ must contain three columns, and $\mathbf{A}_{12}$ must contain two columns. Thus the partitioning shown in Eq. A.52 would be acceptable for executing the product $\mathbf{AB}$:

$$\mathbf{C} = \left[\begin{array}{ccc|cc} 1 & 2 & 3 & 4 & 5 \\ 5 & 4 & 3 & 2 & 1 \\ -1 & 0 & 2 & -3 & 1 \\ 0 & 1 & -1 & 0 & 1 \\ 0 & 2 & 1 & -2 & 0 \end{array} \right] \begin{bmatrix} 2 \\ 0 \\ -1 \\ \cdots \\ 3 \\ 0 \end{bmatrix}. \tag{A.52}$$

If, on the other hand, we partition the **B** matrix so that

$$\mathbf{B}_{11} = \begin{bmatrix} 2 \\ 0 \end{bmatrix} \quad \text{and} \quad \mathbf{B}_{21} = \begin{bmatrix} -1 \\ 3 \\ 0 \end{bmatrix},$$

then $\mathbf{A}_{11}$ must contain two columns, and $\mathbf{A}_{12}$ must contain three columns. In this case the partitioning shown in Eq. A.53 would be acceptable in executing the product $\mathbf{C} = \mathbf{AB}$:

$$\mathbf{C} = \begin{bmatrix} 1 & 2 & | & 3 & 4 & 5 \\ 5 & 4 & | & 3 & 2 & 1 \\ -1 & 0 & | & 2 & -3 & 1 \\ 0 & 1 & | & -1 & 0 & 1 \\ 0 & 2 & | & 1 & -2 & 0 \end{bmatrix} \begin{bmatrix} 2 \\ 0 \\ \cdots \\ -1 \\ 3 \\ 0 \end{bmatrix}. \tag{A.53}$$

For purposes of discussion, we will focus on the partitioning given in Eq. A.52 and leave you to verify that the partitioning in Eq. A.53 leads to the same result.

From Eq. A.52 we can write

$$\mathbf{C} = [\mathbf{A}_{11} \ \mathbf{A}_{12}] \begin{bmatrix} \mathbf{B}_{11} \\ \mathbf{B}_{21} \end{bmatrix} = \mathbf{A}_{11}\mathbf{B}_{11} + \mathbf{A}_{12}\mathbf{B}_{21}. \tag{A.54}$$

It follows from Eqs. A.52 and A.54 that

$$\mathbf{A}_{11}\mathbf{B}_{11} = \begin{bmatrix} 1 & 2 & 3 \\ 5 & 4 & 3 \\ -1 & 0 & 2 \\ 0 & 1 & -1 \\ 0 & 2 & 1 \end{bmatrix} \begin{bmatrix} 2 \\ 0 \\ -1 \end{bmatrix} = \begin{bmatrix} -1 \\ 7 \\ -4 \\ 1 \\ -1 \end{bmatrix},$$

$$\mathbf{A}_{12}\mathbf{B}_{21} = \begin{bmatrix} 4 & 5 \\ 2 & 1 \\ -3 & 1 \\ 0 & 1 \\ -2 & 0 \end{bmatrix} \begin{bmatrix} 3 \\ 0 \end{bmatrix} = \begin{bmatrix} 12 \\ 6 \\ -9 \\ 0 \\ -6 \end{bmatrix},$$

and

$$\mathbf{C} = \begin{bmatrix} 11 \\ 13 \\ -13 \\ 1 \\ -7 \end{bmatrix}.$$

The **A** matrix could also be partitioned horizontally once the vertical partitioning is made consistent with the multiplication operation. In this simple problem, the horizontal partitions can be made at the discretion of the analyst. Therefore **C** could also be evaluated using the partitioning shown in Eq. A.55:

$$\mathbf{C} = \begin{bmatrix} 1 & 2 & 3 & | & 4 & 5 \\ 5 & 4 & 3 & | & 2 & 1 \\ \cdots & \cdots & \cdots & \cdots & \cdots & \cdots \\ -1 & 0 & 2 & | & -3 & 1 \\ 0 & 1 & -1 & | & 0 & 1 \\ 0 & 2 & 1 & | & -2 & 0 \end{bmatrix} \begin{bmatrix} 2 \\ 0 \\ -1 \\ \cdots \\ 3 \\ 0 \end{bmatrix}. \tag{A.55}$$

From Eq. A.55 it follows that

$$\mathbf{C} = \begin{bmatrix} \mathbf{A}_{11} & \mathbf{A}_{12} \\ \mathbf{A}_{21} & \mathbf{A}_{22} \end{bmatrix} \begin{bmatrix} \mathbf{B}_{11} \\ \mathbf{B}_{21} \end{bmatrix} = \begin{bmatrix} \mathbf{C}_{11} \\ \mathbf{C}_{21} \end{bmatrix}, \tag{A.56}$$

where

$$\mathbf{C}_{11} = \mathbf{A}_{11}\mathbf{B}_{11} + \mathbf{A}_{12}\mathbf{B}_{21},$$
$$\mathbf{C}_{21} = \mathbf{A}_{21}\mathbf{B}_{11} + \mathbf{A}_{22}\mathbf{B}_{21}.$$

You should verify that

$$\mathbf{C}_{11} = \begin{bmatrix} 1 & 2 & 3 \\ 5 & 4 & 3 \end{bmatrix} \begin{bmatrix} 2 \\ 0 \\ -1 \end{bmatrix} + \begin{bmatrix} 4 & 5 \\ 2 & 1 \end{bmatrix} \begin{bmatrix} 3 \\ 0 \end{bmatrix}$$

$$= \begin{bmatrix} -1 \\ 7 \end{bmatrix} + \begin{bmatrix} 12 \\ 6 \end{bmatrix} = \begin{bmatrix} 11 \\ 13 \end{bmatrix},$$

$$\mathbf{C}_{21} = \begin{bmatrix} -1 & 0 & 2 \\ 0 & 1 & -1 \\ 0 & 2 & 1 \end{bmatrix} \begin{bmatrix} 2 \\ 0 \\ -1 \end{bmatrix} + \begin{bmatrix} -3 & 1 \\ 0 & 1 \\ -2 & 0 \end{bmatrix} \begin{bmatrix} 3 \\ 0 \end{bmatrix}$$

$$= \begin{bmatrix} -4 \\ 1 \\ -1 \end{bmatrix} + \begin{bmatrix} -9 \\ 0 \\ -6 \end{bmatrix} = \begin{bmatrix} -13 \\ 1 \\ -7 \end{bmatrix},$$

and

$$\mathbf{C} = \begin{bmatrix} 11 \\ 13 \\ -13 \\ 1 \\ -7 \end{bmatrix}.$$

We note in passing that the partitioning in Eqs. A.52 and A.55 is conformable with respect to addition.

A.10 Applications

The following examples demonstrate some applications of matrix algebra in circuit analysis.

Example A.1

Use the matrix method to solve for the node voltages v_1 and v_2 in Eqs. 4.5 and 4.6.

Solution

The first step is to rewrite Eqs. 4.5 and 4.6 in matrix notation. Collecting the coefficients of v_1 and v_2 and at the same time shifting the constant terms to the right-hand side of the equations gives us

$$1.7v_1 - 0.5v_2 = 10,$$
$$-0.5v_1 + 0.6v_2 = 2. \tag{A.57}$$

It follows that in matrix notation, Eq. A.57 becomes

$$\begin{bmatrix} 1.7 & -0.5 \\ -0.5 & 0.6 \end{bmatrix} \begin{bmatrix} v_1 \\ v_2 \end{bmatrix} = \begin{bmatrix} 10 \\ 2 \end{bmatrix}, \tag{A.58}$$

or

$$\mathbf{AV} = \mathbf{I}, \tag{A.59}$$

where

$$\mathbf{A} = \begin{bmatrix} 1.7 & -0.5 \\ -0.5 & 0.6 \end{bmatrix},$$

$$\mathbf{V} = \begin{bmatrix} v_1 \\ v_2 \end{bmatrix},$$

$$\mathbf{I} = \begin{bmatrix} 10 \\ 2 \end{bmatrix}.$$

To find the elements of the $\mathbf{V}$ matrix, we premultiply both sides of Eq. A.59 by the inverse of $\mathbf{A}$; thus

$$\mathbf{A}^{-1}\mathbf{AV} = \mathbf{A}^{-1}\mathbf{I}. \tag{A.60}$$

Equation A.60 reduces to

$$\mathbf{UV} = \mathbf{A}^{-1}\mathbf{I}, \tag{A.61}$$

or

$$\mathbf{V} = \mathbf{A}^{-1}\mathbf{I}. \tag{A.62}$$

It follows from Eq. A.62 that the solutions for v_1 and v_2 are obtained by solving for the matrix product $\mathbf{A}^{-1}\mathbf{I}$.

To find the inverse of $\mathbf{A}$, we first find the cofactors of $\mathbf{A}$. Thus

$$\begin{aligned} \Delta_{11} &= (-1)^2(0.6) = 0.6, \\ \Delta_{12} &= (-1)^3(-0.5) = 0.5, \\ \Delta_{21} &= (-1)^3(-0.5) = 0.5, \\ \Delta_{22} &= (-1)^4(1.7) = 1.7. \end{aligned} \tag{A.63}$$

The matrix of cofactors is

$$\mathbf{B} = \begin{bmatrix} 0.6 & 0.5 \\ 0.5 & 1.7 \end{bmatrix}, \tag{A.64}$$

and the adjoint of $\mathbf{A}$ is

$$\text{adj } \mathbf{A} = \mathbf{B}^T = \begin{bmatrix} 0.6 & 0.5 \\ 0.5 & 1.7 \end{bmatrix}. \tag{A.65}$$

The determinant of $\mathbf{A}$ is

$$\det \mathbf{A} = \begin{vmatrix} 1.7 & -0.5 \\ -0.5 & 0.6 \end{vmatrix} = (1.7)(0.6) - (0.25) = 0.77. \tag{A.66}$$

From Eqs. A.65 and A.66, we can write the inverse of the coefficient matrix, that is,

$$\mathbf{A}^{-1} = \frac{1}{0.77} \begin{bmatrix} 0.6 & 0.5 \\ 0.5 & 1.7 \end{bmatrix}. \tag{A.67}$$

Now the product $\mathbf{A}^{-1}\mathbf{I}$ is found:

$$\mathbf{A}^{-1}\mathbf{I} = \frac{100}{77} \begin{bmatrix} 0.6 & 0.5 \\ 0.5 & 1.7 \end{bmatrix} \begin{bmatrix} 10 \\ 2 \end{bmatrix}$$

$$= \frac{100}{77} \begin{bmatrix} 7 \\ 8.4 \end{bmatrix} = \begin{bmatrix} 9.09 \\ 10.91 \end{bmatrix}. \tag{A.68}$$

It follows directly that

$$\begin{bmatrix} v_1 \\ v_2 \end{bmatrix} = \begin{bmatrix} 9.09 \\ 10.91 \end{bmatrix}, \tag{A.69}$$

or $v_1 = 9.09$ V and $v_2 = 10.91$ V.

Use the matrix method to find the three mesh currents in the circuit in Fig. 4.24.

Solution

The mesh-current equations that describe the circuit in Fig. 4.24 are given in Eq. 4.34. The constraint equation imposed by the current-controlled voltage source is given in Eq. 4.35. When Eq. 4.35 is substituted into Eq. 4.34, the following set of equations evolves:

$$25i_i - 5i_2 - 20i_3 = 50,$$

$$-5i_i + 10i_2 - 4i_3 = 0,$$

$$-5i_1 - 4i_2 + 9i_3 = 0. \qquad (A.70)$$

In matrix notation, Eqs. A.70 reduce to

$$\mathbf{AI} = \mathbf{V}, \qquad (A.71)$$

where

$$\mathbf{A} = \begin{bmatrix} 25 & -5 & -20 \\ -5 & 10 & -4 \\ -5 & -4 & 9 \end{bmatrix},$$

$$\mathbf{I} = \begin{bmatrix} i_1 \\ i_2 \\ i_3 \end{bmatrix},$$

and

$$\mathbf{V} = \begin{bmatrix} 50 \\ 0 \\ 0 \end{bmatrix}.$$

It follows from Eq. A.71 that the solution for **I** is

$$\mathbf{I} = \mathbf{A}^{-1}\mathbf{V}. \qquad (A.72)$$

We find the inverse of **A** by using the relationship

$$\mathbf{A}^{-1} = \frac{\text{adj } \mathbf{A}}{\det \mathbf{A}}. \qquad (A.73)$$

To find the adjoint of **A**, we first calculate the cofactors of **A**. Thus

$$\Delta_{11} = (-1)^2(90 - 16) = 74,$$

$$\Delta_{12} = (-1)^3(-45 - 20) = 65,$$

$$\Delta_{13} = (-1)^4(20 + 50) = 70,$$

$$\Delta_{21} = (-1)^3(-45 - 80) = 125,$$

$$\Delta_{22} = (-1)^4(225 - 100) = 125,$$

$$\Delta_{23} = (-1)^5(-100 - 25) = 125,$$

$$\Delta_{31} = (-1)^4(20 + 200) = 220,$$

$$\Delta_{32} = (-1)^5(-100 - 100) = 200,$$

$$\Delta_{33} = (-1)^6(250 - 25) = 225.$$

The cofactor matrix is

$$\mathbf{B} = \begin{bmatrix} 74 & 65 & 70 \\ 125 & 125 & 125 \\ 220 & 200 & 225 \end{bmatrix}, \qquad (A.74)$$

from which we can write the adjoint of **A**:

$$\text{adj } \mathbf{A} = \mathbf{B}^T = \begin{bmatrix} 74 & 125 & 220 \\ 65 & 125 & 200 \\ 70 & 125 & 225 \end{bmatrix}. \qquad (A.75)$$

The determinant of **A** is

$$\det \mathbf{A} = \begin{vmatrix} 25 & -5 & -20 \\ -5 & 10 & -4 \\ -5 & -4 & 9 \end{vmatrix}$$

$$= 25(90 - 16) + 5(-45 - 80) - 5(20 + 200) = 125.$$

It follows from Eq. A.73 that

$$\mathbf{A}^{-1} = \frac{1}{125}\begin{bmatrix} 74 & 125 & 220 \\ 65 & 125 & 200 \\ 70 & 125 & 225 \end{bmatrix}. \qquad (A.76)$$

The solution for **I** is

$$\mathbf{I} = \frac{1}{125}\begin{bmatrix} 74 & 125 & 220 \\ 65 & 125 & 200 \\ 70 & 125 & 225 \end{bmatrix}\begin{bmatrix} 50 \\ 0 \\ 0 \end{bmatrix} = \begin{bmatrix} 29.60 \\ 26.00 \\ 28.00 \end{bmatrix}. \quad (A.77)$$

The mesh currents follow directly from Eq. A.77. Thus

$$\begin{bmatrix} i_i \\ i_2 \\ i_3 \end{bmatrix} = \begin{bmatrix} 29.6 \\ 26.0 \\ 28.0 \end{bmatrix} \qquad (A.78)$$

or $i_1 = 29.6$ **A**, $i_2 = 26$ **A**, and $i_3 = 28$ **A**. Example A.3 illustrates the application of the matrix method when the elements of the matrix are complex numbers.

Example A.3

Use the matrix method to find the phasor mesh currents I_1 and I_2 in the circuit in Fig. 9.37.

Solution

Summing the voltages around mesh 1 generates the equation

$$(1 + j2)\mathbf{I}_1 + (12 - j16)(\mathbf{I}_1 - \mathbf{I}_2) = 150\underline{/0°}. \quad (\text{A.79})$$

Summing the voltages around mesh 2 produces the equation

$$(12 - j16)(\mathbf{I}_2 - \mathbf{I}_1) + (1 + j3)\mathbf{I}_2 + 39\mathbf{I}_x = 0. \quad (\text{A.80})$$

The current controlling the dependent voltage source is

$$\mathbf{I}_x = (\mathbf{I}_1 - \mathbf{I}_2). \quad (\text{A.81})$$

After substituting Eq. A.81 into Eq. A.80, the equations are put into a matrix format by first collecting, in each equation, the coefficients of $\mathbf{I}_1$ and $\mathbf{I}_2$; thus

$$\begin{aligned}(13 - j14)\mathbf{I}_1 - (12 - j16)\mathbf{I}_2 &= 150\underline{/0°}, \\ (27 + j16)\mathbf{I}_1 - (26 + j13)\mathbf{I}_2 &= 0.\end{aligned} \quad (\text{A.82})$$

Now, using matrix notation, Eq. A.82 is written

$$\mathbf{AI} = \mathbf{V}, \quad (\text{A.83})$$

where

$$\mathbf{A} = \begin{bmatrix} 13 - j14 & -(12 - j16) \\ 27 + j16 & -(26 + j13) \end{bmatrix},$$

$$\mathbf{I} = \begin{bmatrix} \mathbf{I}_1 \\ \mathbf{I}_2 \end{bmatrix}, \quad \text{and} \quad \mathbf{V} = \begin{bmatrix} 150\underline{/0°} \\ 0 \end{bmatrix}.$$

It follows from Eq. A.83 that

$$\mathbf{I} = \mathbf{A}^{-1}\mathbf{V}. \quad (\text{A.84})$$

The inverse of the coefficient matrix $\mathbf{A}$ is found using Eq. A.73. In this case, the cofactors of $\mathbf{A}$ are

$$\begin{aligned} \Delta_{11} &= (-1)^2(-26 - j13) = -26 - j13, \\ \Delta_{12} &= (-1)^3(27 + j16) = -27 - j16, \\ \Delta_{21} &= (-1)^3(-12 + j16) = 12 - j16, \\ \Delta_{22} &= (-1)^4(13 - j14) = 13 - j14. \end{aligned}$$

The cofactor matrix $\mathbf{B}$ is

$$\mathbf{B} = \begin{bmatrix} (-26 - j13) & (-27 - j16) \\ (12 - j16) & (13 - j14) \end{bmatrix}. \quad (\text{A.85})$$

The adjoint of $\mathbf{A}$ is

$$\text{adj } \mathbf{A} = \mathbf{B}^T = \begin{bmatrix} (-26 - j13) & (12 - j16) \\ (-27 - j16) & (13 - j14) \end{bmatrix}. \quad (\text{A.86})$$

The determinant of $\mathbf{A}$ is

$$\det \mathbf{A} = \begin{vmatrix} (13 - j14) & -(12 - j16) \\ (27 + j16) & -(26 + j13) \end{vmatrix}$$

$$= -(13 - j14)(26 + j13) + (12 - j16)(27 + j16)$$

$$= 60 - j45. \quad (\text{A.87})$$

The inverse of the coefficient matrix is

$$\mathbf{A}^{-1} = \frac{\begin{bmatrix} (-26 - j13) & (12 - j16) \\ (-27 - j16) & (13 - j14) \end{bmatrix}}{(60 - j45)}. \quad (\text{A.88})$$

Equation A.88 can be simplified to

$$\mathbf{A}^{-1} = \frac{60 + j45}{5625} \begin{bmatrix} (-26 - j13) & (12 - j16) \\ (-27 - j16) & (13 - j14) \end{bmatrix}$$

$$= \frac{1}{375} \begin{bmatrix} -65 - j130 & 96 - j28 \\ -60 - j145 & 94 - j17 \end{bmatrix}. \quad (\text{A.89})$$

Substituting Eq. A.89 into A.84 gives us

$$\begin{bmatrix} \mathbf{I}_1 \\ \mathbf{I}_2 \end{bmatrix} = \frac{1}{375} \begin{bmatrix} (-65 - j130) & (96 - j28) \\ (-60 - j145) & (94 - j17) \end{bmatrix} \begin{bmatrix} 150\underline{/0°} \\ 0 \end{bmatrix}$$

$$= \begin{bmatrix} (-26 - j52) \\ (-24 - j58) \end{bmatrix}. \quad (\text{A.90})$$

It follows from Eq. A.90 that

$$\begin{aligned} \mathbf{I}_1 &= (-26 - j52) = 58.14\underline{/-116.57°} \text{ A}, \\ \mathbf{I}_2 &= (-24 - j58) = 62.77\underline{/-122.48°} \text{ A}. \end{aligned} \quad (\text{A.91})$$

In the first three examples, the matrix elements have been numbers—real numbers in Examples A.1 and A.2, and complex numbers in Example A.3. It is also possible for the elements to be functions. Example A.4 illustrates the use of matrix algebra in a circuit problem where the elements in the coefficient matrix are functions.

Use the matrix method to derive expressions for the node voltages V_1 and V_2 in the circuit in Fig. A.1.

Solution

Summing the currents away from nodes 1 and 2 generates the following set of equations:

$$\frac{V_1 - V_g}{R} + V_1 sC + (V_1 - V_2)sC = 0,$$

$$\frac{V_2}{R} + (V_2 - V_1)sC + (V_2 - V_g)sC = 0. \quad \text{(A.92)}$$

Letting $G = 1/R$ and collecting the coefficients of V_1 and V_2 gives us

$$(G + 2sC)V_1 - sCV_2 = GV_g,$$

$$-sCV_1 + (G + 2sC)V_2 = sCV_g. \quad \text{(A.93)}$$

Writing Eq. A.93 in matrix notation yields

$$\mathbf{AV} = \mathbf{I}, \quad \text{(A.94)}$$

where

$$\mathbf{A} = \begin{bmatrix} G + 2sC & -sC \\ -sC & G + 2sC \end{bmatrix},$$

$$\mathbf{V} = \begin{bmatrix} V_1 \\ V_2 \end{bmatrix}, \quad \text{and} \quad \mathbf{I} = \begin{bmatrix} GV_g \\ sCV_g \end{bmatrix}.$$

It follows from Eq. A.94 that

$$\mathbf{V} = \mathbf{A}^{-1}\mathbf{I}. \quad \text{(A.95)}$$

As before, we find the inverse of the coefficient matrix by first finding the adjoint of $\mathbf{A}$ and the determinant of $\mathbf{A}$. The cofactors of $\mathbf{A}$ are

$$\Delta_{11} = (-1)^2[G + 2sC] = G + 2sC,$$
$$\Delta_{12} = (-1)^3(-sC) = sC,$$
$$\Delta_{21} = (-1)^3(-sC) = sC,$$
$$\Delta_{22} = (-1)^4[G + 2sC] = G + 2sC.$$

The cofactor matrix is

$$\mathbf{B} = \begin{bmatrix} G + 2sC & sC \\ sC & G + 2sC \end{bmatrix}, \quad \text{(A.96)}$$

and therefore the adjoint of the coefficient matrix is

$$\text{adj } \mathbf{A} = \mathbf{B}^T = \begin{bmatrix} G + 2sC & sC \\ sC & G + 2sC \end{bmatrix}. \quad \text{(A.97)}$$

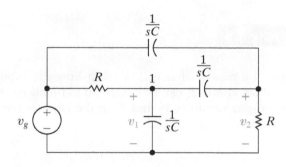

Figure A.1 ▲ The circuit for Example A.4.

The determinant of $\mathbf{A}$ is

$$\det \mathbf{A} = \begin{vmatrix} G + 2sC & sC \\ sC & G + 2sC \end{vmatrix} = G^2 + 4sCG + 3s^2C^2. \quad \text{(A.98)}$$

The inverse of the coefficient matrix is

$$\mathbf{A}^{-1} = \frac{\begin{bmatrix} G + 2sC & sC \\ sC & G + 2sC \end{bmatrix}}{(G^2 + 4sCG + 3s^2C^2)}. \quad \text{(A.99)}$$

It follows from Eq. A.95 that

$$\begin{bmatrix} V_1 \\ V_2 \end{bmatrix} = \frac{\begin{bmatrix} G + 2sC & sC \\ sC & G + 2sC \end{bmatrix}\begin{bmatrix} GV_g \\ sCV_g \end{bmatrix}}{(G^2 + 4sCG + 3s^2C^2)}. \quad \text{(A.100)}$$

Carrying out the matrix multiplication called for in Eq. A.100 gives

$$\begin{bmatrix} V_1 \\ V_2 \end{bmatrix} = \frac{1}{(G^2 + 4sCG + 3s^2C^2)}\begin{bmatrix} (G^2 + 2sCG + s^2C^2)V_g \\ (2sCG + 2s^2C^2)V_g \end{bmatrix}. \quad \text{(A.101)}$$

Now the expressions for V_1 and V_2 can be written directly from Eq. A.101; thus

$$V_1 = \frac{(G^2 + 2sCG + s^2C^2)V_g}{(G^2 + 4sCG + 3s^2C^2)}, \quad \text{(A.102)}$$

and

$$V_2 = \frac{2(sCG + s^2C^2)V_g}{(G^2 + 4sCG + 3s^2C^2)}. \quad \text{(A.103)}$$

In our final example, we illustrate how matrix algebra can be used to analyze the cascade connection of two two-port circuits.

Example A.5

Show by means of matrix algebra how the input variables V_1 and I_1 can be described as functions of the output variables V_2 and I_2 in the cascade connection shown in Fig. 18.10.

Solution

We begin by expressing, in matrix notation, the relationship between the input and output variables of each two-port circuit. Thus

$$\begin{bmatrix} V_1 \\ I_1 \end{bmatrix} = \begin{bmatrix} a'_{11} & -a'_{12} \\ a'_{21} & -a'_{22} \end{bmatrix} \begin{bmatrix} V'_2 \\ I'_2 \end{bmatrix}, \qquad (A.104)$$

and

$$\begin{bmatrix} V'_1 \\ I'_1 \end{bmatrix} = \begin{bmatrix} a''_{11} & -a''_{12} \\ a''_{21} & -a''_{22} \end{bmatrix} \begin{bmatrix} V_2 \\ I_2 \end{bmatrix}, \qquad (A.105)$$

Now the cascade connection imposes the constraints

$$V'_2 = V'_1 \quad \text{and} \quad I'_2 = -I'_1. \qquad (A.106)$$

These constraint relationships are substituted into Eq. A.104. Thus

$$\begin{bmatrix} V_1 \\ I_1 \end{bmatrix} = \begin{bmatrix} a'_{11} & -a'_{12} \\ a'_{21} & -a'_{22} \end{bmatrix} \begin{bmatrix} V'_1 \\ -I'_1 \end{bmatrix}$$

$$= \begin{bmatrix} a'_{11} & a'_{12} \\ a'_{21} & a'_{22} \end{bmatrix} \begin{bmatrix} V'_1 \\ I'_1 \end{bmatrix}. \qquad (A.107)$$

The relationship between the input variables (V_1, I_1) and the output variables (V_2, I_2) is obtained by substituting Eq. A.105 into Eq. A.107. The result is

$$\begin{bmatrix} V_1 \\ I_1 \end{bmatrix} = \begin{bmatrix} a'_{11} & a'_{12} \\ a'_{21} & a'_{22} \end{bmatrix} \begin{bmatrix} a''_{11} & -a''_{12} \\ a''_{21} & -a''_{22} \end{bmatrix} \begin{bmatrix} V_2 \\ I_2 \end{bmatrix}. \qquad (A.108)$$

After multiplying the coefficient matrices, we have

$$\begin{bmatrix} V_1 \\ I_1 \end{bmatrix} = \begin{bmatrix} (a'_{11}a''_{11} + a'_{12}a''_{21}) & -(a'_{11}a''_{12} + a'_{12}a''_{22}) \\ (a'_{21}a''_{11} + a'_{22}a''_{21}) & -(a'_{21}a''_{12} + a'_{22}a''_{22}) \end{bmatrix} \begin{bmatrix} V_2 \\ I_2 \end{bmatrix}. \qquad (A.109)$$

Note that Eq. A.109 corresponds to writing Eqs. 18.72 and 18.73 in matrix form.

B Complex Numbers

Complex numbers were invented to permit the extraction of the square roots of negative numbers. Complex numbers simplify the solution of problems that would otherwise be very difficult. The equation $x^2 + 8x + 41 = 0$, for example, has no solution in a number system that excludes complex numbers. These numbers, and the ability to manipulate them algebraically, are extremely useful in circuit analysis.

B.1 Notation

There are two ways to designate a complex number: with the cartesian, or rectangular, form or with the polar, or trigonometric, form. In the **rectangular form**, a complex number is written in terms of its real and imaginary components; hence

$$n = a + jb, \tag{B.1}$$

where a is the real component, b is the imaginary component, and j is by definition $\sqrt{-1}$.[1]

In the **polar form**, a complex number is written in terms of its magnitude (or modulus) and angle (or argument); hence

$$n = ce^{j\theta} \tag{B.2}$$

where c is the magnitude, θ is the angle, e is the base of the natural logarithm, and, as before, $j = \sqrt{-1}$. In the literature, the symbol $\underline{/\theta^\circ}$ is frequently used in place of $e^{j\theta}$; that is, the polar form is written

$$n = c\underline{/\theta^\circ}. \tag{B.3}$$

Although Eq. B.3 is more convenient in printing text material, Eq. B.2 is of primary importance in mathematical operations because the rules for manipulating an exponential quantity are well known. For example, because $(y^x)^n = y^{xn}$, then $(e^{j\theta})^n = e^{jn\theta}$; because $y^{-x} = 1/y^x$, then $e^{-j\theta} = 1/e^{j\theta}$; and so forth.

Because there are two ways of expressing the same complex number, we need to relate one form to the other. The transition from the polar to the rectangular form makes use of Euler's identity:

$$e^{\pm j\theta} = \cos \theta \pm j \sin \theta. \tag{B.4}$$

---

[1] You may be more familiar with the notation $i = \sqrt{-1}$. In electrical engineering, i is used as the symbol for current, and hence in electrical engineering literature, j is used to denote $\sqrt{-1}$.

A complex number in polar form can be put in rectangular form by writing

$$ce^{j\theta} = c(\cos\theta + j\sin\theta)$$
$$= c\cos\theta + jc\sin\theta \qquad (B.5)$$
$$= a + jb.$$

The transition from rectangular to polar form makes use of the geometry of the right triangle, namely,

$$a + jb = \left(\sqrt{a^2 + b^2}\right)e^{j\theta}$$

$$= ce^{j\theta}, \qquad (B.6)$$

where

$$\tan\theta = b/a. \qquad (B.7)$$

It is not obvious from Eq. B.7 in which quadrant the angle θ lies. The ambiguity can be resolved by a graphical representation of the complex number.

B.2 The Graphical Representation of a Complex Number

A complex number is represented graphically on a complex-number plane, which uses the horizontal axis for plotting the real component and the vertical axis for plotting the imaginary component. The angle of the complex number is measured counterclockwise from the positive real axis. The graphical plot of the complex number $n = a + jb = c\ \underline{/\theta^\circ}$, if we assume that a and b are both positive, is shown in Fig. B.1.

This plot makes very clear the relationship between the rectangular and polar forms. Any point in the complex-number plane is uniquely defined by giving either its distance from each axis (that is, a and b) or its radial distance from the origin (c) and the angle of the radial measurement θ.

It follows from Fig. B.1 that θ is in the first quadrant when a and b are both positive, in the second quadrant when a is negative and b is positive, in the third quadrant when a and b are both negative, and in the fourth quadrant when a is positive and b is negative. These observations are illustrated in Fig. B.2, where we have plotted $4 + j3$, $-4 + j3$, $-4 - j3$, and $4 - j3$.

Note that we can also specify θ as a clockwise angle from the positive real axis. Thus in Fig. B.2(c) we could also designate $-4 - j3$ as $5\ \underline{/-143.13^\circ}$. In Fig. B.2(d) we observe that $5\ \underline{/323.13^\circ} = 5\ \underline{/-36.87^\circ}$. It is customary to express θ in terms of negative values when θ lies in the third or fourth quadrant.

The graphical interpretation of a complex number also shows the relationship between a complex number and its conjugate. The **conjugate of a complex number** is formed by reversing the sign of its imaginary component. Thus the conjugate of $a + jb$ is $a - jb$, and the conjugate of $-a + jb$ is $-a - jb$. When we write a complex number in polar form, we form its conjugate simply by reversing the sign of the angle θ. Therefore the conjugate of $c\ \underline{/\theta^\circ}$ is $c\ \underline{/-\theta^\circ}$. The conjugate of a complex number is

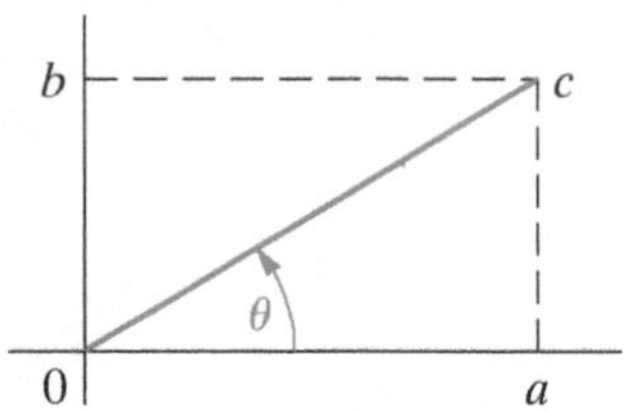

Figure B.1 ▲ The graphical representation of $a + jb$ when a and b are both positive.

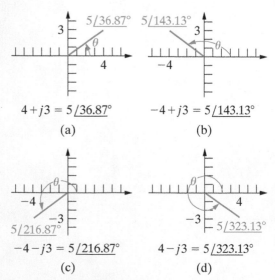

$$4 + j3 = 5\ \underline{/36.87^\circ}$$
(a)

$$-4 + j3 = 5\ \underline{/143.13^\circ}$$
(b)

$$-4 - j3 = 5\ \underline{/216.87^\circ}$$
(c)

$$4 - j3 = 5\ \underline{/323.13^\circ}$$
(d)

Figure B.2 ▲ The graphical representation of four complex numbers.

designated with an asterisk. In other words, n^* is understood to be the conjugate of n. Figure B.3 shows two complex numbers and their conjugates plotted on the complex-number plane.

Note that conjugation simply reflects the complex numbers about the real axis.

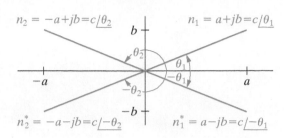

Figure B.3 ▲ The complex numbers n_1 and n_2 amd their conjugates n_1^* and n_2^*.

B.3 Arithmetic Operations

Addition (Subtraction)

To add or subtract complex numbers, we must express the numbers in rectangular form. Addition involves adding the real parts of the complex numbers to form the real part of the sum, and the imaginary parts to form the imaginary part of the sum. Thus, if we are given

$$n_1 = 8 + j16$$

and

$$n_2 = 12 - j3,$$

then

$$n_1 + n_2 = (8 + 12) + j(16 - 3) = 20 + j13.$$

Subtraction follows the same rule. Thus

$$n_2 - n_1 = (12 - 8) + j(-3 - 16) = 4 - j19.$$

If the numbers to be added or subtracted are given in polar form, they are first converted to rectangular form. For example, if

$$n_1 = 10\underline{/53.13°}$$

and

$$n_2 = 5\underline{/-135°},$$

then

$$\begin{aligned} n_1 + n_2 &= 6 + j8 - 3.535 - j3.535 \\ &= (6 - 3.535) + j(8 - 3.535) \\ &= 2.465 + j4.465 = 5.10 \underline{/61.10°}, \end{aligned}$$

and

$$n_1 - n_2 = 6 + j8 - (-3.535 - j3.535)$$

$$= 9.535 + j11.535$$

$$= 14.966 \underline{/50.42°}.$$

Multiplication (Division)

Multiplication or division of complex numbers can be carried out with the numbers written in either rectangular or polar form. However, in most cases, the polar form is more convenient. As an example, let's find the product $n_1 n_2$ when $n_1 = 8 + j10$ and $n_2 = 5 - j4$. Using the rectangular form, we have

$$n_1 n_2 = (8 + j10)(5 - j4) = 40 - j32 + j50 + 40$$

$$= 80 + j18$$

$$= 82\underline{/12.68°}.$$

If we use the polar form, the multiplication $n_1 n_2$ becomes

$$n_1 n_2 = (12.81\ \underline{/51.34°})(6.40\ \underline{/-38.66°})$$

$$= 82\ \underline{/12.68°}$$

$$= 80 + j18.$$

The first step in dividing two complex numbers in rectangular form is to multiply the numerator and denominator by the conjugate of the denominator. This reduces the denominator to a real number. We then divide the real number into the new numerator. As an example, let's find the value of n_1/n_2, where $n_1 = 6 + j3$ and $n_2 = 3 - j1$. We have

$$\frac{n_1}{n_2} = \frac{6 + j3}{3 - j1} = \frac{(6 + j3)(3 + j1)}{(3 - j1)(3 + j1)}$$

$$= \frac{18 + j6 + j9 - 3}{9 + 1}$$

$$= \frac{15 + j15}{10} = 1.5 + j1.5$$

$$= 2.12\ \underline{/45°}.$$

In polar form, the division of n_1 by n_2 is

$$\frac{n_1}{n_2} = \frac{6.71\ \underline{/26.57°}}{3.16\ \underline{/-18.43°}} = 2.12\ \underline{/45°}$$

$$= 1.5 + j1.5.$$

B.4   Useful Identities

In working with complex numbers and quantities, the following identities are very useful:

$$\pm j^2 = \mp 1, \tag{B.8}$$

$$(-j)(j) = 1, \tag{B.9}$$

$$j = \frac{1}{-j}, \tag{B.10}$$

$$e^{\pm j\pi} = -1, \tag{B.11}$$

$$e^{\pm j\pi/2} = \pm j. \tag{B.12}$$

Given that $n = a + jb = c\underline{/\theta°}$, it follows that

$$nn^* = a^2 + b^2 = c^2, \tag{B.13}$$

$$n + n^* = 2a, \tag{B.14}$$

$$n - n^* = j2b, \tag{B.15}$$

$$n/n^* = 1\underline{/2\theta°}. \tag{B.16}$$

B.5 The Integer Power of a Complex Number

To raise a complex number to an integer power k, it is easier to first write the complex number in polar form. Thus

$$n^k = (a + jb)^k$$

$$= (ce^{j\theta})^k = c^k e^{jk\theta}$$

$$= c^k(\cos k\theta + j\sin k\theta).$$

For example,

$$(2e^{j12°})^5 = 2^5 e^{j60°} = 32e^{j60°}$$

$$= 16 + j27.71,$$

and

$$(3 + j4)^4 = (5e^{j53.13°})^4 = 5^4 e^{j212.52°}$$

$$= 625e^{j212.52°}$$

$$= -527 - j336.$$

B.6 The Roots of a Complex Number

To find the kth root of a complex number, we must recognize that we are solving the equation

$$x^k - ce^{j\theta} = 0, \tag{B.17}$$

which is an equation of the kth degree and therefore has k roots.

To find the k roots, we first note that

$$ce^{j\theta} = ce^{j(\theta+2\pi)} = ce^{j(\theta+4\pi)} = \cdots. \tag{B.18}$$

It follows from Eqs. B.17 and B.18 that

$$x_1 = (ce^{j\theta})^{1/k} = c^{1/k}e^{j\theta/k}, \qquad \text{(B.19)}$$
$$x_2 = [ce^{j(\theta+2\pi)}]^{1/k} = c^{1/k}e^{j(\theta+2\pi)/k}, \qquad \text{(B.20)}$$
$$x_3 = [ce^{j(\theta+4\pi)}]^{1/k} = c^{1/k}e^{j(\theta+4\pi)/k}, \qquad \text{(B.21)}$$
$$\vdots$$

We continue the process outlined by Eqs. B.19, B.20, and B.21 until the roots start repeating. This will happen when the multiple of π is equal to $2k$. For example, let's find the four roots of $81e^{j60°}$. We have

$$x_1 = 81^{1/4}e^{j60/4} = 3e^{j15°},$$
$$x_2 = 81^{1/4}e^{j(60+360)/4} = 3e^{j105°},$$
$$x_3 = 81^{1/4}e^{j(60+720)/4} = 3e^{j195°},$$
$$x_4 = 81^{1/4}e^{j(60+1080)/4} = 3e^{j285°},$$
$$x_5 = 81^{1/4}e^{j(60+1440)/4} = 3e^{j375°} = 3e^{j15°}.$$

Here, x_5 is the same as x_1, so the roots have started to repeat. Therefore we know the four roots of $81e^{j60°}$ are the values given by x_1, x_2, x_3, and x_4.

It is worth noting that the roots of a complex number lie on a circle in the complex-number plane. The radius of the circle is $c^{1/k}$. The roots are uniformly distributed around the circle, the angle between adjacent roots being equal to $2\pi/k$ radians, or $360/k$ degrees. The four roots of $81e^{j60°}$ are shown plotted in Fig. B.4.

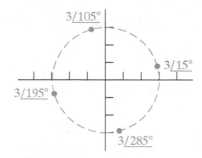

Figure B.4 ▲ The four roots of $81e^{j60°}$.

Answers to Selected Problems

Chapter 1

1.1 104.4 gigawatt-hours

1.5 0.10 mm

1.12 [a] -400 W; power is being delivered by the box

    [b] Entering

    [c] Gaining

1.19 [a] 937.5 mW

    [b] 1.875 mJ

1.24 [a] 223.80 W

    [b] 4 J

1.34 $\sum P_{\text{del}} = \sum P_{\text{abs}} = 2280$ W

Chapter 2

2.6 [a] 20 V

    [b] 8 W (absorbed)

2.12 [a] -16 mA

    [b] 640 mW

    [c] 16 mA; 640 mW

2.15 100 Ω resistor

2.19 [a] 1.2 A, 0.3 A

    [b] 120 V

    [c] $\sum P_{\text{del}} = \sum P_{\text{abs}} = 180$ W

2.29 [a] 20 A in parallel with 5 Ω

    [b] 320 W

2.33 15 V, 1.4167 W

2.42 1800 W, which is 1/2 the power for the circuit in Fig. 2.41

Chapter 3

3.2 [a] 576 W, 288 W, 192 W, 384 W

    [b] 1440 W

    [c] $\sum P_{\text{del}} = \sum P_{\text{abs}} = 1440$ W

3.5 [a] 12 kΩ, 900 Ω, 30 Ω, 120 Ω

    [b] 27 mW, 810 mW, 270 W, 108 mW

3.12 [a] 66 V

    [b] 1.88 W, 1.32 W

    [c] 17,672 Ω, 12,408 Ω

3.14 [a] 1200 Ω, 300 Ω

    [b] 1 W

3.26 [a] 150 mA

    [b] 5.4 V

    [c] 3.6 V

    [d] 1 V

3.34 7.5 A

3.37 [a] 49,980 Ω

    [b] 4980 Ω

    [c] 230 Ω

    [d] 5 Ω

3.51 [a] 1500 Ω

    [b] 28.8 mA

    [c] 750 Ω, 276.48 mW

    [d] 1000 Ω, 92.16 mW

3.60 [a] 80 Ω

    [b] 279 W

3.62 2.4 A, 72.576 W

3.73 [a] 0.2, 0.75

    [b] 384, 200

Chapter 4

4.2 [a] 9

[b] 4

[c] 4

[d] Bottom left-most mesh cannot be used; two meshes sharing dependent source must be combined

4.5 [a] 2

[b] 5

[c] 7

[d] 1, 4, 7

4.11 [a] -6.8 A, 2.7 A, -9.5 A, 2.5 A, -12 A,

[b] 3840 W

4.13 120 V, 96 V

4.18 750 W

4.22 [a] -37.5 V, 75 W

[b] -37.5 V, 75 W

[c] Part (b), fewer equations

4.26 -20 V

4.32 [a] 0.1 A, 0.3 A, 0.2 A

[b] 0.38 A, 0.02 A, -0.36 A

4.40 2700 W

4.43 [a] 2 mA

[b] 304 mW

[c] 0.9 mW

4.49 525 W

4.54 [a] Mesh current method

[b] 4 mW

[c] No

[d] 200 mW

4.62 [a] -0.85 A

[b] -0.85 A

4.68 1 mA down in parallel with 3.75 kΩ

4.72 [a] 51.3 V

[b] -5%

4.79 150 Ω

4.88 2.5 Ω and 22.5 Ω

4.93 [a] 50 V

[b] 250 W

4.105 39.583 V, 102.5 V

Chapter 5

5.5 -1 mA

5.11 [a] $0 \leq \sigma \leq 0.40$

[b] 556.25 μA

5.13 $0 \leq R_\text{f} \leq 60$ kΩ

5.20 [a] 10.54 V

[b] -4.55 V $\leq v_g \leq 4.55$ V

[c] 181.76 kΩ

5.27 [a] -15.1 V

[b] 34.3 kΩ

[c] 250 kΩ

5.30 [a] 16 V

[b] -4.2 V $\leq v_\text{b} \leq 3.8$ V

5.34 2994 $\Omega \leq R_x \leq 3006$ Ω

5.44 [a] -19.9844

[b] 736.1 μV

[c] 5003.68 Ω

[d] -20, 0, 5000 Ω

5.49 [a] 2 kΩ

[b] 12 mΩ

Chapter 6

6.2 [a]
$$i = 0 \qquad t \leq 0$$
$$i = 4t \text{ A} \qquad 0 \leq t \leq 25 \text{ ms}$$
$$i = 0.2 - 4t \text{ A} \qquad 25 \leq t \leq 50 \text{ ms}$$
$$i = 0 \qquad 50 \text{ ms} \leq t$$

[b]
$$v = 0 \qquad t < 0$$
$$v = 2 \text{ V} \qquad 0 < t < 25 \text{ ms}$$
$$v = -2 \text{ V} \qquad 25 < t < 50 \text{ ms}$$
$$v = 0 \qquad 50 \text{ ms} < t$$
$$p = 0 \qquad t \leq 0$$
$$p = 8t \text{ W} \qquad 0 \leq t < 25 \text{ ms}$$
$$p = 8t - 0.4 \text{ W} \qquad 25 < t \leq 50 \text{ ms}$$
$$p = 0 \qquad 50 \text{ ms} \leq t$$
$$w = 0 \qquad t \leq 0$$
$$w = 4t^2 \text{ J} \qquad 0 \leq t \leq 25 \text{ ms}$$
$$w = 4t^2 - 0.4t$$
$$\qquad + 10 \times 10^{-3} \text{ J} \qquad 25 \leq t \leq 50 \text{ ms}$$
$$w = 0 \qquad 50 \text{ ms} \leq t$$

6.8

6.16

6.21 [a] $-50 \times 10^4 t + 15$ V

[b] $10^6 t$ V

[c] $1.6 \times 10^6 t - 12$ V

[d] 52 V

[e]

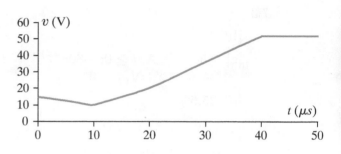

6.27 5 nF with an initial voltage drop of $+15$ V; $10 \,\mu$F with an initial voltage drop of $+25$ V

6.31 [a] $-20e^{-25t}$ V, $\qquad t \geq 0$

[b] $-16e^{-25t} + 21$ V, $\qquad t \geq 0$

[c] $-4e^{-25t} - 21$ V, $\qquad t > 0$

[d] $320 \,\mu$J

[e] $2525 \,\mu$J

[f] $2205 \,\mu$J

[g] $2525 - 320 = 2205$

6.39 [a] $0.2\dfrac{di_2}{dt} + 10i_2 = -0.5\dfrac{di_g}{dt}$

[b] $0.2\dfrac{di_2}{dt} + 10i_2 = 5e^{-10t}$ $\qquad$ and
$$-0.5\dfrac{di_g}{dt} = 5e^{-10t}$$

[c] $-53.125e^{-10t} + 6.25e^{-50t}$ V, $\qquad t > 0$

[d] -46.875 V

6.46 [a] 50 mH, 2.4

[b] 0.2×10^{-6} Wb/A, 0.2×10^{-6} Wb/A

6.50 0.8 nWb/A, 1.2 nWb/A

6.53 [a] $(2.1, 4.3)$; $(3.2, 2.5)$; $(2.1, 2.5)$; $(3.2, 4.3)$

   [b] Zoom in

   [c] Zoom out

Chapter 7

7.3 [a] 0.5 A

   [b] 2 ms

   [c] $0.5e^{-500t}$ A, $t \geq 0$; $-80e^{-500t}$ V, $t \geq 0^+$; $-35e^{-500t}$ V, $t \geq 0^+$

   [d] 35.6%

7.9 [a] 0 A, 100 mA, 0 V

   [b] 400 mA, 100 mA, -20 V

   [c] 500 mA, 0 A, 0 V

   [d] $0.1e^{-4000t}$ A

   [e] $0.5 - 0.1e^{-4000t}$ A

   [f] $-20e^{-4000t}$ V

7.19 [a] $-10e^{-5000t}$ A $t \geq 0$

   [b] 80 mJ

   [c] 1.498τ

7.23 [a] $80e^{-375t}$ V $t \geq 0$

   [b] $1.6e^{-375t}$ mA, $t \geq 0^+$

7.29 [a] 8 kΩ

   [b] $0.25\,\mu$F

   [c] 2 ms

   [d] $648\,\mu$J

   [e] $1139\,\mu$s

7.36 [a] $-0.8 + 2.4e^{-4000t}$ A, $t \geq 0$; $41.6 + 19.2e^{-4000t}$ V, $t \geq 0$

   [b] -48 V, 60.8 V

7.47 17.33 ms

7.53 [a] 90 V

   [b] -60 V

   [c] $1000\,\mu$s

   [d] $916.3\,\mu$s

7.60 3.67 ms

7.68 [a] $40 - 40e^{-5000t}$ mA, $t \geq 0$

   [b] $10e^{-5000t}$ V, $t \geq 0^+$

   [c] $16 - 16e^{-5000t}$ mA, $t \geq 0$

   [d] $24 - 24e^{-5000t}$ mA, $t \geq 0$

   [e] Yes

7.72 -5.013 V

7.80 -5 V, $0 \leq t \leq 5$ s; $-5e^{-0.1(t-5)}$ V, 5 s $\leq t < \infty$

7.88 83.09 ms

7.94 [a] $\dfrac{1}{RC}\displaystyle\int_0^t (v_{\mathrm{b}} - v_{\mathrm{a}})\, dy$

   [b] Output is the integral of the difference between v_{b} and v_{a}, scaled by a factor of $1/RC$

   [c] 120 ms

7.105 73 beats per minute

Chapter 8

8.4 [a] $-10,000$ rad/s, $-40,000$ rad/s

   [b] Overdamped

   [c] $3125\,\Omega$

   [d] $-16,000 + j12,000$ rad/s, $-16,000 - j12,000$ rad/s

   [e] $2500\,\Omega$

8.7 [a] 1.25 H, $125\,\mu$F, -200 V/s, 5 V

   [b] $(2000t - 75)e^{-80t}$ mA, $t \geq 0^+$

8.11 $100e^{-400t}\cos 300t - 800e^{-400t}\sin 300t$ V, $t \geq 0$

8.13 $-300e^{-250t} + 400e^{-1000t}$ V, $t \geq 0$

8.28 $2 + \dfrac{1}{3}e^{-400t} - \dfrac{4}{3}e^{-1600t}$ A, $t \geq 0$

8.39 8 kΩ, 2 H, 7.5 mA, 0

8.50 $20 - 10,000te^{-500t} - 20e^{-500t}$ V, $t \geq 0$

8.56 **[a]** $25e^{-30,000t} \sin 40,000t$ V

[b] $23.18 \, \mu s$

[c] 9.98 V

[d] $100.73e^{-6000t} \sin 49,638.7t$ V, $29.22 \, \mu s$, 83.92 V

8.63 **[a]** $0 \leq t \leq 0.5^- s$:

$$v_{o1} = -1.6t \, \text{V}, \quad v_o = 10t^2 \, \text{V}$$

$$0.5^+ s \leq t \leq t_{sat} :$$

$$v_{o1} = 0.8t - 1.2 \, \text{V}, v_o = -5t^2 + 15t - 3.75 \, \text{V}$$

[b] 3.5 s

8.67 **[a]** 6.33 pF

[b] $5.03 \sin 4\pi \times 10^9 t$ V, $\quad t \geq 0$

Chapter 9

9.3 **[a]** 25 V

[b] 200 Hz

[c] 1256.64 rad/s

[d] 1.0472 rad

[e] 60°

[f] 5 ms

[g] $416.67 \, \mu s$

[h] $25 \cos 400\pi t$ V

[i] 2.92 ms

9.7 $\dfrac{V_m}{2}$

9.11 **[a]** $28.38 \cos(200t + 170.56°)$

[b] $141.33 \cos(50t - 94.16°)$

[c] $16.7 \cos(5000t + 170.52°)$

[d] 0

9.17 **[a]** $160 + j120$ mS

[b] 160 mS

[c] 120 mS

[d] 10 A

9.29 $-120 \cos 8000t$ V

9.35 500 rad/s

9.42 $2/3 \, \Omega$

9.48 $6 + j4$ A in parallel with $-20 + j20 \, \Omega$

9.54 $188.43\underline{/-42.88°}$ V

9.58 $80\underline{/90°}$ V

9.64 $25 \sin 5000t$ V

9.77 **[a]** 0.3536

[b] 2 A

9.84 **[a]** $247 + j7.25$ V

[b] $-j32 \, \Omega$, $241 + j8$ V

[c] $-26.90 \, \Omega$

9.88 **[a]** 0 A

[b] $0.436\underline{/0°}$ A

[c] Yes

Chapter 10

10.1 **[a]** 129.41 W(abs), 482.96 VAR(abs)

[b] -11.65 W(del), 43.47 VAR(abs)

[c] -63.39 W(del), -135.95 VAR(del)

[d] 257.12 W(abs), -306.42 VAR(del)

10.2 **[a]** No

[b] Yes

10.7 5 mW

10.15 **[a]** 15.81 V(rms)

[b] 62.5 W

10.20 **[a]** -6.4 W, -4.8 VAR, 8 VA

[b] $\sum P_{abs} = 6.4 \text{ W} = \sum P_{dev}$

[c] $\sum Q_{abs} = 4.8 \text{ VAR} = \sum Q_{dev}$

10.30 **[a]** 0.96 (lag), 0.28; 0.8 (lead), -0.6; 0.6 (lead), -0.8

[b] 0.74 (lead), -0.67

10.41 **[a]** $2000 - j2000 \, \Omega$

[b] 3.125 mW

[c] $R = 1.8$ kΩ and $C = 47$ nF gives 3.03 mW

10.48 [a] 360 mW

[b] 4000 Ω, 0.1 μF

[c] 443.1 mW

[d] 450 mW

[e] 4000 Ω, 66.67 nF

[f] Yes

10.56 [a] $-21\underline{/0°}$ V(rms)

[b] 63 W

[c] 9.72%

10.62 [a] 125

[b] 26.28125 W

10.67 [a] 15.63 kWh

[b] 11.72 kWh

[c] 9.16 kWh

[d] 6.64 kWh

Chapter 11

11.1 [a] abc

[b] acb

11.11 [a] 15.24 A(rms)

[b] 6583.94 V(rms)

11.12 [a] $5\underline{/-36.87°}$ A(rms), $5\underline{/83.13°}$ A(rms), $5\underline{/-156.87°}$ A(rms)

[b] $216.51\underline{/-30°}$ V(rms), $216.51\underline{/90°}$ V(rms), $216.51\underline{/-150°}$ V(rms)

[c] $122.23\underline{/-1.36°}$ V(rms), $122.23\underline{/118.64°}$ V(rms), $122.23\underline{/-121.36°}$ V(rms)

[d] $211.72\underline{/-31.36°}$ V(rms), $211.72\underline{/88.64°}$ V(rms), $211.72\underline{/-151.36°}$ V(rms)

11.15 $21.64\underline{/121.34°}$ A(rms)

11.16 $159.5\underline{/29.34°}$ V(rms)

11.25 $6120\underline{/36.61°}$ VA

11.27 [a] $1833.46\underline{/22°}$ VA

[b] 519.62 V(rms)

11.35 6990.62 V(rms)

11.45 [a] proof

[b] 2592 VAR, -2592 VAR, 3741.23 VAR, -4172.80 VAR

11.54 [a] 16.71 μF

[b] 50.14 μF

Chapter 14

14.1 [a] 3819.72 Hz

[b] $0.7071\underline{/-45°}$, $0.9923\underline{/-7.125°}$, $0.124\underline{/-82.875°}$

[c] $14.142\cos(24{,}000t - 45°)$ V, $19.846\cos(3000t - 7.125°)$ V, $2.48\cos(192{,}000t - 82.875°)$ V

14.7 [a] 31.42 Ω

[b] 3419.98 Hz

[c] With 33 Ω resistor, 5252.11 Hz

14.13 [a] 5.305 kΩ

[b] 333.86 Hz

14.17 [a] 150 Ω

[b] 680 Ω

14.25 [a] 5 kΩ, 50 mH

[b] 3.52 kHz, 2.88 kHz

[c] 636.62 Hz

14.34 4 kΩ

14.42 [a] 397.89 Ω, 3.17 mH

[b] 4.42 kHz, 3.62 kHz

[c] 800 Hz

14.51 [a] 0.39 H, 0.1 μF

[b] $|V_{697\text{Hz}}| = |V_{941\text{Hz}}| = 0.707|V_{\text{peak}}|$; $|V_{770\text{Hz}}| = |V_{852\text{Hz}}| = 0.948|V_{\text{peak}}|$

[c] $0.344|V_{\text{peak}}|$

Index

E

F

I